Richard G. Oden
71

COPY 2

Introduction to Automata

Introduction to

Automata

R. J. NELSON

Case Institute of Technology

Cleveland, Ohio

John Wiley & Sons, Inc.

New York · London · Sydney

2 3 4 5 6 7 8 9 10

Library of Congress Catalog Card Number: 67-25925
Printed in the United States of America

to

Hendrieka

Preface

Since 1955 a number of mathematical inquiries relating to digital computer circuits, programming, language translation, and nerve networks have begun to form a unified scientific discipline. Although common usage has not yet been established, it seems reasonable to identify this field of study as "The Theory of Automata". For in every one of the inquiries mentioned one encounters problems about *control*, *self-action*, *memory*, and the like, and in each case the objects controlled or remembered are of the nature of symbols, words, or sentences of some kind.

A list of the inquiries alluded to might include:

The logic of sequential circuits; that is, digital computer circuits studied in abstraction from this or that specific hardware embodiment.

Mechanical translation of either vernacular or artificial languages via digital computers, and the study of algebraic properties of languages.

Pattern recognition and the theoretical capabilities of computers (of a given complexity) for detection and discrimination.

Physiology of the nervous system from the discrete-state nerve network point of view.

Structure and analysis of computer programming languages from the algebraic viewpoint.

The logical theory of self-reproduction and of growing systems.

The logic of switching and encoding networks in abstraction from hardware considerations.

This book is an introduction to the main formal mathematical ideas on which these subjects are based, although it does not touch on every one mentioned. My purpose is limited in another way. I do not discuss any of the empirical questions such as the optimal use of computers, efficient language translation, programming, heuristics, simulation of biological behavior (bionics), adaptive and learning nets, or perception—or, in short, any of the various aspects of artificial intelligence.

However, the study of the topics previously listed by way of idealized formal models, as presented here, needs no apology. For surely no great advance can be expected in any of the areas of information science by programmed simulation or experimental design alone, no matter how ingeniously conceived. The question of what *in principle* can be done or cannot be done is basically mathematical, and such a question can never be settled by unaided observation and experimentation.

Briefly, Chapters 2 and 3 introduce the concepts of inductive process and of formal system and explain how several kinds of computing machines and programs may be regarded as sets of rules for manipulating languages. Chapter 4 discusses Turing machines as models of computers with infinite memories, and introduces the notion of problem solution by algorithms or decision procedures. Chapter 5 contains the essential details of the well-established theory of complete sequential machines or transducers. Most of the standard material on state minimization, minimality, and machine structure is included.

Chapter 6 discusses sequential circuits and switching circuits, but only to the extent of including (beyond the necessary material on state assignment, coding, and net structures) the most basic logical topics on the problem of minimization. Chapter 7 deals with the question of which languages can be represented by finite automata, and is an exposition and extension of the Kleene theory of regular sets. Finally, Chapter 8 discusses algebraic linguistics, particularly as developed by Chomsky.

Readers familiar with the field will note the omission of several important topics. For example, there is no discussion of self-reproducing or adaptive automata, of reliability, of definite automata, or of linear automata. The theory of structures of sequential machines is barely sketched. In my opinion none of these topics is essential to an *introductory* treatment. References to readings about further topics, including those in the above list, are found at the end of each chapter.

I hope that the book will be of use to mathematicians and philosophers as well as to computer scientists and engineers. It may be used in a number of ways. Advanced undergraduates and graduate students who have had previous training in modern logic and algebra will be able to master the material in this book in one semester. Such students will omit Chapter 1 altogether, except perhaps for occasional reference, and will be able to absorb Chapters 2 and 3, each in a week.

Engineering or philosophy students who have not had previous training in mathematical logic and algebra will need to spend some time reading the Introduction (Chapter 1). Although the introductory material is hardly a self-contained approach to discrete mathematics, my own experience shows that a student who can work the exercises at the ends of the sections in Chapter 1 can make his way through the rest of the book. For such students the book contains material for a one-year course.

At Case Institute of Technology I myself have taught the Introduction, Chapters 2, 3, 4, 5, and parts of 7 in one semester. Another possible single semester sequence is the Introduction, 5, 6, 7, and 8. As implied in this statement of alternatives, Chapters 1 to 4 may be viewed as independent of the others, although in my opinion they are absolutely basic to automata theory.

For any course arrangement the book presupposes some knowledge of switching and sequential circuits, and propositional logic or boolean algebra. An equivalent of the material in the first six chapters of Phister's *Logical Design of Digital Computers* or the first seven of Bartee, Lebouw, and Reed's *Theory and Design of Digital Machines* is more than enough. Other suitable background books are listed in the first section of the selected Bibliography. Philosophy students with a knowledge of Quine's *Methods of Logic* or Copi's *Symbolic Logic* should be able to read the book, especially if they are willing to master the additional elementary mathematical concepts surveyed in Chapter 1.

Many people have contributed to this book. Almost nothing in it is new, as is evidenced by the short bibliographical and historical discussions at the end of each chapter. Besides my students in Mathematics 193 at Case and in Communication Science 522 at the University of Michigan, I wish to thank the following persons who have read all or part of the book, and who have made many helpful suggestions and corrections: M. Arbib, J. Dugundji, C. Elgot, J. Hartmanis, J. Holland, J. Krack, and R. Lover. Thanks go also to Mrs. Beril Lewis, who was responsible for most of the typing, and to Mrs. Barbara Titus for her preparation of most of the final draft. I also wish to acknowledge the generous support of the National Science Foundation for the development of a course at Case in sequential machines. The book is a modification of notes developed for that course. Deepest thanks go to my wife for her patient and loving support as ever during the writing of this book.

R. J. Nelson

Cleveland, Ohio
June, 1967

Contents

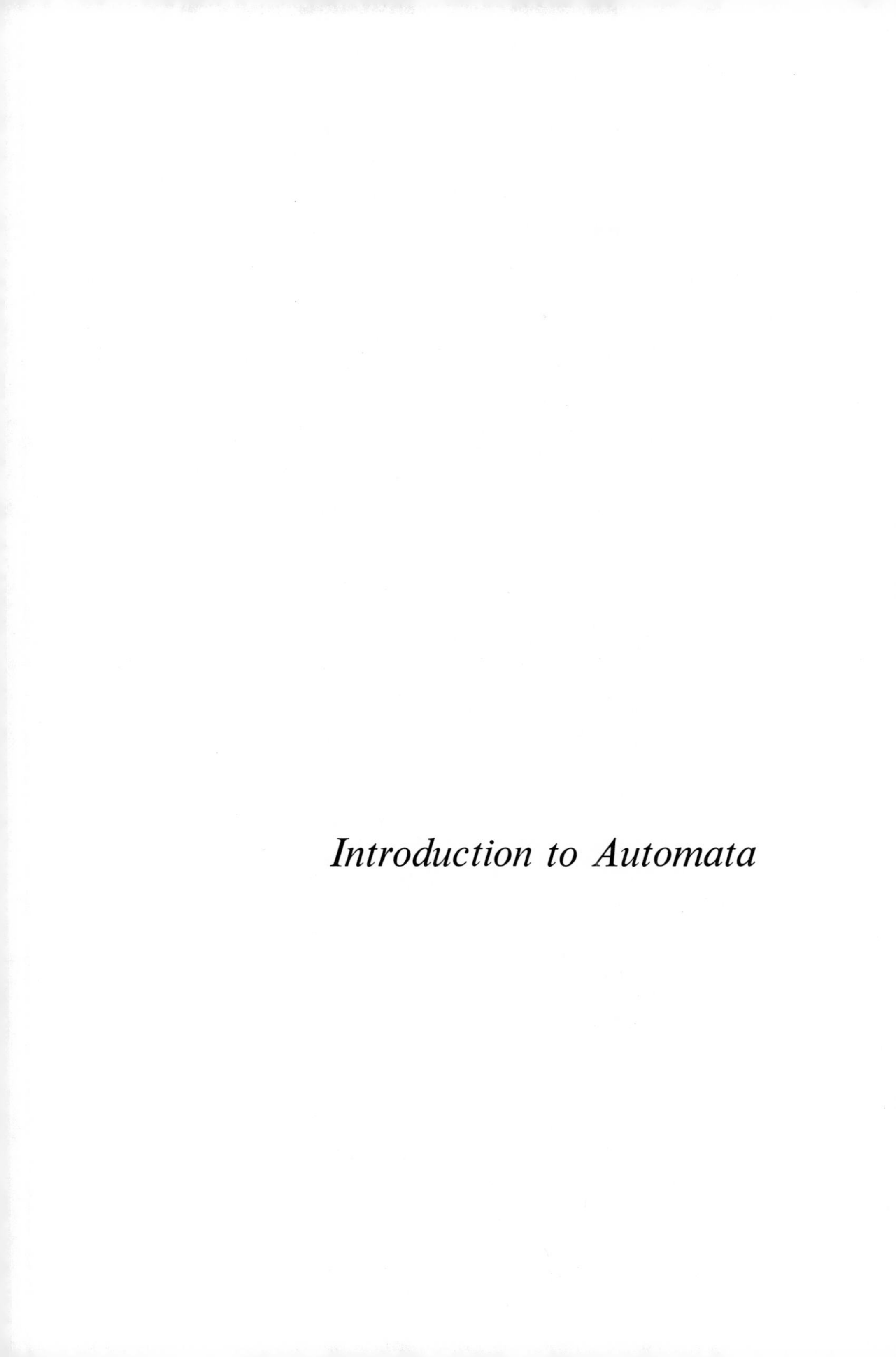

Introduction to Automata

CHAPTER 1

Introduction

1.1 SETS, RELATIONS, AND FUNCTIONS

The basic ingredient of mathematical discourse, indeed of any science, is the statement. A *statement* is any expression which is either true or false. Thus, "the sun is a star," "five is greater than four" or "$5 > 4$," "4 is a negative integer," and "$\int_0^4 x^2\,dx = 100$" are examples of statements, the first pair being true and the last pair false. On the other hand, "Mars was a Roman integer" and "very dogs elixir perhaps" are expressions which are neither true nor false, but meaningless.

Some expressions such as "$x > 5$" or "y is the uncle of John's brother" are not statements as they stand, since without some specification of x and y it is not possible to tell whether they are true or false. However, if the variable x ranges over integers and y ranges over human beings, then replacement of x by the name of an integer and of y by the name of a human being will yield, in each case, a statement which *is* either true or false. Thus replacing "x" by "2" yields "$2 > 5$," which is a false statement, and replacing "y" by "Mary" will yield a false statement; while replacing "y" by "the uncle of John" will yield a true statement (indeed, a trivially true statement).

An expression such as "$x > 5$" in which replacement of variables by *constants* or *names* results in a statement is a *predicate*. Thus "$x > 5$," "x is greater than y," and "x bit the hand that fed him," are predicates. "x is greater than y" is an example of a binary or 2-ary predicate since it has occurrences of two distinct variables. Again, "x gave y to z" is a 3-ary predicate, and "x bit y who ate z who sat on u" is 4-ary, and so on for n-ary predicates, n being a positive integer.

Predicates may also be transformed into statements by attaching as prefixes the pronomial expressions "every x" or "all x." For example "for all x, $x > 5$" or equivalently "for every (or each, or any) x, $x > 5$" is a statement. The expression "for all x" or any of its indicated equivalents is called a *universal quantifier*, and is symbolized "$(\forall x)$." The parentheses are part of the quantifier. Thus we write "$(\forall x)(x > 5)$" for the false statement (assuming x ranges over integers) "every integer x is greater than 5." Similarly, attachment of $(\forall x)$ and $(\forall y)$ to "x is greater than y" yields the statement "$(\forall y)(\forall x)(x > y)$," which is false for the integers.

Throughout this text, whenever we use variables and quantifiers it will clearly be indicated which kinds of objects the variables are intended to range over. If, in a certain discussion, it is clear that the integers are being considered, then "$(\forall x)(x > 5)$" would have the interpretation previously used. In some other discussion, on the other hand, one might mean for "x" to range over just the positive real numbers greater than 10; in such an instance "$(\forall x)(x > 5)$" would of course be true. Sometimes the domain will be mentioned as a part of the statement, as in the example:

$$(\forall x)(x \text{ is a real number and } x > 10 \text{ implies that } x > 5)$$

If P is a 2-ary predicate to which one universal quantifier is prefixed, the resulting expression is still a predicate. Thus $(\forall x)(x$ is greater than $y)$ is neither true nor false. In general, a single quantifier transforms n-ary predicates into $n - 1$-ary predicates; 0-ary predicates are *statements*.

Statements or predicates may be combined with other statements or predicates to form new ones, using the connectives *and*, *or*, *not*, *if then*, etc.[1] Thus "$(\forall x)(x > 5)$" may be combined with "$(\forall x)(\forall y)$(either $x < y$ or $y \leq x$)":

$$(\forall x)(x > 5) \quad \text{and} \quad (\forall x)(\forall y)(\text{either } x < y \text{ or } y \leq x) \tag{1}$$

or

$$\text{if} \quad (\forall x)(x > 5), \quad \text{then} \quad (\forall x)(\forall y)(\text{either } x < y \text{ or } y \leq x) \tag{2}$$

etc.

We will use the symbols indicated for *statement connectives*:

$$\begin{array}{ll} \wedge & \text{for } \textit{and} \\ \vee & \text{for } \textit{or} \\ \Rightarrow & \text{for } \textit{if then}, \text{ or } \textit{only if} \\ \Leftrightarrow & \text{for } \textit{if and only if} \\ \neg & \text{for } \textit{not} \end{array} \tag{3}$$

Less formally we will use "iff" for "if and only if" in ordinary written text, as is customary.

[1] It is assumed that the student is familiar with most of the material in this paragraph either under the guise of "propositional logic" or "boolean algebra," and that he can use truth tables.

Statements (1) and (2) may be written, using the notation above, as follows:

$$(\forall x)(x > 5) \wedge (\forall x)(\forall y)(x < y \vee y \leq x)$$
$$(\forall x)(x > 5) \Rightarrow (\forall x)(\forall y)(x < y \vee y \leq x)$$

In mathematics the symbol $\Rightarrow$ may also be read "implies." Furthermore, a statement formed with $\Rightarrow$ such as "$P \Rightarrow Q$," where P and Q are statements, is understood to mean exactly the same as "$(\neg P) \vee Q$"; that is,

$$(P \Rightarrow Q) \Leftrightarrow ((\neg P) \vee Q) \tag{4}$$

is always true. On this interpretation any implication $P \Rightarrow Q$ such that P is false is true. We also write: $\neg P \vee Q$ for $(\neg P) \vee Q$.

Predicates may also be transformed into statements by attaching as prefixes "there is an x" or "there exists an x" or "for some x." The indicated *existential quantifiers* are all used equivalently and are abbreviated "$(\exists x)$." Thus the result of attaching "$(\exists x)$" to "$x > 5$" is the true statement "$(\exists x)(x > 5)$."

The existential quantifier is used in mathematics with the same meaning as "$\neg(\forall x)\neg$," following the true principle

$$(\exists x)(x > 5) \Leftrightarrow \neg(\forall x) \neg(x > 5) \tag{5}$$

The right side is to be read: "It is not the case that for every x, x is not greater than 5." Other true relations among quantified statements follow. Each of these may be verified by the student by appeal to the meanings of the quantifiers and connectives:

$$(\exists x) \neg(x \text{ is } P) \Leftrightarrow \neg(\forall x)(x \text{ is } P) \qquad (5a)^2$$

$$(\forall x)(x \text{ is } P \wedge x \text{ is } Q) \Leftrightarrow ((\forall x)(x \text{ is } P) \wedge (\forall x)(x \text{ is } Q)) \tag{5b}$$

$$((\forall x)(x \text{ is } P) \vee (\forall x)(x \text{ is } Q)) \Rightarrow (\forall x)(x \text{ is } P \vee x \text{ is } Q) \tag{5c}$$

but not conversely.

Also,

$$(\exists x)(x \text{ is } P \vee x \text{ is } Q) \Leftrightarrow ((\exists x)(x \text{ is } P) \vee (\exists x)(x \text{ is } Q)) \tag{5d}$$

$$(\exists x)(x \text{ is } P \wedge x \text{ is } Q) \Rightarrow ((\exists x)(x \text{ is } P) \wedge (\exists x)(x \text{ is } Q)) \tag{5e}$$

but not conversely;

$$(\forall x)(\forall y)(x \text{ is } R \text{ to } y) \Leftrightarrow (\forall y)(\forall x)(x \text{ is } R \text{ to } y) \tag{5f}$$

and similarly for the existential quantifier.

[2] Using propositional logic (double negation) we also have that

$$\neg(\exists x)(x \text{ is } P) \Leftrightarrow (\forall x) \neg(x \text{ is } P)$$

from (5), and $\neg(\exists x) \neg(x \text{ is } P) \Leftrightarrow (\forall x)(x \text{ is } P)$ from (5a).

Also,

$$(\exists x)(\forall y)(x \text{ is } R \text{ to } y) \Rightarrow (\forall y)(\exists x)(x \text{ is } R \text{ to } y) \tag{5g}$$

but not conversely.

The expression "$a = b$" is used in mathematics to express that two names denote the *same* object. Thus "$\frac{1}{2} = \frac{2}{4}$" means that the symbol "$\frac{1}{2}$" and the symbol "$\frac{2}{4}$" both denote the *same* object, namely the rational number one-half. The equality sign does *not* mean, in *any* context, that two different things are somehow the same. Thus "evening star" and "Venus" are two different *names* (but not two different objects) for the *same* object. So we may write

$$\text{evening star} = \text{Venus}$$

As the example above indicates, we are permitted to use "$=$" (which is a 2-ary predicate!) over domains other than numbers. Thus we will frequently have need to talk about equality of sets, words, sentences, computers, states, etc., but invariably in the sense that two expressions are being used for one object.

A *set* is a collection of objects usually characterized by a predicate which is said to *define* the set. For example, the set of red things is the set of all objects x such that "x is red" is true. If x is P is any predicate, we write

$$\{x \mid P(x)\}$$

for the set of all x such that x is P. So $\{x \mid \text{red}(x)\}$ is the set of red things.

One may freely use any symbols one wants to (attempting to be consistent for clarity) as abbreviations for sets. Thus we might agree to employ R for $\{x \mid \text{red}(x)\}$, from which we have

$$R = \{x \mid \text{red}(x)\}$$

by our notational ruling. We will thus frequently use "$=$" to introduce a new notation.

Sometimes sets are arbitrary collections of objects; for instance, if a and b are objects, we write $\{a, b\}$ to denote the set consisting exactly of a and b. If for some reason we think it is worthwhile to display a defining property, we may write this set

$$\{x \mid x = a \vee x = b\} \tag{6}$$

Expression (6) is about the set of all x such that $x = a$ or $x = b$, and this is, of course, just $\{a, b\}$. The defining predicate in this case is $x = a \vee x = b$. This is a 1-ary predicate. (Why?)

The objects in a set A are called *elements* or *members* of A. If a is a member of A, we write "$a \in A$" for the statement expressing this fact. If a is not an element of A, we write "$\neg(a \in A)$" or more simply "$a \notin A$." Similarly, the U.S.S.R. flag $\in \{x \mid \text{red}(x)\}$.

It is convenient to have at hand the empty set, denoted by $\varnothing$ and the universal set, denoted by V. These may be defined as follows:

$$\varnothing = \{x \mid \neg(x = x)\} \tag{7a}$$

$$V = \{x \mid x = x\} \tag{7b}$$

where in each case we may assume some relevant domain such as integers, human beings, switching circuits, or whatever. If the domain is integers, then (7a) defines the empty set of integers and (7b) the universal set thereof.

The *unit* set, consisting of the single element a, is defined

$$\{a\} = \{x \mid x = a\} \tag{8}$$

A is a *subset* of B if every element of A is also an element of B:

$$A \subseteq B \Leftrightarrow (\forall x)(x \in A \Rightarrow x \in B) \tag{9}$$

We also say that A is *included in B*. Thus the positive real numbers are a subset of the real numbers. The set of Irishmen is a subset of the set of Europeans, which in turn is a subset of the set of men. Castro, on the other hand, is not a subset of Cuba, but is an element of the set of Cubans.

Two sets A and B are *equal* if they have the same members:

$$A = B \Leftrightarrow A \subseteq B \wedge B \subseteq A \tag{10}$$

For example, the set of Philadelphians is equal to the set of Philadelphians less than ten feet tall. The set of positive even numbers is equal to the set of positive multiples of the first prime number.

A is a *proper subset* of B if $A \subseteq B$ but $\neg(B \subseteq A)$. Alternatively,

$$A \subset B \Leftrightarrow A \subseteq B \wedge A \neq B \tag{11}$$

Use of sets is practically indispensable in mathematics, but on the elementary level it is theoretically dispensable in favor of predicates. Observe that it must be true that any object y is an element of the set of all x such that x is P if and only if y is P. For, if y is not P, then it will not be in the set, whereas if y is P, it will be in the set. Symbolically,

$$(\forall y)(P(y) \Leftrightarrow y \in \{x \mid P(x)\}) \tag{12}$$

It is frequently helpful to keep (12) in mind when proving facts about sets, as we shall see shortly. Expressions such as "$x \in A$," where A is the name of a set, are perfectly good predicates since they can be converted into statements by either substitution of a name for x or by quantification.

Hence they may serve as defining conditions for other sets. In particular, the following statements are true:

$$(\forall y)(y \in A \Leftrightarrow y \in \{x \mid x \in A\}) \tag{12a}$$

$$(\forall x)(x \in A \Leftrightarrow x \in \{x \mid x \in A\}) \tag{12b}$$

The *union* of two sets A and B is written $A \bigcup B$ and is defined as

$$A \bigcup B = \{x \mid x \in A \vee x \in B\} \tag{13}$$

The *intersection*, written $A \bigcap B$, is given by

$$A \bigcap B = \{x \mid x \in A \wedge x \in B\} \tag{14}$$

EXAMPLE 1. The union of the positive integers, the negative integers, and $\{0\}$ is the set of integers. The union of $\{a, b, c\}$ and $\{a, c, d\}$ is $\{a, b, c, d\}$. On the other hand, the intersection of the positive integers, the negative integers, and $\{0\}$ is equal to $\varnothing$. The intersection of $\{a, b, c\}$ and $\{a, c, d\}$ is

$$\{a, b, c\} \bigcap \{a, c, d\} = \{a, c\}$$

The union and intersection possess certain algebraic properties such as commutativity (for further discussion see Exercises 1.1). For example,

$$A \bigcup B = B \bigcup A \qquad A \bigcap B = B \bigcap A \tag{15}$$

Using (12b) and (13) we may verify the left side (and similarly, the right) of (15) as follows:

$$\begin{aligned} x \in A \bigcup B &\Leftrightarrow x \in \{x \mid x \in A \vee x \in B\} && \text{by (13)} \\ &\Leftrightarrow x \in A \vee x \in B && \text{by (12b)} \\ &\Leftrightarrow x \in B \vee x \in A && \text{by propositional logic} \\ &\Leftrightarrow x \in \{x \mid x \in B \vee x \in A\} && \text{by (12b)} \\ &\Leftrightarrow x \in B \bigcup A \end{aligned} \tag{16}$$

from which (15) follows by the logical meaning of $\Leftrightarrow$, (9), and (10). In detail,

$$(\forall x)(x \in A \bigcup B \Leftrightarrow x \in B \bigcup A)$$

means the same as

$$(\forall x)[(x \in A \bigcup B \Rightarrow x \in B \bigcup A) \wedge (x \in B \bigcup A \Rightarrow x \in A \bigcup B)] \tag{16a}$$

by the meaning of $\Leftrightarrow$, and it follows that

$$(A \bigcup B \subseteq B \bigcup A) \wedge (B \bigcup A \subseteq A \bigcup B) \tag{16b}$$

is true by (9) and (5b). The desired result then follows from the relation (10).

The *complement* of B with respect to A is $A - B$, where

$$A - B = \{x \mid x \in A \wedge x \notin B\} \tag{17}$$

If A is the universal set, we simply write $\bar{B}$ for $V - B$; since $x \in V$ is trivially true, (17) reduces to

$$\bar{B} = \{x \mid x \notin B\}$$

Two sets are *disjoint* if $A \bigcap B = \varnothing$. If $A \bigcap B = \varnothing$, then $B \subseteq \bar{A}$ and $A \subseteq \bar{B}$.

It is possible for the elements of sets to be sets, or sets of sets, and so on. For example, consider (where x is a integer)

$$A = \{x \mid 0 \leq x \leq 5\}$$

Now we may construct the set $\mathscr{V}$ of unit sets of A:

$$\mathscr{V} = \{\{x\} \mid x \in A\} = \{\{0\}, \{1\}, \{2\}, \{3\}, \{4\}, \{5\}\}$$

Note that $A \neq \mathscr{V}$ (abbreviation of $\neg(A = \mathscr{V})$), and that although $x \in \{x\}$ for all x, it is not generally true that $x = \{x\}$. As another example consider the set of all those subsets of A containing odd numbers:

$$\mathscr{O} = \{\{1\}, \{3\}, \{5\}, \{1, 3\}, \{1, 5\}, \ldots, \{1, 3, 5\}\}$$

The reader should attempt to write down a defining predicate for $\mathscr{O}$. (See Exercises 1.1.)

The formal ideas of quantifiers, logic connectives, and sets are basic to all of mathematics. However, from this point on we shall often revert to more informal mathematical English, leaving it to the student to attempt to supply formally precise definitions where needed (as suggested, for instance, in the previous paragraph). From time to time we shall make exceptions in the interest of perspicuity or in those instances where the subject matter itself requires explicit treatment of quantifiers, etc.

We now treat the concept of a function. Although the concept can be defined in terms of sets together with the machinery of logic, we will present it as a kind of rule.

Let A and B be arbitrary sets; a *function* (or, synonymously, a *mapping* or a *transformation*) f *on* A is a rule which associates to each element of A a unique element of B. By uniqueness the following is meant: Let $x \in A$ and $y, z \in B$ (that is, $y \in B \wedge z \in B$); then if f associates x to y and x to z, $y = z$.

We express the function as a rule associating elements of A to those among B by the notation f: $A \rightarrow B$. A is called the *domain* of the function and B the *co-domain*. If $x \in A$ is associated to $y \in B$, then y is written $f(x)$ and is called the *value* of the function (or *image* under the mapping) for the *argument* x. The set of values $f(x)$ is called the *range*; the range is therefore a subset of the co-domain.

Let us denote the range of f by B'. f is said to be a function on A *into* B. If $B = B'$, then f is a function *onto* B. Every "onto" function is *a fortiori* "into."

Suppose that $x, x' \in A$ and $f(x), f(x') \in B$. We say that f is *one–one* provided that $f(x) = f(x')$ implies $x = x'$; if, further, $B = B'$, then f is a *one–one onto* function or, equivalently, a *one–one correspondence.* We now illustrate these ideas.

EXAMPLE 2. A is the set of real numbers in the interval $-1 \leq x \leq 1$, and B is the set of squares of real numbers; f maps A into B by the rule which associates to each $x \in A$, $x^2 \in B$. Thus $f(x) = x^2$. The range

$$B' = \{x \mid x \in \text{real} \wedge 0 \leq x \leq 1\}$$

and $B' \subset B$. So f is into.

EXAMPLE 3. $A = \{a, b, c\}$; $B = A$. $f\colon A \to B$ is given by the rule

$$a \to b \qquad b \to c \qquad c \to a$$

Or, in the conventional notation, $f(a) = b$, $f(b) = c$, and $f(c) = a$. A is mapped one–one onto A itself. Such a function is called a *permutation.*

EXAMPLE 4. $A = \{\{a, b\}, \{a, c\}, \{a, d\}\}$, $B = \{b, c, d\}$; f is given by the rule

$$\{a, x\} \to x, \qquad x = b, c, d$$

So $f(\{a, b\}) = b$, etc. This is an example of a *set function*: the domain A is a set of sets.

EXAMPLE 5. A is a set of finite sets, B is the set of nonnegative integers; K associates to each set in A an integer which is the number of elements in that set. This is another example of a set function. Thus $K(\{a, b, c, d\}) = 4$.

Other common examples of functions which the student should interpret in the light of our definitions are polynomial functions, derivatives, integrals, vector functions, etc. (See Exercises 1.1.)

If $f\colon A \to B$ and $A' \subseteq A$, then we call $f(A')$ the *direct image* of f. It is the set of all $y \in B$ such that there is an $x \in A'$ for which $f(x) = y$. Similarly, if $B' \subseteq B$, we call $f^{-1}(B')$ the *inverse image.* It is the set of all $x \in A$ such that there is a $y \in B'$ for which $f(x) = y$.

EXAMPLE 6. Suppose $f\colon -I \to I$ is the square function on the negative integers $-I$ into the positive integers I. Then $\{4, 9, 36, 81, 100\}$ is the direct image of $\{-2, -3, -6, -9, -10\}$; that is,

$$f(\{-2, -3, -6, -9, -10\}) = \{4, 9, 36, 81, 100\}$$

Likewise $\{-2, -3, -6, -9, -10\} = f^{-1}(\{4, 9, 36, 81, 100\})$ is an inverse image.

A function whose domain is the set of positive integers I is called an *infinite sequence*. The elements of the range A are also said to be *indexed* by I. A sequence of elements of A is ordinarily written

$$(a_1, a_2, a_3, \ldots)$$

but sometimes without parentheses. We also use the notation $(a_i)_{i \in I}$ for a sequence of elements.

A *finite* sequence of elements of a set A is indexed by a set of integers j such that $1 \leq j \leq n$ for some fixed n; n is called the length of the sequence, and if f is a sequence, we write $l(f)$ to denote its length. A sequence of length n is also called an n-tuple, and a 2-tuple is an *ordered pair*.

EXAMPLE 7. $f(n) = n$, $n \in I$, is the ambiguous value of the sequence

$$(1, 2, 3, 4, 5, \ldots)$$

EXAMPLE 8. $f(n) = 2^n$. Here $n_1 = 2^1$, $n_2 = 2^2$, etc. Explicitly, this function is the sequence

$$(2^1, 2^2, 2^3, \ldots)$$

EXAMPLE 9. $f(n) = a^n$:

$$(a^1, a^2, a^3, \ldots)$$

In this case a is a parameter, and the sequence is determined only when a is specified.

EXAMPLE 10. The range is the abstract (that is, the unspecified) set containing just the objects a_1, a_2, a_3, a_4. That is, $A = \{a_1, a_2, a_3, a_4\}$. An arbitrary sequence of elements of A is written

$$(a_{i_j})_{j \in I} = (a_{i_1}, a_{i_2}, a_{i_3}, \ldots) \tag{18}$$

A specific value of this sequence (here the function itself is variable) might be

$$(a_1, a_1, a_3, a_2, a_1, a_4, \ldots)$$

This function associates 1 to a_1, 2 to a_1, 3 to a_3, etc. Or, alternatively one might write

$$i_1 = i(1) = 1 \quad i_2 = i(2) = 1 \quad i_3 = i(3) = 3 \quad \text{etc.}$$

If (18) is a finite sequence so that $1 \leq j \leq n$ for some n, then there will be exactly 4^n functions of the form

$$(a_{i_j})_{1 \leq j \leq n} = (a_{i_1}, a_{i_2}, \ldots, a_{i_n})$$

Similarly, if the range $\mathscr{A}$ of a sequence is a set of sets, we will call the sequence a *family* of sets. Thus if $\mathscr{A}$ is indexed by the integers, we write for $A \in \mathscr{A}$

$$(A_1, A_2, A_3, \ldots) = (A_i)_{i \in I} \tag{19}$$

for a family of sets. Less formally, we shall at times refer to any set of sets as a *family* and use "D" as an arbitrary (perhaps finite) index set.

The union of a family of sets $(A_i)_{i \in I}$, which is written

$$\bigcup_{i \in I} A_i$$

is defined to be the set of all a such that there exists an $i \in I$ for which $a \in A_i$. Similarly for a finite family,

$$\bigcup_{1 \leq i \leq n} A_i = A_1 \cup A_2 \cup \cdots \cup A_n$$

Similarly the intersection of a family of sets

$$\bigcap_{i \in I} A_i$$

is the set of all a such that for every $i \in I$, $a \in A_i$; and for a finite family we may, in analogy to the union, write

$$A_1 \cap A_2 \cap \cdots \cap A_n = \bigcap_{1 \leq i \leq n} A_i$$

An ordered pair as already noted is a sequence of length two. For example, if $A = \{a, b\}$ then an ordered pair of elements of A is the sequence (a, b). Two other such ordered pairs are (a, a) and (b, a). Note that $(a, b) \neq (b, a)$, and in general $(x, y) = (u, v)$ iff $x = u$ and $y = v$.

If A and B are sets, the set of all pairs (x, y) such that $x \in A$ and $y \in B$ is called the *cartesian* product of A and B and is written $A \times B$. Thus

$$A \times B = \{(x, y) \mid x \in A \wedge y \in B\} \tag{20}$$

In analogy to (12b), the intention is that an ordered pair (a, b) is in $A \times B$ iff $a \in A$ and $b \in B$. Formally stated,

$$(a, b) \in \{(x, y) \mid x \in A \wedge y \in B\} \Leftrightarrow a \in A \wedge b \in B\} \tag{21}$$

Notice that in the foregoing definition $x \in A \wedge y \in B$ is a 2-ary predicate.

Generalizing, let $(A_i)_{i \in I}$ be a family of sets. The cartesian product of the sets of this family is the set of sequences $(a_i)_{i \in I}$ such that $a_i \in A_i$ for all $i \in I$. This product is written

$$\prod_{i \in I} A_i$$

If (A_i) is a finite family with i bounded by some integer n, then the cartesian product is a set of n-tuples $(a_i)_{1 \leq i \leq n}$.

Similarly to (21)

$$(a_1, a_2, \ldots, a_n) \in \{(x_1, x_2, \ldots, x_n) \mid (x_1 \in A_1) \wedge (x_2 \in A_2) \wedge \cdots \wedge (x_n \in A_n)\} \Leftrightarrow (a_1 \in A_1) \wedge (a_2 \in A_2) \wedge \cdots \wedge (a_n \in A_n)$$

EXAMPLE 11. The cartesian product of $A = \{a, b, c\}$ and $B = \{d, e\}$ is

$$A \times B = \{(a, d), (a, e), (b, d), (b, e), (c, d), (c, e)\}$$

On the other hand,

$$B \times A = \{(d, a), (d, b), (d, c), (e, a), (e, b), (e, c)\}$$

A *binary relation* between A and B is a subset of $A \times B$. Thus R is a relation if and only if there are sets A and B such that $R \subseteq A \times B$; a is related to b by R, or simply $a\, R\, b$, is defined:

$$a\, R\, b \Leftrightarrow (a, b) \in R \tag{22}$$

EXAMPLE 12. Let $A = B = I$. Then $I \times I$ is the set of pairs of positive integers $\{(1, 1), (1, 2), (1, 3), \ldots, (2, 1), (2, 2), (2, 3), \ldots, \ldots\}$. The subset $\{(1, 1), (2, 2), (3, 3), (4, 4), \ldots\}$ is the relation of equality of integers. If we denote this subset of $I \times I$ by "$=$," then $(1, 1) \in =$, $(2, 2) \in =$, etc., or by the convention (22) $1 = 1$, $2 = 2$, etc.

EXAMPLE 13. Let $T = \{(x, y) \mid x + y = 100\}$. This is a subset of $I \times I$ and includes (1, 99), (99, 1), (2, 98), (98, 2), etc. We notice, observing this example, that 2-ary predicates define binary relations.

Similarly, an n-ary relation of a family $(A_i)_{1 \leq i \leq n}$ is a subset of

$$\prod_{1 \leq i \leq n} A_i$$

and is a set of n-tuples.

EXAMPLE 14. Let $P = \{(x, y) \mid y = x^2 \wedge x, y \in \text{real numbers}\}$. This is a relation in which each real number is paired with its square. We note that the set of "points" determined by these pairs is a parabola and indeed is a function.

Furthermore, returning to our foregoing characterization of functions (p. 7), we see that if we were to replace the word "associates" with "pairs," our new characterization of "function" would do exactly the same job as before. The uniqueness condition is incorporated by saying that *a function is a set of pairs such that if* (x, y) *and* (x, z) *are in the set,* $y = z$. Continuing, the domain of the function is the set of left-hand members of pairs and the range the set of right-hand members.[3]

[3] We could not, however, have defined functions as kinds of relations since we defined pairs as functions or as sequences in the first instance. In logic it is standard practice to define pairs otherwise, but this would have been irrelevant for our purposes.

EXAMPLE 15. Let A be a set and let

$$X = \{B \mid B \subseteq A\}$$

which is the family of subsets of A. Now consider the product $X \times X$. Any subset of $X \times X$ is a relation. In particular, $\subseteq$ and $=$ are such relations. $\bigcup$ and $\bigcap$ are binary functions: $\bigcup$ associates B_1 and B_2 uniquely to $B_1 \bigcup B_2$. $\bigcup$ and $\bigcap$ are 3-ary relations of a special kind.

An extremely important elementary idea of which we will make much use is that of *equivalence relation.* This concept is a generalization of equality and is defined as follows. Let A be a set, and let $R \subseteq A \times A$. If the following three statements are true, then R is an equivalence relation:

$$\begin{array}{ll} \text{for every } x \in A & x\,R\,x \\ \text{for every } x, y \in A & x\,R\,y \Rightarrow y\,R\,x \\ \text{for every } x, y, z \in A & (x\,R\,y \wedge y\,R\,z) \Rightarrow x\,R\,z \end{array}$$

The first statement says that an equivalence relation R is *reflexive*, which is to say that every x bears the relation R to itself; the second says that an R is *symmetric*—that is, if x is R to y, then conversely y is R to x; the third expresses the *transitivity* of R: x is R related to z if it is related to y, and y is in turn related to z. Any reflexive, symmetric, and transitive relation is an equivalence relation.

EXAMPLE 16. Ordinary equality is an example of an equivalence relation, as is equality between sets. The latter fact is simply verified by checking $A = A$, $A = B \Rightarrow B = A$, and $(A = B \wedge B = C) \Rightarrow A = C$. We do this by going back to (10) and then using the other basic definitions and principles of propositional logic. Thus for symmetry, assume $A = B$. This is the same, by (10), as $A \subseteq B \wedge B \subseteq A$; by the commutativity of $\wedge$, this is the same as $B \subseteq A \wedge A \subseteq B$, or $B = A$. So $A = B \Rightarrow B = A$.

EXAMPLE 17. Let $a, b, c, \ldots$ be positive integers; a is *congruent modulo* m to b iff a and b yield the same remainder when divided by m. This relation is written $a \equiv b(m)$. From the definition it follows immediately that $a \equiv a(m)$ and that $a \equiv b(m)$ implies $b \equiv a(m)$; we go on to show that $a \equiv b(m)$ and $b \equiv c(m)$ imply $a \equiv c(m)$.

Let r_1 be the remainder (which can always be shown to exist) upon dividing a by m, r_2 from b by m, and r_3 from c by m. By hypothesis and the definition of congruence, $r_1 = r_2$ and $r_2 = r_3$. Since "$=$" is an equivalence relation, it is transitive; so $r_1 = r_3$. By the definition this is the desired conclusion, that is, $a \equiv c(m)$. It follows that $\equiv$ is an equivalence relation.

Now let R be an equivalence relation on A. R naturally subdivides the set A into subsets of equivalent members of A. These subsets are called *equivalence classes*. The set of all y such that $x \, R \, y$ is an equivalence class with respect to R is denoted by $[x]_R$. In symbols,

$$[x]_R = \{y \mid x \, R \, y\}$$

A *partition* of a set A is a family $\mathscr{A}$ of nonempty sets such that for every $A_i, A_j \in \mathscr{A} \; (i \neq j)$, $A_i \cap A_j = \varnothing$, and $A = \bigcup_{i \in D} A_i$. That is, $\mathscr{A}$ is a set of *pairwise disjoint* sets, the union of which is A. Each element of $\mathscr{A}$ is a subset of A.

Apparently an equivalence relation induces a partition and, conversely, every partition determines an equivalence relation. Informally, if $[x]_R$ and $[y]_R$ are any two equivalence classes with respect to (w.r.t.) R on A, then no member of A can be in both unless $[x]_R = [y]_R$. Moreover, x is in $[x]_R$ for every x in A. Therefore R partitions A into disjoint subsets which exhaust the members of A. So the collection of classes is indeed a partition. (See Exercises 1.1.)

Conversely, for any partition, since it is a disjoint family, we pair all the members x, y of a set of the family in every possible way and then pair all sets similarly. The union of all the sets thus obtained is a subset of $A \times A$, hence a relation, and, as is easily verified, an equivalence relation.

EXAMPLE 18. Suppose that we take 3 as modulus over the positive integers. Then

$$1 \equiv 4(3) \quad 2 \equiv 5(3) \quad 3 \equiv 6(3) \qquad \text{etc.}$$

are all true. Now, simply writing $[x]$ for $[x]_3$,

$$[1] = \{1, 4, 7, \ldots\} = \{n \mid 1 \equiv n(3)\}$$

$$[2] = \{2, 5, 8, \ldots\} \qquad \text{and} \quad [3] = \{3, 6, 9, \ldots\}$$

Clearly,

$$[x] = [1], [2], \text{ or } [3] \quad \text{for all } x$$

or in other words,

$$I = [1] \cup [2] \cup [3]$$

So the family $\{[1], [2], [3]\}$ is a partition.

EXAMPLE 19. Suppose $\{o_1, o_2, o_3\}$ are outputs of a circuit and that they have been partitioned into $\{\{o_1, o_3\}, \{o_2\}\}$, where o_1 and o_3 are always 1 at time t_0 while o_2 is 0 at t_0. Then from $\{o_1, o_3\}$ we construct the pairs (o_1, o_1), (o_1, o_3), etc., and from $\{o_2\}$ the single pair (o_2, o_2). The abstract relation R is then given by

$$R = \{(o_1, o_1), (o_1, o_3), (o_3, o_1), (o_3, o_3), (o_2, o_2)\}$$

where

$$R \subseteq \{o_1, o_2, o_3\} \times \{o_1, o_2, o_3\}$$

This is very easily seen, at a glance, to be an equivalence relation. Since we actually have an interpretation at hand (on which, of course, the construction does not in any way depend) we may say that R means "has the same output at time t_0."

Two sets A and B are said to be *equipotent* if a one–one correspondence exists between them. Equipotent sets are also said to be *equinumerous.* For this concept we use the notation $A \sim B$. It should be evident that $\sim$ is an equivalence relation.

EXERCISES 1.1

1. Using quantifiers, logic connectives, and the notation $\{\cdots \mid ---\}$ for sets express:

(*a*) The set of all subsets (of positive integers) having odd integers as elements.

(*b*) The set of real numbers whose cosines are greater than y unless $y > 1$.

(*c*) The set of all sets of positive integers divisible by the positive integer m.

(*d*) The set of all pairs (x, y) of human beings such that x is the uncle of y (in this exercise the only predicates explicitly permitted are the 1-ary predicates "male" and "female," and the 2-ary predicate "parent of").

2. If A is a domain of objects a_i $(1 \le i \le k)$ and "x is P" is a predicate and x has the range A, then $(\forall x)P(x)$ may be interpreted to mean $P(a_1) \wedge P(a_2) \wedge \cdots \wedge P(a_k)$. Similarly, $(\exists x)P(x)$ means the same as $P(a_1) \vee P(a_2) \vee \cdots \vee P(a_k)$. Assuming a domain of two objects and $A = \{a_1, a_2\}$, show by truth tables and using the accepted meanings of the connectives (3), that the following statements are true: (5a), (5b), (5c), (5d), and (5f).

3. Prove: (*a*) $A \cap B = B \cap A$, and (*b*) $A \cap (B \cup C) = (A \cap B) \cup (A \cap C)$ using the procedure for proving $A \cup B = B \cup A$ in the preceding text. [*Hint for* (*b*): Begin with $x \in \{x \mid x \in A \wedge x \in \{x \mid x \in B \vee x \in C\}\}$. By (12b) this is equivalent to $x \in \{x \mid x \in A \wedge \ x \in B \vee x \in C|\}$; then proceed as in the text.]

4. Prove: (*a*) $A \subseteq B$ iff $A \cup B = B$. (*b*) $\varnothing \subseteq A$, for every set A. Likewise $A \subseteq V$.

5. Suppose $A = \{a, b, c, d, e, f\}$, $B = \{b, e, f\}$, $C = \{a, b, e\}$, $D = \{f\}$.

(*a*) Prove: $[A - (A - D)] \cap B = A - [(A - B) \cup (A - D)]$.

(*b*) Does the relation (*a*) hold for arbitrary sets A, B, and D? Explain.

(*c*) Is $B \times C \subset C \times A$ true?

6. In the following examples of functions discuss the domain and the range, assuming x, y are restricted to be real.

(*a*) $f(x) = x^2 - 1$

(*b*) $f(x, y) = \sqrt{x - y}$

(*c*) $D[f(x)] = df(x)/dx$ (that is, the derivative transformation)

(*d*) $I_b^a\,[f(x)] = \int_b^a f(x)\,dx$ (the definite integral transformation)

(*e*) $I_b^x\,[f(x)] = \int_b^x f(x)\,dx$ (indefinite integral transformation)

7. In Example 5, how many functions are there on B into C? On B onto C?

How many elements are there in $A \times B \times C \times D$? How many relations are there in $B \times C$?

8. (*a*) Show that $\subseteq$ is not an equivalence relation. (*b*) Discuss why $\Leftrightarrow$ is *not* an equivalence relation. (*c*) Complete the proof, started in the text, that $=$ between sets is an equivalence relation; (*d*) show that $\sim$ between sets is an equivalence relation.

9. Given the common domain I and functions f and g. What is the *union* of f and g, considered as a set of ordered pairs? Is it a function? What about the intersection?

10. Show that if $[x]$ and $[y]$ are equivalence classes under R, then either $[x] = [y]$ or $[x] \cap [y] = \varnothing$.

11. Discuss the concept of *n-ary function* as a kind of $n + 1$-ary relation. (*Hint*: See Examples 14 and 15.)

1.2 CARDINALITY

In the subject of automata, frequent use is made of the concepts of finite and infinite sets, and accordingly it is necessary to review here the precise mathematical meanings of these concepts.

Recall that two sets A and B are equipotent, iff there exists a mapping one–one on A onto B. Also recall, from Exercise 8 in Section 1.1, that $\sim$ so defined is an equivalence relation. Since $\sim$ is such a relation it determines a set of equivalence classes on some given domain $\mathscr{A}$ of sets; or, as we have already seen, it *partitions* $\mathscr{A}$.

We now associate to every member A of an equivalence class $[A]$, and only to those members, an object called the *cardinal number* of A. Informally speaking, this is what occurs. Since all the sets in $[A]$ are in one–one correspondence with each other, they all have the *same number* of elements. We then make this number the cardinal number of all and only the sets in $[A]$. From this characterization it follows that the cardinal number of A equals the cardinal number of B iff $A \sim B$.

We set the cardinal number of $\varnothing$, written $K(\varnothing)$, equal to 0. Furthermore, if $a \notin A$, then we set the cardinal number of $A \cup \{a\}$ equal to the cardinal number of A plus the natural number 1:[4]

$$K[A \cup \{a\}] = K(A) + 1$$

For example, the cardinal number of $A = \{a, b\}$, or alternatively written $A = \varnothing \cup \{a\} \cup \{b\}$, is determined thus: Let $A_1 = \varnothing \cap \{a\}$ and $A_2 = A_1 \cup \{b\}$; then

$$K(A_1) = K(\varnothing \cup \{a\}) = 0 + 1 = 1$$
$$K(A_2) = K(A_1 \cup \{b\}) = K(A_1) + 1 = 1 + 1 = 2$$

[4] The natural numbers are the numbers 0, 1, 2, 3, ...

Similarly, if $I = \{1, 2, 3, \ldots, n\}$, $K(I) = n$; and if $N = \{0, 1, 2, \ldots, n - 1\}$, $K(N) = n$.

Any set whose cardinal number is a natural number is a *finite set*. Both natural numbers and cardinal numbers of finite sets will, throughout our discussion, be denoted by the familiar numerals 0, 1, 2, etc. Any set which is not finite is *infinite*. We shall use the notation $K(A)$ for finite sets only.

Although the idea of the infinite may appear somewhat elusive, especially in theology, it is a perfectly tractable mathematical concept, and one may easily show the existence of infinite sets. To do so, we first show that no finite set A has an equipotent proper subset B. For this, let us assume A to be finite, and also that $A \sim B$. It suffices to prove that $A = B$. Since it is given that $B \subseteq A$, it is only necessary to show that $A \subseteq B$. So we will suppose, to the contrary, that there is an $x \in A$ such that $x \notin B$. By the definition of cardinal number, together with $A \sim B$, we have that

$$K(A) = K(B) \tag{1}$$

Let C be the set of x such that $x \in A$ but $x \notin B$; namely $C = A - B$. Then

$$A = B \bigcup C \quad \text{and} \quad B \bigcap C = \varnothing \tag{2}$$

Since there is no x in C, which is also in B, we get by induction (cf. Section 2.1):

$$K(B \bigcup C) = K(B) + K(C) \tag{3}$$

However, from (2),

$$K(A) = K(B \bigcup C) \tag{4}$$

and so we obtain from (1), (3), and (4) the contradiction

$$K(B) = K(B) + K(C) \tag{5}$$

Hence every element of A is an element of B, and this fact together with $B \subseteq A$ yields the desired result.

Now let us return to our objective of displaying an infinite set. We will take as our example the set of natural numbers

$$N = \{0, 1, 2, 3, \ldots, k, k + 1, \ldots\}$$

From the previous result, all we need to show is that N has a proper subset which is equipotent to N.

Consider, then, the square function on N. This function is clearly onto some *proper* subset M of N: for instance, 3 is *not* in the subset M but it is in N. However, f is a one–one function, because $x^2 = x'^2$ implies $x = x'$ (this is not true for the positive and negative integers). Since f is one–one onto, $M \sim N$. Furthermore, since $M \subset N$, we have the conclusion that N is not finite.

The set N is said to be *countably infinite*; likewise any set equipotent to N is countably infinite. Because functions also determine their values uniquely, the range of a function has at most the cardinality of the domain; also, any sequence of elements is countably infinite.[5] We call a sequence which is used to establish a correspondence with the elements of a set an *enumeration.* For example,

$$0, 1, -1, 2, -2, 3, -3, \ldots \tag{6}$$

is an enumeration of the integers, positive, negative, and zero. Since this sequence is a one–one correspondence, the integers are countably infinite. Similarly, the rational numbers and the algebraic numbers are countably infinite, but we shall not demonstrate these facts.

The real numbers, on the other hand, are not countable as can be shown by the diagonal argument.[6] Since this argument is used so frequently in logical investigations, including the theory of automata, we shall reproduce it quite completely.

It suffices to show that the real numbers in the interval $0 < x \leq 1$ are uncountable (or nondenumerable or nonenumerable—all synonyms) since, if the interval mentioned is uncountable, it is easily shown by an analogous argument—left to the student—that the same holds for all real numbers.

Now any positive real number less than 1 can be written in decimal notation as a nonterminating string

$$.\alpha_1\alpha_2\alpha_3\alpha_4 \cdots$$

Decimals such as .5 can be written as $.4999\cdots$ (see Exercise 5). Next, let us assume that we are able to list, that is, enumerate, the real numbers $0 < x \leq 1$ as x_0, x_1, x_2, etc. Since x_i is nonterminating, this list may be displayed as

$$\begin{array}{llll} x_{00} & x_{01} & x_{02} & x_{03} \cdots \\ x_{10} & x_{11} & x_{12} & x_{13} \cdots \\ x_{20} & x_{21} & x_{22} & x_{23} \cdots \\ x_{30} & x_{31} & x_{32} & x_{33} \cdots \\ \vdots & & & \end{array}$$

where x_{ij} is the jth digit in the decimal expansion of the ith number in the enumeration. For every digit x_{ii} in the array we apply the following rule: if $x_{ii} = 1$, replace x_{ii} by 2; if $x_{ii} \neq 1$, replace x_{ii} by 1. The diagonal line of digits x_{ii}' which results from application of this rule represents a real number not in the list: it differs from x_0 in the x_{00} position, x_1 in the x_{11}

[5] We are here using "sequence" in the sense of a function on N (rather than the positive integers as heretofore).

[6] Due to the mathematician G. Cantor.

position, etc. It follows that our assumption that the real numbers can be listed or enumerated is false. The real numbers comprise an uncountable set.

EXERCISES 1.2

1. Determine the rule for the function used in (6).

2. The set of all the subsets of a given set A is called the *power set* of A. Show that if $K(A) = n$, then the cardinal number of the power set of A is 2^n.

3. Find a scheme for enumerating the rational numbers and hence prove that the set of natural numbers and the set of rational numbers are equipotent.

4. Show that the set of all functions on the natural numbers to the natural numbers is not countable.

5. Show that every nonzero terminating decimal (one ending in a string of 0's) is *equal* to a nonterminating decimal (*Hint*: $\cdot\alpha_1\alpha_2\alpha_3\cdots$ is an abbreviation for the infinite series $\alpha_1 10^{-1} + \alpha_2 10^{-2} + \alpha_3 10^{-3} + \cdots + \alpha_n 10^{-n} + \cdots$. If for some i ($i = 1, 2, 3, \ldots$) and all $k > i$, $\alpha_k = \alpha_i$, the decimal is $\cdot\alpha_1\alpha_2\cdots\alpha_{i-1}\alpha_i\alpha_i\alpha_i\cdots$, then this number may be represented as $\alpha_1 10^{-1} + \alpha_2 10^{-2} + \cdots + \alpha_{i-1} 10^{1-i} + \alpha_i 10^{-i} + \alpha_i 10^{-(i+1)} + \alpha_i 10^{-(i+2)} + \cdots$. Beginning with the term $\alpha_i 10^{-i}$, sum the consequent infinite series.)

6. If $S = \{a, b, ab, ba, aba, bab, \ldots\}$ is the set of alternating strings on the letters a, b, what is its cardinality? Sketch a proof of your statement. Indicate one equipotent subset of A.

7. Prove that a set A is finite iff every one–one function from A into A is onto A.

1.3 CONCEPTS FROM ALGEBRA

The ordinary operations of arithmetic possess properties which are satisfied by a wide variety of mathematical objects other than the integers. For example, addition is associative, which means that the result of adding a to the sum of b and c is the same as the result of adding the sum of a and b to c. This is also true for composition of functions, as we learn implicitly in the calculus, and for multiplication of transformations of geometric spaces. The ubiquity of such properties as associativity suggests the study of *unspecified* or *abstract* objects about which the only things said are the operations they undergo and particularly the properties inhering in the operations.

The reader already knows that switching functions may be realized by a wide variety of different devices. All that is important is that, in the usual practice, there be *two* distinguishable objects, and that any n-ary function on the domain of n-tuples of the two objects into the set comprised of the two objects be realizable by the device in question. For example, two single-pole, single-throw switches in parallel represent the binary "or" function of logic. Here, we might let our objects be {0, 1}. The variable s_1 serves as a name for one switch, s_2 for the other; s_i, $i = 1, 2$, has the value 0 iff the switch labeled s_i is open; s_i has the value 1 iff the switch labeled s_i is closed. The output wire u now has a value which is a function value for the "or" function on the domain {(00), (01), (10), (11)}:

$$f_{\text{or}}(s_1, s_2) = s_1 \vee s_2 = u$$

Similarly f_{or} may be realized by certain diode, transistor, tube, or magnetic circuits in various well-known ways. The student of switching, on the other hand, is indifferent to the hardware varieties of his work and is concerned precisely with the algebraic and structural properties as such. Basically, his motivation for this patently abstract procedure is no different from the algebraist's, although he usually stays closer to the applications.

In this section we shall discuss several kinds of algebraic systems which are of use not only in switching theory but in the broader field of automata and information processing.

Suppose that f and g are two functions on a common domain A into A. The *composition* or *product* h of f and g is written

$$f \circ g = h \tag{1}$$

(read: "f oh g"), and is defined by the rule that if $g(x) = y$ and $f(y) = z$, then $h(x) = z$:

$$(f \circ g)(x) = f(g(x)) = h(x) = z \tag{2}$$

It is clear that for any two such functions f and g, h always exists: g is by assumption defined on all of A; and since its range is again in A and since f is also defined everywhere over A, the result of applying f to g's value is again in A. We say that the set of functions on a common domain into that domain is *closed under composition*. The product function always exists.

We may easily show that composition is *associative*: for any f, g, and h on A to A,

$$(f \circ g) \circ h = f \circ (g \circ h) \tag{3}$$

For, using the definition of composition, (2),

$$((f \circ g) \circ h)(x) = (f \circ g)(h(x)) = f(g(h(x)))$$

and likewise

$$(f \circ (g \circ h))(x) = f((g \circ h)(x)) = f(g(h(x)))$$

Thus far, in our first example, we have a system about functions which possesses two of the properties of addition: like $+$, $\circ$ is closed and associative. In arithmetic we also have the single object 0 which has the property

$a + 0 = 0 + a = a$. Such an object is called an *identity* w.r.t. addition. We next prove, in analogy with arithmetic, that there is a function i in our collection of functions on A to A which serves as an *identity* element w.r.t. composition: for any f of our set of functions there is a function i such that

$$f \circ i = i \circ f = f \tag{4}$$

To prove this we construct the function $i(x) = x$, the *identity function*, which takes every $x \in A$ into x. Then

$$(f \circ i)(x) = f(i(x)) = f(x)$$

and

$$(i \circ f)(x) = i(f(x)) = f(x)$$

verifies (4).

Finally, considering again the arithmetic of the integers with the plus operation, we know that for any integer a we can always find an integer b such that $a + b = b + a = 0$. We call b the *inverse* of a and denote it by $-a$:

$$a + (-a) = (-a) + a = 0$$

Does there also exist, in the instance of our set of functions, an inverse for every function f? If so, then for all f there is a g such that

$$f \circ g = g \circ f = i \tag{5}$$

Suppose that the range of f is the unit set $\{x\}$, $x \in A$. Then for every $y \in A$, $f(y) = x$. It follows that

$$(f \circ g)(y) = f(g(y)) = x \neq i(y)$$

so the inverse does *not* necessarily exist! A little reflection however will show that the inverse function $g = f^{-1}$ does in fact exist when our functions are *one–one* on A *onto* A. Assuming this additional property we may prove (5), which we rewrite,

$$f \circ f^{-1} = f^{-1} \circ f = i \tag{5a}$$

Since f is assumed to be one–one, it follows that corresponding to every $y \in A$ such that $f(x) = y$ there is a *unique* element $x \in A$. Consequently, there exists a function f^{-1} with the property that y determined as above is associated to x: $f^{-1}(y) = x$. It is simple now to carry out the verification of (5a):

$$(f \circ f^{-1})(y) = f(f^{-1}(y)) = f(x) = y = i(y)$$

and

$$(f^{-1} \circ f)(x) = f^{-1}(f(x)) = f^{-1}(y) = x = i(x)$$

for every $x, y \in A$.

What we have demonstrated is that any set of one–one correspondences on a set A with range A satisifies w.r.t. composition the properties *closure*, *associativity*, *existence of an identity*, and existence, for all f, of an *inverse*. Any set of objects, with operation, having these properties is called a *group*. Hence, in particular, the set of all permutations of A is a group [Example 1.1(3), and Exercise 1.3(4)].

Our working example happened to have been a group of functions. However, any set of objects whatsoever satisfying the relations we have been discussing is a group. Thus a group is ordinarily defined to be an ordered triple $G = \langle A, \circ, e \rangle$, where A is any nonempty set, $\circ$ is the group operation, and e is an element of A, which satisfies the following axioms.

For every $a, b \in A$ there is a $c \in A$ such that

$$a \circ b = c \qquad \text{(closure)} \tag{6a}$$

For every $a, b, c \in A$

$$(a \circ b) \circ c = a \circ (b \circ c) \qquad \text{(associativity)} \tag{6b}$$

For every $a \in A$

$$a \circ e = e \circ a = a \qquad \text{(existence of identity)} \tag{6c}$$

For every $a \in A$ there is a $b \in A$ such that

$$a \circ b = b \circ a = e \qquad \text{(existence of inverse)} \tag{6d}$$

As before, b in (6d) is usually written a^{-1}.

If, furthermore, G satisfies the following axiom:

For every a, b,

$$a \circ b = b \circ a \tag{6e}$$

then G is said to be *abelian* or *commutative*.

It is a simple matter to show that there is only one identity in a group and that each element has but one inverse. Moreover, it can be shown that it is sufficient to postulate a *right* (or left) *identity* and a *right* (or left) *inverse* so that (6c) and (6d) could be replaced by

$$a \circ e = a \qquad \text{for every } a \tag{6c$'$}$$

and for every a there exists a b such that

$$a \circ b = e \tag{6d$'$}$$

These additional facts are to be proved by the student in the following exercises.

In every group[7] equations $ax = b$ and $ya = b$ have solutions $x = a^{-1}b$ and $y = ba^{-1}$. For, substituting $a^{-1}b$ for x,

$$a(a^{-1}b) = (aa^{-1})b = eb = b$$

[7] We here write $a \circ x$ as ax.

using successively axioms (6b), (6d), and (6c). Similarly for the solution $y = ba^{-1}$. In addition,

$$ba = ca \Rightarrow b = c \qquad \text{(right cancellation law)} \tag{7}$$

and the companion left cancellation law may easily be verified. We now turn to some examples.

EXAMPLE 1. The set of integers with $+$ and 0. This is an abelian group. Also, the set of positive rational numbers with $\times$ and 1. These are both infinite groups.

EXAMPLE 2. The set of rigid transformations of a rectangle, $G = \langle S, \circ, I \rangle$. The elements of the group are $S = \{R, I, V, H\}$, where the interpretation we have in mind is as follows:

R is a rotation 180° to the right about the center of the rectangle. This transformation carries Fig. 1.3.1 into Fig. 1.3.2. I is the identity, and leaves Fig. 1.3.1 intact. V is the rotation about the vertical axis and H is the rotation about the horizontal axis. With this interpretation we may readily verify that $R \circ V = H$, for instance. That is, a vertical transformation followed by or "multiplied by" a 180° rotation is equal to a horizontal transformation. Similarly we may establish other relations among the elements of S and set up a multiplication table for G.

TABLE 1.3.1

$\circ$	I	R	V	H
I	I	R	V	H
R	R	I	H	V
V	V	H	I	R
H	H	V	R	I

Inspection of Table 1.3.1 shows that each element is its own inverse and that the group is abelian.

EXAMPLE 3. Consider the set N of n-tuples on $\{0, 1\}$. We define *bitwise* addition as

$$0 + 0 = 0 \qquad 1 + 0 = 0 + 1 \qquad 1 + 1 = 0$$

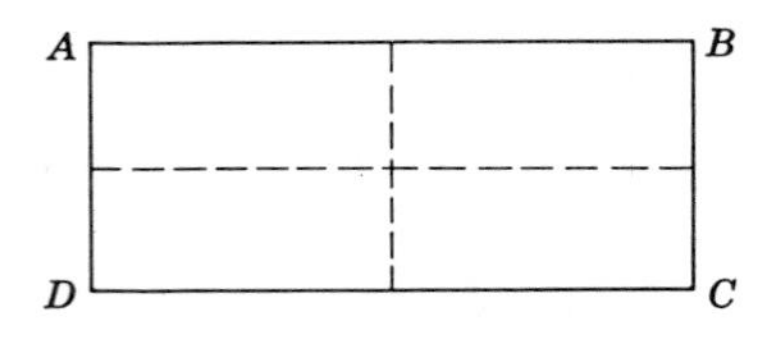

Fig. 1.3.1

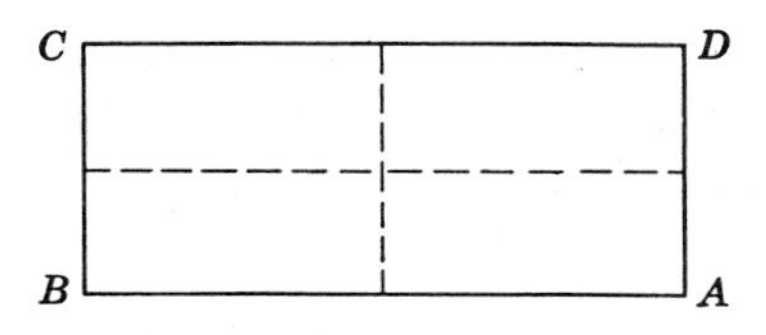

Fig. 1.3.2

The addition of two n-tuples is then given by

$$(x_1, x_2, x_3, \ldots, x_n) + (y_1, y_2, y_3, \ldots, y_n) = (z_1, z_2, z_3, \ldots, z_n)$$

iff $z_i = x_i + y_i$ for each i, where $i = 1, 2, 3, \ldots, n$, and $x_i, y_i, z_i = 0$ or 1. For example, for $n = 4$, $0101 + 1100 = 1001$. $\langle N, +, 000\cdots(n \text{ times})\rangle$ is a group, as may be readily verified, where each element is its own inverse.

EXAMPLE 4. Let $J = 0, 1, 2, 3$ and let addition be defined modulo 4 (compare Example 17, Section 1.1).

TABLE 1.3.2

+	0	1	2	3
0	0	1	2	3
1	1	2	3	0
2	2	3	0	1
3	3	0	1	2

Table 1.3.2 demonstrates that $1 + 2 \equiv 3(4)$ and $1 + 3 \equiv 0(4)$, etc.

Part of the importance of the study of algebra from an abstract point of view stems from the fact that many properties that hold for a group (or, as a matter of fact, for many other mathematical systems), having a given number of elements and a given structure, also carry over to any other group with the same number of elements and the same structure. This truth holds independently of the specific character of the membership of the group. By "structure" we mean here the following. For any group $G = \langle A, \circ, e\rangle$ we may look upon the operation $\circ$ as a *function*, which indeed it is. That is, $\circ$ is a function $\circ: A \times A \to A$, and we could write $\circ(a, b) = c$ as well as $a \circ b = c$. The meaning is the same. By structure we mean, now, simply $\circ$ as a set of pairs of the form $((a, b), c)$. To say that two groups have the same structure, thus possessing the same *algebraic* properties, we mean to say that they have the same function table except for interchanging names of elements. More precisely, two groups $G = \langle A, \circ, e\rangle$ and $G' = \langle A', \cdot, e'\rangle$ are *isomorphic* iff there is a one–one correspondence $f: A \to A'$ such that (8) holds: For every $a, b \in A$,

$$f(a \circ b) = f(a) \cdot f(b) \tag{8}$$

It is usually stated that an isomorphism f "preserves group operations," which means that the image under f of a product in G is equal to the product of the corresponding elements in G'.

EXAMPLE 5. The group G of Example 2 above is nonisomorphic to the group J of Example 4 although they have the same number of elements. A way to verify this failure is to check all 4! possible one–one functions on F onto J, noting that none of them satisfies (8). A simpler procedure is at hand by observing that in G each element is its own inverse, whereas in J this is not the case; for example, 1 and 3 are inverses. From the proposition, proved below, that if two groups are isomorphic their identity elements *and* their inverses are associated under f, it follows that G and J are nonisomorphic.[8]

We next prove that if G is isomorphic to G', then

$$\text{(a)} \qquad f(e) = e'$$

and

$$\text{(b)} \qquad f(a^{-1}) = a'^{-1}$$

Proof of (a): $f(a \circ e) = f(a) \cdot f(e)$, by (8). But $f(a \circ e) = f(a)$, since $a \circ e = a$. Therefore $f(a) \cdot f(e) = f(a)$, and by the uniqueness property of the identity (see Exercise 2), it follows that $f(e) = e'$.

Proof of (b):

$$f(a \circ a^{-1}) = f(a) \cdot f(a^{-1}) = e'$$

These equations follow from (8) and part (*a*) above. Since $f(a) = a'$, we then have $a' \circ f(a^{-1}) = e'$; and since inverses are unique, $f(a^{-1}) = a'^{-1}$.

EXAMPLE 6. Consider $C = \langle \{0, 1\} \times \{0, 1\}, +, (0, 0) \rangle$; this is an instance for $n = 2$ of Example 3. C is isomorphic to the group of symmetries of a rectangle, Example 2. To verify this, we construct the following table for C.

TABLE 1.3.3

x	(00)	(01)	(10)	(11)
(00)	(00)	(01)	(10)	(11)
(01)	(01)	(00)	(11)	(10)
(10)	(10)	(11)	(00)	(01)
(11)	(11)	(10)	(01)	(00)

Then we set up the correspondence $(00) \leftrightarrow I$, $(01) \leftrightarrow R$, $(10) \leftrightarrow V$, and $(11) \leftrightarrow H$, and easily verify that Table 1.3.3 may be obtained from Table 1.3.1 by direct substitution under the correspondence. This accomplishes

[8] In some detail, in G each element is its own inverse, so $x = x^{-1}$ for all $x \in G$. Suppose f is a one–one function and that $f(x) = 1$. Since x is its own inverse, $f(x^{-1}) = 1$. But 3, not 1, is the inverse of 1 in J; so inverses do not correspond to inverses.

the same end as checking all cases of (8). In the case of infinite groups, no such primitive method is open.

EXAMPLE 7. $G = \langle R, +, 0\rangle$ and $G' = \langle R^+, \cdot, 1\rangle$. R is the set of real numbers, and R^+ is the set of positive real numbers. Let the mapping $f\colon R^+ \to R$ be defined by $f(x) = \log_e x$, $x \in R^+$. This function is one–one onto R because every element $y \in R$ has a unique value under $f^{-1}(y) = e^y$ and because f is continuous and monotonic strictly increasing on R^+. But also, $f(x \cdot y) = f(x) + f(y)$, which establishes the isomorphism. Note also that $\log_e(1/x) = -\log_e x$.

Evidently isomorphism is an equivalence relation, and hence partitions the family of groups into classes of isomorphic groups.

EXAMPLE 8. (Cayley's theorem). For any group $G = \langle A, \circ, e\rangle$ we can find an isomorphic group of permutations. This group will be a group of one–one functions on A onto A. We construct these functions as follows. For each $a \in A$, we let f_a be the function which takes $x \in A$ into the element $a \circ x = ax$. Formally, $f_a\colon A \to a \circ A$, where $a \circ A$ denotes the set of elements ax. For a fixed element a, this function is onto. To see this, if b is any element of A, then there exists an element of A, namely $a^{-1}b$, such that b is its image under f_a:

$$f_a(a^{-1}b) = a(a^{-1}b) = (aa^{-1})b = b$$

Moreover, f_a is one–one because $ax_1 = ax_2$ implies $x_1 = x_2$ by cancellation. We therefore conclude that each f_a so constructed is a permutation.

Now let $P = \{f_a \mid f_a\colon A \to a \circ A \wedge a \in A\}$. We must show that (*a*) P is a group and (*b*) P is isomorphic to our given group G.

Proof of (*a*): To show closure, since G is a group, ab exists for all $a, b \in A$. By the method of construction of our functions, f_{ab} also exists and, in fact,

$$f_{ab}(x) = (ab)x = a(bx) = f_a(bx) = f_a(f_b(x)) = (f_a \circ f_b)(x) \tag{9}$$

To show the existence of an identity:

$$f_e(x) = ex = x \qquad \text{for any } x \in A \tag{10}$$

which leads directly to the easy verification of (6c). Finally, to establish the existence of inverses, we let $f_a^{-1} = f_{a^{-1}}$. So,

$$(f_a \circ f_a^{-1})x = f_a(f_{a^{-1}}(x)) = f_a(a^{-1}x) = a(a^{-1}x) = (aa^{-1})x = ex = x = f_e(x)$$

Proof of (*b*): Expression (9) actually establishes the isomorphism. But to be very explicit, there corresponds to each $a \in A$ exactly one function, f_a, and conversely. Let this correspondence be φ. Now two functions are equal iff they have the same values for each argument. Hence from (9), $f_{ab} = f_a \circ f_b$. But then

$$\varphi(ab) = f_{ab} = f_a \circ f_b = \varphi(a) \circ \varphi(b)$$

which satisfies (8). Q.E.D.

A *subgroup* G' of a group $G = \langle A, \circ, e \rangle$ is a group $\langle A', \circ', e \rangle$ where $A' \subseteq A$ and $\circ'$ is the restriction of $\circ$ to A'. A nonempty system G' is a subgroup of G iff G' is closed and every $a \in A'$ has an inverse. The proof from left to right[9] follows trivially from the definition of a group. From right to left, the associativity of G' follows from that of G since $A' \subseteq A$, so all we really have to bother about is the identity. However, since G' is nonempty, there is an $a \in A'$; by hypothesis this has an inverse a^{-1}. Hence $aa^{-1} = e$ is in G' because of closure.

EXAMPLE 9. $G = \langle \{I, R\}, \circ, I \rangle$ is a two-element subgroup of the group of transformations of a rectangle (Example 2). There are obviously others.

A *semigroup* is a system satisfying (6a) and (6b), and a *semigroup with identity* satisfies, in addition, (6c). A system satisfying (6a), (6b), and (6c) is also called a *monoid.*

Actually, in the study of automata, monoids are, if anything, of somewhat more applicability than groups. It so happens that *languages*, as we shall study them from the point of view of automata theory, are subsets of monoids, and that a large part of our task is, therefore, to study various structures of subsets of monoids. Although they may seem much too simple to be interesting, we shall soon find that monoids are sources of embarrassing riches.

All of the examples given of groups are also, of course, monoids. Some properties of groups carry over to monoids. For instance, the *identity* e of a monoid is unique. Suppose that $e' \circ a = a$ for all $a \in A$, then in particular $e' \circ e = e$ holds. But again from (6c), $e' \circ e = e'$; therefore, $e = e'$. However, unlike groups, monoids require the full statement (6c), and the existence of a left identity does not imply that of a right identity or vice versa.

EXAMPLE 10. As a particularly relevant example for our over-all aims, consider a monoid of sequences, $M = \langle A^*, \circ, \Lambda \rangle$.[10] A^* is constructed in the following manner. We begin with a set $A = \{a, b\}$ of *generators* and define

$$A^0 = \{\Lambda\}$$
$$A^{k+1} = A^k \times A \qquad \text{(cartesian product of } A^k \text{ and } A)$$

[9] In proving an iff statement recall P iff Q means $P \Rightarrow Q \wedge Q \Rightarrow P$. Proof of $P \Rightarrow Q$ is from left to right and of $Q \Rightarrow P$ is from right to left.

[10] The identity Λ is the sequence of length zero.

Then we set

$$A^* = \bigcup_{i \in N} (A^i)$$

N is the set of nonnegative integers. A^*, defined in this way, is the set of all sequences of finite (including zero) length with elements a and b. Any element $(s_1, s_2, s_3, \ldots, s_n)$ of A^*, $(s_i \in A)$ is written for convenience as $s_1 s_2 s_3 \cdots s_4$. We have now completely characterized the set A^* of the monoid M. Let the variables x, y, etc., range over the set of sequences A^*.

The operation o is interpreted to be the *concatenation* of sequences to yield sequences. Thus, as an example,

$$abba \circ baba = abbababa \tag{11}$$

By the construction of A^*, the result of concatenation is a sequence on the generators $\{a, b\}$ and thus is in A^*. Hence M is closed. Moreover, for every $x, y, z \in A^*$,

$$(x \circ y) \circ z = x \circ (y \circ z)$$

since

$$(x \circ y) \circ z = (x \circ y)z = (xy)z = x(yz) = x \circ (yz) = x \circ (y \circ z)$$[11]

Finally, if we interpret Λ to be the *null sequence*, that is, the sequence of length zero,

$$\Lambda x = x\Lambda = x$$

holds true. Consequently, M is a monoid. No element of A^* has a negative length, hence no element of A^*, save Λ, has an inverse. Therefore A^* is not a group.

EXAMPLE 11. Let $A = \{a, b\}$ and B equal the set including Λ of all sequences on A beginning with a; then $M' = \langle B, \circ, \Lambda \rangle$ is a monoid.

Examples 10 and 11 are both infinite monoids. To show that this is true for Example 10 we make the correspondence $\varphi(a) = 1$ and $\varphi(b) = 2$. We let I^* be constructed by using $\{1, 2\}$ as generators in the same manner as A^*. Now we extend[12] the mapping φ to sequences by the rule

$$\varphi(sx) = \varphi(s)\varphi(x) \qquad s \in A \quad x \in A^* \tag{12}$$

Thus φ is obviously a one–one correspondence between A^* and I^*. Thus, for example, $abba \leftrightarrow 1221$. The sequence of length zero in I^* represents 0. The positive sequences in I^* represent positive integers. Let $d_i = 1$ or 2. Then $d_n d_{n-1} \cdots d_2 d_1$ is called a *dyadic* number and represents

$$d_1 + 2d_2 + 4d_3 + \cdots + 2^{n-1} d_n \tag{13}$$

[11] $(xy)z = x(yz)$ are equal since two sequences are equal iff they are equal element by element.

[12] The domain of φ is enlarged to include all sequences on $\{a, b\}$.

By this convention, it follows that corresponding to every element of I^* there exists a positive integer. Conversely, to every positive integer there corresponds a unique dyadic representation. Hence, there is a one–one correspondence between I^* and I (the integers) and therefore between A^* and I as well, thereby establishing the fact that A^* is countably infinite.

Suppose we have a monoid M with elements A, all of which are products, under the operation o of the monoid, of just some of the members of A. To make this idea clear suppose $b_1, b_2, b_3, \ldots$ comprise a subset of A and that by b_i^j we mean the product of b_i with itself j times (= the jth power of b_i) where $j \geqslant 0$ and $b_i^0 = e$. Then if every element $a \in A$ can be written

$$a = b_{i_1}^{j_1} b_{i_2}^{j_2} b_{i_3}^{j_3} \cdots b_{i_m}^{j_m}$$

we will say that the b's are *generators* of the monoid, and that if the set of generators is finite that M is *finitely generated*. Examples 10 and 11 are both finitely generated since every element of each monoid can be written as a product of powers of generators. For example, the right side of equality (11) may be written $a^1b^2a^1b^1a^1b^1a^1$.

EXAMPLE 12. The set of positive integers under multiplication is a monoid, with 1 the identity, which is not finitely generated.

Similarly, each element of a group will be the product of powers of a set of generators. Thus the group of transformations of a rectangle (Example 2) is generated by $\{R, V\}$ since $I = R \circ R$ and $H = R \circ V$. Moreover, the monoid of positive integers w.r.t. + is finitely generated by $\{1\}$: for $n = 1^n = 1 + 1 + 1 + \cdots$ (n times) for every n.[13]

Example 10 is an example of a *free* monoid. Roughly speaking, in a free system all its properties follow from the axioms alone, together with the properties of equality and the principles of logic. In the instance of Example 10, two elements x, y of A^* are equal iff they are equal symbol by symbol from left to right.[11] Thus $abba \neq bbbb$ while trivially $abba = abba$. If it *were* true that $abba = bbbb$, then this fact certainly could not be proved by the axioms (6a) to (6c).

As previously seen, however, the group of Example 2 is constructed in such a way that there are nontrivial equalities which hold true. For instance, $V \circ H = R$ is a true *relation* among elements of G, whereas it is fairly obvious that that truth does not follow from (6a) to (6d). Thus G is not free.

We shall make considerable use of the concept, so the student should be aware of the distinction between free and nonfree systems. In Section 5.2

[13] If a monoid (or group) has the operation +, it is often referred to as an *additive* monoid. If this convention is used we speak of *products* rather than *powers* of generators and write $(n)\cdot 1$ in lieu of 1^n. The meaning, however, is the same since $(n)\cdot 1 = 1 + 1 + 1 + \cdots (n \text{ times})$.

we shall see that finite transducers, which are the mathematical counterparts of sequential circuits, process input sequences which are elements of a free monoid. As discussed later there are cases of such a kind that if the input sequences are taken from a monoid in which dependencies exist among the elements (for example, supposing $abba = bbbb$), then the circuit could possibly emit two or more different outputs for one and the same input! Also, as discussed in Chapter 8 we want a language to possess the property that its sentences be uniquely decomposable into grammatical constituents, and this property is guaranteed by requiring that the language be a (subset of a) free monoid. Again, taking our simple example, assuming that *abba* and *bbbb* are sentences of some appropriate language and that they are equal, they do not decompose into the same sequence of generators (grammatical parts). We will return to the concept after another example or two and a definition.

EXAMPLE 13. Let $M = \langle \{a, b\}, \cdot, a \rangle$ have the multiplication table shown.

	a	b
a	a	b
b	b	b

In addition to the relation $ab = b = ba$, which is an instance of axiom (6c), we have the relations $bb = b$, $ababb = b$, etc. So M is not free.

We turn next to a generalization of the concept of an isomorphism. Let G and G' be two groups. A mapping φ on G into G' is a *group homomorphism* iff

$$\varphi(a \circ b) = \varphi(a) \cdot \varphi(b) \tag{14}$$

where $a, b \in G$ and $\circ$ and $\cdot$ are the operations of G and G' respectively. As in the case of isomorphism, a homomorphism on groups transforms identities into identities and inverses into inverses. The proof of this fact is analogous to the one for isomorphism.

EXAMPLE 14. Let G be the group of Example 3 with $n = 3$, and let $G' = C$, the group of Example 6. Let φ be the mapping which takes (x_1, x_2, x_3) into (x_1, x_2) or, using the convention of Example 10 about writing sequences,[14]

$$\varphi: x_1x_2x_3 \rightarrow x_1x_2$$

Thus 000 of G goes into 00 of G' and so does 001. Projection φ is a homomorphism, as may be observed from the fact that bitwise addition is defined without *carries* ($1 + 1 = 0$, not 10). The student should verify this observation in detail.

[14] Such a mapping is called a *projection* since it carries an n-tuple into a k-tuple, $k < n$.

Given two monoids, M and M' with sets of elements A and A' and operations $\circ$ and $\cdot$, $\psi: A \rightarrow A'$ is a *monoid homomorphism* if, in perfect analogy to (14),

$$\psi(a \circ b) = \psi(a) \cdot \psi(b) \tag{15}$$

EXAMPLE 15. Let M be the monoid of Example 10 and M' that of Example 13. Next, let φ be *any* arbitrary mapping of A onto A. Then, using (12) to define the mapping of sequences of A^* onto products in M', it is easily shown that φ is a homomorphism. For if x is $s_1 s_2 \cdots s_k$,

$$\varphi(x \circ y) = \varphi(xy) = \varphi(s_1) \cdot \varphi(s_2) \cdots \varphi(s_k) \cdot \varphi(y)$$

using (12) k times, and

$$\varphi(x) \cdot \varphi(y) = \varphi(s_1) \cdot \varphi(s_2) \cdots \varphi(s_k) \cdot \varphi(y)$$

where $s_i = a$ or b and x, y range over sequences in A^*. As an illustration, if $\varphi: a \rightarrow a$ and $\varphi: b \rightarrow b$, then $\varphi(abab) = \varphi(a) \cdot \varphi(b) \cdot \varphi(a) \cdot \varphi(b) = a.b.a.b$. We have shown by (12) that (15) is satisfied.

To show as in the case of groups that identities go into identities, recalling that Λ (null sequence) is the identity of M and a is the identity of M', we have

$$\varphi(x) = a\varphi(x)$$

since a is an identity, and

$$\varphi(\Lambda x) = \varphi(\Lambda)\varphi(x) = \varphi(x)$$

So $\varphi(\Lambda)$ is also an identity; however, by uniqueness we must have $\varphi(\Lambda) = a$.

Returning to the idea of a free monoid, the technical definition is that a *monoid F with generators A is free* iff, for any monoid M' any mapping φ on A into M' can be extended to a homomorphism of F into M'. According to this definition, M of Example 10, as already mentioned, is free in the formally defined sense by using the argument of Example 15. For quite clearly nothing in the argument proving property (15) depended in any way on the structure of M' or on φ, save that M' be a monoid and φ be any mapping, as required by the above definition. By a perfectly analogous argument we can also easily be convinced that any monoid constructed as in Example 10 with any finite number of generators is free in the sense of the technical definition given above.

Moreover, all of the free monoids on a given set of generators are isomorphic to one another, so in effect there is only one such monoid. We shall not, however, stop to prove this fact here.

There is an important connection between homomorphisms and equivalence classes which we may illustrate here for the case of monoids.

Suppose φ is a homomorphism of $M = \langle A, \text{o}, e\rangle$ into $M' = \langle A', \cdot, e'\rangle$. Let R be a relation over A such that

$$a\,R\,b \Leftrightarrow \varphi(a) = \varphi(b) \qquad \text{for any } a, b \in A$$

R is easily checked to be an equivalence relation, and we may as usual designate by $[a]_R$ the class of elements equivalent to a. It is reasonable to ask whether the set of all such classes itself forms a monoid. Let us try to construct one by defining an operation o as follows:

$$[a]_R \circ [b]_R = [a \circ b]_R$$

For this new operation to yield a unique object we must require that the product be independent of the choice a (or b) as representative of the equivalence class $[a]_R$ (or $[b]_R$). That is, we must show

$$[a \circ b]_R = [d \circ c]_R$$

assuming $a\,R\,d$ and $b\,R\,c$. However, if $a\,R\,d$ and $b\,R\,c$ hold true, then, by the above definition of R, $\varphi(a) = \varphi(d)$ and $\varphi(b) = \varphi(c)$. Since φ is a homomorphism, it follows that

$$\varphi(a \circ b) = \varphi(d \circ c)$$

Consequently, $a \circ b\; R\; d \circ c$, or $[a \circ b]_R = [d \circ c]_R$, which was to be shown.

We say that the new system (or, alternatively, the new operation) is *well-defined*. Such a system, whose set of elements is comprised of equivalence classes of elements of M, is called a *quotient monoid* of M *modulo* R, and is designated M/R. Its identity element is $[e]_R$. The equivalence relation R, in virtue of its satisfying the property that $a\,R\,d$ and $b\,R\,c$ imply $a \circ b\; R\; c \circ d$, is called a *congruence relation*. It can be easily seen that M/R is a homomorphic image of M under the mapping $\varphi'(a) = [a]_R$. For

$$\varphi'(a \circ b) = [a \circ b]_R = [a]_R \circ [b]_R = \varphi'(a) \circ \varphi'(b)$$

Such a function as φ' which maps elements onto equivalence classes is called a *canonical* or *natural* function. [See also Exercise 1.3 (10).]

The circle of ideas just discussed occurs throughout abstract algebra and is used heavily in the theory of automata particularly in Chapter 5 and those following it.

Semigroups and groups are among the very basic ingredients of modern algebra. The familiar high school algebra of complex numbers is an abelian group w.r.t. $+$, also an abelian group (with complex numbers except 0) w.r.t. $\times$; moreover, it obeys distributive laws. Such a system is an example of a *field*. A system of elements, with two operations o and $\cdot$, which is an abelian group w.r.t. o, a semigroup w.r.t. $\cdot$, and such that

$a \cdot (b \circ c) = (a \cdot b) \circ (a \cdot c)$ holds for all a, b, c in the system, is a *ring*. Further, if a system is a monoid w.r.t. $\cdot$ it is a ring with *unit*, the unit being the identity element of the monoid. Finally, if in addition the ring has the property $a \cdot a = a$ for every a, it is said to be a *boolean ring*, and $a \cdot a = a$ is an *idempotent* law. It is possible to convert a boolean ring into a boolean algebra by introducing the familiar "and" and "or" by appropriate definitions. We will discuss this procedure in the exercises. For our central exposition, however, we turn to the development of the basic ideas of boolean algebra, which we need frequently in the theory of automata, as a kind of ordered system.

A partially ordered system is an ordered pair $\langle A, R \rangle$ such that A is a set, $R \subseteq A \times A$, and such that if $a, b, c \in A$ are arbitrary elements:

$$\begin{array}{lll} (a) & a\,R\,a, & \text{(reflexive law)} \\ (b) & a\,R\,b \wedge b\,R\,a \Rightarrow a = b & \text{(anti-symmetry law)} \\ (c) & a\,R\,b \wedge b\,R\,c \Rightarrow a\,R\,c & \text{(transitive law)} \end{array} \qquad (16)$$

EXAMPLE 16. If a and b are positive integers we say a divides b, written $a \mid b$, iff there is a c such that $ac = b$. Divides is clearly a relation on the integers since $ac = b$ is such a relation. To prove reflexivity [item a of (16)] $a \mid a$ means by definition that $a = a \cdot c$ for some c. Such a c does exist and equals 1. The remaining properties are to be verified by the student (see Exercises).

EXAMPLE 17. Let $\mathscr{A}$ be the set of subsets of A. Then $\mathscr{A}$ is partially ordered w.r.t. set inclusion. The reflexive and anti-symmetry properties follow from the definition of inclusion and of equality of sets. The transitivity property follows from the known properties of $\Rightarrow$ in propositional logic, as the student may verify for himself.

EXAMPLE 18. The set of real numbers w.r.t. the relation $\leq$. This may be checked for properties (16) by noting that $x \leq y$ is true iff there is a nonnegative real z such that $x + z = y$ (the notation $x \leq y$ means $x < y \vee x = y$).

A *simply ordered* system A is one which is partially ordered and which in addition possesses the property

$$(d) \quad a\,R\,b \vee b\,R\,a \quad \text{for all } a, b \in A \quad \text{(connective law)} \qquad (16)$$

Example 18 is also simply ordered since for real numbers x, y, either $(x < y) \vee (x = y) \vee (y < x)$.

Suppose now that P is a partially ordered set with $P' \subseteq P$. An element $x \in P$ such that $y\,R\,x$ for all $y \in P'$ is an *upperbound* to P'. Furthermore, if x is an upperbound and there is no other upperbound z to P' such that $z\,R\,x$, then x is a *least upperbound* to P'.

Similarly, an element $x \in P$ is a *lowerbound* if for every $y \in P'$, $x \; R \; y$; and x is the *greatest lowerbound* if there is no other lowerbound z such that $x \; R \; z$.

EXAMPLE 19. Consider the set of integers less than or equal to ten, that is, $P' = \{a \mid a \in \text{integer} \wedge a \leq 10\}$. This is a subset of $P =$ the integers. Any one of the integers 10, 11, 12, etc., is an upperbound, and 10 is the least upperbound. In this case $10 \in P'$. If we consider the set P'' of integers less than 10, then 10 is a least upperbound of P'', but $10 \notin P''$. Neither P' nor P'' has a lowerbound—there is no negative integer less than every negative integer.

EXAMPLE 20. Suppose that $\mathscr{A}$, as in previous examples, is the set of subsets of a finite set A; then A is a least upperbound and $\varnothing$ a greatest lowerbound, w.r.t. $\subseteq$, to $\mathscr{A}$. Similarly, any subset of $\mathscr{A}$ will have a least upperbound and a greatest lowerbound. To be more specific, suppose $A = \{a, b, c\}$, then

$$\mathscr{A} = \{\{a, b, c\}, \{a, b\}, \{a, c\}, \{b, c\}, \{a\}, \{b\}, \{c\}, \varnothing\}$$

Now let $\mathscr{B} = \{\{a, b, c\}, \{a, b\}, \{a, c\}, \{a\}\}$; then $\{a, b, c\}$ is the least upperbound since it contains all other elements of $\mathscr{B}$ and no other element does. Also we can see that $\{a\}$ is the greatest lowerbound. On the other hand, if

$$\mathscr{B}' = \{\{a\}, \{b\}, \{c\}\}$$

then $\{a, b, c\}$ is again the least upperbound while $\varnothing$ is the greatest lowerbound. In this example, neither bound is an element of the subset of $\mathscr{A}$ being considered.

Any partially ordered set L which contains for any $a, b \in L$ both the l.u.b. (least upperbound) and g.l.b. (greatest lowerbound) of $\{a, b\}$ is a *lattice*. It is customary to write $a \cup b$ for the l.u.b. of a and b and $a \cap b$ for the g.l.b. (these symbols are read *join* and *meet* respectively). Thus L is a lattice iff for all $a, b \in L$

$$(\exists c)(c \in L \wedge a \cup b = c) \wedge (\exists c')(c' \in L \wedge a \cap b = c') \tag{17}$$

The set $\mathscr{A}$ of Example 20 is a lattice, as the student may verify by observing that every pair of elements in $\mathscr{A}$ has a l.u.b. and a g.l.b. again in $\mathscr{A}$. In addition, the student should satisfy himself that $\cup$ may be interpreted as set union and $\cap$ as set intersection. *Caution*: There are lattices of sets for which the join is *not* the set union. For instance, $\{\varnothing, \{a\}, \{b\}, \{a, b, c\}\}$ is a lattice under $\subseteq$; but $\{a\} \cup \{b\}$ is $\{a, b, c\}$ and not $\{a\} \cup \{b\} = \{a, b\}$.

From the foregoing definitions it follows that

$$a \; R \; b \Leftrightarrow a \cup b = b \tag{18a}$$

and

$$a \, R \, b \Leftrightarrow a \cap b = a \tag{18b}$$

where $a, b \in L$ and R is the partial ordering. That is, if $a \, R \, b$, then b is the l.u.b. of $\{a, b\}$, and obviously a is the g.l.b. of $\{a, b\}$.

EXAMPLE 21. Let P be the real plane and x_1, x_2, y_1, y_2 real variables. We shall say that a point (x_1, y_1) is less than or equal to a point (x_2, y_2) iff $x_1 \leq x_2 \wedge y_1 \leq y_2$. This will be written $(x_1, y_1) \leq (x_2, y_2)$. It may be easily checked that this relation is a partial (but not a simple) ordering. Now, for any pair of points the l.u.b. exists, since if such a pair is (x_1, y_1) and (x_2, y_2), then the point $(\max(x_1, x_2), \max(y_1, y_2))$ certainly satisfies the definition of l.u.b. Similarly, the g.l.b. is given by

$$(\min(x_1, x_2), \min(y_1, y_2))$$ [15]

We may also write

$$(\max(x_1, x_2), \max(y_1, y_2)) = (x_1, y_1) \cup (x_2, y_2)$$

and similarly for the g.l.b.

EXAMPLE 22. The partially ordered system on $\{0, 1\}$, with $\leq$. By (18a) we have $0 \cup 0 = 0$, $1 \cup 1 = 1$, $0 \cup 1 = 1$; and by (18b) $1 \cap 1 = 1$, $0 \cap 1 = 0$, $0 \cap 0 = 0$. After we have shown commutativity of the join and meet operations we shall have $1 \cup 0 = 1$ and $1 \cap 0 = 0$ as well. Students who are familiar with switching theory will not fail to notice that if we add $\bar{0} = 1$ and $\bar{1} = 0$, this example is a (two-element) boolean algebra.

Lattices are frequently treated as generalizations of boolean algebras. In this sense they are algebraic w.r.t. the operations $\cup$ and $\cap$, and may or may not satisfy the usual distributive or complementation laws of boolean algebras [see (19f) and (19g)]. One system of axioms is given by (19a) to (19d′).

For every $a, b, c \in L$,

$$\left.\begin{aligned} a \cap a &= a \\ a \cup a &= a \end{aligned}\right\} \quad \text{(idempotent laws)} \qquad \begin{aligned} &(19a) \\ &(19a') \end{aligned}$$

$$\left.\begin{aligned} a \cup b &= b \cup a \\ a \cap b &= b \cap a \end{aligned}\right\} \quad \text{(commutative laws)} \qquad \begin{aligned} &(19b) \\ &(19b') \end{aligned}$$

$$\left.\begin{aligned} (a \cup b) \cup c &= a \cup (b \cup c) \\ (a \cap b) \cap c &= a \cap (b \cap c) \end{aligned}\right\} \quad \text{(associative laws)} \qquad \begin{aligned} &(19c) \\ &(19c') \end{aligned}$$

$$\left.\begin{aligned} a \cup (a \cap b) &= a \\ a \cap (a \cup b) &= a \end{aligned}\right\} \quad \text{(absorption laws)} \qquad \begin{aligned} &(19d) \\ &(19d') \end{aligned}$$

[15] Max (x_1, x_2) is the greater of x_1 and x_2, or x_1 if $x_1 = x_2$, and min (x_1, x_2) is the lesser of x_1 and x_2, or x_1 if $x_1 = x_2$.

Each of the four pairs of axioms has the property that either pair member is derivable from the other by systematically replacing joins by meets and meets by joins. Two formulas in lattice theory which reciprocate in this way are *duals*.

The axioms (19a) to (19d′) are immediate consequences of the definition of the lattice in terms of the partial ordering relation. Thus (19a) and (19a′) follow from (18a) and (18b) by substituting a for b and assuming that L is partially ordered. The remaining laws (19) are also implied by the definition; this implication should be followed through by the student.

Conversely, if we assume that L has the properties given by principles (19), we may prove that L is partially ordered and contains the l.u.b. and g.l.b. with every $a, b \in L$. To do this, we now consider the partial ordering relation $\leq$ as a new concept introduced by definition: $a \leq b$ means $a \cup b = b$ [thus we have (18a) not as a consequence of the first definition of a lattice but as a definition introducing a new symbol in terms of the undefined symbol $\cup$ occurring in the assumed axioms]. By this definition $\cup$ has the meaning *least upper bound*. By axiom (19d′), if $a \cup b = b$, then $a \cap (a \cup b) = a \cap b = a$; so $a \cap b$ has the meaning *greatest lower bound*. It can now be shown that every $a, b \in L$ does have a l.u.b. and g.l.b. in L and that the appropriate properties attach to $\leq$ as above defined. [See Exercise 1.3 (15)].

All of the lattices which we shall find useful to us will contain a *greatest* and a *least* element. An element a of a partially ordered set P is greatest iff for every $x \in P$, $x \leq a$, and similarly b is least iff for every $x \in P$, $b \leq x$. These elements are denoted by 1 and 0, respectively, and satisfy the laws

$$0 \cup x = x \quad 0 \cap x = 0 \quad 1 \cup x = 1 \quad 1 \cap x = x \quad \text{for all } x \tag{19e}$$

These relations together with the fact of uniqueness of both 0 and 1 may be established directly from the definition. (See Exercises 1.3).

EXAMPLE 23. Let $A = \{a, b, c\}$ and further let $\mathscr{P}$ be the set of all the partitions (see Section 1.1) of A. This set $\mathscr{P}$ is a family of families and has five elements. For instance, two of them are $P_1 = \{\{a, b, c\}\}$ and $P_2 = \{\{a, b\}, \{c\}\}$. Now let $P_i \leq P_j$ mean that if x, y are in the same set in P_i, then they are in the same set in P_j, for every $x, y \in A$. According to this definition, $P_2 \leq P_1$, since $a, b \in \{a, b\}$ in P_2 and also $a, b \in \{a, b, c\}$ in P_1 etc. Moreover, $x, y, \in P_1 \cap P_2$ means that x, y are in the same set in P_1 and are also in the same set in P_2. Similarly, the join operation $\cup$ may be suitably defined (compare Section 5.5). $\mathscr{P}$, understood in line with these natural constructions, is a lattice.

A *boolean algebra* is a lattice which satisfies, besides (19a) to (19d′), a certain *distributive law* and contains for every element a *complement* as characterized below.

$$a \cap (b \cup c) = (a \cap b) \cup (a \cap c) \quad \text{for all } a, b, c \quad \text{(distributive law)} \qquad (19f)$$

For every a there is an element $\bar{a}$ such that

$$a \cup \bar{a} = 1 \qquad \text{and} \qquad a \cap \bar{a} = 0 \qquad \text{(existence of complement)} \quad (19g)$$

We may prove, as a theorem, the dual of (19f)

$$\begin{aligned}
a \cup (b \cap c) &= (a \cup a) \cup (b \cap c) && \text{by (19a}')\\
&= a \cup (a \cup (b \cap c)) && \text{by (19c)}\\
&= (a \cup (b \cap c)) \cup a && \text{by (19b)}\\
&= (a \cup (b \cap c)) \cup (a \cup (a \cap c)) && \text{by (19d)}\\
&= (a \cup a) \cup ((b \cap c) \cup (a \cap c)) && \text{by associativity and commutativity}\\
&= a \cup ((b \cap c) \cup (a \cap c)) && \text{by (19a}')\\
&= a \cup ((c \cap b) \cup (c \cap a)) && \text{by (19b}')\\
&= a \cup (c \cap (a \cup b)) && \text{by (19f)}\\
&= a \cup ((a \cup b) \cap c) && \text{by (19b}')\\
&= ((a \cup b) \cap a) \cup ((a \cup b) \cap c) && \text{by (19d)}\\
&= (a \cup b) \cap (a \cup c) && \text{by (19f)}
\end{aligned}$$

We may also prove a cancellation law and the uniqueness of complements. The cancellation law we wish to prove asserts that if $a \cup b = a \cup c$ and $a \cap b = a \cap c$ *both* hold, then $b = c$. For, assuming the first,

$$\begin{aligned}
b = (a \cup b) \cap b &= (a \cup c) \cap b && \text{by (19d}') \text{ and (19b}')\\
&= (a \cap b) \cup (c \cap b) &&\\
&= (a \cap c) \cup (c \cap b) && \text{by the second assumption}\\
&= (a \cup b) \cap c &&\\
&= (a \cup c) \cap c = c &&
\end{aligned}$$

using principles which the student may supply for himself. Consequently,

$$(a \cup b = a \cup c) \wedge (a \cap b = a \cap c) \Rightarrow b = c \qquad (19h)$$

To show uniqueness of complements, suppose $a \cup b = 1$ and $a \cap b = 0$; then since $a \cup \bar{a} = 1$ and $a \cap \bar{a} = 0$, we obtain by (19h) the result $b = \bar{a}$. Also $\bar{0} = 1$ and $\bar{1} = 0$ since $0 \cup \bar{0} = \bar{0} = 1$, etc.

EXAMPLE 24. The family $\{A_1, A_2, \ldots\}$ of all subsets of any finite set $A = A_1$. (Example 20 is an instance.) A_1 is the 1 element and $\varnothing$ the 0 element. Using our first characterization of lattices in terms of $\leq$, we note that set inclusion $\subseteq$ is a partial ordering and that, $A_i \bigcup A_j$ and $A_i \bigcap A_j$ (set union and intersection) are defined for all $i, j = 1, 2, \ldots$. Moreover, $A_i \bigcup A_j$ is the l.u.b. since $A_i, A_j \subseteq A_i \bigcup A_j$ by definition of $\bigcup$ and if

$A_i, A_j \subseteq B$, then $A_i \bigcup A_j \subseteq B$, as the student may check for himself. From our previous discussion, this allows us to conclude that (19a) to (19e) are fulfilled with $\bigcup$ in the role of $\cup$ and $\bigcap$ of $\cap$. The distributive law may be proved in the style of (16), Section 1.1.

Finally, we mean by $\bar{A}_i$, $A_1 - A_i$ or $1 - A_i$. Then,

$$\begin{aligned} x \in A_i \bigcup \bar{A}_i &\Leftrightarrow x \in \{x \mid x \in A_i \vee (x \in 1 \wedge x \notin A_i)\} \\ &\Leftrightarrow x \in \{x \mid x \in 1\} \Leftrightarrow x \in 1 \end{aligned} \tag{20}$$

So $A_i \bigcup \bar{A}_i = 1$. In an analogous manner we may obtain $A_i \bigcap \bar{A}_i = \varnothing$.

If B and B' are boolean algebras with 1, 1′ and 0, 0′, respectively, then a function $\varphi: B \rightarrow B'$ is a *boolean homomorphism* if

$$\varphi(a \cup b) = \varphi(a) \cup \varphi(b) \tag{21a}$$

$$\varphi(a \cap b) = \varphi(a) \cap \varphi(b) \tag{21b}$$

and

$$\varphi(\bar{a}) = \overline{\varphi(a)} \tag{21c}$$

where $a, b \in B$. It may be shown that 0 maps into 0′ and 1 into 1′ (cf. Exercise 20).

We note that

$$a \leq b \Rightarrow \varphi(a) \leq \varphi(b) \tag{22}$$

because $a \leq b \Leftrightarrow b = a \cup b$ and by (21a),

$$\varphi(a \cup b) = \varphi(a) \cup \varphi(b) = \varphi(b)$$

An *isomorphism* is a one–one onto homomorphism. It is interesting to observe that if φ is a one–one correspondence, then (22) and its converse imply (21a), (21b), and (21c); so that a boolean isomorphism may be defined as a one–one onto function satisfying (22) and its converse.

EXAMPLE 25. Let $\mathscr{A}$ be the boolean algebra of subsets of $\{a, b, c\}$ and let B be the two element boolean algebra on the elements $\{0, 1\}$ (Example 22). Now let φ be given by the rule that it maps an element $x \in \mathscr{A}$ into 1 if x contains b and into 0 otherwise. Then φ is a homomorphism.

EXAMPLE 26. Let A be the set of all functions of n variables $x_1, x_2, \ldots, x_n$ whose domain is the collection of all n-tuples of 0's and 1's and whose range is $\{0, 1\}$. If f, g, h are such functions, then we stipulate that

$$\begin{aligned} f \cup g = h \Leftrightarrow f(x_1, x_2, \ldots, x_n) &\cup g(x_1, x_2, \ldots, x_n) \\ &= h(x_1, x_2, \ldots, x_n) \end{aligned}$$

and

$$\begin{aligned} f \cap g = h \Leftrightarrow f(x_1, x_2, \ldots, x_n) &\cap g(x_1, x_2, \ldots, x_n) \\ &= h(x_1, x_2, \ldots, x_n) \end{aligned}$$

for all 2^n combinations of values of the variables.

We want further to require that {0, 1} is a two-element boolean algebra (Example 22). The algebra of functions we have constructed in this way is a 2^{2^n}-element boolean algebra. Such functions are *boolean functions.*

We order the values of f_i in some way, obtaining a sequence of 2^n function values $f_{i0}, f_{i1}, f_{i3}, \ldots, f_{i2^n-1}$. To illustrate this technique and to provide one more very convenient convention, consider the case $n = 2$ (Table 1.3.4).

TABLE 1.3.4

	x_1x_2	f_0	f_1						...								f_{15}
(0)	00	0	0	0	0	0	0	0	0	1	1	1	1	1	1	1	1
(1)	01	0	0	0	0	1	1	1	1	0	0	0	0	1	1	1	1
(2)	10	0	0	1	1	0	0	1	1	0	0	1	1	0	0	1	1
(3)	11	0	1	0	1	0	1	0	1	0	1	0	1	0	1	0	1

In the argument column to the left, the values of the variables x_1x_2 are listed in an order determined by the decimal equivalent of x_1x_2 considered as a binary number. Also the functions are indexed by the numbers 0 to $2^{2^n} - 1$ (= 15 in the example) according to the decimal equivalents of the column of function values considered as binary numbers. Moreover, the kth value of the ith function f_i is written f_{ik}. The function labeled f_1, for example, has the value 0 for the 0th argument; that is, $f_{10} = 0$. And similarly, $f_{11} = 0, f_{12} = 0$, and $f_{13} = 1$.

Now, for any two functions f_i, f_j, $0 \leq i, j \leq 2^{2^n} - 1$, and any k such that $0 \leq k \leq 2^n - 1$, $f_{ik} \cup f_{jk}$ and $f_{ik} \cap f_{jk}$ exist since both f_{ik} and f_{jk} are 0 or 1, and {0, 1} is a boolean algebra. Therefore by our definitions, $f \cup g$ and $f \cap g$ exist for all functions f and g. Furthermore, for any n, f_0 is the zero (0-element) and $f_{2^{2^n}-1}$ is the one (1-element) of our system. It is now a routine matter to check the remaining axioms (19).

We next construct the *free boolean algebra on n generators* $F = \langle \mathscr{B}, \cup, \cap, 0, 1 \rangle$. This system is relevant to our subject since it is the algebra used in switching theory. Begin with the sequence of generators $a_1, a_2, \ldots, a_n$, and first construct all possible *elementary meets* of these elements $a_1' \cap a_2' \cap \cdots \cap a_n'$, where $a_i' = a_i$ or $\overline{a}_i$. There are 2^n of these. Call the set of all such elements thus formed B. Second, form all of the joins of these meets taking the elements of B zero at a time, one at a time, two at a time, etc., but in just one fixed order. (That is, do *not* count $b \cup c$ and $c \cup b$ as distinct joins of meets $b, c \in B$.) There are thus 2^{2^n} elements constructed by this procedure, and the result is $\mathscr{B}$. The null join will be the 0 element of the algebra we are constructing and the join of all 2^n meets will be the 1 element.

We demonstrate that F is a boolean algebra by proving that it is isomorphic to the system of functions A of the previous example. To each element $b_i \in \mathscr{B}$ we associate a function f_i of Example 26 in the following manner. If $a_1' \cap a_2' \cap \cdots \cap a_n'$ is an elementary meet in b_i, then to this expression we associate the sequence of arguments $x_1, x_2, \ldots, x_n$ such that x_i is 1 if $a_i' = a_i$ and x_i is 0 if $a_i' = \overline{a_i}$. The function f_i is that function having the value 1 for all and only the combinations of argument values $x_1, x_2, \ldots, x_n$ associated to the elementary meets of b_i by this rule. Thus to each b_i there corresponds a unique function f_i. Conversely, by the same rule, each function f_i corresponds uniquely to a b_i. Under this one–one correspondence, the element 0 of F corresponds to f_0 of A (Example 26), and the 1-element of F corresponds to $f_{2^{2^n}-1}$.

To show isomorphism, let φ be the one–one correspondence constructed in the foregoing discussion. Let us now mean by $b_i \leq b_j$ that every elementary meet in b_i occurs also in b_j. This is a partial ordering, with 0 and 1 the least and greatest elements, respectively. Next assume that $f_i \leq f_j$, $f_i, f_j \in A$. This means [considering that $f_j = f_i \cup f_j$, by (18a)] the same as stating that f_j has the value 1 whenever f_i has the value 1. So if $\varphi(f_i) = b_i$ and $\varphi(f_j) = b_j$, it follows by our constructions that b_j has an elementary meet $a_1' \cap a_2' \cap \cdots \cap a_n'$ whenever b_i does. Therefore $b_i \leq b_j$, and (22) is satisfied. Therefore F is a boolean algebra.

If χ is a mapping on $\{a_1, a_2, \ldots, a_n\}$ into a boolean algebra B, then by appropriate constructions one can show that χ can be extended to a homomorphism of F into B, thus establishing that F is free.

EXERCISES 1.3

1. Given a set A and two permutations on A, prove that their product is a permutation.

2. Prove that the identity of a group is unique and that each inverse is unique. Prove that in any group $(ab)^{-1} = b^{-1}a^{-1}$.

3. Prove that (6c) and (6d) are consequences of (6a), (6b), (6c′), and (6d′).

4. Construct the group of permutations of three letters $\{a, b, c\}$ and prove that your construction is a group. Identify the identity and inverses.

5. Let M be the system $\langle\{1, 5, 7, 11\}, \times, 1\rangle$ where $a \times b$ is defined to be the remainder on division of $a \cdot b$ by 12, $\cdot$ being ordinary multiplication. For example, $5 \times 7 = 11$ $[35 = 2 \cdot 12 + 11]$.

(*a*) Prove that M is a group with identity 1.

(*b*) Prove that M is isomorphic to the group of transformations of a rectangle.

6. Explain why it is that, in the proof of the infinity of the monoid M in Example 10, the binary number system cannot be used to play the role performed by the dyadic system.

7. Prove that the monoid of Example 11 is infinite. Identify the generators alluded to in Example 12.

8. (*a*) Is the system in the following table a monoid?

	a	b
a	b	a
b	a	a

(*b*) Are there any monoids with two elements nonisomorphic to M of Example 13? Are there any two element monoids to which M is homomorphic?

9. Complete the required proof for Example 16.

10. Assume φ is a homomorphism of a monoid M onto M' and that M/R is the quotient monoid modulo R, R having been defined as in the text. Prove M/R and M' are isomorphic.

11. A linearly ordered system L may be defined as one having a relation $<$ such that

(*a*) $(a < b) \wedge (b < c) \Rightarrow (a < c)$

(*b*) $((a < b) \vee (a = b) \vee (b < a)) \wedge \neg(((a < b) \wedge (a = b)) \vee ((a < b) \wedge (b < a)) \vee ((a = b) \wedge (b < a)))$

Show that if L is linearly ordered w.r.t. $<$ then it is simply ordered w.r.t. some R as defined in (16a) to (16d).

12. Formalize the definition of l.u.b. and g.l.b. using quantifiers and the logic connectives $\wedge$, $\vee$, $\neg$.

13. With I being the set of positive integers prove that $\langle I, \cup, \cap \rangle$ is a lattice when $a \cup b$ is interpreted to mean the lowest common multiple of a and b, and $a \cap b$ is interpreted to mean the greatest common divisor of a and b [(19a) to (19d′)].

14. Prove that any lattice has *at most* one greatest and one least element. Prove (19e).

15. Verify that the lattice axioms are consequences of the definition of lattices in terms of partial orderings.

Conversely, continuing the discussion in the text, prove that $\leq$, when *defined* by $a \leq b \Leftrightarrow a \cup b = b$, and assuming the lattice axioms, is, in fact, a partial ordering.

16. Prove that in boolean algebras the following theorems hold. (Prove either one of each dual pair.)

(*a*) $\overline{(a \cup b)} = \bar{a} \cap \bar{b}$ (DeMorgan's theorems)

$\overline{(a \cap b)} = \bar{a} \cup \bar{b}$

Hint: Prove $(a \cup b) \cup (\bar{a} \cap \bar{b}) = 1$ and $(a \cup b) \cap (\bar{a} \cap \bar{b}) = 0$.

(*b*) $\bar{\bar{a}} = a$; hence $\bar{\bar{0}} = 0$, $\bar{\bar{1}} = 1$

(*c*) $(\bar{a} \cap b) \cup (b \cap c) \cup (a \cap c) = (\bar{a} \cap b) \cup (a \cap c)$

$(\bar{a} \cup b) \cap (b \cup c) \cap (a \cup c) = (\bar{a} \cup b) \cap (a \cup c)$

(*d*) $(a \cup b = c \cup b) \wedge (a \cap b = c \cap b) \Rightarrow a = c$

(*e*) $a \leq b \Rightarrow \bar{b} \leq \bar{a}$

17. A *boolean ring with unit* is a system $\langle S, +, \cdot, 0, 1 \rangle$ satisfying the following axioms.

For all $a, b, c \in S$:

There is a $d \in S$ such that $a + b = d$ (1)

$(a + b) + c = a + (b + c)$ (2)

$a + b = b + a$ (3)

$0 + a = a + 0 = a$ (4)

There is an element $-a$ such that $a + (-a) = (-a) + a = 0$ (5)

There is a $d \in S$ such that $a \cdot b = d$ (6)

$(a \cdot b) \cdot c = a \cdot (b \cdot c)$ (7)

$a \cdot 1 = 1 \cdot a = a$ (8)

$a \cdot a = a$ (9)

$a \cdot (b + c) = (a \cdot b) + (a \cdot c)$ (10)

$(b + c) \cdot a = (b \cdot a) + (c \cdot a)$ (11)

(a) Prove $a = -a$ for every $a \in S$.

(b) Prove $a \cdot b = b \cdot a$ for every $a, b \in S$.

Hint for part (a): Show that $a + b = a + ab + ba + b$ and then use (5) and (9) and uniqueness property of inverse.

(c) Define $\bar{a}$ to mean $a + 1$

$a \cup b$ to mean $a + b + ab$

$a \cap b$ to mean $a \cdot b$

Show that $\langle S, \cup, \cap, 0, 1 \rangle$ is a boolean algebra.

18. Given a boolean algebra $\langle S, \cup, \cap, 0, 1 \rangle$, define

$a + b$ to mean $(a \cap \bar{b}) \cup (\bar{a} \cap b)$

$a \cdot b$ to mean $a \cap b$

Prove that the system $\langle S, +, \cdot, 0, 1 \rangle$ is a boolean ring.

19. The boolean expressions which are written as joins of elementary meets as in the construction of the free algebra in the foregoing discussions are said to be *canonical* forms. Show that every boolean function can be written in canonical form.

20. Verify that an *onto* boolean homomorphism may be characterized as a function φ satisfying

$$\varphi(a \cup b) = \varphi(a) \cup \varphi(b)$$

and

$$\varphi(a \cap b) = \varphi(a) \cap \varphi(b)$$

21. Prove the assertion that for a one–one correspondence (22) implies (21a), (21b), and (21c).

1.4 REFERENCES

The foregoing pages are an exposition of standard elementary material. They draw heavily on Birkhoff [1948], Birkhoff and MacLane [1953], Chevalley [1956], and Kleene [1952].

CHAPTER 2

Functions of Integers

2.0 Introduction. Sooner or later in the theory of automata, we must consider the nature of procedures which can be performed mechanically or by following a set of rules. Indeed the idea of an automaton implies not only "self action" or "self-controlled action," but "machinelike" or rote action as well. It turns out that the study of systems of formal rules or of prescribed procedures for applying rules depends heavily on certain ideas in arithmetic and especially on the properties of certain functions of integers. Roughly speaking we are interested in knowing what sorts of problems are subject to solution by rules and what sorts of machines can embody (or are equivalent to) such rules. The standard procedure for answering such questions is to reduce the problem to one about the evaluation of functions of the nonnegative integers. The question, then, is whether the representative function can be calculated by following a recipe (by a clerk) or only by the use of brains.

In the following discussion we will assume that the student is familiar with elementary number theory to the extent of knowing (1) what a prime number is; (2) that there is an infinite number of primes; (3) the fundamental theorem of arithmetic (cf. Example 12 in Section 1.3); and (4) elementary arithmetic operations.

2.1 RECURSIVE FUNCTIONS

Although many properties of the integers[1] may be deduced from the fact that they satisfy certain algebras, these systems fail to elicit certain intrinsic properties of integers evident to the intuition. The principal properties are that (1) the numbers can be constructed (or generated) from 0 uniquely and (2) whenever a property that holds for one number also holds for the next number in the generation, then that property holds for *all* integers.

[1] Throughout this section and later ones "integer" means "nonnegative integer" unless otherwise stated.

The second property noted is the gist of the principle of mathematical induction which is so pervasive that it requires some discussion.

Definition 2.1.1. *Principle of mathematical induction*: If 0 has a property P,[2] and when any integer n is P, then $n + 1$ is P; then every integer is P. The principle is used in proving statements about integers or, derivatively, in proving statements about systems of objects of any kind which can be correlated with the integers. The procedure is to *prove*

(*a*) 0 is P (induction *basis*)

to *assume*

(*b*) n is P (induction *hypothesis*)

to *prove*

(*c*) $n + 1$ is P (induction *step*)

using (*a*) and (*b*); and to *conclude*

(*d*) n is P, for all n

EXAMPLE 1.

$$\sum_{i=0}^{n} i = \frac{n(n + 1)}{2}$$

To begin, we must state the property which we want to prove. This statement is called the *induction proposition*. In this case P is given directly by

$$n \text{ is } P \Leftrightarrow \sum_{i=0}^{n} i = \frac{n(n + 1)}{2}$$

(*a*) For the *basis* of the induction we have, for $n = 0$, $0 = (0 \cdot 1)/2$.

(*b*) The induction *hypothesis* is that k is P for some arbitrary choice of k:

$$\sum_{i=0}^{k} i = 0 + 1 + 2 + \cdots + k = \frac{k(k + 1)}{2}$$

(*c*) For the induction step, proving $k + 1$ is P, we have

$$\sum_{i=0}^{k+1} i = \sum_{i=0}^{k} i + (k + 1) = \frac{k(k + 1)}{2} + (k + 1)$$

(using the induction hypothesis)

$$= \frac{(k + 1)[(k + 1) + 1]}{2}$$

[2] That is, 0 satisfies the predicate P, or simply, 0 is P.

(*d*) Hence k has the property P^2 for any k. Here we have assumed the usual algebraic properties of numbers as learned in high school.

The principle of induction is also valid if at step (*b*), the induction hypothesis, we assume that every $k \leq n$ is P. Moreover, one may choose any integer as a basis and then prove that some property of interest holds for the set of integers greater than or equal to the basis. We will illustrate these equivalent modifications.

The next example not only illustrates the use of induction but introduces some ideas which are of interest in themselves.

EXAMPLE 2. Suppose S is a set of *symbols* $\{s_1, s_2, \ldots, s_n\}$ and $\{o_1, o_2, \ldots, o_m\}$ are *connectives* for constructing *formulas* using elements of S. For instance, our symbols might denote elements of a boolean algebra and our connectives might be $\cup, \cap, -$. Formulas may be constructed using symbols and connectives according to certain rules which prevent formation of meaningless sequences. Thus, in the usual discussions of boolean algebra, we would regard

$$((\overline{s_{i_1} \cup s_{i_2}}) \cap (s_{i_3} \cup \bar{s}_{i_4})) \tag{1}$$

as meaningful, but not

$$) \, s_{i_1} \cap \cup \overline{} (\cap \, s_{i2} \tag{2}$$

The first example is *well-formed* according to rules we have not yet made explicit, whereas the second one is not. Deferring a general discussion of such rules to Chapter 3 note that (1) might be written in *Polish notation* as follows:

$$\cap - \cup s_{i_1} s_{i_2} \cup s_{i_3} - s_{i_4} \tag{3}$$

The rules of translation we have used to derive (3) from (1) are $(x \cup y) \to \cup\, xy$, $(x \cap y) \to \cap\, xy$ and $\bar{x} \to -x$, where x and y are any well-formed formulas or the result of a prior application of the rules. Thus from (1), successively, one might have

$$\begin{array}{l}
(\overline{\cup s_{i_1} s_{i_2}} \cap (s_{i_3} \cup \bar{s}_{i_4})) \\
(- \cup s_{i_1} s_{i_2} \cap (s_{i_3} \cup \bar{s}_{i_4})) \\
\cap - \cup s_{i_1} s_{i_2} (s_{i_3} \cup \bar{s}_{i_4})) \\
\cap - \cup s_{i_1} s_{i_2} \cup s_{i_3} \bar{s}_{i_4} \\
\cap - \cup s_{i_1} s_{i_2} \cup s_{i_3} - s_{i_4}
\end{array}$$

Ignoring this introductory derivation and the original normal formulation of expressions, let us continue again. To each connective o_1, o_2, etc., we associate a *degree n*. In terms of the example, $\cup$ and $\cap$ are of degree 2 since they connect two formulas or symbols, whereas $-$ is of degree 1 since it "connects" one. A *formula* is given by the definition:

(*a*) a single symbol is a formula,
(*b*) if $x_1, x_2, \ldots, x_n$ are formulas and o_i is of degree n, then $o_i x_1 x_2 \cdots x_n$ is a formula,
(*c*) only expressions formed by (*a*) and (*b*) are formulas.

Thus expression (3) may be checked out as a formula since, beginning at the right, s_{i_4} is a symbol and hence by (*a*) a formula; $-$ is of degree 1, so $-s_{i_4}$ is a formula; s_{i_3} is a symbol, hence a formula; $\cup$ is of degree 2, so $\cup s_{i_3} - s_{i_4}$ is a formula, etc.

The *rank* of a formula is determined as follows;

(*d*) the rank of a symbol is -1,
(*e*) the rank of a connective is $n - 1$ where n is the degree,
(*f*) the rank of an arbitrary sequence of symbols and connectives is the sum of the ranks of the individual symbols and connectives.

We shall now prove that if a sequence is a formula in Polish notation, then it has a rank -1. The proof is by *induction on the length* of formulas. Our induction proposition is

> n has the property of being the length of an expression such that if the expression is well-formed it has a rank of -1.

This statement is of course clumsy, but it does emphasize that we are proving a property of numbers.

If F is a formula of length 1, then by (*a*) above it must be a symbol, and by (*d*) it has a rank of -1. So 1 has the property, and this completes the basis step. For the induction step we assume that every formula of length $k \le n$ has rank -1. We must show that if F has length $n + 1$, it has a rank of -1. By (*b*), F is of the form

$$o_i\, x_1 x_2 x_3 \cdots x_m \quad (l(x_j) \le n) \quad j = 1, \ldots, m. \tag{4}$$

where each x_i is well-formed. By the induction hypothesis each x_i has, therefore, a rank of -1. Moreover, by (*e*) o_i must have rank $m - 1$. So by (*f*) the rank of formula (4) must be

$$m - 1 + [(-1) + (-1) + \cdots + (-1)(m \text{ times})] = -1$$

This completes the induction.

The inductive properties of numbers are interesting for their usefulness in proofs by induction and also, more essentially, because automata theory is a part of the larger theory of inductive processes. We proceed to the development of some of the basic ideas.

The notion of formula in the preceding example is inductive, and, in fact, provides for the construction of formulas out of a finite number of starter elements plus a rule of combination giving new elements. Such a procedure for constructing sets of objects of any kind whatsoever is an inductive definition of a set or predicate. The standard form of such a definition is given by the following.

Definition 2.1.2. *Inductive definition* of a property or set P: given a finite set A,

(*a*) the elements of A are P (*basis clause*) (5a)
(*b*) the elements of B, all of which are constructed from A, are P (*inductive clause*) (5b)
(*c*) the elements constructed as in (*a*) and (*b*) are the only elements of P (*extremal clause*) (5c)

As an example, returning to the nonnegative integers, the inductive definition, which uses the operation of successor [compare (6a)] to produce new integers, is written

(*a*) 0 is an integer,
(*b*) if x is an integer, so is the successor of x,
(*c*) the integers are only those entities constructed by 1 and 2.

By a sequence of definitions we are now going to construct a precise formulation of the intuitive idea of a mechanical procedure or algorithm for solving problems. Our first aim will be the inductive definition of a certain class of functions. These will be the functions which can be computed by algorithm.

We consider functions on n-tuples of the integers into the integers. Any n-ary function whose domain is the whole set of n-tuples of integers is *total*, otherwise it is *partial*. The 2-ary function $x_1 + x_2$, for example, is total since the set of integers is closed for addition. We say that the function is *defined* for all pairs (x_1, x_2). On the other hand, subtraction is partial since it is defined only for the set of pairs (x_1, x_2) such that $x_1 \geq x_2$.

We start with an initial set of three functions in order to define a class which we will call the class of *recursive functions*. These functions are:

$$S(x) = x + 1 \quad \text{(successor function)} \tag{6a}$$
$$N(x) = 0 \quad \text{(zero function)} \tag{6b}$$
$$I_i^n(x_1, x_2, \ldots, x_n) = x_i \quad \text{(generalized identity function)} \tag{6c}$$

An example of (6c) is $I_2^4(3, 6, 7, 8) = 6$. The other two are self-explanatory. Turning next to the inductive step of the definition, we introduce three operations on functions: composition, minimalization, and primitive recursion.

Since we are dealing in general with functions of n variables, the concept of composition will be considerably more complicated than it was in Section 1.3. Let the ambiguous values of m partial functions of n variables be

$$g_1(x_1, \ldots, x_n), g_2(x_1, \ldots, x_n), \ldots, g_m(x_1, \ldots, x_n)$$

and let the domains of these functions be the sets of n-tuples of integers D_k, where $1 \leq k \leq m$. Now let f be the m-ary function whose domain includes the set of m-tuples of values

$$(g_1(a_1, \ldots, a_n), g_2(a_1, \ldots, a_n), \ldots, g_m(a_1, \ldots, a_n))$$

of the functions g_i for which

$$(a_1, \ldots, a_n) \in \bigcap_{k \in I} D_k, \qquad I = \{k \mid 1 \leq k \leq m\}$$

Then the *composition* h of $f, g_1, \ldots, g_m$ is given by

$$h(x_1, \ldots, x_n) = f(g_1(x_1, \ldots, x_n), \ldots, g_m(x_1, \ldots, x_n)) \tag{7}$$

and is defined for every $(x_1, \ldots, x_n) \in \bigcap_{k \in I} D_k$.

EXAMPLE 3. Suppose that $f(x, y) = x + y$, $g_1(x, y) = x - y$, $g_2(x, y) = x \cdot y$; then

$$\begin{aligned} h(x, y) &= f(g_1(x, y), g_2(x, y)) \\ &= g_1(x, y) + g_2(x, y) \\ &= (x - y) + x \cdot y \end{aligned}$$

This function h is defined for the set of pairs $(g_1(a, b), g_2(a, b))$ such that $(a, b) \in D_1 \cap D_2 = D_1$; D_1 is the set of pairs (x, y) such that $x \leq y$. D_2 is the set of all pairs. The student should characterize the domain and range of h specifically.

Given the total function f of n-variables $x_1, \ldots, x_n$ and g of $n + 2$ variables $y, z, x_1, \ldots, x_n$, the operation of *primitive recursion* yields a function h of $n + 1$ variables whose values are given by

$$\begin{aligned} h(0, x_1, \ldots, x_n) &= f(x_1, \ldots, x_n) \\ h(y + 1, x_1, \ldots, x_n) &= g(y, h(y, x_1, \ldots, x_n), x_1, \ldots, x_n) \end{aligned} \tag{8}$$

Function h is always a total function. In this definition, y is called the *recursion variable* and $x_1, \ldots, x_n$ are *parameters*. Notice that this function has given to it the value for $y = 0$ outright for each set of parameters, whereas its value for $y + 1$ is provided for by a composition g, in terms of its value for y, y itself, and the parameters. This dependence of the calculation of a function for $y + 1$ in terms of its previously calculated value for y is the motivation for the term "recursive."

Definition 2.1.3. The set of all functions beginning with the initial set (6a) to (6c) or produced from it by the operations of composition and primitive recursion is the set of *primitive recursive functions.*

We also include here the case of primitive recursion without parameters where h is defined as follows, k being a constant:

$$\begin{aligned} h(0) &= k \\ h(y+1) &= g(y, h(y)) \end{aligned} \tag{8a}$$

Function g is a total function of two variables.

EXAMPLE 4. We shall show that addition is a primitive recursive function by the above methods. In the scheme for primitive recursion [see (8)] we are defining the addition function $h(y, x) = x + y$ in terms of $f = I_1^1$, and $g = S \circ I_2^3$.[3]

$$\begin{aligned} h(0, x) &= I_1^1(x) \\ h(y+1, x) &= S(I_2^3(y, h(y, x), x)) \end{aligned}$$

Setting $h(y, x) = x + y$, we have, alternatively,

$$\begin{aligned} x + 0 &= I_1^1(x) = x \\ x + (y+1) &= S(I_2^3(y, x+y, x)) \\ &= S(x+y) = (x+y) + 1 \end{aligned}$$

Using the inductive definition, since I_1^1, I_2^3, and S are primitive recursive functions and since we have defined h using only composition and primitive recursion, h is also primitive recursive.

Notice that this definition succeeds in incorporating our preanalytic notion that the addition function is mechanical. Suppose one wants to calculate $3 + 2$. Here 3 is the parameter, and the first clause of the definition tells us that $3 + 0 = 3$. We then compute $3 + 1 = (3 + 0) + 1 = 3 + 1 = 4$, and $3 + 2 = (3 + 1) + 1 = 4 + 1 = 5$. All anyone (a clerk, say) need know how to do is add 1 in order to perform any addition.

EXAMPLE 5. Let $h(y, x) = x \cdot y$.

We first suppose that addition has already been defined, as above, so that if g is the addition function, then $g(y, x)$ is meaningful. Then we have

$$\begin{aligned} h(0, x) &= N(x) \\ h(y+1, x) &= g(I_2^3(y, h(y, x), x), I_3^3(y, h(y, x), x)) \end{aligned}$$

or

$$\begin{aligned} x \cdot 0 &= N(x) = 0 \qquad \text{by (6b)} \\ x \cdot (y+1) &= g(h(y, x), x) \\ &= g(x \cdot y, x) = x \cdot y + x \end{aligned}$$

[3] As usual, $S \circ I_2^3$ is the composition of S and I_2^3.

Note how the identity functions are used to adhere to the formal requirement that our new function be defined for $y + 1$ in terms of the $n + 2$-ary function g [in accordance with the scheme (8)]. This is clearly a silly requirement for anyone with brains, but we are trying to get a purely mechanical criterion of calculability that can be understood even by the most unimaginative clerical worker.

All the familiar functions one runs across in computational problems such as $|x - y|$, polynomial functions, etc., are primitive recursive.

A wider class of functions is obtained by adding an operation of *minimalization*. Given a total function f of $n + 1$ variables, minimalization yields the n-ary function h whose values are

$$h(x_1, \ldots, x_n) = \mu y(f(y, x_1, \ldots, x_n) = 0) \tag{9}$$

where μy means "the least y." Further, h may or may not be a total function. For instance, $x/3 = \mu y(|3 \cdot y - x| = 0)$, where $|3 \cdot y - x|$ is total, is only defined for multiples of 3. A function f whose minimalization is a total function is said to be *regular*.

Definition 2.1.4. A *partial recursive function* is any function definable from the initial functions (6) with the aid of composition, primitive recursion, and minimalization. If minimalization is restricted to regular functions, then the functions thus defined are *recursive functions*.

All recursive functions, as is implied by the absence of the adjective "partial," are total. The set of primitive recursive functions is included in the set of recursive functions, which, in turn, is included in the partial recursive functions.

EXAMPLE 6. In this example several functions are defined. We do this, however, without always using the full formality required by the rules, leaving it to the student to fill in the gaps.

$$\begin{aligned} P(0) &= 0 \\ P(y + 1) &= I_1^2(y, P(y)) && \text{(predecessor)} \\ x \dot{-} 0 &= I_1^1(x) \\ x \dot{-} (y + 1) &= P(I_2^3(y, x \dot{-} y, x)) && \text{(proper difference)} \\ |x - y| &= (x \dot{-} y) + (y \dot{-} x) && \text{(absolute value)} \\ \overline{sg}(x) &= 1 \dot{-} x \\ sg(x) &= 1 \dot{-} \overline{sg}(x) && \text{(sign)}^4 \\ x^2 &= I_1^1(x) \cdot I_1^1(x) && \text{(square)} \end{aligned}$$

$$\begin{aligned} [\sqrt{x}] \quad \text{(integral part of } \sqrt{x}) &= \mu y(\overline{sg}((S(I_2^2(x, y)))^2 \dot{-} I_1^2(x, y))) = 0 \\ &= \mu y(1 \dot{-} ((y + 1)^2 \dot{-} x) = 0) \\ &= \mu y(((y + 1)^2 \dot{-} x) \neq 0) \end{aligned}$$

[4] This is a specialization of the real function sign $(x) = 0, 1, -1$ for 0, positive or negative values of x.

Although the class of partial recursive functions is an inductive class by virtue of its generation by the procedure (5), we say that any function in the class is defined *recursively* or *by induction.*

The partial recursive functions are precisely those functions which we would naturally say are calculable by an algorithm or equivalently by some computer. The evidence for this assertion will be easier to weigh after we have formalized the appropriate concept of a computer (in Chapter 4). Let us assume, however, that there is an algorithm or purely mechanical procedure for computing a function f for any value in its domain iff f is partial recursive. This latter statement is a generalized form of a mathematical proposition known as *Church's thesis.*

EXERCISES 2.1

1. State in words the induction proposition for Example 1.

2. Given $\mathscr{A}$ the family of subsets of a set A, show by induction that the unions $A_{i_1} \cup A_{i_2} \cup A_{i_3} \cdots$ exist for all integers j; that is, show that all finite unions exist.

3. (*a*) State a generalized distributive law for boolean algebra and prove it by induction.

(*b*) State likewise a generalized DeMorgan's law and prove it by induction.

4. Given addition of integers as defined primitive recursively (Example 4), prove addition is associative.

5. Define the identity function I_1^1 in terms of minimalization supposing given any of the functions introduced in Example 6 or earlier.

6. Show the recursiveness, by actual constructions, of the following functions and predicates.

(*a*) $f(y, x) = x^y$

(*b*) $f(y) = y!$

(*c*) Assume that $[x/y]$ is recursive, where $[x/y] = 0$, if $y = 0$, or $=$ greatest integer $\leq x/y$, if $y \neq 0$.
Prove that the remainder function $r(x, y)$ is recursive. $r(x, y)$ is the remainder on dividing x by y.

(*d*) Prove that subtraction is partial recursive.

(*e*) Prove that $[x/2]$ is recursive.

2.2 RECURSIVE SETS AND PREDICATES

We next discuss a precise way of dealing with the concept of decision making by rules. Suppose we are given a set of elements of some kind and then are asked whether an independently given object is in that set. If the set is finite, we can answer the question by examining every element. Any one capable of identifying that object could in a finite time decide the question about membership in the set purely mechanically. On the other hand, if the set is *infinite,* we might not ever, by following any conceivable systematic procedure, be able to settle the question. We state therefore that there is a *decision procedure* for a set if there is an algorithm for deciding whether any object is in that set. It will turn out that there is a decision procedure just in case the set in question (whether finite or infinite) is, in a sense to be specified, *recursive*.

Since we already have an exact notion of the functions calculable by algorithm, it would seem worthwhile to consider first the question of decision procedures for sets of integers. Suppose we had a function defined on a set with value $f(x) = 0$ (= yes) if x is in the set and $f(x) = 1$ (= no) otherwise. If $f(x)$ were recursive, a clerk could take an integer x, calculate $f(x)$, and thus settle the decision question. We shall proceed to follow out this suggestion.

Definition 2.2.1. The *characteristic function* of a set A is the function C_A such that $C_A(x) = 0$ if $x \in A$ and $C_A(x) = 1$ if $x \notin A$. A set is said to be *recursive* iff its characteristic function is recursive.

EXAMPLE 1. The set of integers itself is recursive since its characteristic function $N(x)$ is recursive. A less trivial example is the set of even integers. Its characteristic function is given by $C_E(x) = x \dot{-} (2 \cdot [x/2])$, where $[x/2]$ is the greatest integer $\leq x/2$. If x is even, then $2 \cdot [x/2] = x$, so $C_E(x) = 0$. If x is odd, then $1 + 2 \cdot [x/2] = x$, and so $C_E(x) = 1$.

A useful and interesting fact is that recursiveness of sets is preserved under the set operations union, intersection, and complementation. To see this, suppose A and B are recursive sets. The characteristic function of $A \bigcup B$ is

$$C_{A \cup B} = C_A \cdot C_B \tag{10}$$

If $x \in A$ or $x \in B$, then the product is 0; but if $x \notin A$ and $x \notin B$, then the product is 1. So our definition of $C_{A \cup B}$ is adequate to the task. Finally, since multiplication is recursive, (10) must be recursive since C_A and C_B are given to be so. Hence $A \bigcup B$ is a recursive set. To prove recursiveness of the complement, suppose A is recursive. The characteristic function of $\bar{A}$ is

$$C_{\bar{A}} = \overline{sg}(C_A) \tag{11}$$

If $x \in A$, then $C_A = 0$ and $\overline{sg}(C_A) = 1$. If $x \notin A$, then $C_A = 1$ and $\overline{sg}(C_A) = 0$. But since the sign function is recursive, it follows that $\bar{A}$ is a recursive set. The recursiveness of $A \bigcap B$ is left as an exercise for the student, as is the completion of the proof of the following theorem.

Theorem 2.2.2. The family of recursive sets is closed under union, intersection, and complementation; hence it is a boolean algebra.

EXAMPLE 2. From the preceding conclusions the null set (of integers) is recursive and the odd integers are recursive.

EXAMPLE 3. The set of all divisors of some fixed integer n. This set is

$$D = \{x \mid (\exists y)(y \leq n \wedge x \cdot y = n)\}$$

Its characteristic function is

$$C_D(x) = \prod_{i=1}^{n} sg|x \cdot i - n|$$

where $\prod$ is the customary manifold product. $sg|x \cdot i - n|$ is primitive recursive. To show that

$$\prod_{i=1}^{n} sg|x \cdot i - n|$$

is recursive, we prove that if $f(i, x_1, \ldots, x_n)$ is recursive, so is

$$g(m, x_1, \ldots, x_n) = \prod_{i=0}^{m} f(i, x_1, \ldots, x_n)$$

We define g by primitive recursion:

$$g(0, x_1, \ldots, x_n) = f(0, x_1, \ldots, x_n)$$
$$g(m + 1, x_1, \ldots, x_n) = g(m, x_1, \ldots, x_n) \cdot f(m + 1, x_1, \ldots, x_n)$$

Hence for our special case

$$\prod_{i=0}^{n} sg|x \cdot 1 - n|$$

is recursive. But then, so is $C_D(x)$ since for this function

$$\prod_{i=0}^{n} sg|x \cdot i - n| = \prod_{i=1}^{n} sg|x \cdot i - n|$$

as the reader may check for himself.

A predicate (see Section 1.1) is a certain kind of expression which determines sets. Any predicate which determines a set of integers is called a *number-theoretic* predicate, and the set of integers determined by it is the *extension* of the predicate. A predicate of this kind is (primitive) recursive iff its extension is (primitive) recursive.

EXAMPLE 4. The predicates "is an integer," "is even," "is odd," "is a divisor of n" are all recursive.

The *characteristic function of a predicate* is the characteristic function of its extension. Thus if P is a predicate and A its extension, we set $C_P = C_A$. Also, using $\vee$, $\wedge$, and $\neg$ as logic connectives (Section 1.1), we set $C_{P \vee Q} = C_{A \cup B}$, $C_{P \wedge Q} = C_{A \cap B}$, and $C_{\neg P} = C_{\bar{A}}$, where A is the extension of P and B of Q. It is obvious that if P and Q are recursive so are $P \vee Q$, $P \wedge Q$, and $\neg P$.

Our next discussion introduces a modification of the universal and existential quantifiers $\forall$ and $\exists$. We rule that these quantifiers be applied to number-theoretic predicates and that their range be restricted to the integers. With this understanding we define *bounded quantifiers* as follows:

$$(\overset{z}{\forall}x)P \quad \text{means} \quad (\forall x)(0 \leq x \leq z \Rightarrow P)$$

and

$$(\overset{z}{\exists}x)P \quad \text{means} \quad (\exists x)(0 \leq x \leq z \wedge P)$$

where z is an integer and P any number-theoretic predicate.

In order to talk about binary, ternary, and in general n-ary predicates we use the notation

$$P(x_1, \ldots, x_n) \qquad \text{for} \quad x_1, \ldots, x_n \text{ is } P$$

Thus "x is prime" becomes "prime (x)," and a 3-ary relation such as "x is between y and z" is expressed by the predicate "between (x, y, z)."

Theorem 2.2.3. The set of recursive predicates is closed under bounded quantification.

Proof. Let $P(y, x_1, \ldots, x_n)$ be an $n + 1$-ary recursive predicate. We now will show that

$$(a) \quad (\overset{z}{\exists}y)P(y, x_1, \ldots, x_n) \quad \text{and} \quad (b) \quad (\overset{z}{\forall}y)P(y, x_1, \ldots, x_n)$$

are recursive n-ary predicates.

Proof of (a). The characteristic function of

$$P(y, x_1, \ldots, x_n)$$

is

$$C_P(y, x_1, \ldots, x_n)$$

Owing to the boundedness of the quantifier,

$$(\overset{z}{\exists}y)P(y, x_1, \ldots, x_n)$$

means

$$P(0, x_1, \ldots, x_n) \vee \cdots \vee P(z, x_1, \ldots, x_n)$$

[cf. Exercise 1.1(2)]. Thus the characteristic function by (10) and a simple induction is

$$\prod_{y=0}^{z} C_P(y, x_1, \ldots, x_n) \tag{12}$$

Then, from the recursiveness of $P(y, x_1, \ldots, x_n)$, we have by definition the recursiveness of $C_P(y, x_1, \ldots, x_n)$; and by Example 3 above, (12) is recursive. Hence the result of attaching the bounded existential quantifier to $P(y, x_1, \ldots, x_n)$ is recursive.

Proof of (*b*). Since

$$P(y, x_1, \ldots, x_n) \qquad \text{and} \quad (\overset{z}{\exists} y)P(y, x_1, \ldots, x_n)$$

are recursive—by assumption and by part (*a*), respectively—it follows that

$$(\overset{z}{\forall} y)P(y, x_1, \ldots, x_n)$$

is recursive, since

$$(\overset{z}{\forall} y)P(y, x_1, \ldots, x_n) \Leftrightarrow \neg(\overset{z}{\exists} y)\neg P(y, x_1, \ldots, x_n)$$

by Footnote 2, Chapter 1, and Theorem 2.2.2. Q.E.D.

Summarizing all of the above, the property of (primitive) recursiveness of predicates is preserved under the operations $\wedge$, $\vee$, $\neg$, and bounded quantification.

In order to go on to more complicated examples we need the recursiveness of $=$ and $<$. The characteristic function of the latter is

$$\overline{sg}(y \dot{-} x) \tag{13}$$

For, if $y > x$ then $y \dot{-} x \geq 1$ and $1 \dot{-} (y \dot{-} x) = 0$ and if $y \leq x$, then $y \dot{-} x = 0$ and $1 \dot{-} 0 = 1$. It follows that $<$ is primitive recursive since its characteristic function is. It also follows immediately that $=$ is primitive recursive, since

$$x = y \Leftrightarrow \neg(x < y) \wedge \neg(y < x)$$

and, as we have seen, recursiveness is preserved under $\wedge$ and $\neg$.

EXAMPLE 5. Every finite set A is recursive (as we know anyway, on intuitive grounds), since we may write

$$\begin{aligned} A &= \{a_1, a_2, a_3, \ldots, a_k\} \\ &= \{x \mid x = a_1 \vee x = a_2 \vee x = a_3 \vee \cdots \vee x = a_k\} \end{aligned}$$

[cf. (6) in Section 1.1].

EXAMPLE 6. We may determine the recursiveness of a set, as in Example 5, by checking the defining predicate rather than the characteristic function for recursiveness; so

$$x \text{ is even} \Leftrightarrow (\overset{x}{\exists} y)(2 \cdot y = x)$$

is a recursive predicate and hence so is its extension. (In examples such as this one the student should verify the claim step by step.) As the next example shows, the recursiveness of predicates may be of use in the establishment of the recursiveness of certain functions.

EXAMPLE 7. Let us assume that the predicate prime (x) is recursive [see Exercise 2.2(5)] and show that the function $Pr(x)$, the xth prime, is also recursive. Since we deal with the nonnegative integers, we adopt the convention that the 0th prime is 0. Then

$$Pr(0) = 0$$
$$Pr(n + 1) = \mu y(y \leq (Pr(n)! + 1) \wedge \text{Prime}\,(y) \wedge y > Pr(n))$$

Thus the third prime is the least y less than or equal to $3! + 1 = 7$ such that y is prime and $y > 3$. The complete demonstration that this function is primitive recursive may be found in Davis [1958].

We now have a precise way of stating, for the integers at least, what we mean by a decision problem. It is the problem whether the characteristic function of a set, or alternatively the defining predicate of a set, is recursive. If so, we say that the decision problem for a set is *recursively solvable*, and if not, that it is *recursively unsolvable*. Clearly this notion of solvability does not tell us what problems are solvable by rational, nonroutine procedures. For example, the question whether a given problem is recursively solvable or not is itself no trivial matter, in general, and frequently requires high-order ability. In Chapter 4 we shall discuss some recursively unsolvable problems.

Corresponding to the concept of an inductively generated class (such as the formulas of a system, the integers themselves, or the recursive functions) is the notion of a class of integers generated by a systematic process. An enumeration, as discussed in Section 1.2, is such a process provided the sequence is a recursive function.

Now suppose that a set of integers is, as suggested, the range of a recursive function. Such a set is said to be *recursively enumerable*. If y is in the set, then within a finite number of computations of the recursive function of which the set is the range, y will turn up. This is true simply because the evaluation of argument x for which y is the value has its turn in a finite number of steps from 0. It appears therefore that if a set A is recursively enumerable and $y \in A$, then there is a procedure for discovering this fact. If, on the other hand, $y \notin A$, we may never know it: we could systematically run through the computations for arguments 0, 1, 2, etc., of the function generating the set, but failure to turn out y after a finite number of steps would not be evidence that y is not in the set.

According to the preceding remarks about recursively enumerable sets, recursive sets are among the recursively enumerable ones. This fact will be proved later. Assuming this, all the foregoing examples of recursive sets and those in the exercises which follow are recursively enumerable. In Chapter 4 we shall also find a set which is recursively enumerable but not recursive.

From this fact it will follow that there are recursively enumerable sets having unsolvable decision problems.

EXERCISES 2.2

1. Prove that if A and B are recursive sets, then $A \cap B$ is also. Prove it in *two* ways.

2. Show that the set of all integers excluding the squares is recursively enumerable.

3. Prove that if $f(i, x_1, \ldots, x_n)$ is recursive so is

$$\sum_{i=0}^{m} f(i, x_1, \ldots, x_n)$$

(*Hint*: See Example 3.)

4. Why cannot "characteristic function" be defined as a partial recursive function?

5. Prove that prime (x)—x is prime—is a recursive predicate.

2.3 GÖDEL NUMBERINGS

In the theory of automata and elsewhere in logical studies we are interested in the existence of algorithms for solving problems which do not deal directly with integers. For example, the computer engineer is interested in the problem of whether two switching circuits (or two sequential circuits) behave in the same way. It turns out that such problems are recursively solvable. Again, the programmer may wish to know whether a given program will do what it was meant to do. This question, unfortunately, is recursively unsolvable.

To extend the concept of solvability to domains outside the realm of arithmetic, we resort to the technique of *Gödel numbering*.[5] We start with a set A and construct A^* as in Example 10, Section 1.3. A *Gödel function* is a one–one function on a subset of A^* into the integers. With this device one can translate statements about the elements of the subset of A^* (whatever they may be) into statements about integers. Similarly, ordinary predicates applicable to these elements become number-theoretic predicates, and functions become functions of integers.

Returning to Example 2 of Section 2.1 we will in outline show that the property of being a boolean formula in Polish form is primitive recursive.

According to the definition of *formula* in Example 2 of Section 2.1, a sequence σ is a formula if (a) it is a symbol of the set

$$\{s_1, \ldots, s_n\}$$

[5] This device is due to the mathematician Kurt Gödel and is meant to apply mainly to cases where the subset is a *language*.

or (*b*) it is the result of combining a formula σ' with $-$ yielding $-\sigma'$ or by combining two formulas σ' and σ'' with $\cup$ or $\cap$ yielding either $\cup\sigma'\sigma''$ or $\cap\sigma'\sigma''$.

The class of formulas is a subset of $\{s_1, \ldots, s_n, -, \cup, \cap\}^*$ and is inductive (as previously noted immediately after Example 2 of Section 2.1), with the alphabet of symbols as basis and the combinations provided for in clause (*b*) above the inductive step. In analogy to the usage for the set of integers,[6] we will term the result of combining $-$ with σ', or of combining $\cup$ or $\cap$ with σ' and σ'', the *successor* to $-, \sigma''$; or $\cup, \sigma', \sigma''$; or $\cap, \sigma', \sigma''$; as the case may be. Consider, as an instance,

$$\sigma = \cup - \cap s_1 s_2 \cap s_1 s_2$$

Formula σ itself is the successor to $\cup$, $-\cap s_1 s_2$, $\cap s_1 s_2$, since it is a combination, under clause (*b*), of the formulas $-\cap s_1 s_2$ and $\cap s_1 s_2$ with the connective $\cup$. Continuing, $-\cap s_1 s_2$ is the successor to $-$, $\cap s_1 s_2$, and is the combination of the formula $\cap s_1 s_2$ with $-$; etc., on to the basis symbols. If σ is the successor to $\alpha_1, \alpha_2, \ldots$, then $\alpha_1, \alpha_2, \ldots$, are *predecessors* of σ.

The Gödel numbers are constructed using the correlation φ of odd numbers to the alphabet of the boolean language as follows:

$$\varphi\colon \begin{array}{cccccccc} - & \cup & \cap & s_1 & s_2 & \cdots & s_n \\ 3 & 5 & 7 & 9 & 11 & \cdots & 2n+7 \end{array}$$

Now the Gödel number $g_n(s_i)$ of a formula with one symbol is $2i + 7$. If $\alpha_1, \ldots, \alpha_m$ are predecessors of $\alpha_1 \cdots \alpha_m$ and if $x_1, x_2, x_3, \ldots, x_m$ are their assigned Gödel numbers, then

$$\prod_{i=1}^{m} Pr(i)^{x_i} = \text{Gödel number of } \alpha_1 \cdots \alpha_m$$

In this instance $m \leq 3$ always.

EXAMPLE 1. Let us suppose $\sigma = -\cap s_1 s_2$; then

$$g_n(\sigma) = 2^3 \cdot 3^{2^7 \cdot 3^9 \cdot 5^{11}}$$

Explanation: σ is the successor to $-$, $\cap s_1 s_2$; so by the definition

$$g_n(\sigma) = 2^3 \cdot 3^{g_n(\cap s_1 s_2)}$$

and $\cap s_1 s_2$ is the successor to $\cap$, s_1, s_2; so

$$g_n(\cap s_1 s_2) = 2^7 \cdot 3^9 \cdot 5^{11}$$

Although these numbers are out of this world, they do correspond one–one with formulas of the sample language, and in principle, by using

[6] That is, in the inductive definition of the integers.

the dictionary φ above, a formula can always be recovered from its Gödel number (see exercises).

Continuing with our project of showing the primitive recursiveness of "is a formula" we shall construct a numerical predicate corresponding to the predicate "formula." This definition means to say that x, an integer, is F iff x is the Gödel number of a boolean formula σ. First, we write the definition; second, we prove it means what we want it to mean; third, we show the predicate F introduced in this way is primitive recursive. First,

$$\begin{aligned} F(x) \Leftrightarrow ((\overset{x}{\exists} i)(x = 2i + 7) \vee (\overset{x}{\exists} y)(x = 2^3 \cdot 3^y \wedge F(y)) \\ \vee (\overset{x}{\exists} y)(\overset{x}{\exists} z)(x = 2^5 \cdot 3^y \cdot 5^z \wedge F(y) \wedge F(z)) \\ \vee (\overset{x}{\exists} y)(\overset{x}{\exists} z)(x = 2^7 \cdot 3^y \cdot 5^z \wedge F(y) \wedge F(z))) \end{aligned} \tag{14}$$

Proceeding to the second task, which is to establish (14), we will use induction on the number of occurrences r of connectives $\neg$, $\cup$, and $\cap$ in σ. If $r = 0$, by the definition of formula, $\sigma = s_i$ for some i. But then, $x = g_n(s_i) = 2i + 7$, using the correspondence table φ. Therefore

$$(\overset{x}{\exists} i)(x = 2i + 7)$$

holds, and consequently $F(x)$ holds by (14). Assume now that the desired implication is true for $r < n$. If σ has n connectives it is either of the form:

$$(1) \qquad \sigma = -\sigma'$$

or

$$(2) \qquad \sigma = \cup\sigma'\sigma''$$

or

$$(3) \qquad \sigma = \cap\sigma'\sigma''$$

CASE 1: $g_n(\sigma) = x = 2^3 \cdot 3^{g_n(\sigma')}$. By induction hypothesis, since σ' has less than n connectives, $F(g_n(\sigma'))$ is true. Hence

$$(\overset{x}{\exists} y)(x = 2^3 \cdot 3^y \wedge F(y))$$

and therefore $F(x)$. The remaining cases (2) and (3) are similar and are left to the student.

To sketch the converse, if $F(x)$ is true, then exactly one of the four disjuncts of (14) must be true. If it is the first, then x is of the form $2i + 7, i = 1, \ldots, n$, and by φ the corresponding expression is s_i, which is a formula. If the second disjunct is true, then $\sigma = -\sigma'$ follows from the correspondence φ, the fact that $F(y)$ is true, together with the hypothesis of a kind of induction and the definition of Gödel number. There are similar arguments for the third and fourth disjuncts. This establishes

$$\sigma \text{ is a formula is true} \Leftrightarrow F(g_n(\sigma)) \text{ is true} \tag{15}$$

To see that $F(x)$ is primitive recursive, we note that each disjunct of (14) consists of the bounded quantification of either an equality relation, which in each case is primitive recursive, or the conjunction of an equality and an expression $F(y)$. Hence $F(x)$ is primitive recursive if $F(y)$ is.

Actually, (14) is an instance of a form of definition by recursion of predicates which can be shown to yield recursive predicates; our proof, if it were complete, would hinge on this. The details are, however, irrelevant to our purpose—which was to indicate how nonnumerical decision problems can be handled—and the reader interested in a complete discussion should consult the references (Kleene [1952]).

To summarize the discussion of solvability of nonnumerical problems, we have indicated how the objects of a set whose solvability is in question can be made to correspond to numbers using a certain numbering scheme. The function used to effect numbering, φ, is itself *effective*[7] in the sense that it associates numbers to objects by a mechanical scheme. The defining predicate of the set is translated into the defining (numerical) predicate of the set of integers and, using the correspondence φ, the two predicates are shown to be equivalent. Finally, if it can be shown that the numerical predicate is recursive, then the original problem will be solvable, and if it is not, the problem is unsolvable.

Although we have taken some space to introduce recursive solvability and unsolvability and to suggest applications to nonnumerical problems, most of the decision questions which arise in this book will require a less elaborate treatment. Frequently, one can show a problem solvable by either indicating a finite-step procedure for solving it or showing that the problem is in some sense equivalent to a known solvable one. If a problem yields to this type of quick treatment, there is little point to a formal verification via the complete procedure of Gödel numbering; indeed, it is standard mathematical practice to avoid such formalities. The criterion is satisfaction of the simple rule that proof of the workability of a procedure could itself be routinely supplied on numerical grounds.

In the treatment of Example 2 in Section 2.1, for instance, we might have argued informally as follows. Since every boolean expression E in Polish notation is of finite length, we can tell whether or not it is a formula in a finite number of steps. One would give a recipe for finding the expressions of which E is the successor, and then the expressions of which these expressions are successors, and so on. If at any stage there is no successor, according to the definition of formula, the answer would be negative, whereas if the test succeeds at each one of a number of stages, it would be affirmative. A proof, usually inductive, of the efficacy of the

[7] But not recursive, since its domain is not the integers.

recipe would then be proof of solvability (or, contrarywise, of unsolvability). Still other algorithms are suggested by deeper studies of the properties of language. In Example 2 of Section 2.1 we found that every formula has a rank of -1. It turns out that this property and another routinely calculated property are necessary and sufficient for an expression to be a formula. [See Exercise 3.3 (4).]

To prove unsolvability of a problem, more powerful techniques, based on arithmetization of the problem, are usually required. In Chapter 4 we will continue with this formal discussion and demonstrate the unsolvability of certain problems.

In the sequel we shall talk freely about "recursive sets," "recursive predicates," and "recursive definition" or "definition by induction" when it is clear that the formal counterpart in the realm of integers could be constructed in a straightforward way. Also, as is customary, we shall refer to any definition of a predicate F, either numerical or nonnumerical, as a *recursive definition* when either the predicate is defined for the integer x in terms of $F(y)$, where $x > y$—as in (14) above—or where the truth of the predicate $F(y)$ depends on its truth for a predecessor x such that $F(x)$.

EXERCISES 2.3

1. A dyadic Gödel function is a rule that assigns to each element of a free monoid on n generators a dyadic numeral as follows: If $\{a_1, a_2, \ldots, a_n\}$ is the set of generators, then replace each a_{i_j} in each sequence of the monoid by $1222\cdots(i_j$ times). Show that this function is one–one *into* the integers and show that it is an isomorphism w.r.t. the operation o of the monoid and "juxtaposition" of numerals in the dyadic representation system [see Example 1.3 (10)].

2. Prove that the Gödel function used in the boolean language example is a one–one function into the integers.

3. Given P, Q, R, etc., as a list of statement variables and the formal symbols $\vee$, $\wedge$, $\neg$, $\Rightarrow$, $\Leftrightarrow$, (, and); write an inductive definition for "statement" in the ordinary sense in propositional logic so that $(\neg P \vee Q)$, for example, is a statement.

2.4 HISTORICAL AND BIBLIOGRAPHICAL REMARKS

The material in this chapter is taken almost entirely from Davis [1958], Kleene [1952], and Rosenbloom [1950]. The recursive functions are of importance in logic because they turn out to be precisely the functions representable in elementary formal logical systems (Gödel [1931]). Their use in automata theory will become apparent in later chapters. Unfortunately, no easily readable and elementary discussion of further topics in the theory of recursive functions is yet available except for an early paper by Post [1944] and a survey paper by Rogers [1959]. However, the books in the Selected Bibliography by Rogers (in press) and by Kreider and Ritchie (in press) should fill the gap.

CHAPTER 3

Formal Systems

3.0 Introduction. At the beginning of Chapter 2 we emphasized the importance of studying systems of rules which can be applied mechanically to objects we are interested in manipulating. It so turns out that such systems are not only important to the study of automata but are also *central.* In fact, we shall *define* automata as certain systems of rules called formal systems. This basic characterization will apply to sequential machines or transducers, pattern recognizers, generative grammars, Turing machines, nerve networks, program schemes, self-reproducing machines, and indeed to any object one could reasonably term a (discrete state) automaton, or "data processing" device.

On this approach, automata theory is closely related to logic, which is also largely occupied with the study of formal systems. However, the emphasis is somewhat different. The logician is principally concerned with *inference* as it occurs in any rational discipline, and he sets up formal logical systems in such a way that "inference" can be given an exact meaning and its properties thereby studied. The logician deals with statements which, like the scientific or mathematical statements he models, are interpretable as true or false and as a body form a language that has a meaningful structure. The logician is therefore tempted to think of formal systems as language systems having associated grammars, semantic rules, rules of inference, and rules of translation.

The automata logician is also concerned with questions of language, but in a somewhat more general way. He is not concerned principally with inference as such but with any process by which sequences of symbols can be transformed into others. Inference is a special case. Thus a sequential circuit for controlling an automatic elevator system transforms collections of input signals into output signals.

But the analogy (one might argue) implied by such locutions as "input statement" and "hypothesis" or "output statement" and "theorem" is somewhat strained. The transformation performed by the circuit in producing the output from the input, at any time, is hardly an inference. Indeed, the common engineer would be likely to say that elevator control does not seem to have anything to do with languages or logical inferences at all, but rather with efficient and reliable design, and perhaps with the kinds of automation which are physically and logically possible, as well as with mechanical synthesis. The neurophysiologist, to use another relevant instance, would hardly find it fruitful to call a stimulus-response pattern in neural networks "inference" or congeries of stimuli "languages."

Similarly, the systems programmer does not think of scanning of a "problem language" statement, or even of compilation as such, as an inference. Here, perhaps, the analogies are somewhat more suggestive, but it is still very difficult to see how the programmer could benefit from studying formal systems of logic.

Nevertheless, from a strictly abstract point of view—one which is not oriented solely to the study of models of the languages of the sciences or mathematics—it is useful to consider all kinds of automata as formal systems and moreover, because of the abstract similarity to processes studied in logic, to employ terms such as "theorem," "proof," "hypothesis," "formula," "well-formed formula," etc. Some of these terms are already in use in algebraic linguistics, programming language theory, and the theory of infinite automata (Turing machines); so we shall feel justified in extending the terminology and basic style of approach to all of automata theory.

The study of formal systems, and therefore of automata, is a part of mathematics and is related to the broader field of computer science in much the same way as analysis is to well-established empirical sciences such as physics or chemistry. It is the mathematical part of the study of finite-state complex systems, in the engineers' jargon. As such it is helpful to contrast the methods and problems with those of traditional mathematics.

Postponing the definition of formal systems until Section 3.1, let us proceed with an example and a descriptive characterization. A formal system, like a mathematical system such as a group, comprises a set of objects, perhaps of several kinds, some axioms, and rules for changing sequences of objects called *words* into other words. In a formal system no change (or transformation) whatsoever is permitted unless it be by use of an explicit rule of the system. There may be several categories of rules and likewise several categories of words.

EXAMPLE 1. As a very simple example, let us consider the system with objects $\{a, b\}$, called the *alphabet*, the axioms

Ax.1. a ***Ax.2.*** b

and the four rules of "inference"

R.1.	$a \rightarrow aa$	***R.2.***	$a \rightarrow ab$
R.3.	$b \rightarrow bb$	***R.4.***	$b \rightarrow ba$

R.1 says that a may be written as aa in any context, ***R.2*** says that a may be written as ab in any context, and ***R.3*** and ***R.4*** may be read similarly. Such rules are called "productions." A *proof* is a finite sequence of words such that each element of the sequence is either (1) an axiom, or (2) the result of applying one of the productions to an earlier element of the sequence. For example, to prove *bbbba*, we form the sequence, written as a vertical list:

1.	b	axiom ***Ax.2***
2.	ba	applying ***R.4*** to 1
3.	bba	applying ***R.3*** to 2 (rewrite b in 2 as bb)
4.	$bbba$	similar to 3
5.	$bbbba$	

The reader should verify that this system generates precisely the elements (except for Λ) of the set of expressions on the letters $\{a, b\}$ [cf. Example 1.3 (10)]. Also, he should note carefully that the intended proof is indeed one: there is a finite sequence of words; the first is an axiom, the second is the result of applying ***R.4*** to the first, etc., as annotated to the right of the list.

Proceeding with the promised comparisons to ordinary mathematical systems (such as groups), in these latter systems we think of a fixed set of objects as being given to us together with certain specific operations. In group theory, for example, we have a set, an operation o, and some axioms. We then proceed to prove certain properties about the system. The student himself has worked at several examples concerned with finding or verifying properties of groups. In a formal system, on the other hand, we begin with a set of objects, such as $\{a, b\}$ in the introductory example, and generate a further set by proving expressions from the axioms. Again, on the one hand we study established properties of a *ready-made* system, whereas on the other we *generate* a system by a sequence of operations. [To avoid possible misunderstanding, observe the distinction that generators in the theory of groups (or monoids) are *given* as a basis of group elements by certain stipulated equalities or relations, whereas in a formal system the generators are put together by a rule-abiding process to form new elements of a collection.] The mathematician Hilbert introduced this distinction and termed the first method of mathematical study *postulational* and the second *genetic* or *constructive*.

Second, in a formal system we may speak of any word which follows from the axioms as a "provable" word or theorem. Similarly, in postulational mathematics, we also produce theorems. However, the procedures differ in some important respects. In group theory our proofs are informal; this means that the proofs do not always follow explicitly written-down rules, but depend instead on our prior intuitive understanding of the properties of equality, the principles of logic, elementary facts about numbers and sets, etc. For example, consider the proof, in Section 1.3, that in every group equations $ax = b$ and $ya = b$ have solutions. The first equality was

$$a(a^{-1}b) = (aa^{-1})b$$

This relation may be obvious, but it does not follow *from explicitly given rules* by the axioms, since no such rules were stated at all. (It does follow, in a vague way, from the associativity axiom.) A more explicit (but still not entirely so) proof would be

1.	$(\forall a)(\forall b)(\forall c)((ab)c = a(bc))$	Axiom (6b) Section 1.3
2.	$(aa^{-1})b = a(a^{-1}b)$	by the logical rule that whatever is true for every a, b, c is true for a, a^{-1}, b in particular
3.	$(\forall x)(\forall y)(x = y \Rightarrow y = x)$ $x, y \in$ any nonempty domain	this is the property of symmetry of equality.
4.	$(aa^{-1})b = a(a^{-1}b) \Rightarrow a(a^{-1}b) = (aa^{-1})b$	by the same logical rule as used at step 2.
5.	$a(a^{-1}b) = (aa^{-1})b$	from steps 2 and 4 by another logical rule which says that if P is true and $P \Rightarrow Q$ is true, then Q is true.

This example shows that in ordinary postulational mathematics many of the rules we use in reasoning are never explicitly referred to but are taken to be part of the basic reservoir of ideas of the mature mathematical reasoner.

In formal systems, no step may be written down in the proof of a theorem which is not justified by a stipulated rule. It should be fairly clear that a clerk could turn out theorems in our example formal system and that a properly designed machine could do so as well.[1]

Third, in group theory, analysis, or arithmetic we want to discover mathematically interesting and scientifically applicable properties of

[1] It does not follow, however, that, given a theorem w in the formal system, a machine could find a proof cleverly; it only follows that sooner or later (in a finite time) it would turn out a proof.

integers, geometrical spaces of various kinds, functions, integrals, etc. In formal mathematics, on the other hand, we usually but not always have in mind a kind of *language* as the object of our study. What we usually discuss are alphabets, strings of symbols, statements, theorems, formulas, etc., all of which are *linguistic* entities.

The foregoing distinction, however, does not always hold, as may be seen by the fact that "linguistic" objects can often be studied by algebraic means, in a way reminiscent of ordinary algebra; whereas, oppositely, entities such as numbers can be studied genetically. Three examples will suffice to sustain the point. In modern linguistics, languages of various kinds are being studied profitably by algebraic techniques (Chapter 8 is devoted entirely to the elements of this subject). Second, if we interpret our sample formal system above such that $a = 1$ and $b = 2$, then it generates the nonnegative integers in dyadic notation. Third, we are going to see that automata—to be specific let us say sequential circuits—are formal systems in the sense that, beginning with a formal system of a certain kind, by a sequence of linguistic translations we can derive the circuit. Whether the circuit is "really" a language or something else is irrelevant and beside the point.

EXAMPLE 2. A simple example will perhaps make the preceding remarks plausible. We want to construct an ordinary pulse divider having one input wire and one output wire such that the output ejects a 1 at time t iff the number of inputs up until t is even but not zero. We will discuss the design of this automaton, in analogy with our earlier sample of a formal system, as a set of rules.

The alphabet is $\{0, 1, \#, q_0, q_1\}$, and we have one axiom scheme where w is a variable ranging over the elements of $\{0, 1\}^*$:

Ax.1. $q_0 w\#$

Also $P, R, \ldots$ are variables whose range is the set of words, including Λ, on the whole alphabet. The rules of inference are the following six:

R.1. $Pq_0 0R \to P0q_0 R$ ***R.2.*** $Pq_0 1R \to P0q_1 R$
R.3. $Pq_1 0R \to P0q_1 R$ ***R.4.*** $Pq_1 1R \to P1q_0 R$
R.5. $Pq_1\# \to P$ ***R.6.*** $Pq_0\# \to P$

These rules are to be employed in a manner similar to that of Example 1. Thus if $010q_0011$ is a word, then using ***R.1*** with P being 010 and R being 11, we obtain $0100q_011$.

Let us now consider the axiom (with input 010111) $q_0010111\#$. Counting P as Λ and R as $10111\#$, ***R.1*** states that we may rewrite $q_0010111\#$ as

$0q_0 10111\#$. Proceeding in the list form of Example 1, we have the following proof:

1.	$q_0 010111\#$	***Ax.1.***
2.	$0q_0 10111\#$	***R.1.***
3.	$00q_1 0111\#$	***R.2.***
4.	$000q_1 111\#$	***R.3.***
5.	$0001q_0 11\#$	***R.4.***
6.	$00010q_1 1\#$	***R.2.***
7.	$000101q_0\#$	***R.4.***
8.	000101	***R.6.***

This sequence 1 to 8 is a proof of 000101. Now if we interpret this latter expression as an output sequence so that the first bit occurs at time 1, the second at time 2, etc., we may easily check that it does satisfy the original design specifications: times 4 and 6 are all and only the times when the past input sequence had an even, nonzero number of 1's.

One might argue that this system is not an automaton but only works like one. However, since the theory does not distinguish among different realizations or embodiments, we insist this *is* an automaton—in fact, a sequential machine or transducer.

However, this formulation is not necessarily the most useful for all purposes. For instance, we may construct a transition[2] and output function from ***R.1*** to ***R.4***. These will be the functions $M: S \times Q \rightarrow Q$ and $N: S \times Q \rightarrow S$ where $S = \{0, 1\}$, $Q = \{q_0, q_1\}$ (the set of states), so that $M(s_j, q_i) = q_l$ and $N(s_i, q_j) = s_k$ iff there is a rule

$$Pq_i s_j R \rightarrow P s_k q_l R$$

Thus each production determines a pair of functions. The rules ***R.5*** and ***R.6*** correspond to deactivating the circuit at the end of the sequence. In tabular form, as is customary in switching theory, these functions are for the current example

$q \backslash s$	M: 0	M: 1
q_0	q_0	q_1
q_1	q_1	q_0

$q \backslash s$	N: 0	N: 1
q_0	0	0
q_1	0	1

Fig. 3.0.1

As the reader already knows, if we "encode" this pair of functions so that $q = 0$ and $q = 1$, we eventually obtain the diagram in Fig. 3.0.2, where the blocks marked $\wedge$, $\vee$, I, δ are "and," "or," "not," or "inverter," and unit delay devices respectively.

[2] It is assumed the reader knows about sequential circuits. However, the technical ideas involved will be discussed in Chapter 6.

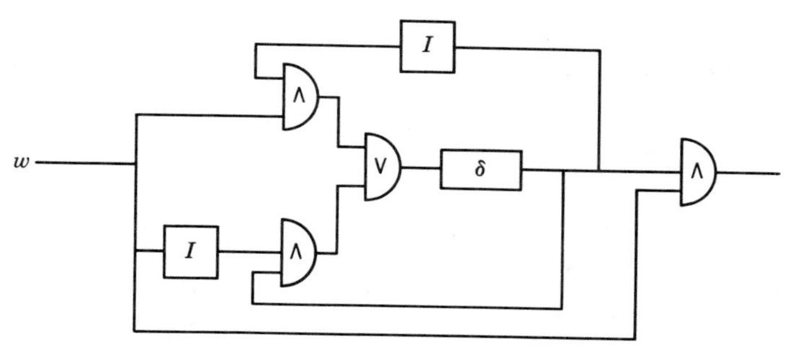

Fig. 3.0.2

EXERCISES 3.0

1. Show that the sample system in Example 1 generates the elements of the set $\{a, b\}^*$. Is your proof a "formal proof"? Explain.

2. Write a system of axioms and rules for formally proving as theorems elements of the infinite set $S = \{a, b, aa, bb, aaa, bbb, \text{etc.}\}$.

3. Construct a formal system for changing a to b, b to c, and c to a, given any "input" word w on $\{a, b, c\}$. Design the productions and determine the complete alphabet.

3.1 DEFINITION OF FORMAL SYSTEM

The examples used in Section 3.0 suggest that we think of a formal system as a purely mechanical device for turning out theorems from axioms (or, more picturesquely, producing outputs from inputs). In many instances, such as those of Section 3.0, the sequences of symbols occurring in the axioms or theorems are hardly "structured" in any way analogous to the sentences of ordinary language, mathematics, or informal logic. At other times—usually in the formalization of logics—we desire to deal with sequences forming sentences or formulas which are to be given meaningful interpretations. We already noted this distinction in the boolean language example in Section 2.1. We need therefore to characterize formal systems broadly enough to consider not only the generation of theorems, but the generation of well-formed formulas and other entities as well. In algebraic linguistics, moreover, the formulas in the foregoing sense will be theorems—that is, the set of theorems will comprise a language.

Definition 3.1.1. Given a finite nonempty set A, a *word* is an element of the set of finite sequences on A. The length of a word $l(w)$ is the number of occurrences of symbols in it and $l(\Lambda) = 0$. The alphabet A may conceivably be (cf. Example 3 of Section 1.3) a collection of pairs, triples, or in general of n-tuples. In such a case, if $(a_{11}, a_{12}, \ldots, a_{1n})$, $(a_{21}, a_{22}, \ldots, a_{2n}), \ldots, (a_{m1}, a_{m2}, \ldots, a_{mn})$ are elements of A, we set the m-length word

$$(a_{11}, a_{12}, \ldots, a_{1n})(a_{21}, a_{22}, \ldots, a_{2n}) \cdots (a_{m1}, a_{m2}, \ldots, a_{mn})$$

equal to

$$(a_{11}a_{21} \cdots a_{m1};\ a_{12}a_{22} \cdots a_{m2};\ \cdots;\ a_{1n}a_{2n} \cdots a_{mn})$$

which is an n-tuple of words. The set of all such words is a universal n-ary relation any subset of which is a *word relation*. For any n-tuple there exists an m such that $l(a) = m$ for every element a of the n-tuple. This follows directly from the foregoing convention. Still more general word relations are possible. As an example, take the relations defined by the predicates $\mathscr{P}$ in Definition 3.1.2 below, and the word relations used in Section 7.3.

We will use the letters x, y, z, x_1, y_1, z_1, etc., as variables ranging over words. Such variables are termed *syntactic variables.*

In this usage the set A is called the *alphabet*, and we require that it be a recursively enumerable set—sometimes even finite. An alphabet may consist, speaking informally, of a class of single objects such as a, b, c, or may be "words" of ordinary English, or other spoken language, such as "the," "boy," "house," "computer," etc.

Definition 3.1.2. A *formal system* is a quadruple $\mathbf{F} = \langle A, \mathscr{B}, \mathscr{A}, \mathscr{P} \rangle$ as follows: A is an alphabet; $\mathscr{B}$ is a subset of the set of words on A, and the elements of $\mathscr{B}$ are called *formulas*; $\mathscr{A}$ is a subset of $\mathscr{B}$ whose elements are called *axioms*; $\mathscr{P}$ is a finite set of at-least-binary recursive predicates of words of $\mathscr{B}$, and the elements of $\mathscr{P}$ are called *rules of inference*. $\mathscr{A}$ and $\mathscr{B}$ are recursive. If $P(x_1, \ldots, x_n, y) \in \mathscr{P}$, we say *$y$ follows from $x_1, \ldots, x_n$* by P. The axioms may be specified by *axiom schemes* which are forms indicating how axioms may be constructed. We shall give examples in Section 3.1 below.

Perhaps a word of explanation is useful. We require of a formal system not only that it turn out theorems or whatever by a procedure such that no step is made without a rule, but moreover that an observer can check exactly whether the given rules and only such rules have been indeed followed in any proof. (We want to be able to *trace* the operation of a machine—or a program.) For this reason we require $\mathscr{A}$ and $\mathscr{B}$ to be recursive. $\mathscr{P}$ is recursive since it is finite. In abstract form, what we expect of a formal system is summarized in the following Theorems 3.1.4 and 3.1.6.

Definition 3.1.3. A *proof* in $\mathbf{F}$ is a finite sequence of words $(x_i)_{i \leq n}$, such that for every i either $x_i \in \mathscr{A}$ or there exists a sequence $(j_k)_{k<i}$ such that x_i follows from (x_{j_k}) by P, P being $k + 1$-ary.

Theorem 3.1.4. The set of proofs in **F** is recursive.

Proof. A sequence of words S is in the set of proofs iff S is finite and each element of S is an element of $\mathscr{A}$ or is the last term of a predicate P (a rule of inference). However, by definition, $\mathscr{A}$ is recursive and P is recursive.[3] Q.E.D.

Definition 3.1.5. x_n is a *theorem* of **F** iff there is a proof $x_1, \ldots, x_n$ in **F**, $n \geq 1$.

Theorem 3.1.6. The set of theorems of **F** is recursively enumerable.

Precisely speaking, this theorem means that the set T of Gödel numbers of theorems of **F**, according to some appropriate Gödel function, is recursively enumerable—there is a recursive function f such that T is the range of f. Informally, the theorem means that the system **F** generates theorems by a mechanical procedure analogous to the cranking out of values of a recursive function. Thus if y is a theorem, sooner or later **F** will yield a proof of it: going through the integers, we consider whether i, for instance, is the Gödel number of a proof; this is a decidable question by Theorem 3.1.4; if it is a proof, we check whether it is a proof of y, also a decidable procedure; if it is, y is put in the set of theorems. But if y is not a theorem, this process will not terminate; therefore one would never know whether y was a theorem.

EXAMPLE 1. Rudimentary arithmetic. This is the system

$$\boldsymbol{R} = \langle A, \mathscr{B}_{\mathbf{R}}, \mathscr{A}, \mathscr{P} \rangle$$

as follows.

1. The alphabet $A = \{0, ', =\}$.
2. $\mathscr{B}_{\mathbf{R}}$ is the set of formulas defined in two steps:
   (*a*) 0 is a *term*. If x is a term, then x' is a *term*.
   (*b*) If x and y are terms, then $x = y$ is a *formula*.
3. $\mathscr{A}$ is a unit set consisting of $0 = 0$.
4. $\mathscr{P}$ is a unit set consisting of the binary irreflexive predicate

$$\rightarrow (x = y, x' = y'),$$

also written $x = y \rightarrow x' = y'$, and where $\alpha \rightarrow \beta$ means α may be written β at some occurrence of α (that is, $\rightarrow$ is a production).

$\mathscr{B}_{\mathbf{R}}$, the set of formulas, is the set as follows: the terms are 0, $0'$, $0''$, $0'''$, ...; the formulas are $0 = 0$, $0 = 0'$ $0' = 0$, $0' = 0'$, $0 = 0''$, $0' = 0''$, $0'' = 0''$, $0'' = 0$, ... Both of these sets, are recursive. Consider the

[3] For this as well as later theorems which depend on Gödel numbers, Davis [1958] should be consulted for details. Also, see remarks at the end of Section 2.3.

following sequence: $0 = 0$, $0' = 0'$, $0'' = 0''$. $0 = 0$ is the axiom; by the rule of inference this may be rewritten $0' = 0'$, etc. Thus the set of theorems is $\{0 = 0, 0' = 0', 0'' = 0'', \ldots\}$.

EXAMPLE 2. In this example the set of theorems will include all of the boolean formulas in Polish notation.[4] Hence we use here "theorem" in a derivative and purely formal sense. The formulas are "theorems" strictly in the sense that they are yielded by the rules of the system, not that they may be interpreted as "true" sentences in some "theory." We have $\mathbf{B} = \langle A, \mathscr{B}_{\mathbf{B}}, \mathscr{A}, \mathscr{P} \rangle$ where now

1. $A = \{a, b, c, a_1, b_1, c_1, \ldots, \cup, \cap, -, F\}$.
2. $\mathscr{B}_{\mathbf{B}}$ = set of words on A.
3. $\mathscr{A} = \{F\}$.
4. $\mathscr{P}$ consists of the following productions:

R.1. $F \to x$
R.2. $F \to -F$
R.3. $F \to \cup FF$
R.4. $F \to \cap FF$

x is a variable over the symbols $\{a, b, c, a_1, b_1, c_1, \ldots\}$. To show that

$$-\cap-\cup ab - c$$

is a theorem (that is, a formula), we construct the following sequence:

1.	F	Axiom
2.	$-F$	***R.2***
3.	$-\cap FF$	***R.4***
4.	$-\cap - FF$	***R.2***
5.	$-\cap-F - F$	***R.2***
6.	$-\cap-F - c$	***R.1***
7.	$-\cap-\cup FF - c$	***R.3***
8.	$-\cap-\cup ab - c$	***R.1*** twice

The variable x in ***R.1*** may be eliminated and the alphabet rendered finite by eliminating all the symbols except a, $\cup$, $\cap$, $-$, F and adding the symbols $'$ and T. The alphabet of the new system $\mathbf{B}'$ is then

$$A' = \{a, ', \cup, \cap, -, F, T\}$$

[4] It should be noted that in this formal system we allow the proof of junk—not all theorems are boolean formulas (for example, Step 3 in the proof, since F is not to be interpreted as a boolean symbol, but rather as meaning "formula"). In Section 3.3 we will effect the necessary discrimination by use of the concept terminal theorem.

and the new set of rules $\mathscr{P}'$ comprises ***R.2*** to ***R.4*** above and in addition the following three:

$$\textbf{\textit{R.5.}}\quad F \to T' \qquad \textbf{\textit{R.6.}}\quad T \to a \qquad \textbf{\textit{R.7.}}\quad T \to T'$$

The single axiom is still F.

To derive $\cup a'a''$, we have the proof

$$F, \quad \cup FF, \quad \cup TF, \quad \cup T'F, \quad \cup a'F$$
$$\cup a'T, \quad \cup a'T', \quad \cup a'T'', \quad \cup a'a''$$

Returning to the first formulation of the example, if we use $(3i + k)$ to stand for $3i + k$ primes $''''\ldots$; then for every boolean formula which is a theorem x of the system **B** above there exists a theorem x' in **B**$'$ such that x' is the result of substituting primed letters for each a_i, b_i, or c_i according to Table 3.1.1.

TABLE 3.1.1

$a = a'$	$a_i = a^{(3i+1)}$	
$b = a''$	$b_i = a^{(3i+2)}$	$(1 \leq i)$
$c = a'''$	$c_i = a^{(3i+3)}$	

To prove this, we introduce some new concepts. In Example 1 the desired interpretation of the theorems of the system is the set of trivial equalities of integers $0 = 0$, $0' = 0'$, etc., where we may understand $0'$ to mean 1, $0''$, 2, etc. In this system the alphabet contains just those symbols which are the ingredients of the formulas we want to be able to prove. Moreover, the class of formulas, $\mathscr{B}_{\mathbf{R}}$, is specified independently of the rules of inference. Otherwise stated, the rules of inference apply only to formulas, and hence formulas must be appropriately defined beforehand. Let us designate as *atomic symbols* those symbols from which are formed terms, formulas, etc., by definitions given antecedent to the rules. In Example 1, the only sequences occurring in proofs will be sequences of formulas defined beforehand.

In system **B**$'$ of Example 2, the intended interpretation is the set of boolean formulas made up out of the terms a', a'', a''', etc., $\cup$, $\cap$, and $-$. The composition of terms out of the letter a and the prime is accomplished, however, *within* the system of rules—in particular, by ***R.5*** to ***R.7***; furthermore, the system of rules is intended to generate boolean formulas among the theorems. The set of boolean formulas is not defined antecedently. The given "formulas" are the *words* of $\mathscr{B}_{\mathbf{B}}$.

This rulewise composition of terms and formulas is accomplished by use of the symbols T and F. In effect, the concepts "term" and "formula" which are predicates of words in Example 1 are represented instead by abstract symbols T and F *within* the system of rules of Example 2. This is borne out by the fact that in **B**′ these symbols are included in the alphabet, whereas in **R** the same role is played by *syntactical* predicates.[5] When syntactical concepts (under the intended interpretation of the system) are incorporated as symbols *within* the alphabet of the system under study itself, the symbols are called *auxiliary* symbols. Thus in Example 2, F and T are auxiliary symbols.

Continuing with the verification that **B**′ produces all of the boolean formulas which are theorems of **B**, with primed letters, we proceed by induction on the length of a proof l.[6]

If $l = 1$, then the proof consists simply of the axiom, which is the same for **B**′ as it is for **B**. For the induction step, assume that to every proof in **B** of length $l \leq m$ there corresponds one (not necessarily of the same length) in **B**′ such that the theorem x_m' (the last element of the proof sequence) in **B**′ is the result of substituting primed a's for the atomic symbols of **B** occurring (perhaps there are zero occurrences) in the theorem x_m of the proof in **B**. Now let $(y_j)_{j \leq m+1}$ be a proof of length $m + 1$ in **B**. Then its last element y_{m+1} is the result of applying a rule of inference to some subsequence of a proof of length $l \leq m$. At this step either the auxiliary symbol F is rewritten using ***R.2*** to ***R.4***, or ***R.1*** is used, replacing an occurrence of F with an atomic symbol. If F is rewritten by ***R.2*** to ***R.4*** in y_j for some j, then using the induction hypothesis find the corresponding y_j' in the proof in **B**′ and apply ***R.2*** to ***R.4*** as needed. If, turning to the other possible case, F is rewritten by an atomic symbol in y_j using ***R.1***, then, in the corresponding y_j': (1) apply ***R.5*** to the subject F; (2) apply ***R.7*** either 0, 1, 2, or $3i + k$ $(k = 1, 2, 3)$ times as determined by the atomic symbol replacing F' in y_j using the correspondence Table 3.1.1; (3) finally, use ***R.6***. The result is a sequence of formulas ending in y_j', which is the result of replacing an atomic symbol in y_j by primed a's. Q.E.D.

The preceding proof, though tied to an example, can, in fact, be easily generalized to establish Theorem 3.1.7.

Theorem 3.1.7. For every formal system **F** there exists a formal system **F**′ such that **F**′ yields, except for notation, every theorem of **F**; furthermore **F**′ has a finite set of atomic symbols.

One can also show that any formal system whatsoever (in our sense) can be reduced to one in which there is a finite alphabet containing auxiliary symbols, a finite set of axioms or axiom schemes and a finite set of rules

[5] That is, they are predicates of words. In mathematical logic, the language in which a formal system is discussed is called the *metalanguage*, and that part of it which expresses the definitions for terms, formulas, sentences, theorems, etc., and their properties is termed the *syntactical metalanguage*.

[6] This concept is meaningful since we already have defined the *length* of a sequence.

of inference, all of them productions, as in Example 2. The system to be reduced may have any number of antecedently given syntactical categories of words such as terms, formulas, sentences, etc., all of which may be reflected in the rules themselves in a manner very similar to the one in which we collapsed a denumerable infinity of atomic symbols into the auxiliary T. These formulas as in the preceding example, become theorems of a kind, and if the system is interpreted as a logic, the sentences wanted as theorems in the mathematical sense are distinguished as *asserted* theorems. Such very general, simple formal systems are called *canonical systems*, and a certain variety of these will be the subject of our study.

We complete this subsection with some other general ideas pertaining to formal systems.

Definition 3.1.8. We say that the *decision problem* for a formal system is *solvable* iff the set of Gödel numbers of theorems of the system is recursive. Alternatively, the theorems of such a system are said to be *decidable*.

We have already seen (in Section 2.3) that the set of boolean formulas is recursive, hence the system **B** of Example 2 is solvable.[7] Similarly, if we interpret $=$ as ordinary (arithmetic) equality and $0''' \cdots (n \text{ times})$ as $0 + n$ in the ordinary sense; then **R** may also easily be shown solvable.

Theorem 3.1.9. Let T be the set of theorems of a formal system **F**. If the complement $\overline{T}$ of T w.r.t. $\mathscr{B}$ is the set of theorems of some system **F**$'$, then T is recursive.

This theorem follows from a later result (Corollary 4.4.7) which states that if both a set A and $\overline{A}$ are recursively enumerable, then A is recursive. By the hypotheses stated in Theorems 3.1.9 and 3.1.6, the result then follows. More intuitively, arguing along the same lines as used in Theorem 3.1.6, if x is a theorem of T then a proof can effectively be found; if it is not a theorem of T, then it is a theorem of $\overline{T}$ and can therefore be found in an effective way not to be a theorem of T. Q.E.D.

EXAMPLE 3. Let $A = \{a, b, c, d, e\}$ and let $A' = \{a, b, c\}$. We shall show that the set of words $\mathscr{A}'$ on A' is solvable by inventing systems which generate all words $\mathscr{A}'$ and which generate all words $\mathscr{A} - \mathscr{A}'$, where $\mathscr{A}$ is the set of words on A.

The first system has axioms

Ax.1. a ***Ax.2.*** b ***Ax.3.*** c

and the rule of inference:

R.1. $x, y \rightarrow xy$

where x and y are variables on $\mathscr{A}'$, and the rule means that if x and y are won as theorems, then xy comes out a theorem, as well. It is rather easily

[7] Assuming, of course, that **B** turns out only boolean formulas. See Exercises 3.1.

seen that precisely $\mathscr{A}'$ is the set of theorems, and thus $\mathscr{A}'$ is recursively enumerable. Next consider the system with $A = \{a, b, c, d, e\}$, axioms,

Ax.1. d **Ax.2.** e

and rules,

R.1. $x \to xy$ **R.2.** $x \to yx$

with x, y ranging over all of $\mathscr{A}$.
Since the theorems of this system include all words on A with at least one occurrence of either d or e, it follows that this set is $\mathscr{A} - \mathscr{A}'$. Thus this set is recursively enumerable and is at the same time the complement of $\mathscr{A}'$. Hence $\mathscr{A}'$ is solvable.

This latter procedure is not the only one available for showing solvability. We may, in a more technical vein, actually go to the trouble of demonstrating the recursiveness of the set of Gödel numbers of theorems, or as suggested at the end of Section 2.3, devise a way of indicating membership in the set of theorems by a finitary test.

EXERCISES 3.1

1. Given the formal system with alphabet $\{a, b\}$ with axioms

Ax.1. a **Ax.3.** ab
Ax.2. b **Ax.4.** ba

and rules of inference

R.1. $xa \to xab$ **R.2.** $xb \to xba$

where x ranges over the words on $\{a, b\}$ and where rules are used as in Example 3. Redesign the system so that the variable x is not used. (*Hint*: What subset of the set of words on the alphabet $\{a, b\}$ is generated by the given system? Knowing this, attempt to define a meaning of formula applicable to just these words and then proceed to construct a system in the style of **B**′ of Example 2.)

2. Give a formal proof in **B**′ of Example 2 of the formula corresponding to

$$(a) \quad -\cap-\cup ab - c \qquad (b) \quad (\bar{a} \cup (b \cup (c \cap b)))$$

3. Explain in detail, using Definition 3.1.3 and the rules of system **B**′ as *recursive word predicates*, why what you produced in Exercise 2a is indeed a proof.

4. Prove informally that **B** yields all of the boolean formulas in the sense of Section 2.1.

5. Prove that the set of theorems of **R** (Example 1) is recursive.

6. Prove that the second system of Example 3 does, in fact, generate as theorems exactly $\mathscr{A} - \mathscr{A}'$.

7. Is it true according to Definitions 3.1.2, 3.1.3, and 3.1.5 that if a word is not a formula, then it is not a theorem?

8. Is the universal relation of Definition 3.1.1 a monoid? Explain. What about the more general relations such as those defined by the predicates $\mathscr{P}$ of Definition 3.1.2?

3.2 EXAMPLES OF FORMAL SYSTEMS

All of the preceding examples of formal systems are trivial. In this section we discuss two nontrivial systems which are of immediate interest.

Definition 3.2.1. **P** is a formulation of the *propositional calculus*. The alphabet is the following (where p, q, etc., are called *variables*).

$$A = \{p, q, r, s, t, p_1, q_1, r_1, s_1, t_1, \ldots, \Rightarrow, \neg, (,),\}$$

A *formula* is defined as follows:

1. any variable is a formula,
2. if x is a formula, so is $\neg x$,
3. if x and y are formulas, $(x \Rightarrow y)$ is a formula,
4. a word x is a formula only if this fact follows from 1 to 3.

The *axioms* are:

Ax.1. $(p \Rightarrow (q \Rightarrow p))$.
Ax.2. $((p \Rightarrow (q \Rightarrow r)) \Rightarrow ((p \Rightarrow q) \Rightarrow (p \Rightarrow r)))$.
Ax.3. $((\neg p \Rightarrow \neg q) \Rightarrow (q \Rightarrow p))$.

The *rules of inference* are:

R.1. From x and $(x \Rightarrow y)$ to infer y.

R.2. If x is a formula, from x to infer the result of substituting y for all occurrences of a variable in x.

In ***R.1*** and ***R.2***, and hereafter in this discussion, x and y have formulas as values. Note that this is a formal system: the set of formulas is recursive, as can be checked by the Gödel procedure given for the boolean language in Section 2.3; the set of axioms is finite, hence recursive; and ***R.1*** and ***R.2*** are easily shown to be recursive word predicates.

EXAMPLE 1. Prove $(p \Rightarrow ((p \Rightarrow q) \Rightarrow p))$.

1.	$(p \Rightarrow (q \Rightarrow p))$	***Ax.1***
2.	$(p \Rightarrow ((p \Rightarrow q) \Rightarrow p))$	1 and ***R.2***

This is a sequence of formulas of length 2. The first element is an axiom. The second one is the result of substituting $(p \Rightarrow q)$ for q in $(p \Rightarrow (q \Rightarrow p))$ Thus this sequence is a proof by Definition 3.1.3.

EXAMPLE 2. A less trivial example is to prove $(p \Rightarrow p)$.

1. $((p \Rightarrow (q \Rightarrow r)) \Rightarrow ((p \Rightarrow q) \Rightarrow (p \Rightarrow r)))$ ***Ax.2***
2. $((p \Rightarrow (q \Rightarrow p)) \Rightarrow ((p \Rightarrow q) \Rightarrow (p \Rightarrow p)))$ ***R.2***, p for r in 1
3. $(p \Rightarrow (q \Rightarrow p))$ ***Ax.1***
4. $((p \Rightarrow q) \Rightarrow (p \Rightarrow p))$ ***R.1***, 2, and 3
5. $((p \Rightarrow (q \Rightarrow p)) \Rightarrow (p \Rightarrow p))$ ***R.2***, $(q \Rightarrow p)$ for q in 4
6. $(p \Rightarrow p)$ ***R.1***, 3, and 5

The student should carefully check that formulas 1–6 constitute a proof.

EXAMPLE 3. To prove $(\neg p \Rightarrow (p \Rightarrow q))$.

1. $((\neg q \Rightarrow \neg p) \Rightarrow (p \Rightarrow q)) \Rightarrow (\neg p \Rightarrow ((\neg q \Rightarrow \neg p) \Rightarrow (p \Rightarrow q)))$

Here we have written the result of substituting $((\neg q \Rightarrow \neg p) \Rightarrow (p \Rightarrow q))$ for p and $\neg p$ for q in ***Ax.1*** without writing the latter down first. So there are two steps we have merged into one.

2. $((\neg q \Rightarrow \neg p) \Rightarrow (p \Rightarrow q))$

Similarly, we made here the obvious substitution directly in ***Ax.3***.

3. $(\neg p \Rightarrow ((\neg q \Rightarrow \neg p) \Rightarrow (p \Rightarrow q)))$ ***R.1***, 1, and 2
4. $((\neg p \Rightarrow ((\neg q \Rightarrow \neg p) \Rightarrow (p \Rightarrow q))) \Rightarrow ((\neg p \Rightarrow (\neg q \Rightarrow \neg p)) \Rightarrow (\neg p \Rightarrow (p \Rightarrow q))))$

This is the result of substituting $\neg p$ for p, $(\neg q \Rightarrow \neg p)$ for q, and $(p \Rightarrow q)$ for r in ***Ax.2***.

5. $((\neg p \Rightarrow (\neg q \Rightarrow \neg p)) \Rightarrow (\neg p \Rightarrow (p \Rightarrow q)))$ ***R.1***, 3, and 4
6. $(\neg p \Rightarrow (\neg q \Rightarrow \neg p))$ ***R2, Ax.1***
7. $(\neg p \Rightarrow (p \Rightarrow q))$ ***R.1***, 5, and 6

These examples may demonstrate that the construction of a proof of as simple a formula as $\neg p \Rightarrow (p \Rightarrow q)$ is hardly a trivial task. Nevertheless since the set of proofs is recursive, it is purely clerical to check out the foregoing or any other alleged proof; and since the set of theorems is recursively enumerable, by Theorem 3.1.6, these theorems could be proved by a machine, but not necessarily exactly in the same sequence as the foregoing.

The propositional calculus formalizes that sort of reasoning in science and mathematics which turns on the locutions "if-then," "not," "or," "and," etc. Thus ***Ax.3*** is a formalization of the principle called the *contrapositive*. To see this we interpret $\neg$ to mean "not" (as in Section 1.1) and $\Rightarrow$ to mean "if-then." Thus $(\neg p \Rightarrow q)$ is read "if not-p, then q." The variables, q, p, etc., may be replaced by any declarative sentences. Hence with this in mind the theorems are meant to express logical truths. By turning back to ***Ax.3***, which reads

If, if not p, then not q, then if q, then p

an application of it, replacing p by the sentence

2 is an odd number

and q by

2 is divisible by 3

results in the logical truth

> If, if 2 is not an odd number, then 2 is not divisible by 3, then if 2 is divisible by 3, then 2 is an odd number.

Although this statement is not very informative it is true as a little thought given to it will confirm. The reasoning that this axiom is meant to convey, however, would more likely be as follows. Assume not-p. But then, for such and such reason, not-q. Therefore if q, then p.

Technically, to explain "logical truth" we interpret the variables p, q, etc., as ranging over a set of two objects $\{t, f\}$ which we *define* as having the properties:

$$\begin{aligned} &(t \Rightarrow t) = (f \Rightarrow t) = (f \Rightarrow f) = t \\ &(t \Rightarrow f) = f \\ &\neg t = f, \neg f = t \end{aligned} \tag{1}$$

Our motivation for this is that statements are true or false. If a statement p is true, we assign to it the value t = true; if it is false, the value f = false. The properties attributed to t and f by (1) are those, experience shows, which are sufficient for mathematical inference insofar as it hinges on if-then, not, etc. The first expression in the first line of (1) states that if true, then true is (identically) true; or using the variables, if p has the value true and q has the value true, then if p then q has the value true. Using (1) we may introduce *truth tables* for $\Rightarrow$ and $\neg$ which with this interpretation are called *truth functions*.

p	$\neg p$
f	t
t	f

(2)

and

p	q	$p \Rightarrow q$
f	f	t
f	t	t
t	f	f
t	t	t

or

p \ q	f	t
f	t	t
t	f	t

(3)

Thus $\neg$ and $\Rightarrow$ are functions onto $\{t, f\}$ from $\{t, f\}$ and $\{(t, t), (t, f), (f, t), (f, t)\}$, respectively.

Definition 3.2.2. Any formula which under the interpretation has a function table with all t's in the function column is a logical truth or *tautology*; any formula with all f's in the function column is a logical falsehood or *contradiction.*

Returning to the motivation behind the construction of the calculus, our objective is to build a formal system, which when interpreted, produces all and only the tautologies. Analogously, the rudimentary arithmetic of Example 1 in Section 3.1 was meant to turn out all arithmetical truths such as $0' = 0'$ and only those, whereas in Example 2 of that section the purpose was to turn out all and only the boolean formulas. Similarly, the pulse divider discussed at the end of Section 3.0 was intended to turn out all and only sequences of 0's and 1's of the kind described, given any input.

A formal system which yields a set of theorems including all of those desired under a given interpretation is said to be *complete*; one which yields only the desired objects (as theorems) is *consistent.* Still more generally speaking, any system, which succeeds in producing (with a mechanically applicable set of rules) every output desired, is complete, and if it furnishes only such outputs, it is consistent. In Exercises 4 and 6 of Section 3.1, the student was asked to establish certain results of this kind. We will now indicate how this may be done for the propositional calculus.

Definition 3.2.3. A propositional calculus is *consistent* iff there is no formula x such that both x and $\neg x$ are provable.

This definition does what we require, since by Example 3, if both p and $\neg p$ were provable, then any statement, including any false statement, could be proved (by using Example 3 and ***R.1*** twice).

Theorem 3.2.4. Every theorem of the system of Definition 3.2.1 is a tautology.

The detailed proof,[8] which we will not include here, also establishes the consistency of the system. For if x is a theorem it has all t's in its truth table by Theorem 3.2.4. But then $\neg x$ has, by (2), all f's, and hence is not a theorem.

Definition 3.2.5. A propositional calculus is *complete* iff every tautology is a theorem.

This definition also performs its required function since our declared intention was to construct a system yielding every logically true statement.

[8] Each axiom is a tautology and ***R.1*** and ***R.2*** preserve tautologies.

Theorem 3.2.6. The system of Definition 3.2.1 is complete.

The proof is omitted.[9]

Theorem 3.2.7. The decision problem for the propositional calculus is solvable.

This proposition follows immediately from Theorems 3.2.4 and 3.2.6. For the construction of a truth table is an effective task; then x is a theorem iff it is a tautology, by the two preceding theorems.

Another interpretation of the propositional calculus is the one indicated at the beginning of Section 1.3 in the discussion of switching circuits. In order to discuss it in a way that will be worthwhile later (Chapter 6) we must introduce the connectives which are most useful to the interpretation. For either relay, diode, or transistor circuitry, the geometry of the equipment makes the or, and, nor, and nand connectives particularly useful. We may introduce them in terms of our primitive connectives, given earlier with the alphabetical listing, as follows (where "$=$" means "equal by definition"):

$$\begin{array}{ll} (p \vee q) = (\neg p \Rightarrow q) & \text{(or)} \\ (p \wedge q) = \neg(p \Rightarrow \neg q) & \text{(and)} \\ (p \mid q) = (p \Rightarrow \neg q) & \text{(nand—Sheffer stroke)} \\ (p \downarrow q) = \neg(\neg p \Rightarrow q) & \text{(nor—Peirce stroke)} \end{array} \tag{4}$$

And while we are at it,[10]

$$(p \Leftrightarrow q) = (p \Rightarrow q) \wedge (q \Rightarrow p) \tag{5}$$

For the switching interpretation, we now use 0 and 1 for f and t; for and, or, and not "logic," (1) becomes in virtue of the definitions (4):

$$\begin{array}{l} (0 \vee 0) = (\neg 0 \Rightarrow 0) = (1 \Rightarrow 0) = 0 \\ (1 \vee 0) = (\neg 1 \Rightarrow 0) = (0 \Rightarrow 0) = 1 = (0 \vee 1) \\ (1 \vee 1) = (\neg 1 \Rightarrow 1) = (0 \Rightarrow 1) = 1 \\ (0 \wedge 0) = \neg(0 \Rightarrow \neg 0) = \neg(0 \Rightarrow 1) = \neg 1 = 0 \\ (0 \wedge 1) = \neg(0 \Rightarrow \neg 1) = \neg(0 \Rightarrow 0) = \neg 1 = 0 = (1 \wedge 0) \\ (1 \wedge 1) = \neg(1 \Rightarrow \neg 1) = \neg(1 \Rightarrow 0) = \neg 0 = 1 \end{array} \tag{6}$$

Finally, as is customary in switching, we will write $\bar{p}$ for $\neg p$, so that $\bar{0} = 1$ and $\bar{1} = 0$. Evidently, $\{0, 1\}$ w.r.t. $\vee$, $\wedge$, and $-$ is a two-element boolean algebra [cf. Example 1.3 (22)].

[9] See, for example, Church [1956].

[10] To be formally correct, we should have used a different set of connectives for the formal propositional calculus than the ones used for our informal mathematical discourse beginning in Section 1.1 and elsewhere. However, the ambiguity should not cause confusion.

We might emphasize at this time that the propositional calculus, which is a formal system, is *not* boolean algebra, or even *a* boolean algebra, even though $\{t, f\}$ is. The logic using $\wedge$, $\vee$, and $-$, however, is essentially the same as a free boolean algebra. A brief discussion of this point will provide the opportunity to introduce additional useful material.

Definition 3.2.8. *x implies y* iff y has the value t whenever x does.

This is simply a formulation of the ordinary meaning of implication used in mathematical proofs. In this discussion it is necessary to distinguish "if p then q" from "x implies y." By Definition 3.2.1, "if p then q" or "$p \Rightarrow q$" is a *formula* in the propositional calculus, and "x implies y" is not. The latter statement asserts a relation between two statements, indeed a partial ordering, as the reader should verify. *Implies* is a binary word predicate, and for the propositional calculus, in virtue of the effectiveness of truth tables, a recursive one.

Definition 3.2.9. x is *equivalent* to y iff x implies y and y implies x.

Theorem 3.2.10. x is equivalent to y iff x and y have the same truth table. The proof follows from the definition. It is obvious that equivalence partitions the formulas of the propositional calculus into equivalence classes.

Theorem 3.2.11. x implies y iff $x \Rightarrow y$ is a theorem; x is equivalent to y iff $x \Leftrightarrow y$ is a theorem (or, using only the connectives $\Rightarrow$ and $\neg$, iff

$$\neg((x \Rightarrow y) \Rightarrow \neg(y \Rightarrow x))$$

is a theorem).

Proof is left to the student.

Definition 3.2.12. Let $\mathbf{P}$ be a formulation of the propositional calculus using just the distinct variables $p_1, \ldots, p_n$, the connectives $\wedge$, $\vee$, $-$. Any formula $p_1' \wedge p_2' \wedge \cdots \wedge p_n'$ with each p_i' either a variable p_i or a negated variable $\bar{p}_i$, is a *fundamental* formula. Any formula $x \wedge y$ is a *conjunction*; and any formula $x \vee y$ is a *disjunction*. $\bar{x}$ is the *negation* of x. Any disjunction of conjunctions of variables p or their negations is said to be in *disjunctive normal form*; any disjunction (including the null disjunction which we write f) of fundamental formulas without repetition is in *complete disjunctive normal form*.[11] Dually,[12] with the appropriate companion formulation for disjunction of "fundamental formula," one may define *conjunctive normal form* and *complete conjunctive normal form*.

[11] This is the counterpart in logic of the canonical expansion in boolean algebra. See Exercises. The only substantive difference is in notation.

[12] Recall that the dual of an expression in lattice theory is the result of interchanging $\cup$ and $\cap$ everywhere.

As the reader may verify, all of the relations which hold for (free) boolean algebras with $\cup$, $\cap$ hold as true equivalences in logic with $\vee$, $\wedge$, and may be so established by the use of truth tables using Theorem 3.2.10.

EXAMPLE 4. $\bar{x} \vee \bar{y}$ is equivalent to $\overline{x \wedge y}$.

Alternatively, by Theorem 3.2.11 one finds that $(\bar{x} \vee \bar{y}) \Leftrightarrow (\overline{x \wedge y})$ is a theorem of the formal system. Using the axioms ***Ax.1*** to ***Ax.3*** above, however, one would first have to translate the formula into a version using only $\Rightarrow$ and $\neg$ by (4).

Thus every formula, in complete disjunctive normal form in a logic with n propositional variables, corresponds to an element in a free boolean algebra on n generators. In this sense propositional calculus is the same as boolean algebra.

More exactly, we can say that the set of *equivalence classes* of formulas of n variables w.r.t. $\wedge$ and $\vee$ is isomorphic to the free boolean algebra on n generators. For, if $\mathscr{P}$ is a partition with $P_1, P_2, \ldots$ the equivalence classes, then $P_i \vee P_j$—which is the class of all formulas x such that there is a $y \in P_i$, $z \in P_j$, and $x = (y \vee z)$—is a well-defined equivalence class, as is $P_i \wedge P_j$. To each class corresponds a unique formula, the complete disjunctive normal form. There is a canonical mapping from each formula into its equivalence class; this function is a homomorphism, as is shown by noting the definitions of $\vee$ and $\wedge$ for equivalence classes. Also by Exercise 1.3(19), each equivalence class maps into a unique *representative*, the formula in complete disjunctive normal form.

Theorem 3.2.13. The system $\mathscr{P} = \langle\{P_1, \ldots, P_{2^{2^n}}\}, \wedge, \vee, f, t\rangle$ is isomorphic to the free boolean algebra on n generators.

Using the technique for showing isomorphism between the system of boolean functions of n-variables and the free system on n variables, one may always expand a logic function into normal form by way of the truth table. Except for notation, a truth function with $\wedge$, $\vee$, and $\overline{}$ is a boolean function with $\cap$, $\cup$, and $-$.

EXAMPLE 5. Let $x = p \vee \overline{(q \wedge r)}$. Its truth table, by (2), (3), and (4), is as follows:

pqr	$p \vee \overline{(q \wedge r)}$
fff	t
fft	t
ftf	t
ftt	f
tff	t
tft	t
ttf	t
ttt	t

By the previously mentioned proof, for every function value t of x we write down a fundamental formula $x_1x_2x_3$ where x_1 is p if its value in the argument column is t and $\bar{p}$ if its value is f; similarly, for x_2 and x_3. Thus, corresponding to the first row in the table, we have $\bar{p} \wedge \bar{q} \wedge \bar{r}$. The entire expanded form is

$$(\bar{p} \wedge \bar{q} \wedge \bar{r}) \vee (\bar{p} \wedge \bar{q} \wedge r) \vee (\bar{p} \wedge q \wedge \bar{r}) \vee$$
$$(p \wedge \bar{q} \wedge \bar{r}) \vee (p \wedge \bar{q} \wedge r) \vee (p \wedge q \wedge \bar{r}) \vee$$
$$(p \wedge q \wedge r)$$

Although we have used a formulation of the propositional calculus with the notion of variable and formula given antecedently to the axiom set, we can formulate it strictly as a canonical system in the sense explained just after Theorem 3.1.7. In this form, however, it would be much more work to elicit the interpretation of the objects as true or false sentences and to work out the algebraic properties discussed above.

The next example is concerned with a class of systems called *programs.* Although programs, strictly speaking, are not full formal systems, they can be formalized in various ways. In particular, they are equivalent to Turing machines (as is shown in Chapter 4), and since the latter are formal systems we feel justified in treating programs as such in the present context. [See also Exercise 3.3(11).]

Definition 3.2.14. A *program* is any system with an alphabet consisting of a denumerable set of pairs of the form (i, x_j) where i is a nonnegative integer, x_j is a *symbol*, j an integer. The set includes at least one pair (i, p). A program has one axiom, which is a finite word of pairs without repetitions of symbols x_j including at least one pair (i, p). The *rules of inference* are any *finite sequences* selected from the following *sub-rules.*

$$\begin{array}{llll} \text{(i)} & x_j \to x_i & \text{(iv)} & x_i \to p \\ \text{(ii)} & x_i + 1 \to x_i & \text{(v)} & (0, x_i) \Rightarrow j, k \\ \text{(iii)} & x_i - 1 \to x_i & \text{(vi)} & \text{Stop} \end{array} \tag{7}$$

where i, j, and k are integers.

In a proof, the *sub*-rules must be applied beginning with the first in the sequence, and we apply the $(k + 1)$st after the kth unless k is a rule of form (v) of (7). Note that here we are discussing *two sequences*: a proof, and a system of rules which is undefined unless it is a sequence.

A *proof* is any finite sequence of words (recall the symbols here are pairs)

$$w_1, w_2, w_3, \ldots, w_n$$

such that w_1 is the axiom; w_{k+1} is the result of applying one of the rules (i) to (iv) of the rule sequence to w_k, $k = 1, 2, \ldots, n - 1$; w_n is a *theorem.*

A proof is *terminal* iff there is no w_{n+1} such that it follows by application of one of (i) to (iv) of the rule sequence to w_n. Here w_n is a *terminal theorem*.

The informal interpretation of the preceding definition is as follows. The pair (i, x_j) means that i is in x_j or, equivalently, that the content of x_j is i; p means "print-out position." An axiom

$$(i_1, x_{j_1})(i_2, x_{j_2}) \cdots (i_k, x_{j_k})(i_{k+1}, p)$$

should be interpreted to be any array of *registers* with addresses x_{j_r} and contents i_r. The rules of the form $\alpha \to \beta$, that is, (i) and (iv), mean "to replace the contents of β with the contents of α."[13] Rules (ii) and (iii) mean to perform the indicated operation on the contents of x_i and to replace the contents of x_i with the result. Thus suppose two pairs $(0, x_1)$ $(2, x_2)$ occur in the axiom and that the rules of inference include $x_1 + 1 \to x_1$. The result of an application will then be $(1, x_1)$ $(2, x_2)$. The rule $(0, x_1) \Rightarrow j, k$ means that if x_1 contains 0, apply rule j next, otherwise apply rule k. This kind of rule is applicable since the system of rules for any program is a sequence, and j, k are indices thereof.

EXAMPLE 6. This is a program for adding two integers. The alphabet is

$$A = \{(0, x_1), (1, x_1), (2, x_1), \ldots, (0, x_2)(1, x_2)(2, x_2), \ldots, (0, p)\}$$

The single axiom is

$$\mathscr{A} = (a, x_1)(b, x_2)(0, p)$$

Technically, this is an *axiom scheme*, and becomes an axiom when a and b are specified with integers; a and b are syntactical variables. The rules of inference are

1. $(0, x_1) \Rightarrow 5, 2$
2. $x_1 - 1 \to x_1$
3. $x_2 + 1 \to x_2$
4. $(0, x_2) \Rightarrow 1, 1$
5. $x_2 \to p$
6. Stop

To add $2 + 3 = 5$, the axiom is specified: $(2, x_1)(3, x_2)(0, p)$. The proof follows.

1. $(2, x_1)(3, x_2)(0, p)$ Axiom $\mathscr{A}$
2. $(1, x_1)(3, x_2)(0, p)$ Rule 2
3. $(1, x_1)(4, x_2)(0, p)$ Rule 3
4. $(0, x_1)(4, x_2)(0, p)$ Rule 2
5. $(0, x_1)(5, x_2)(0, p)$ Rule 3
6. $(0, x_1)(5, x_2)(5, p)$ Rule 5

[13] As given, these rules are *not* productions.

The answer in step 5 occurs in location p.

Obviously, no one literally handles calculations in this way, but the foregoing construction nevertheless is instructive in that is shows programs to be analogous to formal systems in our strict sense.

Definition 3.2.15. To any program **P** and for any n we associate an n-ary function of nonnegative integers $\Phi_{\mathbf{P}}$ such that if there exists a terminal proof of w_m in **P** from $(a_1, x_1)(a_2, x_2)\cdots(a_n, x_n)(0, p)$, then we set

$$\Phi_{\mathbf{P}}(a_1, \ldots, a_n) = \text{contents of } p \text{ in } w_m$$

Or, if there is no terminal proof from the axiom indicated,

$$\Phi_{\mathbf{P}}(a_1, \ldots, a_n) \text{ is undefined}$$

Explanation. According to Definition 3.2.14, a program, if it has a proof, is in effect a mapping from the axiom to the theorem and hence from n-tuples of integers to integers. If there is no proof, the word sequence beginning with the axiom is infinite (goes into a "loop"). To show that whenever there is a proof there is a mapping of the sort required, we need observe only that by the definition of proof, for every word w_i there is at most one word w_{i+1} following it in the sequence. For one always applies the $(k + 1)$st instruction after the kth, unless rule (v) of list (7) is used, in which case the next applicable rule is uniquely determined. Such formal systems are said to be *monogenic* (see Section 3.3). This discussion proves, as corollary to Definition 3.2.14,

Corollary 3.2.16. Programming systems are *monogenic*.

The Corollary justifies Definition 3.2.15.

Definition 3.2.17. A function f is *program partial computable* iff there exists a program **P** such that[14]

$$f(x_1, \ldots, x_n) = \Phi_{\mathbf{P}}(x_1, \ldots, x_n)$$

Program **P** is said to *compute* f.

The set of rules (7) is complete in that it includes sufficient rules or instructions for computing any partial recursive function. For recalling that a partial recursive function is one derived from the successor function $S(x)$, the identity function $I_i^n(x_1, \ldots, x_n)$, and the zero function $N(x)$ by composition, primitive recursion, or minimalization, we can show programs for each calculation or operation on functions. We now do so, using the alphabet A (Example 6).

The *successor function*:

$$\mathscr{A} = (a, x_1)(0, p)$$

[14] Recall that two functions are equal if they have the same values for each element of a common domain.

RULES	*Proof*:
1. $x_1 + 1 \to x$	1. $(a, x_1)(0, p)$
2. $x_1 \to p$	2. $(a + 1, x_1)(0, p)$
3. Stop	3. $(a + 1, x_1)(a + 1, p)$

The associated function here, by Definition 3.2.15, is Φ, and $\Phi(a) = a + 1 =$ contents of p.

Equally trivial are the program systems for the *zero* and *identity* functions.

If **P** computes a function f, then $(f(a_1, \ldots, a_n), x)$ can appear as a symbol for another Program **P**′. Rather than rewrite **P** as a part of **P**′, which is always possible, we determine **P**′ once and for all and introduce the rule

$$f(x_{i_1}, \ldots, x_{i_n}) \to x_j \tag{8}$$

where $x_{i_1}, \ldots, x_{i_n}$ and x_j are locations in **P**′ and $f(x_{i_1}, \ldots, x_{i_n})$ means the result of computing $f(a_{i_1}, \ldots, a_{i_n})$. Such a rule indicates a *subroutine*. For example, a system for *multiplication* would be

$$\mathscr{A}: (a_1, x_1)(a_2, x_2)(0, x_3)(0, p)$$

RULES

1. $(0, x_1) \Rightarrow 2, 4$
2. $x_3 \to p$
3. Stop
4. $x_1 - 1 \to x_1$
5. $x_2 + x_3 \to x_3$
6. $(0, x_1) \Rightarrow 1, 1$

Step 5 represents the insertion of a subroutine for addition.

Proceeding inductively, suppose that

$$f_1(x_1, \ldots, x_n), \ldots, f_m(x_1, \ldots, x_n)$$

are program computable over a common domain D and that

$$g(x_1, \ldots, x_m)$$

is computable as well. Then, if we have

$$\mathscr{A} = (a_1, x_1)\cdots(a_n, x_n)(a_{n+1}, x_{n+1})\cdots(a_{n+m}, x_{n+m})(0, p)$$

and the rules

$$\begin{aligned} 1.\quad & f_1(x_1, \ldots, x_n) \to x_{n+1} \\ \vdots\quad & \\ m.\quad & f_m(x_1, \ldots, x_n) \to x_{n+m} \\ m + 1.\quad & g(x_{n+1}, \ldots, x_{n+m}) \to p \\ m + 2.\quad & \text{Stop} \end{aligned}$$

we have a program for the composition

$$g(f_1(x_1, \ldots, x_n), \ldots, f_m(x_1, \ldots, x_n))$$

Suppose that we next have a function defined by primitive recursion (cf. Section 2.1)

$$h(0, x_1, \ldots, x_n) = f(x_1, \ldots, x_n)$$
$$h(y + 1, x_1, \ldots, x_n) = g(y, h(y, x_1, \ldots, x_n), x_1, \ldots, x_n)$$

where f and g are program computable. To show that h is program computable, let $a_1, \ldots, a_n$ be arbitrary values of $x_1, \ldots, x_n$ and b be an arbitrary value of y. We will now construct a system whose axiom is the scheme:

$$(a_1, x_1)(a_2, x_2)\cdots(a_n, x_n)(b, x_{n+1})(0, x_{n+2})(0, x_{n+3})(0, p)$$

RULES

1. $f(x_1, \ldots, x_n) \rightarrow x_{n+3}$
2. $(0, x_{n+1}) \Rightarrow 3, 5$
3. $x_{n+3} \rightarrow p$
4. Stop
5. $x_{n+1} - 1 \rightarrow x_{n+1}$
6. $g(x_{n+2}, x_{n+3}, x_1, \ldots, x_n) \rightarrow x_{n+3}$
7. $x_{n+2} + 1 \rightarrow x_{n+2}$
8. $(0, x_1) \Rightarrow 2, 2$

By a subroutine, this program computes f and places the result in x_{n+3}. At this point the content of x_{n+3} is the value of h for $y = 0$. Next the program checks whether the argument value of y is given as 0. If so, the computation is over and there is a stop at 4. If not, x_{n+1} is decremented, g is computed for $x_{n+2}, x_{n+3}, x_1, \ldots, x_n$; that is, for $y = 0$, $h(0, x_1, \ldots, x_n)$, $x_1, \ldots, x_n$; then x_{n+2} is incremented, and so on.

Finally, let us suppose that $f(y, x_1, \ldots, x_n)$ is a total function of $n + 1$ variables which is program computable. Then the minimalization

$$g(x_1, \ldots, x_n) = \mu(f(y, x_1, \ldots, x_n) = 0)$$

is also program computable. The proof, again by construction of a suitable program system, is left to the student. Altogether this discussion has demonstrated Theorem 3.2.18.

Theorem 3.2.18. Every partial recursive function is program computable.

Corollary 3.2.19. Every recursively enumerable set is the set of contents of p for some program system.

For, if S is such a set, it is the range of some recursive function which, in turn, can be calculated by a program.

EXERCISES 3.2

1. Write the proof for $(\neg p \Rightarrow (p \Rightarrow q))$, Example 3, completely.

2. In the formulation of the propositional calculus used above prove the formula

$$((q \Rightarrow r) \Rightarrow ((p \Rightarrow q) \Rightarrow (p \Rightarrow r)))$$

3. Prove that the rules of inference ***R.1*** and ***R.2*** of the propositional calculus preserve the property of being a formula.

4. Show that "formula" as in Definition 3.2.1 is a recursive word predicate. (*Hint*: See the comparable analysis for boolean formulas in Section 2.3.)

5. Give a definition of "proof" for the system of Definition 3.2.1.

6. Show by truth tables that the definitions (4) are adequate to the meaning of $\vee$, $\wedge$, $|$, and $\downarrow$ as used in switching theory.

7. Check whether (*a*) every truth function of two variables can be represented using $|$ (nand) alone; (*b*) using $\neg$ and $\wedge$; (*c*) using $\neg$ and $\Leftrightarrow$.

8. Prove that x implies y iff $x \Rightarrow y$ is a theorem.

9. Expand $(p \vee (q \wedge \bar{r}))$ into complete disjunctive normal form by (*a*) algebraic manipulation (that is, applying laws of boolean algebra); (*b*) by the method of Example 5.

10. Is the propositional calculus monogenic? Explain. What about the pulse divider example, end of Section 3.0? The system of rudimentary arithmetic, Example 3.1(1)? The system for generating boolean formulas?

11. Write a program for minimalization.

12. Write a program for testing whether $x_1 = x_2$ using only (7).

13. Write a program for subtraction. Recall that the subtraction $x - y$ is undefined for the nonnegative integers x, y if $y > x$.

3.3 SEMI-THUE SYSTEMS AND AUTOMATA

We have examined a rather large variety of formal systems and studied some properties which are of use in the theory of automata. We now begin to concentrate on automata as such.

Definition 3.3.1. A *semi-thue*[15] system is a quadruple, $\mathbf{T} = \langle A, \mathscr{B}, \mathscr{A}, \mathscr{P} \rangle$ where

A is a finite, nonempty *alphabet*.

$\mathscr{B}$ is the set of words on A.

$\mathscr{A}$ is a single *axiom* or *axiom scheme*, an element of $\mathscr{B}$.

$\mathscr{P}$ is a finite set of *rules of inference* of the form

$$PgR \rightarrow Pg'R$$

where $g, g' \in \mathscr{B}$, and P, R are syntactic variables on $\mathscr{B}$. The interpretation is that some occurrence of g in PgR may be written g' yielding $Pg'R$.

[15] Named after the Norwegian mathematician Axel Thue.

EXAMPLE 1. The formal system $\mathbf{B}'$ for producing boolean formulas is a semi-thue system. To see this, observe routinely that A' is finite, $\mathscr{B}$ is $(A')^*$, $F \in \mathscr{B}$ is an axiom, and that each element of $\mathscr{P}$ is of the form specified. ***R*.2**, of this example, is now written

***R*.2.** $PFR \to P - FR$

The other productions can be treated similarly.

Another example is the pulse divider at the end of Section 3.0. Again, its alphabet is finite, and the rules are already written explicitly in semi-thue form.

Definition 3.3.2. A word w' *follows from* w in $\mathbf{T}$ iff $w = PgR$ and $w' = Pg'R$ and $PgR \to Pg'R$ is a rule of $\mathbf{T}$.

Definition 3.3.3. A *proof* is a finite sequence of words $w_1, w_2, \ldots, w_n$ such that w_1 is the axiom and for every i, $1 < i \leq n$, w_i follows from w_{i-1}.

Specific versions of the general concepts follows from and proof introduced in Section 3.1, are embodied in the two foregoing definitions. Notice that here our rules of inference may be construed as binary word predicates $K(w_1, w_2)$ meaning w_2 follows from w_1. By Definition 3.3.2 $K(w_1, w_2)$ is true iff there exist words P and R such that $w_1 = PgR$ and $w_2 = Pg'R$. The definition of proof is more restrictive than it is in the general case of Definition 3.1.3, in two ways. First, all of the rules here are binary and second, each w_i follows from w_{i-1} in the sequence, and not from any other w_j, $j < i - 1$.

Theorem 3.3.4. Every semi-thue system is a formal system.

Definition 3.3.5. w is a *theorem* of $\mathbf{T}$ iff there is a proof $w_1, \ldots, w_n$ such that $w = w_n$.

The basic theorems for formal systems concerning the recursiveness of proofs, enumerability of theorems, etc., may be summarized for the special case of semi-thue systems in the following corollary.

Corollary 3.3.6. Let $\mathbf{T}$ be any semi-thue system.

(*a*) The set of proofs in $\mathbf{T}$ is recursive.

(*b*) The set of theorems in $\mathbf{T}$ is recursively enumerable.

(*c*) If a set of words and its complement are also sets of theorems of, say, $\mathbf{T}$ and $\mathbf{T}'$ respectively, then both sets are recursive.

Each part follows from the respective general theorems for formal systems together with the fact that any $\mathbf{T}$ is a formal system.

Definition 3.3.7. A *terminal* theorem is a theorem w such that no word w' follows from w.[16]

[16] These concepts may in obvious ways be applied to any formal system.

Definition 3.3.8. A semi-thue system is *monogenic* iff at most one theorem w' follows from a theorem w. Otherwise, a system is *polygenic*.[16]

EXAMPLE 2. The program system for addition (Example 6 in Section 3.2) has terminal theorems. Explain.

EXAMPLE 3. The propositional calculus has no terminal theorems (using, of course, the meaning of "follow from" appropriate there). Explain.

EXAMPLE 4. The boolean formula generator (Example 2 in Section 3.1) has terminal theorems. In particular, no word lacking in auxiliary symbols T, F, has any consequence at all, as can be verified by inspection of the rules.

EXAMPLE 5. The addition program is monogenic (Example 6, Section 3.2).

EXAMPLE 6. The rudimentary arithmetic (Example 1 in Section 3.1) is monogenic.

EXAMPLE 7. Both the boolean formula generator and the propositional calculus are polygenic.

Definition 3.3.9. Let $S = \{s_0, s_1, s_2, \ldots\}$ and $Q = \{q_0, q_1, q_2, \ldots\}$ be finite nonempty sets. S is called a set of (atomic) *symbols* and Q a set of *auxiliary symbols*; $S \cap Q = \varnothing$. The set $A = S \cup Q$ is called an alphabet with *auxiliaries.*

In much of the following discussion we will take the sets S and Q as simply abstract, unspecified objects, such that each s_j and q_i designates itself and each occurs in some rule of inference. As usual we will employ x, y, etc., as variables ranging over S^*. We will also use P, R, etc., as variables on the words on all of $A = S \cup Q$, and s and q with and without primes as variables ranging over the individual elements of S and Q.

We are finally able to specify what we mean by an automaton.

Definition 3.3.10. An *automaton* is a semi-thue system having an alphabet with auxiliaries.

Of the systems discussed so far the example of the semi-thue pulse divider at the end of Section 3.0 and the $\mathbf{B}'$ form of the boolean formula generator are automata. We will introduce several varieties of automata.

Definition 3.3.11. Any word containing only auxiliary symbols is said to be *auxiliary*. Any word containing only atomic symbols s is *pure*. Any other word is *mixed.*

Definition 3.3.12. An *acceptor* is an automaton with a mixed axiom (scheme) qx such that every terminal theorem is auxiliary.[17]

EXAMPLE 8. Let **A** have the alphabet with $\# = s_0$, $s_1 = a$, $s_2 = b$, and the auxiliary symbols $\{q_0, q_1, \ldots, q_5\}$. The axiom of **A** is $q_0x\#$; the rules are as follows, with $P = \Lambda$.

1.	$q_0aR \to q_1R$	6.	$q_0bR \to q_3R$
2.	$q_1bR \to q_2R$	7.	$q_3aR \to q_4R$
3.	$q_1aR \to q_5R$	8.	$q_3bR \to q_5R$
4.	$q_2aR \to q_1R$	9.	$q_4bR \to q_3R$
5.	$q_2bR \to q_5R$	10.	$q_4aR \to q_5R$
11.	$q_1\# \to q_1$	15.	$q_5aR \to q_5R$
12.	$q_2\# \to q_2$	16.	$q_5bR \to q_5R$
13.	$q_3\# \to q_3$	17.	$q_5\# \to q_5$
14.	$q_4\# \to q_4$	18.	$q_5 \to q_5$

This automaton *accepts* all of the alternating words $abab\cdots\#$ or $babab\cdots\#$ on S in a manner which will now be explained.

Definition 3.3.13. An automaton **A** *accepts* a word x on the symbols S of **A** iff there is a proof $qx = w_1, w_2, \ldots, w_n$, and w_n is terminal and auxiliary. The set of all words x such that x is accepted by **A** is an *accepted set.*

To avoid the somewhat ungainly business of introducing the idea of a proof every time we want to say a certain word is a theorem w.r.t. a formal system, we will say that such a word w_n is a *consequence* of the axiom (*by* the rules of inference).

Continuing with Example 8, any alternating word x in $q_0x\#$ will have as a consequence q_1, q_2, q_3, or q_4 as an auxiliary terminal theorem. On the other hand, any nonalternating non-null word x in $q_0x\#$ will yield the consequence q_5 and, in fact, the infinite sequence $q_5, q_5, q_5, \ldots$; hence q_5 is not terminal (though auxiliary), and thus x is not accepted.

We next discuss the use of the symbol # in this example. In many languages we want to have a tangible indication of a blank space to mark either separations of words or ends of words. In this example, # marks the end of a word. We could also have introduced # as the beginning of the word x at the slight cost of adding more rules to Example 8. Moreover, we could have omitted # as an end marker in $x\#$ and eliminated every one of the Rules 11 to 17. When # is a necessity or when it is an option is a subject that will be considered in the appropriate places.

[17] The question is left open as to whether an acceptor does in fact have any terminal theorems. We will want to say later that some acceptors accept *no* set of words. This is equivalent to the practical question of whether a given "pattern recognizer" really recognizes anything.

The foregoing example suggests the possibility of a nonalternating axiom $q'x$ having a terminal theorem as consequence. For if we were simply to lop off Rule 18, q_5 would be terminal, since there would be no word following from it. An automaton of the kind suggested by this example is able to detect or recognize a given word as being or not being in a certain class.

Definition 3.3.14. Let $\mathbf{A} = \langle S \cup Q, \mathscr{B}, qx, \mathscr{P} \rangle$ be an acceptor. $\mathbf{A}$ is a *detector* iff there is a partition $\{S_1, S_2\}$ on S^* and a partition $\{Q_1, Q_2\}$ on Q such that if $x \in S_1$, the terminal consequence of the axiom qx is in Q_1; and if $x \in S_2$, the terminal consequence is in Q_2. An accepted set of a detector is a *detected set.*

If Rule 18 is omitted from the acceptor of Example 8, the shortened system is a detector. To show this, according to Definition 3.3.14, we must show that the required partition exists. In this case S_1 = the set of alternating strings and $S_2 = \bar{S}_1 - \{\#\}$. This is a partition since $S_1 \cap S_2 = \varnothing$ and $S_1 \cup S_2 = S^* - \{\#\}$. Assuming that $\mathbf{A}$ is, in fact, the acceptor it is designed to be (we have not proved this), then every alternating word $x \in S_1$ does have as consequence a terminal theorem in the set $\{q_1, q_2, q_3, q_4\}$.

If $x \notin S_1$, then there must be somewhere in x at least two adjacent occurrences of a or b or both. If aa occurs as the first two symbols of x, then by Rules 1 and 3 of the example we have q_5R as a theorem, and thence by either Rule 15 or Rule 16, applied a finite number of times (every word in a set of words is of finite length), $q_5\#$, and finally q_5 is terminal. If aa occurs not as the first two symbols in x but somewhere in the interior, then either Rule 4 or Rule 7 applies. If we have proved q_2aaR, then by Rule 7 we rewrite this q_1aR and by Rule 3 start the termination to q_5. Similarly if we have q_3aaR and apply Rule 7. By the analogous examination of cases we find that bb likewise yields q_5. Thus every $x \in S_2$ has q_5 as a consequence of qx, and therefore every consequence is an element of $\{q_0, q_5\}$. Therefore the required partition of Q exists.

In Example 8 we converted the acceptor into a detector by a trivial change of the rules. This conversion will not always be possible. There exist infinite (in a certain sense characterized in Chapter 4) acceptors which are not detectors and which cannot be made into detectors without changing the definition of the set of words it accepts.

Perhaps it has occurred to the reader that accepted sets are recursively enumerable and detected sets recursive. This is true, although we shall show it to be so only for special cases in the sequel.

Definition 3.3.15. A *generator* is an automaton with a single auxiliary axiom, all of whose terminal theorems are pure.

Definition 3.3.16. A terminal theorem of a generator **G** is called a *sentence* or a *formula*; and the set of all sentences generated by a generator **G** is a *language*.

Later it will also be convenient to think of an accepted set of words as a language and of its elements as sentences.

Corollary 3.3.17. Every language in the sense of Definition 3.3.16 is recursively enumerable.

This corollary is immediate from the definition and Corollary 3.3.6.

The adequacy and usefulness of such a conception of a generator as a *grammar* will be discussed in Chapter 8. Example 10 will perhaps suggest such an interpretation.

EXAMPLE 9. The system $\mathbf{B}'$ of Example 2 in Section 3.1. As already pointed out, $\mathbf{B}'$ is semi-thue, the axiom is auxiliary, namely F, and according to examination of the rules ***R.2*** to ***R.7*** of the system only the symbols a, $'$, $\cup$, $\cap$, and $-$ allow no rewriting, and hence have no consequences.

EXAMPLE 10. Let **G** be $\langle A = \{\text{the, a, dog, boy, ran}; q_0, q_1, q_2, q_3, q_4\}, \mathscr{B}, \mathscr{A}, \mathscr{P}\rangle$. Here $\mathscr{B}$ is the set of words on A, $\mathscr{A} = q_0$, and the elements of $\mathscr{P}$ follow.

1. $Pq_0R \rightarrow Pq_1q_2R$
2. $Pq_1R \rightarrow Pq_3q_4R$
3. $Pq_3R \rightarrow P \text{ the } R$
4. $Pq_3R \rightarrow P \text{ a } R$
5. $Pq_4R \rightarrow P \text{ dog } R$
6. $Pq_4R \rightarrow P \text{ boy } R$
7. $Pq_2R \rightarrow P \text{ ran } R$

The symbols in this example are English words, s_0 = the, $s_1 = a$, etc., whereas words in our technical sense are any elements of $\mathscr{B}$, such as q_0 a q_1 a ran q_2 boy.[18] To show that "the dog ran" is a sentence, we have the proof:

1.	q_0	Axiom
2.	q_1q_2	Rule 1, $P = \Lambda$, $R = \Lambda$
3.	$q_3q_4q_2$	Rule 2, $P = \Lambda$, $R = q_2$
4.	the q_4q_2	Rule 3, $P = \Lambda$, $R = q_4q_2$
5.	the dog q_2	Rule 5, P = the, $R = q_2$
6.	the dog ran	Rule 7, P = the dog, $R = \Lambda$

Definition 3.3.18. A *transducer* or *sequential machine* is an automaton with a mixed axiom (scheme) qx such that every terminal theorem is pure.

[18] Some clarity could have been gained here by using space markers # to separate symbols and to begin and end words. However, this use would have required a clumsier set of rules.

Quite frequently it will be convenient to make a distinction between the alphabet on which x of the axiom qx is a word and the alphabet on which a theorem is a word. If we do make the distinction, then the first is the *input* alphabet and the second the *output*. A, in the general definition of a semi-thue system, is then the union of the two alphabets and the auxiliary alphabet.

EXAMPLE 11. The pulse divider discussed at the very end of Section 3.0. As already noted, this is a semi-thue system.

The alphabet is $S[= \{\#, 0, 1\}] \bigcup Q[= \{q_0, q_1\}]$, satisfying the definition of an automaton; the axiom is a mixed word since it has the part w, which is by definition a word on S; and finally every terminal theorem is pure. The proof is left to the student (see Exercises).

Transducers are models of input-output sequential circuits used in digital control and computing systems. They also provide fairly adequate models for neural switching activity, as we shall see in Chapter 6.

In Chapter 4 we shall demonstrate that programs are transducers in the sense that for every program and correlated function Φ_P there exists a transducer which "computes" Φ_P. The axiom of the transducer represents an assignment of values to the arguments of Φ_P and a terminating theorem represents the value of the function if it is defined; if it is not defined, there is no terminating theorem.

EXERCISES 3.3

1. Does it follow from the definition of "proof" that all semi-thue systems are monogenic?

2. Suppose $PgR \to Pg'R$ and $Pg_1R \to Pg_1'R$ are any two distinct productions of some semi-thue system and that for any such pair $PgR \neq Pg_1R$. Does it follow that the system is monogenic? If so, give a proof; if not, provide a counterexample.

3. Suppose we have a semi-thue system such that there are two distinct productions $PgR \to Pg'R$ and $Pg_1R \to Pg_1'R$ such that $PgR = Pg_1R$. Does it follow that the system is polygenic? If so give a proof; if not provide a counterexample.

4. A *Markov algorithm* (Markov [1954]) is like a semi-thue system but has the following additional properties. (*a*) There is a finite *sequence* of productions—that is, the productions are indexed 1, 2, 3, etc. (*b*) A production of the form $PgQ \to .$ is a *stop*. (*c*) Beginning with the axiom w_1, if more than one production is applicable to w_1 to yield w_2, then apply the earliest, according to the indexing. (*d*) If a production PgR is applicable to a word w containing more than one occurrence of g, apply it to the leftmost occurrence of g. Reference system $\mathbf{B}'$ in Example 2 of Section 3.1. Devise an algorithm for checking whether a word of at most length k on the alphabet $\{a, ', \cap, \cup, -\}$ is a boolean formula in Polish notation. If the word is a formula, the algorithm is to place a

t beside the word, and if not a formula, an f. No other symbols, auxiliary or otherwise, are to appear in the result except the alphabetical ones and t and f. (*Hint*: w is a formula iff every proper head of w is nonnegative in rank and the rank of w is -1. A *head* of $w = xz$ is x, and x is a *proper* head if $z \neq \Lambda$. Now let $0, -1, 1, 2, \ldots, k$ be themselves the auxiliary symbols.)

5. Prove that the following semi-thue system has some terminal theorems. The alphabet is $\{a, b, q\}$ with q auxiliary; axiom scheme qx; rules are:

R.1. $PqbR \rightarrow PbqR$
R.2. $PaqaR \rightarrow PqaaR$
R.3. $PbqaR \rightarrow PqbaR$

Characterize the set of such theorems.

6. Prove that the system **A** of Example 8 in Section 3.3 accepts words which alternate on a and b.

7. One might define the alphabet of a semi-thue system as being the set of symbols used in the words g, g' of all the productions of the system, instead of displaying the set of symbols in advance. Why did we not follow this procedure throughout Section 3.3?

8. Design an acceptor for the set of all words axb on the alphabet $\{a, b\}$ where x is any word on $\{a, b\}$. (It is permitted, if possible, to design a detector.) Do not use markers #.

9. Design a generator for the set of all words xx^{-1} on $\{a, b\}$ where x^{-1} is the *reflection* of x; that is, if $x = s_{i_1}s_{i_2}\cdots s_{i_{n-1}}s_{i_n}$, then

$$x^{-1} = s_{i_n}s_{i_{n-1}}\cdots s_{i_2}s_{i_1}$$

10. Design a transducer that counts modulo 10 and steps one at each injection of a step signal. The counter returns to zero when stepped from nine. (*Hint*: Let 1 be a step signal and $q11111\cdots$ an axiom. Then design in analogy with the pulse divider of Section 3.0.) A theorem for this system should be an arabic numeral, say 5, if the axiom is $q11111$.

11. Show how a program system can be reconstructed as a strictly formal system.

(*a*) The alphabet should be redefined as symbols of pairs (together with auxiliaries as below) with the left members being *numerals* [try a tally system where the integer n is represented by $1^n = 111\cdots(n \text{ times})$].

(*b*) In the inference sequence (program), replace each Rule $\mathbf{m}\cdot x_i + 1 \rightarrow x_i$ by a production $mR\ x_i\ P \rightarrow m + 1\ R1x_i\ P$ where the indices m are incorporated into the alphabet as auxiliaries. Complete the exercise for other program rules and argue recursiveness of these rules.

3.4 HISTORICAL AND BIBLIOGRAPHICAL REMARKS

Formal logic dates back to Aristotle who studied certain forms of reasoning in abstraction from the material propositions that can occur as premises or conclusions. A strictly formal approach to logic as exemplified by our formulation of the propositional calculus was advocated by

Hilbert and his followers. The broad characterization we have used of formal systems is from Davis [1958]. The very general formal canonical systems, of which semi-thue systems are a species, are Post's [1934]. Program systems [but not explicity considered as formal systems as we have done in Exercise 3.3(11)] of the kind we have discussed have been studied by Myhill [1963b], Sheperdson and Sturgis [1963], Hermes [1954], and Kaphengst [1959], among others.

The present general formulation of automata and its three main species is new, although it is an extension of a point of view advanced in a series of papers by Chomsky. See also, for example, Davis [1958], Evey [1963], Rosenbloom [1950], Smullyan [1961], and Nelson [1965].

CHAPTER 4

Turing Machines

4.0 Introduction. One of the aims of the theory of automata is to classify machines on the basis of their powers. A transmission wire capable of carrying signals from a finite alphabet is an automaton (in our terminology it will be a single-state transducer) of the weakest kind, as is obvious. At the other extreme, a device which would be capable of imitating the behavior of any algorithm-executing device would be the strongest. According to Church's thesis[1] every effectively calculable function is recursive and, by various means which we have already discussed, non-numerical calculability problems can be converted into numerical ones. Hence an automaton capable of computing a recursive function would seem, according to this thesis, to be of the strongest class. Again, in more commonplace terms, the strongest automaton would be able to handle any algorithm.

A large-scale digital computer comes close to filling the requirements. Such a machine, however, has one shortcoming: it has a finite, bounded memory. Although existing computers can retain billions of bits (probably a practical bound is ten or eleven billion), they are limited. This seems to be a generous enough bound, since it is close to the memory capacity of ten human beings. However this may be, a good deal of mathematical freedom can be secured by studying models of computers with *unlimited* but finite memory. Such automata have available to them at any time t, after an initial t_0, only finite storage, but their memory cells can be endlessly increased in number.

Historically speaking, the first automata studied were infinite transducers. It is an interesting fact that such theoretical devices were investigated by both Post and Turing in the mid-1930's—about a decade prior to the design of the first stored-program digital computer. They were invented expressly to formalize the concept of algorithm or effective process, as a tool in mathematical logic. The equivalence to the recursive function

[1] Introduced at the end of Section 2.1.

criterion of solvability was discovered a year later. The form of automaton with which we begin the detailed study is widely known today as a *Turing machine.*

Informally, imagine a finite tape divided into squares, with each square holding a symbol from a finite alphabet, or otherwise a blank. Next imagine an organism—say a clerk—which by means of appropriate organs is able to read the symbol on a square—one square at a time—and is capable of three kinds of act: it can print any symbol (including the blank) of the alphabet, but only in the square being read, in such a way that whatever symbol occupied the square prior to printing is erased and replaced by the symbol printed; it can move right w.r.t. tape, one square; it can move left w.r.t. tape, one square; when it moves left or right at the end of the tape, a new square appears which holds a blank.

In Fig. 4.0.1 we have depicted such a tape, with an arrow representing a versatile organ capable of reading and printing. Whatever means are required to move the tape left or right may be imagined by the reader as he wishes. This is the tape of a Turing machine which moves from left to right, replacing a's by b's unless the a scanned is preceded by b, in which case it replaces a by c. When it sees a, b, or c it moves right. Assuming the machine has scanned the first b and has moved right, it scans a and, according to the specification of its task, prints c. Then it moves right one square. In Fig. 4.0.2 it scans b, then moves right and scans a. By the rules, a must be replaced by c. Suppose this replacement is made, followed by another move right. Then we have Fig. 4.0.3.

It then scans b, moves right, scans c, moves right, and scans a (Fig. 4.0.4). Here, since c precedes a, a is replaced by b. The machine now moves right twice, the second time growing a new square. Since the machine has no specified rule for doing anything at all when scanning a blank, it stops. The final situation is shown in Fig. 4.0.5.

Looking at this "computation" from the outside, as we have, one ingredient is lacking. When scanning an a, in order to "know" what to do next the machine must somehow remember whether it previously scanned b, c, or a. In order to recall past experience, therefore, the machine must be endowed with a memory. So we add to our informal description of a

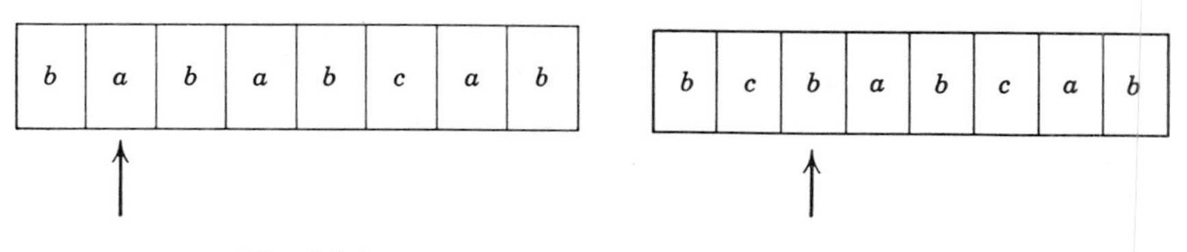

Fig. 4.0.1

Fig. 4.0.2

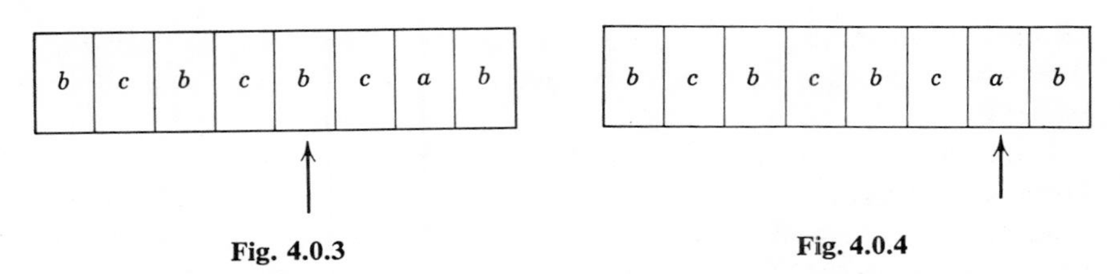

Fig. 4.0.3 **Fig. 4.0.4**

Turing machine, *memory states* or briefly, *states*. We may think of a Turing machine as being in a state (or having a memory state q_i) at some point in its actions while scanning a symbol. The state and symbol determine both the next act and the subsequent (perhaps the same) state.

Thus, in the foregoing example, suppose the machine has an *initial* or *starting* state q_0 and that *if it scans an a it prints b* and then *assumes state q_0 again*. This is clearly a rule which can be expressed by a *production* because all the rule specifies is that if the automaton (1) has a determinate position of the organ w.r.t. tape, (2) is in a certain state, and (3) is scanning a certain symbol, then this condition is to be replaced by some other one. All we need do now is establish notational conventions for conditions (1) to (3).

We will represent (1) to (3) by replacing the arrow in our pictorial conception of a Turing machine by the state symbol q_0 (Figure 4.0.6) and, furthermore, exchanging, in the example, the word $bq_0ababcab$ for the diagram. The word represents conditions (1) to (3). The machine is in state q_0, scanning a, in a position marked by q_0's occurrence in the word.

Returning to the task of defining productions, we have for the rule if scan a then print b

$$q_0a \rightarrow q_0b$$

and since this rule clearly applies no matter what the surrounding tape context, for arbitrary words P and R we have

R.1. $Pq_0aR \rightarrow Pq_0bR$

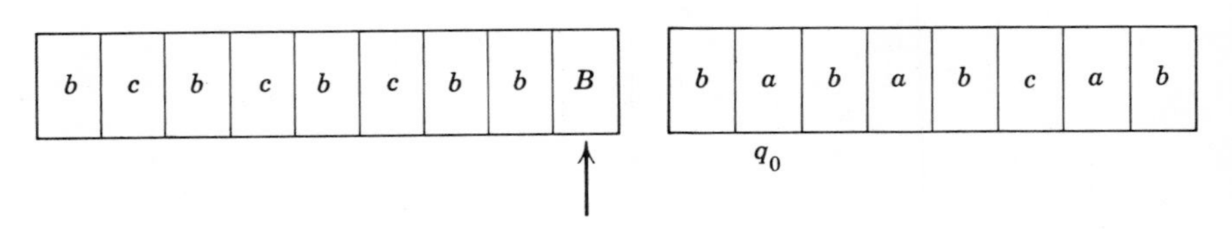

Fig. 4.0.5 **Fig. 4.0.6**

Next we stipulate that if b is scanned, the machine is to remember this fact by going into state q_1, and second that the machine action, no matter what its state, when scanning b is to move right. Hence we have

R.2. $Pq_0bR \to Pbq_1R$
R.3. $Pq_1bR \to Pbq_1R$

However, for c we have

R.4. $Pq_0cR \to Pcq_0R$
R.5. $Pq_1cR \to Pcq_0R$

and finally

R.6. $Pq_1aR \to Pq_0cR$

From the definition of Section 3.1 it is plain that what we have obtained is a semi-thue system with $q_0ababcab$ an axiom. Moreover, since the axiom is mixed, if we add the production

R.7. $Pq_iBR \to PBR \qquad i = 0, 1, 2$

the result will be that every terminal theorem is pure. For when the Turing machine, moving always to the right in this case, reaches the end of the word, it will see a blank B; then the Rule 7 in effect deletes the auxiliary symbol q_i, yielding a pure word. This word is terminal. In terms of the tape model, it is the printed output of the Turing machine.

We now proceed to develop the main aspects of the theory of Turing machines which are pertinent to our study.

EXERCISES 4.0

1. Verify the action of the Turing machine given in Section 4.0.

4.1 TURING MACHINE DEFINITION AND REPRESENTATIONS

The formal definition of a Turing machine will be introduced in this section. We will discuss several examples and then introduce a convenient way of representing Turing machines as sets of quadruples of a certain kind, or as diagrams.

Definition 4.1.1. A *Turing machine* is a semi-thue system

$$\mathbf{Z} = \langle A, \mathscr{B}, \mathscr{A}, \mathscr{P}\rangle$$

The alphabet includes a disjoint auxiliary alphabet and the set of symbols has a distinguished element #. Thus, using the conventions of Definition 3.3.9, $A = S \cup Q$; $S \cap Q, = \varnothing$, $\# \in S$, $s_0 = B$; $\mathscr{B}$ is the set of words on A;

the axiom is $\#xqy\#$ where x and y are words on $S - \{\#\}$ and y is not null; the set $\mathscr{P}$ is as follows.

1. $\mathscr{P}$ is a finite collection of productions of the forms:

(*a*)	$Pq_is_jR \to Pq_ls_kR$	(overprint s_k)
(*b*)	$Pq_is_js_kR \to Ps_jq_ls_kR$	(move right)
(*c*)	$Pq_is_j\#R \to Ps_jq_is_0\#R$	(move right at end of tape)
(*d*)	$Ps_kq_is_jR \to Pq_ls_ks_jR$	(move left)
(*e*)	$P\#q_is_jR \to R\#q_ls_0s_jR$	(move left at end of tape)
(*f*)	$Pq_is_jR \to Ps_jR$	(terminate)

2. Every pair $q_is_j \in Q \times (S - \{\#\})$ occurs either exactly once on the left side of a production of form a or f; or it occurs, instead, in the left of both b and c type productions for every s_k and for q_l fixed; otherwise, it occurs in the left of both d and e type productions for every s_k and for q_l fixed.[2] The occurrences on the right side are immaterial—anything is permitted, provided that Rule 1 is not violated.

3. The only productions in $\mathscr{P}$ are those whose being so follows from Rules 1 or 2 above.

The definitions of "follow from" and "proof" are precisely Definitions 3.3.2 and 3.3.3.

Recalling the informal discussion of a machine equipped with tape, as in Section 4.0, we may interpret these formalities in the following way: S is the alphabet proper; Q the set of states; $\#$ marks the two ends of the tape, which is finite at any time; $s_0 = B$ is conventionally taken as a blank, but $\# \neq B$, since $\#$ is distinguished. In some examples, however, $B = 0$; in *any* case we want to distinguish between a word of B's (a stretch of blank tape) and $\#$ which signifies the end of a tape—not followed by any cells at all.

Definition 4.1.2. An *instantaneous description* (abbreviated i.d.) is a word of the form $\#xqy\#$ where x and y are elements of the words on $S^* - \{\#\}$ and $y \neq \Lambda$. An axiom is an *initial* i.d.

Corollary 4.1.3. A proof $w_1, \ldots, w_n$ of a Turing machine system terminates iff w_{n-1} does not satisfy the left side of any productions of the forms a to e.

Proof is immediate.

[2] Our intention is that each state-symbol combination is defined and occurs exactly once in the left-hand side of a production. The reason for requiring that q_is_j occur in *both* b and c is that, in the case b, a move right is called for someplace in the interior of the tape and, in the case c, it is called for at the end. Similar statements can be made for d and e. Since both situations cannot exist at once, the rules retain their monogenic character. See Corollary 4.1.5.

Corollary 4.1.4. Every nonterminal theorem of a Turing machine is an i.d.

Proof. By Definition 4.1.1 the axiom is $\#yqx\#$, which is an i.d. Assume that every nonterminal theorem w_k of proofs $w_1, \ldots, w_k$ of length k is an i.d. Suppose now that w_{k+1} is a nonterminal theorem following from w_k by some production. It cannot follow from f, since if it did, w_{k+1} would be terminal contrary to hypothesis. Since w_k is an i.d., P and R, in applying one of productions a to e, must contain only symbols of S, and no auxiliaries Q. It follows then that the right hand of every applied production a to e is an i.d. and hence w_{k+1} is an i.d. as well. Q.E.D.

Corollary 4.1.5. Every Turing machine is monogenic—every theorem has at most one consequence.

Proof. This Corollary follows from Clause 2 of Definition 4.1.1 and from Corollary 4.1.4. For from Clause 2, at most one production applies to any theorem. Moreover, since every nonterminal theorem is an i.d., it has as immediate consequence either another i.d. or a terminal theorem. If the former is true, then again exactly one production applies. Note that Clause 2 in itself does not guarantee monogenicity. [See Exercise 3.3(3).] Q.E.D.

Corollary 4.1.6. Every **Z** is a transducer.

Proof. That **Z** is an automaton and that its axiom is mixed follows from the definition; that every terminal theorem is pure follows 1 to 3 of the basic definition of $\mathscr{P}$; because if w_k were mixed and a theorem, then by Definition 4.1.2 it would be an i.d. and therefore equal to $\#xqy\#$. Since every pair qy is defined by some production, w_k would therefore have a consequence, hence it would not be terminal. Q.E.D.

We now continue the interpretive discussion of Definition 4.1.1. It would perhaps be helpful if the reader were to read this description while using the running example of Section 4.0, or the ensuing Example 1, or both.

The axiom $\#yqx\#$ is an i.d. describing that **Z** is in state q scanning the input $x = s_{i_1}s_{i_2}\cdots s_{i_k}$ and that the tape (Fig. 4.1.1) is just long enough for x and y; type a productions mean that if **Z** is in state q_i scanning s_j, then **Z** overprints s_k and goes into state q_l. "Overprinting" implies "erasure

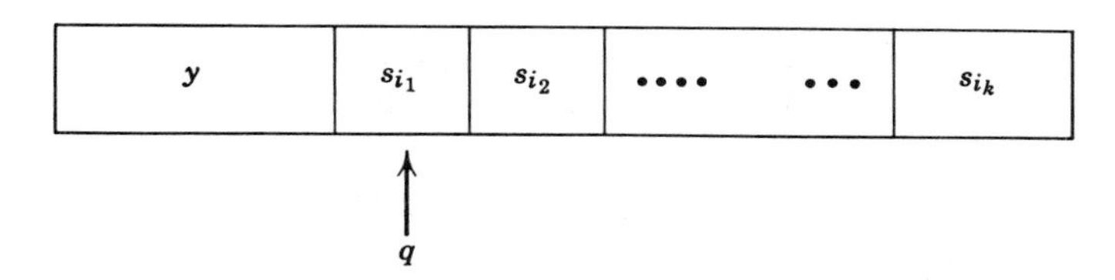

Fig. 4.1.1

followed by printing." Type b productions mean that if $\mathbf{Z}$ is in q_i scanning s_j, it moves right, goes into state q_l, scanning the symbol s_k to the right of s_j in the given i.d. Type c productions mean the same, except that the symbol scanned s_j is at the right end of the tape. Consequently, a new square holding $s_0 = B$ is added. Note that # marks the end of a tape, now one cell longer. Similar explanations may be used to interpret type d and type e productions; type f productions replace the q symbol in an i.d. by Λ.

EXAMPLE 1. This Turing machine counts up to 999,999. $S = \{\alpha, \beta, 0, 1, \ldots, 9\}$; $Q = \{q_0, q_1, q_2\}$. The axiom is $\alpha 00000 q_0 0 \beta$; α and β are *sentinels* marking the ends of the counter cells which are initially all zero's. In violation of Definition 4.1.1, but in the interest of economy, we have omitted the # symbol. Since this machine will never move left of α or right of β, it will never need to grow tape. Hence # is here inessential. (The reader is, however, to supply a fully legal set of instructions—see exercises at end of section.) $\mathscr{P}$ is the following set of 17 productions.

1. $Pq_0 0R \to Pq_1 1R$
2. $Pq_0 1R \to Pq_1 2R$
3. $Pq_0 2R \to Pq_1 3R$
4. $Pq_0 3R \to Pq_1 4R$
5. $Pq_0 4R \to Pq_1 5R$
6. $Pq_0 5R \to Pq_1 6R$
7. $Pq_0 6R \to Pq_1 7R$
8. $Pq_0 7R \to Pq_1 8R$
9. $Pq_0 8R \to Pq_1 9R$
10. $Pq_0 9R \to Pq_2 0R$
11. $Pq_0 \alpha R \to P\alpha R$
12. $Pq_0 \beta R \to P\beta R$
13. $Pq_1 ijR \to Piq_1 jR$ $\Big\}$ $i = 0, \ldots, 9$
14. $Piq_1 \beta R \to Pq_0 i\beta R$ $\Big\}$ $j = 0, \ldots, 9, \beta$
15. $Pq_1 \alpha R \to P\alpha R$
16. $Piq_2 0R \to Pq_0 i0R$ $\quad i = 0, \ldots, 9, \alpha$
17. $Pq_2 jR \to PjR$ $\quad j = 1, \ldots, 9, \alpha, \beta$

Before we examine the behavior of this machine, some explanation of the presentation of the productions is in order. In productions 13, 14, 16, and 17 we have taken the liberty of representing large sets of productions using variables i, j with ranges indicated to the right of the subject productions. Thus

13. $Pq_1 ijR \to Piq_1 jR$

stands for $(i = 10) \times (j = 11) = 110$ productions:

13_1. $Pq_1 00R \to P0q_1 0R$
13_2. $Pq_1 01R \to P0q_1 1R$
⋮
13_{110}. $Pq_1 9\beta R \to P9q_1 \beta R$

Bearing this inessential abbreviation in mind, we must next verify that the preceding is really a Turing machine. All the rules consist of one of the approved forms *a* to *f*. Second, Clause 2 of Definition 4.1.1 is satisfied (except for the fact that in this example we are not using the end-of-tape marker #). Every symbol $q_0 0$, $q_0 1$, etc., occurs in productions 1 to 12; every symbol $q_1 0$, $q_1 1$, etc., also occurs in productions 13, 14, or 15 (by the previously explained conventions). Finally, every pair $q_2 0$, $q_2 1$, etc., occurs in productions 16 or 17.

It is instructive to verify the workings of this machine, starting with the axiom or initial i.d. $\alpha 00000 q_0 0 \beta$ (see Exercises).

Since a Turing machine has a potentially infinite tape and since it is able to read anything previously printed, its "memory" is not limited to the finite states represented by the auxiliary alphabet. For this reason a Turing machine is sometimes said to have an *infinite memory* or to be an *infinite transducer*.

The way of characterizing a Turing machine as a kind of semi-thue system is instructive and emphasizes its membership in the domain of formal systems. However, there are far more useful and intuitively manageable representations of Turing machines. We now introduce two of them.

Definition 4.1.7. Given an alphabet $\{s_0, s_1, s_2, \ldots, q_0, q_1, q_2, \ldots, \mathbf{R}, \mathbf{L}\}$ a *quadruple* is a word of the form

(*a*) $q_i s_j s_k q_l$ (*b*) $q_i s_j \mathbf{R}\, q_l$ (*c*) $q_i s_j \mathbf{L}\, q_l$

A *Turing machine* is any finite set of quadruples such that no two quadruples have the same pair $q_i s_j$ on the left.

The quadruple formulation accords nicely with the intuitive conception of a Turing machine as used in Section 4.0. There we observed that a Turing machine embodies two functions: one a mapping of *pairs* consisting of a state and a scanned symbol (also represented in an i.d.) into a *next state*, and the other a mapping from pairs into an operation set consisting of print, move right w.r.t. tape, or move left w.r.t. tape. This is exactly the interpretation to be given to quadruple *a* of Definition 4.1.7: when in state q_i scanning the symbol s_j, print s_k and go to state q_l; similarly for quadruples *b* and *c*, where **R** and **L** mean move right and move left, respectively.

Although it is a routine matter to prove the equivalence of the two formulations in the sense that for every axiom and set of theorems in the one formulation there exists a counterpart in the other, we will indicate here only how to construct a quadruple set from the productions of a given machine $\mathbf{Z}'$ and vice versa.[3]

[3] See Davis [1958] pp. 6–7 and pp. 88–89.

Corollary 4.1.7a. Let $\mathbf{Z}$ be a quadruple and $\mathbf{Z}'$ a semi-thue formulation of a machine over the same alphabet and with the same initial i.d. (axiom); then

1. $q_i s_j s_k q_l \in \mathbf{Z} \Leftrightarrow Pq_i s_j R \to Pq_l s_k R \in \mathscr{P}_{\mathbf{Z}'}$
2. $q_i s_j \mathbf{R}\, q_l \in \mathbf{Z} \Leftrightarrow (\forall k)(Pq_i s_j s_k R \to Ps_j q_l s_k R \in \mathscr{P}_{\mathbf{Z}'})$ $(k = 0, 1, 2, \ldots)$ and $Pq_i s_j \# R \to Ps_j q_l s_0 \# R \in \mathscr{P}_{\mathbf{Z}'}$
3. $q_i s_j \mathbf{L}\, q_l \in \mathbf{Z} \Leftrightarrow (\forall k)(Ps_k q_i s_j R \to Pq_l s_k s_j R \in \mathscr{P}_{\mathbf{Z}'})$ and $P\# q_i s_j R \to P\# q_l s_0 s_j R \in \mathscr{P}_{\mathbf{Z}'}$
4. Let O vary over $S \cup \{\mathbf{R}, \mathbf{L}\}$:
   $q_i s_j O q_l \notin \mathbf{Z}$ for all $O \Leftrightarrow Pq_i s_j R \to Ps_j R \in \mathscr{P}_{\mathbf{Z}'}$

These latter quadruples are "undefined" in that $q_i s_j$ causes the machine to stop.

EXAMPLE 2. We indicate in this example the construction of a quadruple list from the semi-thue system of Example 1. From production 1, we have $q_0 0 1 q_1$. From 2, we have $q_0 1 2 q_1$; similarly for 3 to 10. There are no quadruples at all to be found from productions 11, 12, 15, and 17 (by the last equivalence in the foregoing construction). From production 13 we have $q_1 0\, \mathbf{R}\, q_1$, $q_1 1\, \mathbf{R}\, q_1$, etc.

Definition 4.1.8. The *transition diagram* of a Turing machine, given a quadruple formulation $\mathbf{Z}'$, is a directed linear graph[4] in which there is a node for every symbol Q; each node is labeled by the symbol with which it is associated; for each quadruple $q_i \cdots q_l$ there is a branch (q_i, q_l); for each branch (q_i, q_l) (where $i = l$ is possible) there is a label of one of the following forms:

$$s_j : s_k$$
$$s_j : \mathbf{R}$$
$$s_j : \mathbf{L}$$

depending on the quadruple $q_i s_j O q_l$, $O = s_k, \mathbf{R}, \mathbf{L}$.

EXAMPLE 3. Given the Turing machine in quadruple form:

(i)	$q_0 a b q_1$	(vi)	$q_1 c\, \mathbf{R}\, q_0$
(ii)	$q_0 b c q_1$	(vii)	$q_0 B\, \mathbf{L}\, q_2$
(iii)	$q_0 c a q_1$	(viii)	$q_2 a\, \mathbf{L}\, q_2$
(iv)	$q_1 a\, \mathbf{R}\, q_0$	(ix)	$q_2 b\, \mathbf{L}\, q_2$
(v)	$q_1 b\, \mathbf{R}\, q_0$	(x)	$q_2 c\, \mathbf{L}\, q_2$

This machine starts from $\# q x \#$, where x is on $\{a, b, c\}$, and realizes the permutation $a \to b$, $b \to c$, $c \to a$. It then finds the left end of the tape, grows a new square, and stops. For example,

[4] A *directed linear graph* is formally the union of a set A with a binary relation on A. If $(a, b) \in R$, then a is a *node*, b is a *node*, and the pair a *branch*. Thus $\{a, b, (a, b)\}$ may be depicted $a \rightsquigarrow b$.

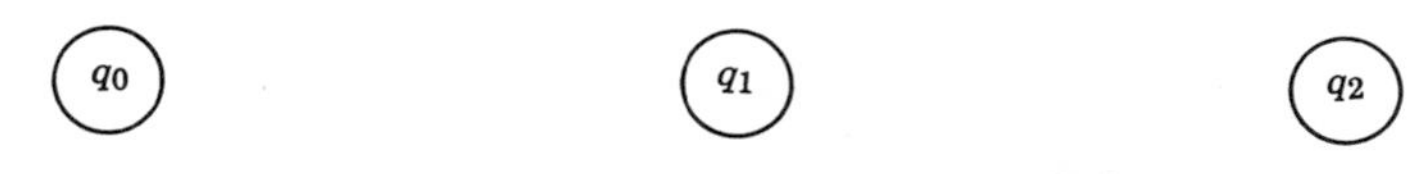

Fig. 4.1.2

1.	$\#q_0bca\#$	Axiom (or initial i.d.)
2.	$\#q_1cca\#$	(ii) or, more formally by the equivalence 1 of Corollary 4.1.7a, $Pq_0bR \to Pq_1cR$
3.	$\#cq_0ca\#$	(vi)
4.	$\#cq_1aa\#$	(iii)
5.	$\#caq_0a\#$	(iv)
6.	$\#caq_1b\#$	(i)
7.	$\#cabq_0B\#$	(v) or by equivalence 2 of Corollary 4.1.7a, $Pq_1b\#R \to Pbq_0B\#R$
8.	$\#caq_2bB\#$	(vii)
9.	$\#cq_2abB\#$	(ix)
10.	$\#q_2cabB\#$	(viii)
11.	$\#q_2BcabB\#$	(x)

Since there is no quadruple $q_2B\ldots$, the machine stops. By clause (4) of Corollary 4.1.7*a*, we may delete q_2, yielding the *output* or terminal theorem. In the future, when using the quadruple formulation, our convention will simply be that if a Turing machine stops on an undefined pair, such as q_2B above, the q may be deleted.

The transition diagram of this example is constructed as follows. We draw labeled circles (nodes), for each state in any convenient pattern, say as in Fig. 4.1.2. Then branches are added for each quadruple beginning in q_i and ending in q_l. For q_0abq_1, Fig. 4.1.2 becomes Fig. 4.1.3.

Continuing in this manner, we obtain Fig. 4.1.4. Note that since q_2 always goes back into state q_2 on scanning a, b, or c, the branch is looped back in each case from the node q_2 to itself.

In designing Turing machines it is convenient to start with a diagram and then derive a quadruple list by using Definition 4.1.8. As an analysis of the machine, to be certain it is one, a full formal system may be derived by the equivalences of Corollary 4.1.7a.

Very complicated machines may be handled somewhat more economically by using the following conventions.

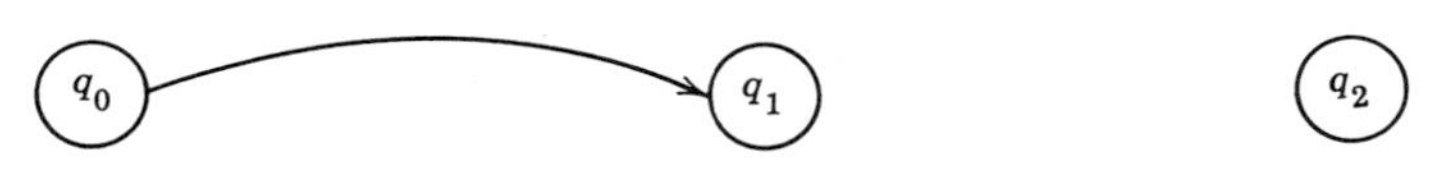

Fig. 4.1.3

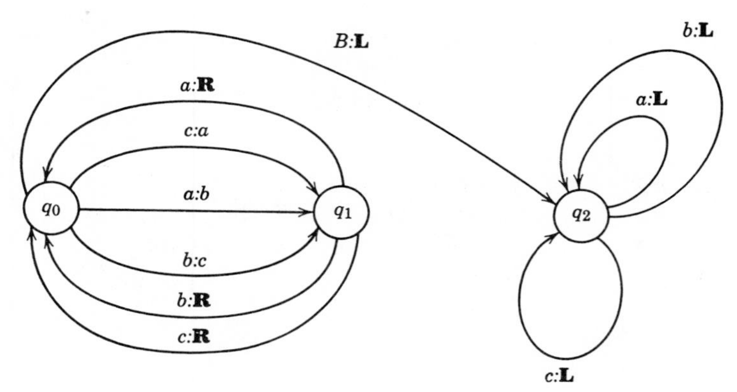

Fig. 4.1.4

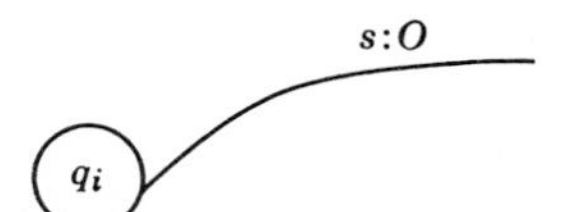

Fig. 4.1.5

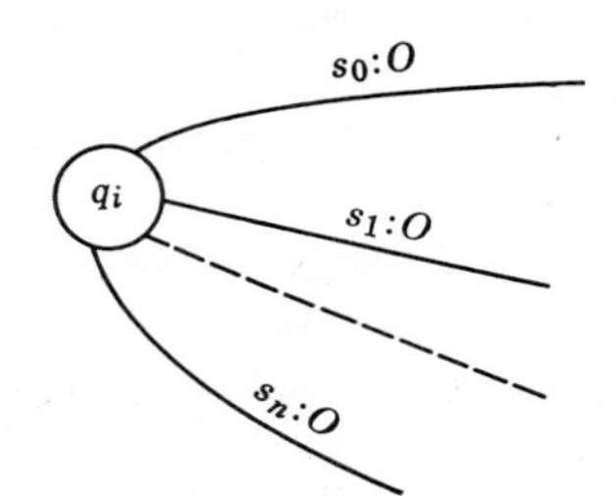

Fig. 4.1.6

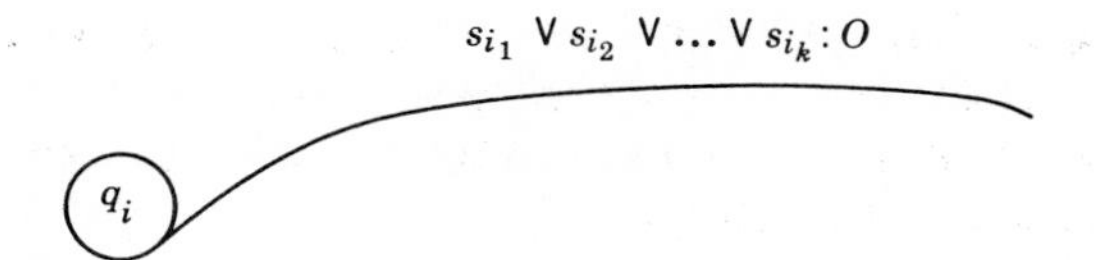

Fig. 4.1.7

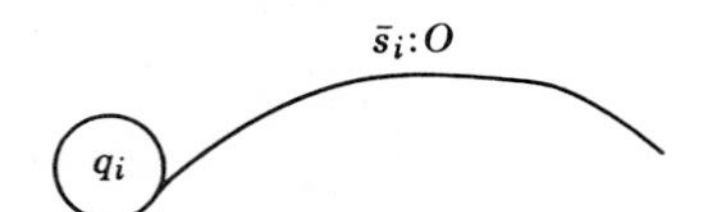

Fig. 4.1.8

1. If a unique operation O is defined for *every* symbol in S, given a state q_i, use the symbol variable s and draw Fig. 4.1.5 instead of Fig. 4.1.6.

2. If a unique operation is defined for *more than one* symbol in S, use the "or" sign ($\vee$), and one branch (Fig. 4.1.7).

3. If a unique operation is defined for every symbol except s_i, then use the complement sign $\overline{}$ (Fig. 4.1.8); or two or more exceptional symbols s_{i_1}, s_{i_2} can be treated as in Fig. 4.1.9.

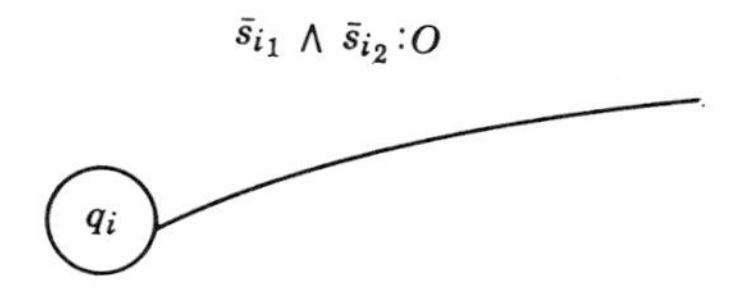

Fig. 4.1.9

4. Finally, an operation **R** or **L** which is to occur over and over again may be superscripted with a numeral indicating the number of squares to be moved. For example, Fig. 4.1.10 means, starting in state q_i, to move left

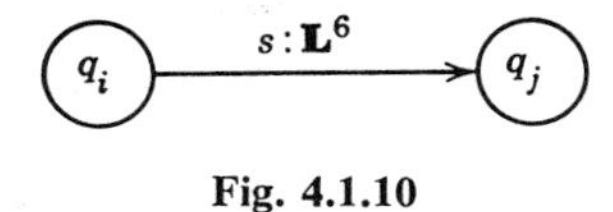

Fig. 4.1.10

six squares, independently of the symbol scanned, and go into state q_j. If we repeat Example 3, using some of these conventions, we obtain Fig. 4.1.11.

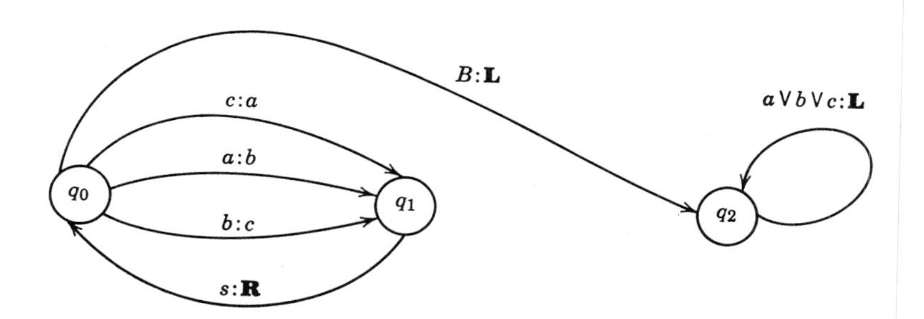

Fig. 4.1.11

EXERCISES 4.1

1. Redesign the counter of Example 1, including productions of type c and e from Definition 4.1.1 (which were excluded in the formulation in Example 1).

2. Design a semi-thue form of Turing machine for *counting down* from 999,999. Freely use abbreviations, where applicable, as we did in the text for Example 1.

3. Write the full system of productions for Example 3 and verify the alleged proof given there.

4. Draw a transition diagram for the counter of Example 1 using, where possible, the conventions introduced in the text.

5. Beginning with a diagram, design a Turing machine with alphabet $S = \{B, 0, 1, \alpha, \beta\}$ such that, if the initial i.d. is

$$\alpha q_0 s_{i_1} s_{i_2} \cdots s_{i_k} \beta \qquad s_{i_j} = 0, 1, B$$

the one terminal theorem is

$$\alpha \sigma_{i_1} \sigma_{i_2} \cdots \sigma_{i_l} BBB \cdots \beta$$

where the $\sigma_{i_j} = 0$, 1 and occur in the same order as the 0's and 1's in the axiom and the number of B's preserved. For example,

$$\alpha q_0 0B11B0BB10\beta$$

is to go into

$$\alpha 011010BBBB\beta$$

6. Design a Turing machine for *sorting* any arrangement with repetitions of {1, 2, 3, 4, 5} into monotonic order, that is, into the "natural" arrangement $111 \cdots 222 \cdots 333 \cdots 444 \cdots 555 \cdots$. Thus an axiom might be $\# q_0 51423 \#$. Design using as little "tape" as possible. A transition diagram counts as a "design."

7. If $S = 0, 1$ where 0 serves as a blank, show that the four operations, print 0, print 1, **R**, and **L** can be replaced by two: **L** and **CR**, where the latter means the composition of complement ($\bar{0} = 1$ or $\bar{1} = 0$) and move right as *one* operation. For example $q_1 0$ **CR** q_2 applied to $\# q_1 0 B \#$ yields $\# 1 q_2 B \#$.

8. Is the set of Turing machines recursive?

4.2 COMPUTABLE FUNCTIONS

Although Turing machines are capable of only the most primitive operations it appears, as hinted at in Section 4.0, that they are more powerful than real computers. The fact is that Turing machines compute all the partial recursive functions. Turing generators and acceptors, which we shall introduce in Section 4.3, are able to generate or to accept any recursively enumerable set. Several topics, concerning the limits of the behavior of Turing machines, will now be discussed.

Definition 4.2.1. A *computation* of a Turing machine is a terminal proof. We also call the terminal theorem of the axiom $\mathscr{A}$ the *resultant* or *answer* to $\mathscr{A}$, written Res ($\mathscr{A}$).

In order to handle numerical problems, some kind of representation has to be chosen. That is, we must deal, by Definition 4.1.1, with a finite alphabet S of symbols. If $K(S) = k$, then to handle integers $n \geq k$ requires a code of some sort. Any base number system will, in principle, suffice, but for convenience we choose a *tally* system as follows.

Definition 4.2.2. (1) The symbols B and 1 are tallies. (2) If x is a tally, then Bx and $x1$ are tallies. (3) A word is a tally only if this fact follows from statements 1 and 2.

Interpretation. Any word made up of B's designates the nonnegative integer 0. Any positive integer n equals n tallies $111\cdots$. By the definition, we countenance words such as $BB\cdots B11111$; this word is to be interpreted as denoting the same integer as 11111, namely 5. Hence B's are used as insignificant 0's to the left as in standard computer words. For abbreviations, we write $1^0 = B$, $1^n = 1111\cdots$ (n times).

All of the Turing machines we shall discuss in connection with numerical computation will use part of the alphabet $S = \{\alpha, B, 1, \mathbf{x}_1, \mathbf{x}_2, \ldots, \mathbf{x}_k, \ldots, p, \#\}$; $\mathbf{x}_1$, etc., are simply called *symbols*. This alphabet is infinite, though recursively enumerable; however, any given machine will use only a finite number of the $\mathbf{x}$ symbols.

Definition 4.2.3. To any n-tuple $(a_1, a_2, \ldots, a_n)$ of integers, we associate the word $a_1\mathbf{x}_1a_2\mathbf{x}_2\ldots a_n\mathbf{x}_n = 1^{a_1}\mathbf{x}_1 1^{a_2}\mathbf{x}_2\ldots 1^{a_n}\mathbf{x}_n$. Also, we adopt the convenient policy that to any n-tuple of integers $(a_1, a_2, \ldots, a_n)$ we may equally associate any rearrangement by pairs $a_i\mathbf{x}_i$ of $a_1\mathbf{x}_1\cdots a_n\mathbf{x}_n$. Thus we also associate to $(a_1, a_2, \ldots, a_n)$ $a_2\mathbf{x}_2a_4\mathbf{x}_4a_1\mathbf{x}_1a_3\mathbf{x}_3\cdots a_n\mathbf{x}_n$, for example.[5] Again, to the triple (2, 0, 3) we associate the word $11\mathbf{x}_1B\mathbf{x}_2111\mathbf{x}_3$, or else $B\mathbf{x}_211\mathbf{x}_1111\mathbf{x}_3$, etc. In numerical computations the symbols $\mathbf{x}_i$ are used to identify the location on tape of the ith argument of the n-tuple; and in a manner reminiscent of our programming schemes the reader may wish to read $a_i\mathbf{x}_i$ as "a_i is in the $\mathbf{x}_i$ location." We also use the location p for the printout position for answers so that if a_ip occurs on tape at the end of a computation from an axiom w_1, a_i is the value of the computation.

Definition 4.2.4. If $a_ip = 1^{a_i}p$ occurs in a terminal theorem of $\mathbf{Z}$, and w is the axiom, then $\langle \mathrm{Res}_{\mathbf{Z}}(w)\rangle = a_i$. That is, "corner" of resultant equals contents of p.

Definition 4.2.5. With any Turing machine $\mathbf{Z}$ and for any n, we associate an n-ary function of integers $\Psi_{\mathbf{Z}}(x_1, \ldots, x_n)$ such that if there exists a

[5] In other words, any word $a_{i_1}\mathbf{x}_{i_1}a_{i_2}\mathbf{x}_{i_2}\cdots a_{i_n}\mathbf{x}_{i_n}$ to within the order of the symbols by pairs $a_i\mathbf{x}_i$ designates $(a_1, a_2, \ldots, a_n)$. Thus although words are unequal, symbol by symbol, they designate the same object. This procedure is possible because of our use of the $\mathbf{x}$ symbols.

computation $w_1, w_2, \ldots, w_m$ from initial i.d. $w_1 = \#\alpha q_1 a_1 \mathbf{x}_1 a_2 \mathbf{x}_2 \cdots a_n \mathbf{x}_n Bp\#$, we set

$$\Psi_{\mathbf{Z}}(a_1, \ldots, a_n) = \langle \mathrm{Res}_{\mathbf{Z}}(w_1) \rangle$$

or, if there is no computation from w_1,

$$\Psi_{\mathbf{Z}}(a_1, \ldots, a_n)$$

is undefined.

Definition 4.2.6. A function $f(x_1, \ldots, x_n)$ is said to be *partial computable* iff there exists a Turing machine $\mathbf{Z}$ such that

$$f(x_1, \ldots, x_n) = \Psi_{\mathbf{Z}}(x_1, \ldots, x_n)$$

If f is defined for all n-tuples, it is *total.*

We now state the principal result of this section.

Theorem 4.2.7. Every partial recursive function is partial computable.

The procedure in our proof will be to show that every program (partial) computable function is partial computable. But first, in the interests of simplifying our task, we want to see if we can eliminate some of the types of rules of inference for program systems.

Theorem 4.2.8. The rules (ii), (iii), and (v) of Definition 3.2.14 suffice for any program.

To prove this we have to show that subroutine programs exist for (*a*) $x_j \to x_i$, (*b*) $x_i \to p$, and (*c*) stop, in terms of (ii), (iii), and (v) alone.

(*a*) For any program containing the rule $x_j \to x_i$ which occurs mth in the sequence of rules indexed $1, 2, \ldots, m, m + 1, \ldots, n$ and which has the axiom $(i_1 x_1)(i_2 x_2) \cdots (i_k x_k)(i_{k+1}, p)$ we construct, with axiom

$$(i_1 x_1)(i_2 x_2) \cdots (i_k x_k)(i_{k+1} p)(0, x_{k+2})$$

the program system:

m_1 $(0, x_i) \Rightarrow m_4, m_2$
m_2 $x_i - 1 \to x_i$ (clear x_i to zero)
m_3 $(0, x_i) \Rightarrow m_4, m_2$

m_4 $(0, x_j) \Rightarrow m + 1, m_5$ (if x_j is zero, continue main program)

m_5 $x_j - 1 \to x_j$
m_6 $x_i + 1 \to x_i$ (copy x_j into x_i and x_{k+2})
m_7 $x_{k+2} + 1 \to x_{k+2}$

m_8 $(0, x_j) \Rightarrow m_9, m_5$
m_9 $x_{k+2} - 1 \to x_{k+2}$ (copy x_{k+2} back into x_j)
m_{10} $x_j + 1 \to x_j$

m_{11} $(0, x_{k+2}) \Rightarrow m + 1, 9$

Explanation. x_i is first cleared to zero. Since x_j is copied into x_i by exhaustion, its contents are destroyed. To preserve the contents, x_j is copied also into x_{k+2} which is then copied back into x_j. x_{k+2} is then at zero and ready to be used for any other copy subroutine which may be called for in the main program. It is assumed that $m = m_1$ and that $m_1 < m_2 < \cdots < m_{11} < m + 1$ so that this program is a sequence as required. This sequence is inserted in the given program to yield the sequence $1, 2, 3, \ldots, m_1, m_2, \ldots, m_{11}, m + 1, \ldots, n$.

The routine verification that this program simulates $x_j \to x_i$ is left to the student.

(*b*) $x_i \to p$ is a special case of *a*.

(*c*) By definition, a program system is comprised of a finite *sequence* of rules of inference. Hence when the nth step is executed, unless there is a transfer to k or l $(k, l < n)$, the program stops. If *stop* is the last step of a program, delete it. If stop is the kth step, $k < n$, in an n-step program, replace *stop* by $(i, x_i) \Rightarrow n + 1, n + 1$ for arbitrary (i, x_i).

Continuing with Theorem 4.2.7, we shall need the following lemma.

Lemma 4.2.9. Every program (partial) computable function is (partial) computable.

Proof. Assume that $f(x_1, \ldots, x_n)$ is program computable; then by Definition 3.2.17 there exists a program **P** such that

$$f(x_1, \ldots, x_n) = \Phi_{\mathbf{P}}(x_1, \ldots, x_n) \tag{1}$$

To show that f is computable in the Turing sense we will have to show there is a machine **Z** such that

$$f(x_1, \ldots, x_n) = \Psi_{\mathbf{Z}}(x_1, \ldots, x_n) \tag{2}$$

We will accomplish this by constructing a machine **Z** such that

$$\Phi_{\mathbf{P}}(x_1, \ldots, x_n) = \Psi_{\mathbf{Z}}(x_1, \ldots, x_n) \tag{3}$$

Let $(a_1, \ldots, a_n)$ be any defined value of $(x_1, \ldots, x_n)$ for any arbitrary $\Phi_{\mathbf{P}}$. By hypothesis and using Definition 3.2.15, there is a program **P**,

$$1.\ (\ ),\qquad 2.\ (\ ),\qquad \ldots,\quad r.\ (\ )$$

[where, by Theorem 4.2.8, each step ( ) is either the rule $x_i + 1 \to x_i$, $x_i - 1 \to x_i$, or $(0, x_i) \Rightarrow k, l$]; and there is a proof $w_1, w_2, \ldots, w_t$ where w_1 is the axiom

$$(a_1, x_1)(a_2, x_2)\cdots(a_n, x_n)(0, p)(0, x_{n+1})$$

w_t the theorem,[6]

$$(a_1', x_1)(a_2', x_2)\cdots(a_n', x_n)(b, p)(a_{n+1}, x_{n+1})$$

[6] Recall that x_{n+1} is used as a copy location only.

and $\Phi_{\mathbf{P}}(a_1, \ldots, a_n) = b$. We construct the Turing machine **Z** with axiom

$$\#\alpha q_1 a_1 \mathbf{x}_1 \cdots a_n \mathbf{x}_n B p \#$$

To each index m of the program **P** we associate a q-symbol q_m, $m = 1, 2, \ldots, r$, so that when **P** begins to execute step m, **Z** is in state q_m. For each step m in **P** we construct a set of quadruples such that if step m takes w_j into w_{j+1} in the proof, **Z** takes the corresponding word w_j' into w_{j+1}', where words "correspond" iff they denote the same n-tuple of integers and the same contents of p (print out).

We now proceed to construct quadruple sets for the three required cases.

CASE 1. Suppose $m(\ )$ is $mx_i + 1 \rightarrow x_i$ and that w_{k+1} follows from w_k by m. Consider the set of quadruples in Table 4.2.1.[7]

TABLE 4.2.1

(i)	$q_m \bar{\alpha}\, \mathbf{L}\, q_m$	(ix)	$q_{m3} \mathbf{x}_i\, \mathbf{L}\, q_{m4}$	(xvii)	$q_{m7} B \alpha q_{m+1}$
(ii)	$q_m \alpha \mathbf{x}_i q_{m1}$	(x)	$q_{m4} B\, \mathbf{L}\, q_{m4}$	(xviii)	$q_{m4} 1 B q_{m8}$
(iii)	$q_{m1} \mathbf{x}_i\, \mathbf{L}\, q_{m1}$	(xi)	$q_{m4} \mathbf{x}\, \mathbf{R}\, q_{m5}$	(xix)	$q_{m8} \bar{\mathbf{x}}_i\, \mathbf{L}\, q_{m8}$
(iv)	$q_{m1} B \alpha q_{m1}$	(xii)	$q_{m5} \bar{\mathbf{x}}_i\, \mathbf{R}\, q_{m5}$	(xx)	$q_{m8} \mathbf{x}_i\, \mathbf{L}\, q_{m9}$
(v)	$q_{m1} \alpha\, \mathbf{R}\, q_{m2}$	(xiii)	$q_{m5} \mathbf{x}_i B q_{m6}$	(xxi)	$q_{m9} 1\, \mathbf{L}\, q_{m9}$
(vi)	$q_{m2} \bar{\mathbf{x}}_i\, \mathbf{R}\, q_{m2}$	(xiv)	$q_{m6} \bar{\alpha}\, \mathbf{L}\, q_{m6}$	(xxii)	$q_{m9} \alpha 1 q_{m10}$
(vii)	$q_{m2} \mathbf{x}_i\, \mathbf{R}\, q_{m3}$	(xv)	$q_{m6} \alpha 1 q_{m7}$	(xxiii)	$q_{m10} B \alpha q_{m2}$
(viii)	$q_{m3} \bar{\mathbf{x}}_i\, \mathbf{R}\, q_{m3}$	(xvi)	$q_{m7} 1\, \mathbf{L}\, q_{m7}$	(xxiv)	$q_{m10} 1\, \mathbf{L}\, q_{m10}$

This Turing machine replaces α by $\mathbf{x}_i$, finds $\mathbf{x}_i$ to the right in the initial i.d., copies the 1's (1^{a_i}) to the left of the $\mathbf{x}_i$ which replaces α, and adds one tally. For example, if we have

$$\#\alpha q_m 111 \mathbf{x}_1 1111 \mathbf{x}_2 B p \#$$

and the program step is $\mathbf{x}_2 + 1 \rightarrow \mathbf{x}_2$, the quadruples produce

$$\# q_{m+1} \alpha 11111 \mathbf{x}_2 111 \mathbf{x}_1 BBBBBBp \#$$

The transition diagram for this machine, with explanatory remarks, appears in Fig. 4.2.1.

With these informal remarks in mind, we now prove that the constructed machine indeed simulates $\mathbf{x}_i + 1 \rightarrow \mathbf{x}_i$.

Suppose that $m\mathbf{x}_i + 1 \rightarrow \mathbf{x}_i$ is the rule taking

$$(a_1, x_1) \cdots (a_i, x_i) \cdots (a_n, x_n)(0, p)$$

into

$$(a_1, x_1) \cdots (a_i + 1, x_i) \cdots (a_n, x_n)(0, p)$$

[7] The reader should review conventions 1 to 4 following Example 3 in Section 4.1. Moreover, in Table 4.2.1, we let **x** be a variable over $\{\mathbf{x}_1, \mathbf{x}_2, \ldots\}$.

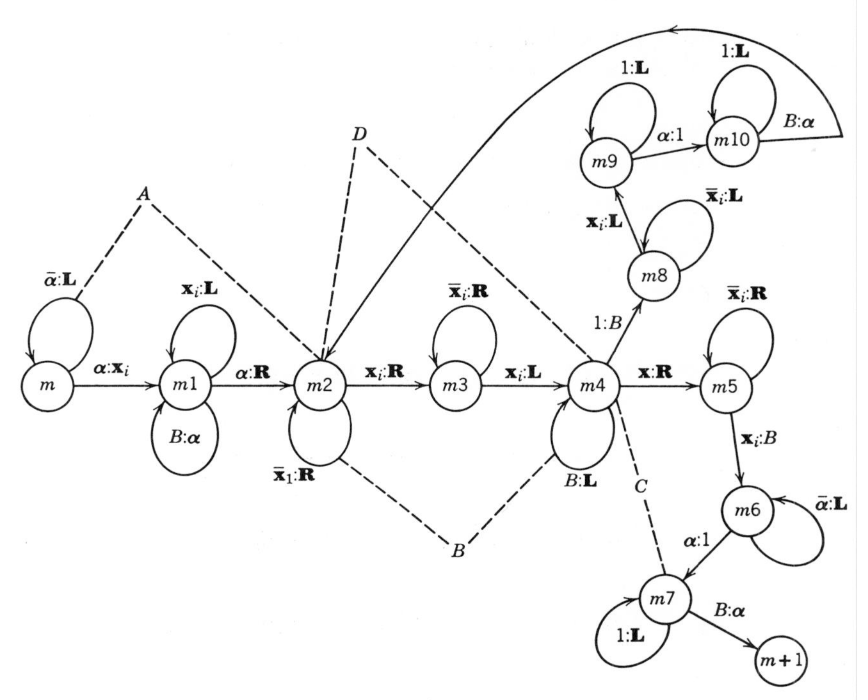

Fig. 4.2.1

A. Replace α by $\mathbf{x}_i$.
B. Find $\mathbf{x}_i$ to the right.
C. If "contents" of $\mathbf{x}_i = 0 = BB\ldots$, erase $\mathbf{x}_i$, add tally at left of tape at new $\mathbf{x}_i$. Exit to simulate next instruction.
D. Copy tallies left of $\mathbf{x}_i$ into new $\mathbf{x}_i$ position at end of tape.

We will show that our Turing machine (Table 4.2.1) takes

$$\#\alpha 1^{a_1}\mathbf{x}_1 \cdots 1^{a_{i-1}}\mathbf{x}_{i-1}1^{a_i}\mathbf{x}_i 1^{a_{i+1}}\mathbf{x}_{i+1}\cdots 1^{a_n}\mathbf{x}_n q_m Bp\# \tag{4}$$

into

$$\#q_{m+1}\alpha 1^{a_i+1}\mathbf{x}_i 1^{a_1}\mathbf{x}_1\cdots 1^{a_{i-1}}\mathbf{x}_{i-1}B^{a_i+1}1^{a_{i+1}}\mathbf{x}_{i+1}\cdots 1^{a_n}\mathbf{x}_n Bp\# \tag{5}$$

where the q_m in (4) has been placed arbitrarily. Thus, beginning by using the quadruple (i) with $\bar{\alpha} = B$, and by Clause 3 of Corollary 4.1.7a, using the production

$$P\mathbf{x}_n q_m BR \rightarrow Pq_m\mathbf{x}_n BR$$

we have from (4)

$$\#\alpha 1^{a_1}\mathbf{x}_1\cdots 1^{a_i}\mathbf{x}_i\cdots 1^{a_n}q_m\mathbf{x}_n BP\#$$

Continuing with (i) which still applies, and using the appropriate instances of Corollary 4.1.7a, we eventually have

$$\#q_m\alpha 1^{a_1}\mathbf{x}_1 \cdots 1^{a_i}\mathbf{x}_i \cdots 1^{a_n}\mathbf{x}_n BP\#$$

By (ii) (and thus indirectly by the appropriate production),

$$\#q_{m1}\mathbf{x}_i 1^{a_1}\mathbf{x}_1 \cdots 1^{a_i}\mathbf{x}_i \cdots 1^{a_n}\mathbf{x}_n Bp\#$$

By (iii) and (iv),

$$\#q_{m1}\alpha\mathbf{x}_i \cdots$$

By (v) to (viii),

$$\#\alpha\mathbf{x}_i 1^{a_1}\mathbf{x}_1 \cdots 1^{a_i}q_{m3}\mathbf{x}_i \cdots 1^{a_n}\mathbf{x}_n Bp\#$$

By (ix),

$$\#\alpha\mathbf{x}_i 1^{a_1}\mathbf{x}_1 \cdots 1^{a_i-1}q_{m4}1\mathbf{x}_i \cdots 1^{a_n}\mathbf{x}_n Bp\#$$

By (xviii),

$$\#\alpha\mathbf{x}_i 1^{a_1}\mathbf{x}_1 \cdots 1^{a_i-1}q_{m8}B\mathbf{x}_i \cdots 1^{a_n}\mathbf{x}_n Bp\#$$

By (xix),

$$\#\alpha q_{m8}\mathbf{x}_i 1^{a_1}\mathbf{x}_1 \cdots 1^{a_i-1}B\mathbf{x}_i \cdots 1^{a_n}\mathbf{x}_n Bp\#$$

By (xx),

$$\#q_{m9}\alpha\mathbf{x}_i \cdots$$

By (xxi)

$$\#q_{m10}1\mathbf{x}_i \cdots$$

By (xxiv),

$$\#q_{m10}B1\mathbf{x}_i \cdots \qquad \text{(added blank at end of tape)}$$

By (xxiii),

$$\#q_{m2}\alpha 1\mathbf{x}_i 1^{a_1}\mathbf{x}_1 \cdots 1^{a_i-1}B\mathbf{x}_i \cdots 1^{a_n}\mathbf{x}_n Bp\#$$

Using the same sequence of productions $a_i - 1$ more times, each time beginning with (vi), we obtain

$$\#q_{m2}\alpha 1^{a_i}\mathbf{x}_i 1^{a_1}\mathbf{x}_1 \cdots B^{a_i}\mathbf{x}_i \cdots 1^{a_n}\mathbf{x}_n Bp\#$$

and we have copied 1^{a_i} to the extreme left of tape.

Continuing now with (vi) to (ix),

$$\#\alpha 1^{a_i}\mathbf{x}_i 1^{a_1}\mathbf{x}_1 \cdots B^{a_i}q_{m4}B\mathbf{x}_i \cdots 1^{a_n}\mathbf{x}_n Bp\#$$

By (x),

$$\#\alpha 1^{a_i}\mathbf{x}_i 1^{a_1}\mathbf{x}_1 \cdots 1^{a_{i-1}}q_{m4}\mathbf{x}_{i-1}B^{a_i}\mathbf{x}_i \cdots 1^{a_n}\mathbf{x}_n Bp\#$$

By (xi), (xii),

$$\#\alpha 1^{a_i}\mathbf{x}_i 1^{a_1}\mathbf{x}_1 \cdots 1^{a_{i-1}}\mathbf{x}_{i-1} B^{a_i} q_{m5}\mathbf{x}_i \cdots 1^{a_n}\mathbf{x}_n Bp\#$$

By (xiii), (xiv),

$$\#q_{m6}\alpha 1^{a_i}\mathbf{x}_i 1^{a_1}\mathbf{x}_1 \cdots 1^{a_{i-1}}\mathbf{x}_{i-1} B^{a_i+1} \cdots 1^{a_n}\mathbf{x}_n Bp\#$$

And finally, using (xv) to (xvii),

$$\#q_{m+1}\alpha 1^{a_i+1}\mathbf{x}_i 1^{a_1}\mathbf{x}_1 \cdots$$

which is of the desired form (5).

CASE 2. Suppose $m(\ )$ is $m\ x_i - 1 \to x_i$. Consider, then, the following set of quadruples.

$$\begin{array}{ll} q_m\bar{\alpha}\,\mathbf{L}\,q_m & q_{m2}\mathbf{x}\,\mathbf{R}\,q_{m3} \\ q_m\alpha\,\mathbf{R}\,q_{m1} & q_{m3}1Bq_{m+1} \\ q_{m1}\bar{\mathbf{x}}_i\,\mathbf{R}\,q_{m1} & q_{m2}B\,\mathbf{R}\,q_{m3} \\ q_{m1}\mathbf{x}_i\,\mathbf{L}\,q_{m2} & q_{m3}B\,\mathbf{R}\,q_{m3} \\ q_{m2}1\,\mathbf{L}\,q_{m2} & \end{array}$$

By a tiresome procedure imitative of Case 1, one can show that this set takes

$$\#\alpha 1^{a_1}\mathbf{x}_1 \cdots 1^{a_i}\mathbf{x}_i \cdots 1^{a_n}\mathbf{x}_n q_m Bp\#$$

into

$$\#\alpha 1^{a_1}\mathbf{x}_1 \cdots 1^{a_{i-1}}\mathbf{x}_{i-1} B \cdots q_{m+1} B 1^{a_i-1}\mathbf{x}_i \cdots 1^{a_n} x_n Bp\#$$

whenever $m\ x_i - 1 \to x_i$ takes

$$(a_1, x_1) \cdots (a_i, x_i) \cdots (a_n x_n)(0, p)$$

into

$$(a_1, x_1) \cdots (a_i - 1, x_i) \cdots (a_n, x_n)(0, p)$$

CASE 3. Suppose $m(\ )$ is $m\ (0, x_i) \Rightarrow k, l$ where $1 \le k, l \le n$. Consider the quadruples

$$\begin{array}{ll} q_m\bar{\alpha}\,\mathbf{L}\,q_m & q_{m2}BBq_k \\ q_m\alpha\,\mathbf{R}\,q_{m1} & q_{m2}11q_l \\ q_{m1}\bar{\mathbf{x}}_i\,\mathbf{R}\,q_{m1} & \\ q_{m1}\mathbf{x}_i\,\mathbf{L}\,q_{m2} & \end{array}$$

If $\mathbf{x}_i$ is zero, the program step $m(0, x_i) \Rightarrow k, l$ takes us to k, otherwise to l. Similarly, the quadruple set above causes a Turing machine to find $\mathbf{x}_i$. In state q_{m2} if there is a blank, then by our conventions (Definition 4.2.2), the word represents zero and the machine goes into state q_k. If there is a 1, it goes into q_l.

Since **Z** is monogenic, each one of the consequences in the foregoing three cases is unique. So, finally, corresponding to the given proof

$$w_1, w_2, w_3, \ldots, w_t$$

of **P**, we have constructed a proof

$$w_1', \ldots, w_2', \ldots, w_3', \ldots, \ldots, w_t'$$

of **Z** such that if w_t is terminal so is w_t' and moreover $\langle \text{Res}(w_1') \rangle =$ contents of p in w_t. This proves the equality (3), and hence Theorem 4.2.7.

Q.E.D.

Corollary 4.2.10. Every recursively enumerable set is enumerated by a Turing machine, hence by an infinite transducer.

EXERCISES 4.2

1. The Turing machine, given in quadruple formulation as below, has the axiom $\#\alpha q_0 1^{a_1} \mathbf{x}_1 1^{a_2} \mathbf{x}_2 \#$, where the printout has been (illegally) omitted.

$q_0 \alpha \mathbf{R} q_0$	$q_2 \alpha \mathbf{R} q_3$
$q_0 \bar{\mathbf{x}}_1 \mathbf{R} q_0$	$q_3 1 B q_0$
$q_0 \mathbf{x}_1 \mathbf{R} q_1$	$q_3 B \mathbf{R} q_3$
$q_1 B \mathbf{R} q_1$	$q_3 \mathbf{x}_1 \mathbf{x}_1 q_3$
$q_1 1 B q_2$	$q_1 \mathbf{x}_2 \mathbf{L} q_4$
$q_2 \bar{\alpha} \mathbf{L} q_2$	$q_4 \bar{\mathbf{x}}_1 \mathbf{L} q_4$

$$q_4 \mathbf{x}_1 p q_5$$

(*a*) Determine the associated function Ψ of this machine.
(*b*) Reformulate the machine in semi-thue form.
(*c*) Supply a legal formulation using $\#\alpha q_0 1^{a_1} \mathbf{x}_1 1^{a_2} \mathbf{x}_2 Bp\#$.

2. Prove that $x_1 + x_2$ is computable by direct construction of a Turing machine whose associated function is $\Psi(x_1, x_2) = x_1 + x_2$. Use our symbol conventions for representing numbers as given in Definitions 4.2.2 and 4.2.3. The machine must be constructed in such a way that the original encoded arguments a_1 and a_2 are preserved on tape at the end of the computation. The construction should result in a quadruple formulation.

3. Complete the proof of Lemma 4.2.9 for Case 2.

4. Construct a (nonnumerical) Turing machine for translating any boolean formula F in parenthetical form into Polish form (cf. Example 2 in Section 2.1). Explain, by supplying appropriate definitions, a natural sense in which such a translation is *recursive*. The alphabet is to be as in the example cited. To keep to the linear style of writing, write $-F$ for $\overline{F}$, where F is a boolean formula. To facilitate the translation use parentheses completely as in (1), Section 2.1.

4.3 TURING GENERATORS AND ACCEPTORS

According to Corollary 4.2.10, every recursively enumerable set is *enumerated* by some Turing machine, which is intended to mean that (for 1-ary computable functions) if $x = 1$ is encoded on tape, then $f(1)$ is printed out; if $x = 2$, $f(2)$, etc. We are additionally interested in the question whether the recursively enumerable sets are also the sets *accepted* and/or *generated* by Turing machines in the technical sense of Definitions 3.3.13 and 3.3.16. The answer is affirmative in both cases.

In Section 2.2 we promised to show that not all recursively enumerable sets are recursive. From this result it will follow that Turing machines "process" exactly the recursively enumerable sets *properly included* within which are the recursive sets. This also establishes the existence of recursively unsolvable problems, which we shall discuss in Section 4.4.

In the following exposition (Sections 4.3 and 4.4) we draw heavily upon Davis [1958]. Since the theory is developed in that book in painstaking detail, there is little point in reproducing it here in full. The reader interested in the details should consult the reference mentioned. On occasion, we shall present some of the proofs quite fully in order to emphasize the role played by some of the key concepts.

The discussion initiated in this section requires first a proof of the equivalence of the partial recursive with the partial computable functions.[8] To accomplish this, suppose for the moment that f is partial computable. Then we know there is a Turing machine **Z** which computes it. Of this machine we can assert the following salient facts. (1) If we code the argument values of f in some appropriate way, this encodement serves as axiom for **Z**; (2) if f is defined for a given assignment of values, then there is a computation (or terminal proof from the axiom) and the terminal theorem represents the function value. Using the device of Gödel numbers, we may assert the above facts about an $n + 2$-tuple of numbers, one standing for the Turing machine, n of them for its axiom encodement of the argument, and one for its proof. Since the axiom is (represents) already an n-tuple of integers, we let the n-tuple stand for the axiom. With this construction of the indicated numerical predicate in mind, we see at once that if f is partial computable, then the predicate is true for the defined arguments, for the number of the machine, and for the number of some proof on it. This predicate turns out to be primitive recursive. By two further operations, to be discussed later, the predicate yields a *partial recursive function* equal to f.

We base the Gödel numbering to be used for any Turing machine in the alphabet $\{s_0, s_1, s_2, \ldots\} \cup \{q_1, q_2, \ldots\} \cup \{\mathbf{R}, \mathbf{L}\}$ on the correspondence in Table 4.3.1. Thus s_i is associated with $4i + 7$ and q_i with $4i + 5$.

[8] Hence leading to another formulation of Church's thesis.

TABLE 4.3.1.

3	5	7	9	11	13
R	**L**	s_0	q_1	s_1	q_2

To continue, by the correlations 1 to 4 of Corollary 4.1.7a, any numerical predicate which is true about Gödel numbers of Turing machines construed as quadruples corresponds to a true statement about Turing semi-thue systems. Hence, following Davis, we use the quadruple formulation.[9]

Definition 4.3.1. Let $x = \sigma_1\sigma_2\cdots\sigma_n$ be a word on the aforementioned alphabet, and let $a_1a_2\cdots a_n$ be the numerical sequence corresponding to x by Table 4.3.1. Then

$$gn(x) = \prod_{k=1}^{n} Pr(k)^{a_k}$$

If $x = \Lambda$, then $gn(x) = 1$.

By the fundamental theorem of arithmetic it follows that $gn(x) = gn(y)$ implies $x = y$.

Definition 4.3.2. Let $x_1, x_2, \ldots, x_n = X$ be a sequence of words. Then

$$gn(X) = \prod_{k=1}^{n} Pr(k)^{gn(x_k)}$$

EXAMPLE 1. The sequence of quadruples $q_1s_1\,\mathbf{L}\,q_2$, $q_2s_1s_2q_1$, $q_1s_3\,\mathbf{R}\,q_2$ has associated to it the number

$$2^{2^9\cdot 3^{11}\cdot 5^5\cdot 7^{13}}\cdot 3^{2^{13}\cdot 3^{11}\cdot 5^{15}\cdot 7^9}\cdot 5^{2^9\cdot 3^{19}\cdot 5^3\cdot 7^{13}}$$

As in the example, the Gödel number of a sequence of quadruples is called the *Gödel number of the Turing machine* provided of course that the set from which the sequence is drawn (without repetition) is in fact a Turing machine (Definition 4.1.7). In general, the variable z will be used to range over Gödel numbers of Turing machines. Each machine has $n!$ Gödel numbers, n being the number of quadruples in its formulation.

EXAMPLE 2. Suppose we have a computation $w_1, \ldots, w_n$. Then the Gödel number of the computation will be

$$2^{gn(w_1)}\cdot 3^{gn(w_2)}\cdot\ldots\cdot Pr(n)^{gn(w_n)}$$

If the student wishes to examine such a number he should set $s_0 = B$, $s_1 = 1$, $s_2 = \alpha$, $s_3 = p$ (recalling our alphabet for numerical computation

[9] Since a Turing machine is explicitly (rather than inductively) defined as a set of quadruples, the ensuing Gödelization of Turing machines will be in a natural way simpler than that of the boolean formalism in Section 2.3.

given in Definitions 4.2.2 and 4.2.3). In general, the variable y will be used to represent Gödel numbers of computations.

Definition 4.3.3. The *predicate* $T_n(z, x_1, \ldots, x_n, y)$ is defined to mean for a given $n + 2$-tuple $(z, x_1, \ldots, x_n, y)$, that z is the Gödel number of a Turing machine for which there exists a computation beginning with the axiom

$$\#\alpha q_1 1^{x_1}\mathbf{x}_1 1^{x_2}\mathbf{x}_2 \cdots 1^{x_n}\mathbf{x}_n Bp\#$$

and y is the Gödel number of the computation on $\mathbf{Z}$.

Theorem 4.3.4. The predicate $T_n(z_1, x_1, \ldots, x_n, y)$ is primitive recursive.

The proof consists in the establishment of a long sequence of definitions culminating in the definition of a numerical predicate expressing y as the Gödel number of a computation on the machine whose Gödel number is z, and another predicate expressing the Gödel number of the axiom as the exponent of the first prime in y. By the construction both predicates are primitive recursive. T_n is then equivalent to the conjunction of the two predicates.[10]

A suitable predicate $P(x_1, \ldots, x_n)$ about integers can be transformed into a function of integers by minimalization (see Section 2.1); however, we now, of course, think of the μ operator as applying more generally, not just to the special predicate $f(y, x_1, \ldots, x_n) = 0$. In particular, we also apply it to T_n, so that $\mu yT(z, x_1, \ldots, x_n, y)$ is the value of the function defined on a subset of the set of $n + 1$-tuples $(z, x_1, \ldots, x_n)$. Therefore $\mu yT_n(z_0, x_1, \ldots, x_n)$ is a partial recursive function on the domain of n-tuples $(x_1, \ldots, x_n)$ for some given, fixed, Turing machine $\mathbf{Z}_0$ whose number is z_0. Its value is the least integer y which is the Gödel number of a computation on $\mathbf{Z}_0$ with the initial i.d. $\mathscr{A} = \#\alpha\, q_1 1^{x_1}\mathbf{x}_1 1^{x_2} \cdots 1^{x_n}\mathbf{x}_n Bp\#$.

If $\mathscr{A}$ is the axiom for a numerical computation, recall that, by Definition 4.2.4, $\langle \text{Res}\,(\mathscr{A})\rangle = a_p = 1^{a_p}$, the contents of p. We now use $\mathbf{U}(y)$ to mean $\langle \text{Res}\,(\mathscr{A})\rangle$ when y is the number of the computation $\mathscr{A} = w_1, \ldots, w_n = \text{Res}\,(\mathscr{A})$. It can be shown that $\mathbf{U}$ is again a recursive function. Consequently, by composition, $\mathbf{U}(\mu yT_n(z, x_1, \ldots, x_n, y))$ is partial recursive since μy is.

Theorem 4.3.5. For any n-ary partial computable function f there exists a Gödel number z_0 such that

$$f(x_1, \ldots, x_n) = \mathbf{U}(\mu yT_n(z_0, x_1, \ldots, x_n, y)) \tag{1}$$

[10] *Caution:* For the reader who follows the construction in Davis, note that n-tuples $(a_1, \ldots, a_n)$ of integers are there coded $1^{a_1+1}B1^{a_2+1}B \cdots B1^{a_n+1}$ with the tally convention that $n = 1^{n+1}$, $0 = 1^1$, and $\langle x\rangle$, for any word, is the number of tallies 1 occurring in x. For a really thoroughgoing adaptation of Davis' exposition, we should, of course, have to alter the definitions given in his Chapter 4, Section 1, so as to accommodate our notational conventions.

Proof. By the hypothesis of the theorem and Definition 4.2.6 there exists a Turing machine $\mathbf{Z}_0$ such that

$$f(x_1, \ldots, x_n) = \Psi_{\mathbf{Z}_0}(x_1, \ldots, x_n)$$

Furthermore, by the construction of T_n the function $\mu y T_n(z_0, x_1, \ldots, x_n, y)$, z_0 being the Gödel number of $\mathbf{Z}_0$, is defined for exactly the same set of values as $\Psi_{\mathbf{Z}_0}$: $\mu y T_{n_0}(z_0, x_1, \ldots, x_n)$ exists when and only when there is a computation from $\mathscr{A}$, and this is also the criterion of definition for $\Psi_{\mathbf{Z}_0}$. Moreover, from the construction of the **U** function,

$$\mathbf{U}(\mu y T_n(z_0, x_1, \ldots, x_n, y))$$

is $\langle \text{Res}(\mathscr{A}) \rangle$ which is, by Definition 4.2.5, the value of $\Psi_{\mathbf{Z}_0}$ for $(x_1, \ldots, x_n)$. Hence $f = \mathbf{U}(\mu y)$. Q.E.D.

Corollary 4.3.6. An n-ary function f is partial computable iff there exists a Gödel number z_0 such that (1) holds.

Proof. Since $\mathbf{U}(\mu y)$ is partial recursive, it follows by Theorem 4.2.7 that it is equal to a partial computable function. This statement with the previous theorem proves the Corollary. Corollary 4.3.6 is the *Kleene normal form* theorem.

Corollary 4.3.7. An n-ary function f is partial computable iff it is partial recursive.

In order to develop the results about Turing generators and acceptors we state here without proof a certain equivalence between domains and ranges of partial recursive functions.

Theorem 4.3.8. For every partial recursive function f with range R, there exists a partial recursive function g such that its domain D is equal to R. Conversely, for every such function g with domain D there exists another such function f with range R such that $D = R$.[11]

Corollary 4.3.9. A set is recursively enumerable iff it is the domain of a partial recursive (partial computable) function.

Corollary 4.3.10. A set S is recursively enumerable iff it is the domain $D_{\mathbf{Z}}$ of the associated function $\Psi_{\mathbf{Z}}$ of a Turing machine **Z**.

In order to build a Turing acceptor we augment the basic definition of a Turing machine, 4.1.1. A Turing acceptor will by Definition 4.3.11 have only auxiliary symbols in every terminal theorem. That is, it will be a

[11] This theorem is quite profound and depends both on the results of Gödelization of Turing machine predicates and on the existence of recursive correspondences between integers and n-tuples of integers. (See Davis, Chapter 5, Section 4.) At this stage of development, automata theory must make use of results which are far deeper than any it itself has established.

device without "output." To achieve such a construction, we use Definition 4.1.1 but replace f by f' and add some new productions g to i as in the following definition.

Definition 4.3.11. A Turing *acceptor* is a semi-thue system $\langle A, \mathscr{B}, \mathscr{A}, \mathscr{P}\rangle$ with alphabet and axiom as in Definition 4.1.1 except that Q includes additional auxiliaries q' and q'': $A = S \cup Q$ and $\{q_1, \ldots, q', q''\} = Q$; $q_i \neq q', q''$ for any $i = 0, 1, \ldots$. The set of productions $\mathscr{P}$ is as follows (as usual, P and R range on $\mathscr{B}$).

1. $\mathscr{P}$ is a finite set of rules with the forms

(a) $Pq_is_jR \rightarrow Pq_ls_kR$
(b) $Pq_is_js_kR \rightarrow Ps_jq_ls_kR$
(c) $Pq_is_j\#R \rightarrow Ps_jq_ls_0\#R$
(d) $Ps_kq_is_jR \rightarrow Pq_ls_ks_jR$
(e) $P\#q_is_jR \rightarrow P\#q_ls_0s_jR$
(f′) $Pq_is_jR \rightarrow Pq's_jR$ (replace q_i by q')
(g) $Pq's_jR \rightarrow Pq'R$ (delete s symbols to the right of q')
(h) $Pq'\#R \rightarrow Pq''\#R$
(i) $Ps_jq''R \rightarrow Pq''R$[12] (delete s symbols to the left of q'')

2. Every pair $(q_i, s_j) \in Q \times S$ (excluding pairs q', s_j, and q'', s_j) occurs either exactly once on the left side of a production of the form a or f', or in the left of both b- and c-type productions for every s_k and for fixed q_l; otherwise it occurs on the left in both d- and e-type productions for every s_k and for fixed q_l. Every $q's_j$ occurs exactly once on the left in a g-type production, and every pair s_jq'' occurs exactly once on the left in an i-type.

3. The only productions in $\mathscr{P}$ are those whose being so follows from clauses 1 and 2.

Definition 4.3.12. A word in $\mathscr{B}$ is in *standard form* iff it is of the form $\#xqy\#$ where $x = y = \Lambda$ is possible and q ranges over the auxiliary alphabet.

Corollary 4.3.13. Every theorem of a Turing acceptor is in standard form.
Proof is left to the student (cf. Corollary 4.1.4).

Lemma 4.3.14. Turing acceptors are monogenic.
Proof is left to the student.

[12] If we think of acceptors as machines with tapes we might redefine the concept of an acceptor so that the final theorem is of the form $\#BB\cdots q''BBB\#$. But then we should have to rearrange our conventions about representing numbers as well. Another possibility would be to introduce a convention for shrinking tape. Strictly speaking, in our formulation we should also add productions to delete $\#$.

Lemma 4.3.15. w_n is terminal iff $w_n = \#q''\#$.

Proof. If w_n is terminal then there is no w_{n+1} following from w_n by any of the rules a to i. By Corollary 4.3.13 every theorem is in standard form, and hence so is w_n. Thus w_n is either of the form (i) $\#xq_i y\#$; (ii) $\#xq'y\#$; or (iii) $\#xq''y\#$.

(i) By Definition 4.1.2 and Corollary 4.1.4, $y = \Lambda$ is impossible, so $y \neq \Lambda$; therefore, rules a to f' apply and $\#xq_i y\#$ is not terminal.

(ii) If $y \neq \Lambda$, rule g applies, and if $y = \Lambda$, rule h applies. So $\#xq'y\#$ is not terminal.

(iii) If $x \neq \Lambda$, rule i applies. If $x = \Lambda$, however, then none of rules a to i apply so that $\#q''y\#$ is terminal. But by the way in which q'' arises, which is only in rule h, it is clear that $y = \Lambda$. Hence $\#q''\#$ and only this expression is terminal. Q.E.D.

Recalling Definition 3.3.13, we have the following corollary.

Corollary 4.3.16. A word x is accepted by $\mathbf{Z}$ iff $\#q''\#$ is a terminal theorem from the axiom $\#q_i x\#$.

Theorem 4.3.17. A set S is recursively enumerable iff there exists a Turing acceptor which accepts each integer $x \in S$.

Proof. By Corollary 4.3.10, S must be the domain of a function $\Psi_{\mathbf{Z}}$ associated to a Turing transducer $\mathbf{Z}$. Let $\mathbf{Z}$ have the pure alphabet

$$\{\alpha, B, 1, \mathbf{x}_1, \mathbf{x}_2, \ldots, \mathbf{x}_k, \ldots, p\}$$

The axiom is $\#\alpha q_1 1^{x_0} \mathbf{x}_1 Bp\#$. Since $x_0 \in S$, $\Psi_{\mathbf{Z}}$ is defined for x_0, so

$$\text{Res}\ (\#\alpha q_1 1^{x_0} \mathbf{x}_1 Bp\#)$$

exists and equals w_n. By Definition 4.1.1, w_n arises only from a production

$(f)\quad Pq_i s_j R \rightarrow Ps_j R$

where s_j is an element of w_n. We construct the acceptor with f' replacing f and with added productions of the form g to i. Call this acceptor $\mathbf{Z}'$. Now consider the theorem $\#w_n\#$ (where w_n is like w_{n-1} except for the q symbol), which is a consequence of w_{n-1} using f'. By productions g to i there is a terminal theorem $\#q''\#$. Hence $\mathbf{Z}'$ accepts x_0.

Conversely, if $\mathbf{Z}'$ accepts the integer x_0 then we have $\#q''\#$ as a theorem, by Corollary 4.3.16. By the construction of productions g to i it can be seen that $\#q''\#$ can follow only from $\#Pq's_j R\#$ for some s_j; so the latter word is a theorem. Hence there is a sequence $w_1 = \#\alpha q_1 1^{x_0} \mathbf{x}_1 Bp\#$, $w_2, \ldots, w_n$, $\#Pq's_j R\#$ such that each w_{i+1} follows from w_i, $i = 1, 2, \ldots, n-1$, by a rule of $\mathbf{Z}'$. Hence by Definition 4.2.5 x_0 is an element of the domain of $\Psi_{\mathbf{Z}}$, where $\mathbf{Z}$ is a transducer with production f replacing f'. Therefore S is the domain of a partial recursive function and consequently is recursively enumerable. Q.E.D.

An interesting question now may be posed concerning the possibility of Turing *detectors* (cf. Definition 3.3.14). Proceeding by example, let us consider the set of even numbers. Since it is the range of the recursive function $2x$ (counting 0 as even), the set is recursively enumerable and hence equally the domain of some partial recursive function. By Theorem 4.3.17 it is accepted by some acceptor. It is an easy matter (left to the student) to construct a detector such that $\#\alpha q_1 1^{2a}\mathbf{x}0p\#$ leads to a terminal theorem $\#q''\#$, while $\#q_1 1^{2a+1}\mathbf{x}0p\#$ leads to a *terminal* theorem $\#q\#$, where $Q = \{q_1, q_2, \ldots, q', q''\}$ and $q \in \{q_1, q_2, \ldots\}$. Hence by Definition 3.3.14 there is the required partition $\{Q_1, Q_2\}$ with even numbers leading to terminal theorems with auxiliary in Q_1 and odd numbers leading to terminal theorems with auxiliary in Q_2. As we shall see in Section 4.4, if *every* recursively enumerable set were of this kind, then all of them would be recursive, and all decision problems for recursively enumerable sets would be solvable. In our present terminology, such problems would all be solvable by Turing detectors. However, there are acceptors for some sets for which there are no detectors.

We now start to demonstrate that every recursively enumerable set can be generated by an appropriate Turing-like system.

By Definition 3.3.15, a generator is an automaton with a single auxiliary axiom all of whose terminal theorems are pure.

Definition 4.3.18. The *inverse* of a semi-thue production $PgR \to Pg'R$ is $Pg'R \to PgR$.

REMARK. It is clear that if y follows from x by $PgR \to Pg'R$, then and only then x follows from y by $Pg'R \to PgR$ where $x, y \in \mathscr{B}$.

Definition 4.3.19. A (numerical) Turing *generator* is a semi-thue system $\mathbf{Z} = \langle A', \mathscr{B}, \mathscr{A}, \mathscr{P}\rangle$ with alphabet as in Definition 4.2.2 with the symbol r added, with axiom $\#q''\#$, and whose productions are precisely the inverses of those for acceptors, together with the following productions.

(j) $P\#\alpha q_1 B\mathbf{x}Bp\#R \to PBR$
(k) $P\#\alpha q_1 1R \to P1rR$
(l) $Pr1R \to P1rR$
(m)[13] $P1r\mathbf{x}Bp\#R \to P1R$

Theorem 4.3.20. A set S is recursively enumerable iff there exists a Turing generator $\mathbf{Z}''$ which generates each integer $x \in S$.

Proof in outline. Any integer x_0 is generated iff 1^{x_0} is a theorem of some $\mathbf{Z}''$. Also $x_0 \in S$ iff $\#\alpha q_1 1^{x_0}\mathbf{x}Bp\#$ is the axiom for some acceptor $\mathbf{Z}'$ with terminal theorem $\#q''\#$. Let $\mathbf{Z}''$ be, now, the generator constructed

[13] Since $\#$ is not an auxiliary we could have also arranged for our terminal theorems to be of the form $\#1^a\#$, $a = 0, 1, 2, \ldots$.

from $\mathbf{Z}'$ in the manner specified in Definition 4.3.19; then by the remark following Definition 4.3.18, $\#q''\#$ is a theorem of $\mathbf{Z}'$ iff $\#\alpha q_1 1^{x_0}\mathbf{x}Bp\#$ is a theorem of $\mathbf{Z}''$. Hence $x_0 \in S$ iff $\#\alpha q_1 1^{x_0}\mathbf{x}Bp\#$ is a theorem of $\mathbf{Z}''$.

Owing to the construction of $\mathbf{Z}''$, however, $\#\alpha q_1 1^{x_0}\mathbf{x}Bp\#$ is not terminal; in fact, production j or k applies. Continuing with rules j to m we have the sequence

$$\begin{array}{ll} \#\alpha q_1 1^{x_0}\mathbf{x}Bp\# & \\ \quad B & \text{(by rule } j \text{ above)} \end{array}$$

provided that $x_0 = 0$ (that is, $1^0 = B$); or the sequence

$$\begin{array}{ll} \#\alpha q_1 1^{x_0}\mathbf{x}Bp\# & \\ 1r1^{x_0-1}\mathbf{x}Bp\# & \\ \vdots & \\ 1^{x_0}r\mathbf{x}Bp\# & \\ \quad 1^{x_0} & \text{(by rules } k \text{ to } m) \end{array}$$

Therefore $x_0 \in S$ implies 1^{x_0} is a theorem of Z''. Q.E.D.

The proof of the converse is omitted.

Corollary 4.3.21. Every recursively enumerable set is generated by a semi-thue system.

Although somewhat aside from our main interest, Corollary 4.3.21 entails the remarkable result, by Theorem 3.1.6, that the theorems of any formal system can be obtained as theorems of a semi-thue system. Also every *language* (cf. Definition 3.3.16), as that term is used in modern mathematical linguistics, is generated by a Turing generator.

Another consequence of the foregoing development is that Turing acceptors and generators are equivalent in the sense that they "process" exactly the same family of sets. A companion truth holds for certain *finite* acceptors and generators, as we shall see in Chapter 8. However, there are automata of intermediate powers for which the analogous statement is false.

EXERCISES 4.3

1. In view of the fact that Turing generators are polygenic, the remark following Definition 4.3.18 and particularly the statement appearing in the proof of Theorem 4.3.20, that $\#q''\#$ is a theorem of $\mathbf{Z}'$ iff $\#\alpha q_1 1^{x_0}\mathbf{x}Bp\#$ is a theorem of $\mathbf{Z}''$, requires some discussion. Provide a proof.

2. Prove that no integer is the Gödel number of both a word and a sequence of words.

3. How many different Turing machines are there?

4. Construct a partial recursive function having the even integers, including zero, as domain.

5. Construct a detector for the even integers.

6. Construct an acceptor for the domain of the subtraction function.

7. Prove Corollary 4.3.13 and Lemma 4.3.14.

8. Example 10 in Section 3.3 is not, as it stands, a Turing generator, although it is a semi-thue system. Reformulate the example as a Turing generator. For convenience let s_0 = the, $s_1 = a$, etc.

9. Are all program computable functions partial recursive? Explain.

4.4 UNSOLVABLE PROBLEMS

In this section we shall prove the existence of unsolvable problems and give several examples of such problems which will be useful. Our approach to the question of unsolvability is, in essence, to use a kind of diagonal procedure as in the proof of the nondenumerability of the real numbers presented in Section 1.2. In fact, we construct a set of integers which cannot occur by that very construction, in a certain enumeration of all of the recursively enumerable sets. Hence this set will be non-recursively enumerable. Assuming, furthermore (we will prove this in Corollary 4.4.7), that S is recursive iff both S and $\bar{S}$ are recursively enumerable, it will then follow that the complement of the set constructed as described will be nonrecursive.

Carrying this informal description further, we leave it to the student to prove that there is only a denumerable number of Turing machines, say generators, on an alphabet of the integers. By Theorem 4.3.20 there is only a denumerable number of recursively enumerable sets. Suppose now that we begin to generate *Turing machines* as follows. We consider the integers in turn, reducing them to products of powers of primes, in order by primes. When we hit upon a Turing machine [cf. Exercise 4.1(8)] $\mathbf{Z}''$, we then generate the companion recursively enumerable set of integers S_i, and if $i \in S_i$, we then put i in a set U, otherwise in $\bar{U}$. Now any integer is in U iff it is in the ith set S_i; hence the integers in $\bar{U}$ are in no set of the enumeration and hence $\bar{U}$ is not recursively enumerable. Hence by the proposition of the foregoing paragraph, U is nonrecursive. Since every recursively enumerable set is generated by some semi-thue system (Corollary 4.3.21) it follows that there are formal systems whose decision problems are recursively unsolvable.

We now formalize this argument.

Definition 4.4.1. A predicate is *recursively enumerable* iff its extension (see Section 2.2) is recursively enumerable. That is, if

$$S = \{(x_1, \ldots, x_n) \mid P(x_1, \ldots, x_n)\}$$

is recursively enumerable, then and only then is $P(x_1, \ldots, x_n)$ recursively enumerable.[14]

EXAMPLE 1. The domain of $x - y$ is the set $\{(x, y) \mid x \geq y\}$. Hence $x \geq y$ is recursively enumerable (we already know, of course, that it is also recursive).

Theorem 4.4.2. If P is recursive, then it is recursively enumerable.

Proof. By hypothesis $\{(x_1, \ldots, x_n) \mid P(x_1, \ldots, x_n)\}$ is recursive and its characteristic function is $C_P(x_1, \ldots, x_n)$. But then it is also the domain of the partial recursive function

$$\mu y(C_p(x_1, \ldots, x_n) + y = 0)$$

and therefore is recursively enumerable. Q.E.D.

Corollary 4.4.3. Recursive sets are recursively enumerable.

Theorem 4.4.4. Assume that $P(y, x_1, \ldots, x_n)$ is a recursive predicate. Then

$$(\exists y)P(y, x_1, \ldots, x_n)$$

is recursively enumerable. The existential quantification of a recursive predicate is recursively enumerable.

Proof. $\{(x_1, \ldots, x_n) \mid (\exists y)P(y, x_1, \ldots, x_n)\}$ = domain of

$$\mu y(C_P(y, x_1, \ldots, x_n) = 0)$$

Q.E.D.

Hence whereas recursive predicates are closed under *bounded* existential quantification (see Section 2.2), the recursively enumerable predicates are precisely the predicates that arise when recursive predicates are operated on by *unbounded* existential quantifiers.

Theorem 4.4.5. If $R(x_1, \ldots, x_n)$ is recursively enumerable, then there exists an integer z_0 such that

$$R(x_1, \ldots, x_n) \Leftrightarrow (\exists y)T(z_0, x_1, \ldots, x_n, y)$$

By definition $S = \{(x_1, \ldots, x_n) \mid R(x_1, \ldots, x_n)\}$ is recursively enumerable and hence S is the domain of a partial recursive function $f(x_1, \ldots, x_n)$. By Corollary 4.3.6 there is a z_0 such that

$$f(x_1, \ldots, x_n) = \mathbf{U}(\mu y T_n(z_0, x_1, \ldots, x_n, y))$$

It follows that S is the domain of $\mathbf{U}$ and therefore of the predicate $(\exists y)T_n(z_0, x_1, \ldots, x_n, y)$; thus

$$\{(x_1, \ldots, x_n) \mid R(x_1, \ldots, x_n)\} = \{(x_1, \ldots, x_n) \mid (\exists y)T_n(z_0, x_1, \ldots, x_n, y)\}$$

and the theorem follows. Q.E.D.

[14] Davis uses computable and semicomputable as we use recursive and recursively enumerable. Moreover, he defines a recursively enumerable predicate as one whose extension is the domain of a partial computable function, which of course is equivalent to our definition.

Theorem 4.4.6. $R(x_1, \ldots, x_n)$ is recursive iff $R(x_1, \ldots, x_n)$ and

$$\neg R(x_1, \ldots, x_n)$$

are both recursively enumerable.

Proof. By Theorem 4.4.2 and the fact that if a predicate is recursive, its negation is also, the theorem holds from left to right. Suppose that $R(x_1, \ldots, x_n)$ and $\neg R(x_1, \ldots, x_n)$ are recursively enumerable. By Theorem 4.4.5 it follows that there are predicates $P(y, x_1, \ldots, x_n)$ and

$$Q(y, x_1, \ldots, x_n)$$

which are both recursive, and

$$\begin{aligned} R(x_1, \ldots, x_n) &\Leftrightarrow (\exists y)P(y, x_1, \ldots, x_n) \\ \neg R(x_1, \ldots, x_n) &\Leftrightarrow (\exists y)Q(y, x_1, \ldots, x_n) \end{aligned}$$

By elementary logic, for any value $(a_1, \ldots, a_n)$ either $R(a_1, \ldots, a_n)$ or $\neg R(a_1, \ldots, a_n)$ must be true. Hence

$$(\exists y)(P(y, x_1, \ldots, x_n) \vee Q(y, x_1, \ldots, x_n))$$

is true for each choice of values.

Recalling that μy transforms predicates into functions,

$$h(x_1, \ldots, x_n) = \mu y(P(y, x_1, \ldots, x_n) \vee Q(y, x_1, \ldots, x_n))$$

is a *total* recursive function since P and Q are recursive, their disjunction is recursive, and the disjunction holds for *all* values $(x_1, \ldots, x_n)$, for some y.

Setting $y_0 = h(x_1, \ldots, x_n)$,

$$R(x_1, \ldots, x_n) \Leftrightarrow P(y_0, x_1, \ldots, x_n)$$

So R is recursive since P is. Q.E.D.

Corollary 4.4.7. S is a recursive set iff both S and $\bar{S}$ are recursively enumerable.

We are now able to show that a nonrecursive set exists.

Theorem 4.4.8. $(\exists y)T(x, x, y)$ is recursively enumerable but not recursive. (The converse of Theorem 4.4.2 is false).

Proof. Assume that $(\exists y)T(x, x, y)$ is recursive. From the preceding theorem it follows that $\neg(\exists y)T(x, x, y)$ is recursively enumerable. If this is so, by Theorem 4.4.5, there exists a z_0 such that

$$\neg(\exists y)T(x, x, y) \Leftrightarrow (\exists y)T(z_0, x, y) \tag{1}$$

for every x.

In particular, then, if (1) holds for any x it must hold for $x = z_0$:

$$\neg(\exists y)T(z_0, z_0, y) \Leftrightarrow (\exists y)T(z_0, z_0, y)$$

But this is a contradiction, and therefore our assumption that $(\exists y)T(x, x, y)$ is recursive is false. That it is recursively enumerable follows from Theorem 4.4.4. Q.E.D.

$\neg(\exists y)T(x, x, y)$ is not even recursively enumerable, so the property is not preserved under negation. It can be shown that recursive enumerability is preserved under existential quantification, but not under universal quantification.

Corollary 4.4.9. The set $K = \{x \mid (\exists y)T(x, x, y)\}$ is recursively enumerable but not recursive.

Corollary 4.4.10. The decision problem for K is recursively unsolvable.

Corollary 4.4.11. There exist Turing acceptors and generators with nonrecursive accepted and generated sets respectively. There exists a semi-thue (and hence a formal) system with a recursively unsolvable decision problem, that is, with a nonrecursive set of theorems.

These results all follow from the fact that every recursively enumerable set is accepted by, is generated by, or is a theorem of, the relevant systems.

Although, as indicated at the end of Section 2.3, many problems, including nonnumerical problems, can be shown to be solvable by mechanical means on rather simple intuitive grounds, the unsolvability proofs require a rather sophisticated apparatus. The basis for these methods has been laid in the foregoing theorems. There are several slightly more concrete decision problems which can be shown unsolvable by a fairly direct application of Theorem 4.4.8. Surprisingly enough, these latter problems in turn have applications to more or less realistic automaton problems concerning machines and languages of far less power than the Turing machines and the recursively enumerable sets. We proceed now to a discussion of some of the more important examples of unsolvability.

EXAMPLE 1. *The Halting Problem.* Suppose one were to ask whether there is an algorithm for deciding if a given Turing machine $\mathbf{Z}$ computes anything from a given i.d. or axiom, or instead goes into an "infinite loop." In numerical terms this is the problem whether the following predicate is recursive.

$H_{\mathbf{Z}}(x) \Leftrightarrow x$ is the Gödel number of the axiom of $\mathbf{Z}$ and there is computation on Z.

The unsolvability proof is by construction of a Turing machine $\mathbf{Z}_0$ such that the recursiveness of $H_{\mathbf{Z}_0}(x)$ implies that of

$$(\exists y)T(x, x, y)$$

(see Davis [1958]).

EXAMPLE 2. *The Printing Problem.* A related question is: Can one decide whether a Turing machine ever prints a given symbol s_i of its alphabet? More precisely we have

$P_{\mathbf{Z},i}(x) \Leftrightarrow x$ is the Gödel number of the axiom of $\mathbf{Z}$ and there is a proof (not necessarily terminal) $\mathscr{A} = w_1, w_2, \ldots, w_k$ such that w_k contains an occurrence of s_i.

The unsolvability of this problem is obtained by showing that the halting problem would be solvable for a Turing machine $\mathbf{Z}_0$ (as required in the desired construction above) iff the printing problem were solvable for a certain Turing machine $\mathbf{Z}_1$ which is the union of the quadruples of $\mathbf{Z}_0$ and a set which causes $\mathbf{Z}_1$ to print s_i whenever $\mathbf{Z}_0$ halts. s_i is not in the alphabet of $\mathbf{Z}_0$.

EXAMPLE 3. *Equivalence.* The reader already knows that two switching circuits may be mechanically checked for equivalence (by use of truth tables), and also that two sequential circuits may be so checked by a finite procedure.[15] However, two Turing machines with the same pure alphabet S and the same axiom scheme (except perhaps for indices on the auxiliary symbols) cannot be determined to be computationally equivalent (or inequivalent) by an algorithm. Suppose we say that $\mathbf{Z}$ and $\mathbf{Z}'$, both on S, are *equivalent* iff for every specification of $\mathscr{A}$ either there is no computation on $\mathbf{Z}$ or $\mathbf{Z}'$, or $\text{Res}_{\mathbf{Z}}(\mathscr{A}) = \text{Res}_{\mathbf{Z}'}(\mathscr{A})$. The unsolvability of this problem follows immediately from that of the halting problem.

EXAMPLE 4. *Efficacy of Algorithms.* In data processing enterprises it is reasonable to ask whether a given program (or special purpose computer) does what it is supposed to do. We will restrict the discussion to programs for computing 1-ary recursive functions.

If there were an algorithm for determining whether an alleged program is one, then the set of programs (Gödel numbers of programs) would be recursive. We might, however, be willing to settle for less. Even if there were no algorithm for checking programs, there might be a *partial* algorithm which would terminate in the identification of an alleged program if it were one, but would loop infinitely otherwise. In this case the set of programs would be only recursively enumerable. We will see that not even this much can be expected of programs for total functions.

[15] This fact is discussed in detail in Section 5.2.

If a set of programs, say in ALGOL or FORTRAN, were recursively enumerable, then the set of programs in the formal sense of Definition 3.2.14 also would be.[16] And if the set of formal programs is recursively enumerable, then so is the set of Turing machines. For if **P** computes some function, it is in the set of programs and by the method of construction in Lemma 4.2.9 a Turing machine computing the same function can be obtained effectively.

Now assume the set R of Gödel numbers of Turing machines which compute total 1-ary recursive functions is recursively enumerable. This set is

$$R = \{z \mid (\forall x)(\exists y)T(z, x, y)\}$$

By definition there exists a recursive function f whose range is R. It follows that

$$\mathbf{U}(\mu y T(f(x), x, y))$$

is (total) recursive, and by composition that

$$\mathbf{U}(\mu y T(f(x), x, y)) + 1$$

is also recursive. Hence by Corollary 4.3.6 and the definition of f,

$$\mathbf{U}(\mu y T(f(x), x, y)) + 1 = \mathbf{U}(\mu y T(f(x_0), x, y))$$

for every x. Choosing x to be x_0 gives a contradiction. It follows that R is not even recursively enumerable and consequently that the set of programs for total functions is not either.

EXAMPLE 5. *Word Problem for Semigroups.* Let S be any finite alphabet with *at least two elements* and let $\mathscr{S}$ be the free semigroup generated by S. Let g, g' be variables on $\mathscr{S}$ and let H be a finite relation on $\mathscr{S}$, namely a finite set of pairs (g, g').

Suppose x and y are any elements of the semigroup $\mathscr{S}$, and also let P and R be words on $\mathscr{S}$. If $x = PgR$ and $y = Pg'R$, or alternatively, if $x = Pg'R$ and $y = PgR$, then write $x \sim y$. Also, if there is a sequence of elements $x_1, x_2, \ldots, x_n$ such that $x_i \sim x_{i+1}$, $i = 1, \ldots, n - 1$, we write $x_1 \approx x_n$. It can be seen easily that $\approx$ is an equivalence relation, and hence determines a set of equivalence classes on $\mathscr{S}$.

The word problem for semigroups is whether there exists, for arbitrary semigroups, an algorithm for determining membership in an equivalence class—or, in other words, for checking $x \approx y$ for arbitrary elements, given H. For example, let $S = \{a, b\}$ and $H = \{(aa, ba), (ba, bb), (a, bbb)\}$. If $x = PgR = abbaa$, then $Pg'R = abbba$, or $bbbbbaa$, etc. Suppose we ask whether $aaaabb \approx bababa$. A little searching will show the equivalence

[16] We claim that ALGOL and FORTRAN, in the case of numerical computations, compute exactly the same functions as formal programs.

holds, but it is hardly a trival matter to prove that there exists (or does not exist) a solvable procedure for this class of problem.

We prove this problem to be recursively unsolvable by showing that if it were solvable the problem for a certain class of generators would also be solvable.

A *thue generator* $\mathbf{Z}'''$ is a system with the same alphabet as the Turing generator $\mathbf{Z}''$ (Definition 4.3.19), except for omission of the special symbol r, a set of productions consisting of the union of the productions of $\mathbf{Z}''$ and their inverses but omitting the productions j to m and their inverses. The axiom is the same as for $\mathbf{Z}''$. (Equivalently, $\mathbf{Z}'''$ consists of an acceptor together with its inverse productions, but with the axiom of a generator.) Thus for every production $PgR \to Pg'R$ in $\mathbf{Z}''$ (excepting j to m), $\mathbf{Z}'''$ includes $Pg'R \to PgR$ as well. We distinguish the productions of $\mathbf{Z}''$ as α rules and their inverses as β rules. We remark that no β rules apply to the axiom $\#q''\#$ and that the β rules are rules of an acceptor, and hence as a subsystem, *monogenic*, by Lemma 4.3.14.

Obviously every theorem of $\mathbf{Z}''$ (except for use of j to m) is also a theorem of $\mathbf{Z}'''$. Conversely, assume w_n is a theorem of $\mathbf{Z}'''$; then there exists a sequence

$$w_1, w_2, \ldots, w_n \tag{2}$$

in $\mathbf{Z}'''$. If each rule taking w_i into w_{i+1} for $i = 1, \ldots, n - 1$ is an α rule, then w_n is also a theorem of $\mathbf{Z}''$. Suppose, however, that w_j is the first theorem in the sequence (2) in which application is made of a β rule. Let us write

$$w_{j-1} \xrightarrow{\beta} w_j \tag{3}$$

By the above remark, $w_{j-1} \neq q''$. Consequently w_{j-1} must follow from w_{j-2} by an α rule (since w_j was the first to follow by a β rule):

$$w_{j-2} \xrightarrow{\alpha} w_{j-1} \tag{4}$$

By construction $\mathbf{Z}'''$ must also include the inverse of (4)

$$w_{j-1} \xrightarrow{\beta} w_{j-2} \tag{5}$$

By (3) and (5), w_{j-1} has *two* consequences, so the system of β rules is polygenic. But the β rules must be, as remarked above, monogenic. Hence w_n follows only by α rules and consequently every theorem of $\mathbf{Z}'''$ is a theorem of $\mathbf{Z}''$. By a few steps which we omit, we find that every recursively enumerable set is generated by a thue generator, and there exists a thue generator with an unsolvable decision problem.

Now let $\mathscr{S}$ be the semigroup whose alphabet is the same as that of some thue system $\mathbf{Z}$ and whose relations (g, g') are determined by the semi-thue productions of **Z** and their inverses. Let $\mathscr{A}$ be the axiom of **Z**. Let w be a word in $\mathscr{S}$. It is obvious by the construction that w is a theorem of **Z** iff $\mathscr{A} \approx w$ w.r.t. to $\mathscr{S}$. Consequently if there were a decision procedure for $\mathscr{S}$, constructed in this way, there would also be one for **Z**. Since there exists a thue generator with an unsolvable decision problem, therefore, it follows that there exists a semigroup on a finite set of generators and pairs (g, g') whose word problem is recursively unsolvable.

EXAMPLE 6. *The Correspondence Problem.* Let $(x_1, \ldots, x_n)$, $(y_1, \ldots, y_n)$ be two n-tuples of words on a common alphabet S with at least two elements. Does there exist a sequence of integers $i_1, i_2, \ldots, i_k$, where $k \geq 1$ and $1 \leq i_j \leq n$ for $n = 1, \ldots, k$ such that $x_{i_1}x_{i_2} \cdots x_{i_k} = y_{i_1}y_{i_2} \cdots y_{i_k}$?

For instance, given (aa, ab, ba, bb) and (a, bab, b, ab) is there a sequence of indices yielding $aabbab = aabbab$? In this case there is such a sequence, which is 1, 4, 2.

Using only the apparatus now at our disposal, the full proof of the unsolvability of this problem is fairly complicated. The student interested in the details should look up the original paper (Post, [1946]).

In outline, it is possible to show that a formal system, called a *normal* system, corresponds to every semi-thue system. The normal system is like a semi-thue system, except that all of its productions are of the form

$$gP \rightarrow Pg'$$

As in the proof of the unsolvability of the word problem, we could show here that if the normal system derived by a certain construction from a semi-thue system were solvable, then the semi-thue system would also be solvable. Since there is a semi-thue system with a recursively unsolvable set of theorems, the same fact holds true for normal systems.

Now let N be a normal system with $\mathscr{A}$ an axiom and w a theorem. There then exists a proof

$$w_1 = \mathscr{A}, w_2, \ldots, w_n, w$$

so that w_2 follows from $\mathscr{A}$ by a production $g_{i_1}P_1 \rightarrow P_1g'_{i_1}$, w_3 from w_2 by $g_{i_2}P_2 \rightarrow P_2g'_{i_2}, \ldots$, and w from w_n by $g_{i_n}P_n \rightarrow P_ng'_{i_n}$. Hence w is a theorem iff the following set of equations is satisfied by integers $n, i_1, i_2, \ldots, i_n$.

$$\mathscr{A} = g_{i_1}P_1 \quad P_1g'_{i_1} = g_{i_2}P_2, \ldots, \quad P_{n-1}g'_{i_{n-1}} = g_{i_n}P_n \quad P_ng'_{i_n} = w \tag{6}$$

Consider the first two equations in (6). Since $\mathscr{A} = g_{i_1}P_1$ and $P_1g'_{i_1} = g_{i_2}P_2$, we have

$$\mathscr{A}P_1g'_{i_1} = g_{i_1}P_1g_{i_2}P_2$$

and canceling P_1,

$$\mathscr{A}g'_{i_1} = g_{i_1}g_{i_2}P_{i_2} \tag{7}$$

Thus starting with $\mathscr{A}g'_{i_1}g'_{i_2}\cdots g'_{i_n}$ and substituting from left to right by using (6), we obtain

$$\mathscr{A}g'_{i_1}g'_{i_2}\cdots g'_{i_n} = g_{i_1}g_{i_2}\cdots g_{i_n}w \tag{8}$$

Or, for something less than the whole proof, as in (7),

$$\mathscr{A}g'_{i_1}g'_{i_2}\cdots g'_{i_{m-1}} = g_{i_1}g_{i_2}\cdots g_{i_m}P_m \qquad m = 1, \ldots, n \tag{9}$$

Moreover, it follows from (6) and (9) that

$$l(\mathscr{A}g'_{i_1}g'_{i_2}\cdots g'_{i_{m-1}}) \geq l(g_{i_1}g_{i_2}\cdots g_{i_m}) \tag{10}$$

Hence if there is a proof, represented by (6), then equation (8) holds subject to the length condition (10). Conversely, if (8) is true with the condition (10), then (9) can be shown for each m, yielding a proof (6). In summary, there is a proof of w iff there exist i_1, i_2, i_n, and n satisfying (8) with the length condition (10).

The student should observe that if we rewrite the pairs (g_1, g_1'), (g_2, g_2'), $\ldots$, (g_r, g_r'), which determine the normal productions $g_1P \rightarrow Pg_1'$, $g_2P \rightarrow Pg_2'$, etc., in the form $(g_1, g_2, \ldots, g_r) = (g_1', g_2', \ldots, g_r')$ we succeed in recasting the correspondence problem approximately as one about normal systems. We have failed to do so only in that, (a) in the equations (8), unlike the equation

$$x_{i_1}x_{i_2}\cdots x_{i_k} = y_{i_1}y_{i_2}\cdots y_{i_k}$$

of the formulation of the problem itself, the unwanted symbols $\mathscr{A}$ and w occur; and (b) the correspondence problem does not suffer the restriction of the length condition (10). In Post's original treatment, the essential point is to show that there is a normal system without these limitations which is constructible from a correspondence problem. Hence the correspondence problem is recursively unsolvable.

EXERCISES 4.4

1. Explain how the informal argument at the opening of the section uses the diagonal argument. Why doesn't the argument simply prove that there is a nondenumerable number of Turing machines, in analogy with the real number argument?

2. Which of the following predicates are recursively enumerable according to the results discussed in this section?

(a) $(\overset{3}{\exists}y)(\exists z)(yz = 3x)$
(b) $(\overset{x}{\exists}z)(\exists y)(yz = x)$
(c) $(\exists x)(\mu y(x^2 + y = z) = x)$
(d) $(\overset{5}{\exists}x)(\text{Prime}\,(y) \wedge x = y)$
(e) $\neg(\exists y)((y \dot{-} x) \dot{-} z = [x/2])$

3. Complete the details of the proof of the unsolvability of the halting problem.

4. Similarly, complete the proof of unsolvability of the printing problem.

5. Explain how the proof about the nonrecursive enumerability of Gödel numbers of Turing machines (or programs) would fail if extended to the partial recursive functions.

6. Prove that the $\approx$ between words in a semigroup is an equivalence relation.

7. Invent a formal generator (not necessarily Turing) for generating the words, and perhaps other words, of the example used in the discussion of the correspondence problem so that a word such as *aabbab* of the example is generable in at least two ways (at least two distinct proofs).

4.5 UNIVERSAL MACHINES

Among all Turing machines (transducers) there exists a *Universal machine* which can compute all of the partial recursive functions of a single variable. The existence of such a machine may be shown from the fact that

$$\mathbf{U}(\mu y T(z, x, y))$$

is a partial recursive function of z and x. Hence by Theorem 4.2.7 and Definition 4.2.6, there exists a Turing machine $\mathscr{U}$ such that

$$\Psi_{\mathscr{U}}(z, x) = \mathbf{U}(\mu y T(z, x, y))$$

If z_0 is the Gödel number of a machine $\mathbf{Z}_0$ which computes the partial recursive function $\Psi_{\mathbf{Z}_0}(x)$, then $\Psi_{\mathbf{Z}_0}(x) = \Psi_{\mathscr{U}}(z_0, x)$.

A Universal machine, given the argument pair (z_0, x), recovers the quadruple list of $\mathbf{Z}_0$ from the integer z_0 (see Example 1 after Definition 4.3.2), and then given that list encoded on tape, computes $\Psi_{\mathbf{Z}_0}$ for an inscribed value of x.

In formal terms, a complete treatment would involve the construction of a semi-thue Turing machine with the axiom comprised of a representation of *both* the quadruple list of the special machine to be imitated, and an encodement of the argument value. However, it is much simpler, since we know we can always reconstruct a system with all the formalities absent, merely to use a quadruple formulation along with the intuitive tape model used in Section 4.0. We shall adopt this procedure, and also hold the assumption that $\mathbf{Z}_0$ is already prepared in quadruple form.

In the following development we shall suppose that every machine to be simulated operates with just the alphabet $\{0, 1\}$. The universal Turing machine may of course use any alphabet so long as it includes $\{0, 1\}$. The one we construct will in fact use $\{0, 1\}$ only. In view of these conventions, it is necessary to show that any Turing machine can in fact be reduced to one with an alphabet of two symbols.

Definition 4.5.1. A *code* is an isomorphism between a free monoid $\mathscr{S}$ and a subset of a free monoid $\mathscr{S}'$.

Generally a coding problem arises when of two alphabets S and S', $K(S) > K(S')$. Ordinarily, one chooses a mapping φ so that if $K(S) = m$ and $K(S') = n$, φ takes the letters of S into words on the letters S' of length $\{\log_n m\}$, where $\{i\}$ is the least integer greater than or equal to i. Then φ is extended to a code by $\varphi(xs) = \varphi(x)\varphi(s)$, $x \in \mathscr{S}$, $s \in S$.

EXAMPLE 1. $S = \{a, b, c\}$ and $S' = \{0, 1\}$. Then $m = 3$, $n = 2$, $\{\log_n m\} = 2$. We let φ be explicitly given by $a \leftrightarrow 00$, $b \leftrightarrow 01$, $c \leftrightarrow 10$. So $\leftrightarrow$ is a one–one correspondence between $\{a, b, c\}$ and $\{00, 01, 10\}$. As a mapping (code) on *words*, we have, for instance,

$$\begin{aligned}\varphi(aabc) &= \varphi(aab)\varphi(c) = \varphi(aab)10 \\ &= \varphi(aa)\varphi(b)10 = \varphi(aa)0110 = \cdots = 00000110\end{aligned}$$

Not all codes need arise in this way. In particular, we need not hold that all words on S' in the range of φ be of equal length. However, we will not pursue this interesting possibility here.

Next, we want to discuss *equivalent* Turing machines.

Definition 4.5.2. Let $\mathbf{Z}_1$ and $\mathbf{Z}_2$ be Turing machines with pure alphabets S_1 and S_2 (we are not concerned here with auxiliaries q, or $\#$, if used). Suppose that $K(S_1) \geq K(S_2)$ and that a code of some sort is defined on $\mathscr{S}_1$ into $\mathscr{S}_2$ such that if $l(x) = l(y)$ then $l(\varphi(x)) = l(\varphi(y))$, $x, y \in \mathscr{S}_1$. Let $d(w)$ be the result of replacing each auxiliary q occurring in w by Λ. Then $\mathbf{Z}_1$ and $\mathbf{Z}_2$ are *equivalent* iff

(i) If there is a terminal proof of $w_n{}^1$ from $w_1{}^1$ in $\mathbf{Z}_1$, then there is a $w_m{}^2$ and a terminal proof of $w_m{}^2$ from $w_1{}^2$ in $\mathbf{Z}_2$ such that $\varphi(d(w_1{}^1)) = d(w_1{}^2)$ and $\varphi(w_n{}^1) = w_m{}^2$.

(ii) If there is a terminal proof of $w_m{}^2$ from $w_1{}^2$ in $\mathbf{Z}_2$, then there is a $w_n{}^1$ and a terminal proof of $w_n{}^1$ from $w_1{}^1$ in $\mathbf{Z}_1$ such that $\varphi^{-1}(d(w_2{}^1)) = \varphi(w_1{}^1)$ and $\varphi^{-1}(w_m{}^2) = w_n{}^1$.

Since φ is into, there will be many instances where (i) is satisfied whereas (ii) is not. In such instances we say that $\mathbf{Z}_2$ *simulates* $\mathbf{Z}_1$.

Two machines on the *same* alphabet but with different states and unequal proof sequences $w_1{}^1 = w_{i_1}{}^1, w_{i_2}{}^1, \ldots, w_{i_n}{}^1 = w_n{}^1$ and $w_1{}^2 = w_{j_1}{}^2, w_{j_2}{}^2, \ldots, w_{j_m}{}^2 = w_m{}^2$ might be equivalent.

We will now take up the specific case where $S_1 = \{s_0, s_1, \ldots, s_n\}$ and $S_2 = \{0, 1\}$. With each symbol s of S_1 we associate a word $x_1x_2\cdots x_r$ of

S_2, $x_i = 0, 1$. We also assume that $\mathbf{Z}_1$ is given as a set of quadruples $q_i s_j \mathbf{M} q_l$ where $\mathbf{M} = \mathbf{R}$, $\mathbf{L}$, or s_k. If a quadruple $q_i s_j s_k q_l$ derives from a production $Pq_i s_j R \to Pq_l s_k R$ [according to (1) of Corollary 4.1.7a], we will say that $q_i s_j s_k q_l$ *operates on* $Pq_i s_j R$ yielding $Pq_l s_k R$. The quadruples of the other two forms can be treated in similar fashion.

Theorem 4.5.3. For every Turing machine $\mathbf{Z}_1$ there exists a machine $\mathbf{Z}_2$ with an alphabet of two symbols $\{0, 1\}$ which simulates $\mathbf{Z}_1$.

Proof. The construction makes use of the idea that the states of a machine may be used to remember a sequence of symbols scanned. Thus if $011 \leftrightarrow s_1$, a two-symbol machine must go through three states to identify and remember the coded word. So $q_i s_1 \mathbf{R} q_i$, on $\mathbf{Z}_1$, let us say, is matched by the *set* $q_i 0 \mathbf{R} q_{i_0}$, $q_{i_0} 1 \mathbf{R} q_{i_0}$, $q_{i_{01}} 1 \mathbf{R} q_i$ on $\mathbf{Z}_2$. It is easy to see that if $q_i s_1 \mathbf{R} q_i$ operates on a word $Pq_i s_1 s_j R$ yielding $Ps_1 q_i s_j R$, then the triple of quadruples displayed operates to yield

$$\begin{aligned} &P' q_i 011\varphi(s_j)R' \\ &P' 0 q_{i_0} 11\varphi(s_j)R' \\ &P' 01 q_{i_{01}} 1\varphi(s_j)R' \\ &P' 011 q_i \varphi(s_j)R' \end{aligned}$$

successively.

So much for motivation.

For every quadruple $q_i s_j s_k q_l$ of $\mathbf{Z}_1$ we construct the following set for $\mathbf{Z}_2$ (where $x_1 x_2 \cdots x_r \leftrightarrow s_j$ and $y_1 y_2 \cdots y_r \leftrightarrow s_k$):

$$\begin{array}{cl} 1 & q_i x_1 \,\mathbf{R}\, q_{ix_1} \\ 2 & q_{ix_1} x_2 \,\mathbf{R}\, q_{ix_1x_2} \\ \vdots & \quad\vdots \\ r-1 & q_{ix_1x_2\cdots x_{r-1}} x_r y_r q'_{iy_1y_2\cdots y_{r-1}} \\ r & q'_{iy_1y_2\cdots y_{r-1}} y_r \,\mathbf{L}\, q''_{iy_1y_2\cdots y_{r-1}} \\ \vdots & q''_{iy_1y_2\cdots y_{r-1}} x_{r-1} y_{r-1} q'_{iy_1y_2\cdots y_{r-2}} \\ \vdots & \quad\vdots \\ \vdots & q''_{iy_1y_2} x_2 y_2 q'_{iy_1} \\ \vdots & q'_{iy_1} y_2 \,\mathbf{L}\, q''_{iy_1} \\ 3r-2 & q_{iy_1} x_1 y_1 q_l \end{array}$$

Suppose now that $q_i s_j s_k q_l$ operates on $Pq_i s_j R$, yielding $Pq_l s_k R$. By coding, we have $P' q_i x_1 x_2 \cdots x_r R'$. In the first $r - 1$ steps, $\mathbf{Z}_2$ detects $x_1 x_2 \cdots x_r$ and overprints y_r. In the remaining steps, the states q_i' and q_i'' "remember" what to print, and symbol by symbol replace x_j by y_j ($j = 1 \cdots r - 1$) moving left. At step $3r - 2$, $\mathbf{Z}_2$ is in state q_l scanning y_1 in the i.d. $Pq_l y_1 y_2 \cdots y_r R'$. Hence when $\varphi(d(Pq_i s_j R)) = d(P' q_i x_1 \cdots x_r R')$,

$$\varphi(d(Pq_l s_k R)) = d(P' q_l y_1 \cdots y_r R')$$

For every quadruple $q_i s_j \mathbf{L} q_l$ of $\mathbf{Z}_1$, we construct the list for $\mathbf{Z}_2$ with the same form of coding as before.

$$
\begin{array}{l}
q_i x_1 \mathbf{R} q_{ix_1} \\
\vdots \\
q_{ix_1x_2\cdots x_{r-1}} x_r \mathbf{L} q'_{ix_1x_2\cdots x_{r-1}} \\
q'_{ix_1x_2\cdots x_{r-1}} x_{r-1} \mathbf{L} q'_{ix_1x_2\cdots x_{r-2}} \\
\vdots \\
q'_{ix_1} x_1 \mathbf{L} q''_{ix_1'x_2'\cdots x_r'} \\
q''_{ix_1'x_2'\cdots x_r'} x_r' \mathbf{L} q''_{ix_1'x_2'\cdots x_{r-1}'} \\
\vdots \\
q''_{ix_1'x_2'} x_2' \mathbf{L} q_l
\end{array}
$$

Again, it is easily seen that if $w^1 \rightarrow y^1$ under operation of $q_i s_j \mathbf{L} q_l$, then $w^2 \rightarrow \cdots \rightarrow y^2$ under the listing above and $\varphi(d(w^1)) = d(w^2)$, and $\varphi(d(y^1)) = d(y^2)$.

By a similar construction, which is left to the reader, it can be shown that for every quadruple $q_i s_j \mathbf{R} q_l$ in $\mathbf{Z}_1$ one may obtain a desired corresponding set for $\mathbf{Z}_2$. The theorem then follows by a kind of induction on the length of a proof in $\mathbf{Z}_1$. Q.E.D.

On theoretical grounds, briefly reviewed above, it is possible to show that a Turing machine capable of imitating any other Turing machine exists. We now describe the construction of such a machine, letting the construction itself suffice to show that such a machine is indeed universal.

Definition 4.5.4. If w as i.d. contains $q_i s_j$ and if a machine $\mathbf{Z}$ is in state q_i, $q_i s_j$ is called the *active determinant* and the quadruple of which it forms a part is called the *active quadruple.*

A Universal machine $\mathcal{U}$ simulates another machine $\mathbf{Z}$ as follows. Certain regions on $\mathcal{U}$'s tape are reserved for quadruples of $\mathbf{Z}$, which are coded in binary words. Other regions are used for active determinants of $\mathbf{Z}$ (so $\mathcal{U}$ "knows" where it is in the simulation of $\mathbf{Z}$), and finally, still other regions are used to replicate the tape of $\mathbf{Z}$. It is assumed that any $\mathbf{Z}$ simulated is a two-symbol machine, which by Theorem 4.5.3 is certainly no restriction on the generality of the treatment.

$\mathcal{U}$ will be constructed so as to operate as follows:

1. The first active determinant of $\mathbf{Z}$ (that is, the determinant defined by the axiom), the entire set of quadruples, and the axiom $d(\mathscr{A})$ are coded on $\mathcal{U}$ tape.
2. $\mathcal{U}$ scans the first (next) active determinant and finds the corresponding active quadruple (which by Definition 4.1.7 is unique).

3. $\mathscr{U}$ executes the **Z** operation specified by the quadruple found in Step 2.

4. $\mathscr{U}$ forms the next active determinant from the new state, determined by the quadruple found in Step 2, and the symbol scanned, as determined by Step 3.

We design $\mathscr{U}$ with operations 0, 1, **R**, **L**; the representation of quadruples of **Z** is as follows:

Determinants (Note q_i0 and q_i1 are the only possible forms.)

$$q_i0 \leftrightarrow 1^{3i+1}$$
$$q_i1 \leftrightarrow 1^{3i+2}$$

Operations

$$\text{Print } 0 \leftrightarrow 0$$
$$\text{Print } 1 \leftrightarrow 00$$
$$\text{Move } \mathbf{R} \leftrightarrow 000$$
$$\text{Move } \mathbf{L} \leftrightarrow 0000$$

Next State

$$q_l \leftrightarrow 1^{3l}$$

An arbitrary number of 0's may be used to separate quadruples when written on tape, with the obvious convention that $3l$ 1's on tape is always the 4th member of a quadruple, and any subsequent string of 0's is part of no quadruple.

EXAMPLE 2. The representation on $\mathscr{U}$ of the quadruples $q_2 0\,\mathbf{R}\,q_3$, $q_3 10 q_4$ is

$$1111111000111111111\cdots01111111111101111111111111$$

The layout of symbols on the $\mathscr{U}$ tape is in groups of seven cells as in the Fig. 4.5.1. The tape to the left of E_1 is not used, but it is infinite to the right (that is, for any q_i and s_j, $Pq_is_j\#R \to Ps_jq_l0\#R$, $B = 0$).

The cells E are used to mark the end of the tape. E_1 contains 1, the other E's hold 0's, and none of the E's are ever overprinted. $\mathscr{U}$ in general finds E_1 by moving to the right to the nearest E_i, then moving left in jumps of seven cells until it scans 1 (at E_1). It is convenient to represent such jumps by the special notational conventions (1) to (4) introduced just after Example 3 in Section 4.1.

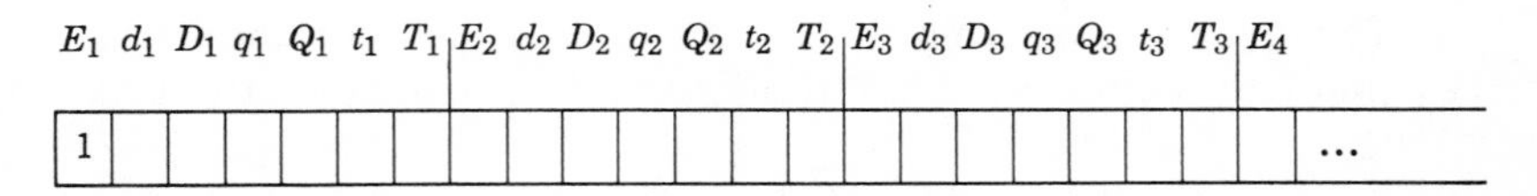

Fig. 4.5.1

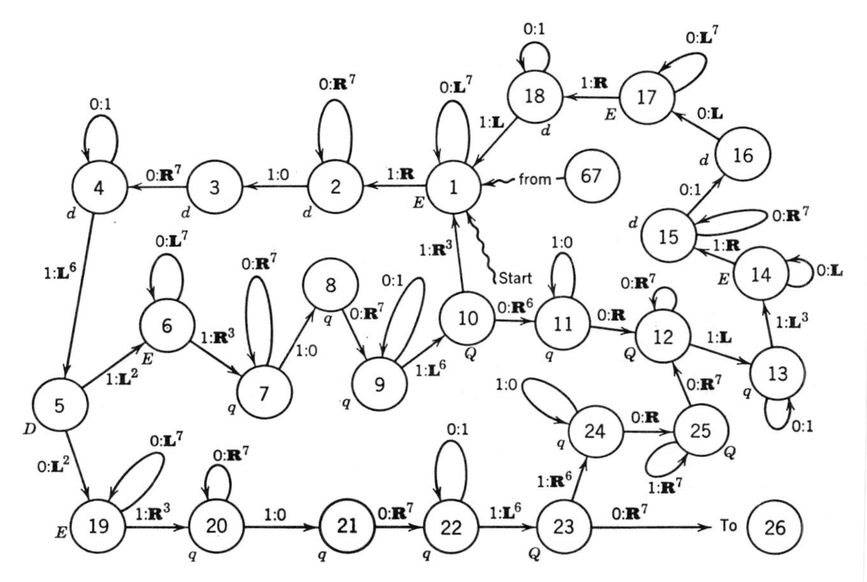

Fig. 4.5.2 Algorithm Step I: Given active determinant, find active quadruple.

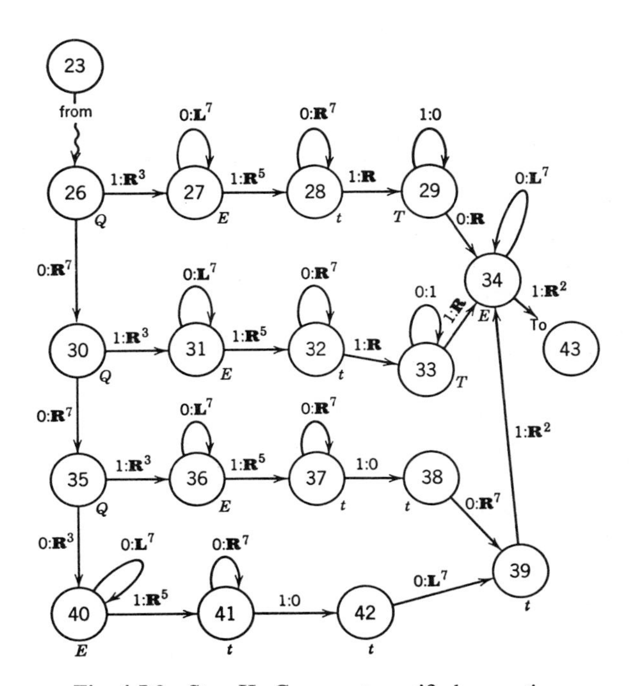

Fig. 4.5.3 Step II: Carry out specified operation.

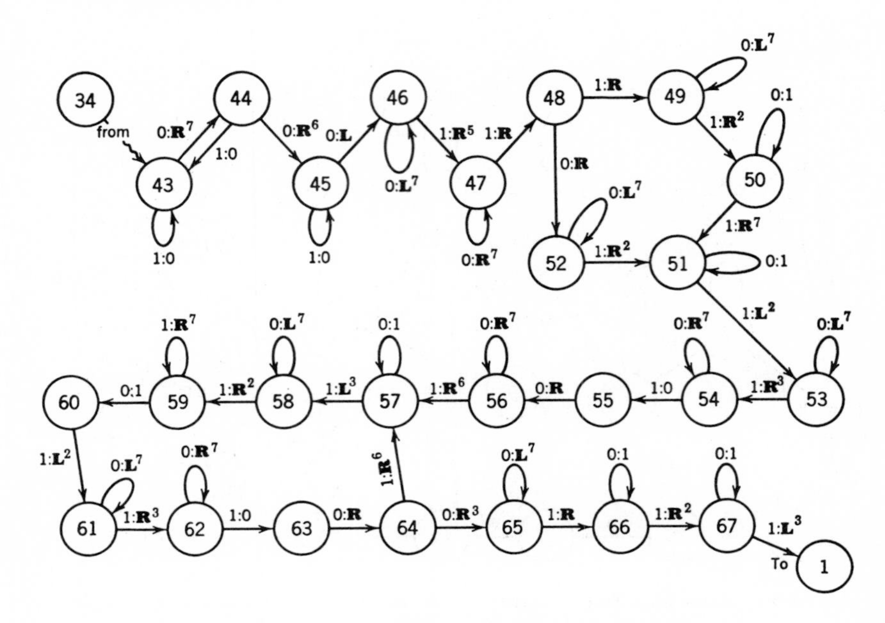

Fig. 4.5.4 Step III: Form next active determinant.

The D cells of the $\mathscr{U}$ tape contain the active determinant of **Z**. The Q cells contain the entire quadruple list defining **Z**. The T cells correspond to the tape on **Z**.

The letters d, q, and t are used by $\mathscr{U}$ to mark which D, Q, and T cells respectively of **Z** are next to be "considered" by $\mathscr{U}$. For example, a 1 in t_3 means that **Z** is scanning T_3. Only a single d, a single q, and a single t are marked with a 1 for any i.d.

$\mathscr{U}$ starts in q_1 scanning E_1. The quadruple list for **Z** is printed on the Q squares beginning with Q_1, and q_1 is marked.

The first active determinant is printed on D_1, D_2, etc., and d_1 is marked. The T cells are marked with the initial tape expression of **Z** and t_1 is marked.

Finally $\mathscr{U}$ is defined by the transition diagram appearing in Figs. 4.5.2, 4.5.3, and 4.5.4.

EXERCISES 4.5

1. Is any one–one map of an alphabet into another alphabet a useful code? Explain.

2. Two Turing machines are given by the following lists of quadruples:

$\mathbf{Z}_1$	$\mathbf{Z}_2$
$q_1 0 \mathbf{R} q_1$	$q_1 a a q_2$
$q_1 1 \mathbf{R} q_2$	$q_1 b \mathbf{R} q_1$
$q_2 0 \mathbf{R} q_2$	$q_2 b \mathbf{L} q_2$
$q_2 1 \mathbf{R} q_3$	$q_2 a \mathbf{R} q_3$
$q_3 0 \mathbf{R} q_3$	$q_3 b \mathbf{R} q_3$
$q_3 1 0 q_4$	$q_3 a \mathbf{R} q_4$
$q_4 0 \mathbf{R} q_1$	$q_4 b \mathbf{R} q_4$
	$q_4 a b q_5$
	$q_5 a \mathbf{L} q_5$
	$q_5 b \mathbf{R} q_1$

Show that these two Turing machines are equivalent according to Definition 4.5.2.

3. Two Turing machines are weakly equivalent if they compute the same class of recursive functions. Construct an example using two machines (adders, for example) which are weakly equivalent but not equivalent.

4. Complete the proof of the reducibility of Turing machines to binary machines.

5. Is the "code" for representing quadruples of a machine Z on the Universal machine a code in our technical sense? Is the one–one function for operation "coding"

Print $0 \leftrightarrow 0$
Print $1 \leftrightarrow 00$
Move $\mathbf{R} \leftrightarrow 000$
Move $\mathbf{L} \leftrightarrow 0000$

a code?

6. "Program" the universal machine for adding 1 to an integer and follow through the computation. Is this machine limited to the computation of 1-ary functions? Explain.

4.6 POST MACHINES

A strikingly simple mode of an infinite transducer was suggested by the logician Emil Post.[17] We will discuss his machines briefly, leaving it to the student (Exercise 1) to explicitly formulate the model as a semi-thue system and to verify that the concepts of proof, terminal proof, etc., are precisely those of, and have the same properties as, Turing machines.

Definition 4.6.1. Given a sequence of symbols $q_1, q_2, \ldots$; 0, 1; $\mathbf{R}$, $\mathbf{L}$; a pair is any expression of one of the forms $q_i 0$, $q_i 1$, $q_i \mathbf{R}$, $q_i \mathbf{L}$, $q_i(x)$, where x is a nonnegative integer. $0 = B$ (blank).

[17] Actually, our exposition is based more directly on the work of Hao Wang and of C. Y. Lee.

Definition 4.6.2. A *Post machine* is an ordered set of n pairs $q_1y_1, q_2y_2, \ldots, q_ny_n$, where yi is either 0, 1, **R**, **L**, or (x) and the range of x is $\{1, 2, \ldots, n\}$.

We suppose that Post machines, like Turing machines, are endowed with infinite two-way tape. Then, from the point of view of one watching the tape, the behavior of a Post machine is very much like that of a Turing machine. In fact, in Theorem 4.6.4 it is proved that the two kinds of machine are equivalent.

The action of Post machines is to be explained as follows. Every machine begins in state q_1; then in state q_k, it either prints a 0 or a 1 (q_k0 or q_k1), or moves **R** or **L** one cell ($q_k\mathbf{R}$ or $q_k\mathbf{L}$), and then goes to state q_{k+1}; or it jumps to state q_r if it scans a 1 ($q_k(r)$), or proceeds to q_{k+1} otherwise.

EXAMPLE 1. The following machine starts at the right of a tape and moves left, complementing symbols:

W:		
	$q_1(7)$	q_70
	q_21	$q_8\mathbf{L}$
	$q_3\mathbf{L}$	$q_9(7)$
	$q_4(7)$	$q_{10}1$
	q_51	$q_{11}(2)$
	$q_6(2)$	

An equivalent Turing machine (which starts at the left) is:

$$q_101q_2 \qquad q_21\,\mathbf{R}\,q_1 \qquad q_110q_2 \qquad q_20\,\mathbf{R}\,q_1$$

Definition 4.6.3. A *flow-chart* of a Post machine **W** is a labeled, directed, connected linear graph where each node is labeled with a pair of **W** and each directed branch connects a node labeled q_i with one labeled q_{i+1}, unless q_i calls for a jump to q_r, in which case q_i is connected by a branch with q_r.

The chart associated with **W** of the foregoing example is Fig. 4.6.1.

Theorem 4.6.4. (*a*) For every Post machine there exists a simulating[18] Turing machine **Z**; (*b*) for every Turing machine **Z** there exists a simulating Post machine **W**.

Proof of (*a*). Make a pair of Turing machine quadruples q_i1sq_{i+1}, q_i0sq_{i+1} correspond to each pair q_is of **W**; make two quadruples $q_is\,\mathbf{R}\,q_{i+1}$ $s = 0, 1$ or $q_is\,\mathbf{L}\,q_{i+1}, s = 0, 1$ correspond to each pair $q_i\mathbf{R}$ or $q_i\mathbf{L}$; make the pair of quadruples q_i00q_{i+1} and q_i11q_x correspond to each pair $q_i(x)$. Now verify each of the cases developed in Exercise 1 below.

The proof of part (*b*) depends on the following definitions and lemma.

[18] We have in mind Definition 4.5.2 for equivalence and simulation.

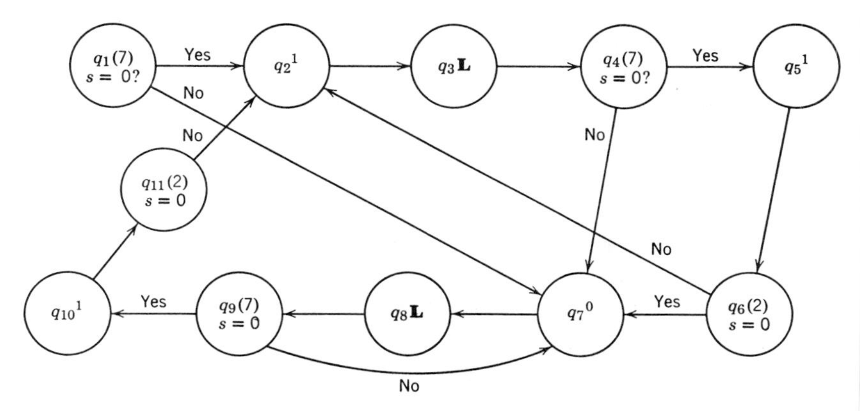

Fig. 4.6.1

Definition 4.6.5. Let $\mathbf{M}$ be either $\mathbf{R}$ or $\mathbf{L}$. By the *successor* set of a quadruple $q_is_js_kq_l \in \mathbf{Z}$, we mean the submachine of $\mathbf{Z}$ whose elements are $q_is_js_kq_l$, $q_ls_ks_{k'}q_{l'}$, $q_{l'}s_{k'}s_{k''}q_{l''}, \ldots, q_{l^{n-1}}s_{k^{n-1}}\mathbf{M}q_{l^n}$ for some $\mathbf{M}$.

Remark 4.6.6. From the definition, it is evident that for every successor set $\mathbf{Z}'$ determined by $q_is_js_kq_l$ there exists an equivalent $\mathbf{Z}''$ containing two quadruples, $q_is_js_{k^{n-1}}q_{l^{n-1}}$ and $q_{l^{n-1}}s_{k^{n-1}}\mathbf{M}q_{l^n}$. Following is an alternative definition of Turing machines in terms of quintuples.[19]

Definition 4.6.7. A *Turing machine* is a finite set of quintuples such that no two distinct quintuples have the same determinant; a determinant is the left-hand pair of a quintuple and the quintuples are expressions of one of the two forms:

$$q_is_js_k \, \mathbf{R} \, q_l \qquad q_is_js_k \, \mathbf{L} \, q_l$$

The first quintuple, for example, is interpreted to mean that if a machine is in state q_i scanning s_j, it prints s_k, moves right, and goes into state q_l. All of the definitions of theorems, computations, etc., are the same as for the quadruple formulation with the exception of slight changes in the basic definition of Turing machines as semi-thue systems, which we omit.

Lemma 4.6.8. For every quadruple Turing machine there exists an equivalent quintuple Turing machine.

Proof. First, consider quadruples of the form $q_is_j \, \mathbf{R} \, q_l$ and $q_is_j \, \mathbf{L} \, q_l$ which are not elements of any successor set. Determination of these quadruples is clearly an effective procedure, since a Turing machine is a finite set of quadruples. Replace these by $q_is_js_j \, \mathbf{R} \, q_l$ and $q_is_js_j \, \mathbf{L} \, q_l$, respectively. Next, for every successor set of quadruples construct, by

[19] This is essentially the original formulation of Turing.

Remark 4.6.6 a simpler equivalent set. Then, for each pair $q_i s_j s_{k^{n-1}} q_{l^{n-1}}$, $q_{l^{n-1}} s_{k^{n-1}} \mathbf{M} q_{l^n}$ so constructed make correspond the quintuple $q_i s_j s_{k^{n-1}} \mathbf{M} q_{l^n}$. If $q_i s_j s_k q_l$ does not determine a successor set, make correspond the quintuples $q_i s_j s_k$ **R** q_i and $q_i ss$ **L** q_j for all $s \in S$. Clearly, this resulting set of quintuples is equivalent to the original machine. If $K(S)$ (S the alphabet) of the resulting quintuple Turing machine is equal to n, then there must be, for our projected construction, n quintuples $q_i s_j s_k \mathbf{M} q_l$ for each i with $j = 1, \ldots, n$. To ensure this requirement, if $q_i s_j$, any i, j, is undefined for the given quadruple machine **Z**, then add $q_i s_j s_j$ **R** q_m, where q_m is *not* an element of the auxiliaries of **Z**, to the collection of quintuples.

EXAMPLE 2. Let $\mathbf{Z} = \{q_1 0 \,\mathbf{R}\, q_2, q_2 1 \,\mathbf{L}\, q_1\}$. Then the quintuple machine

$$\mathbf{C} = \{q_1 00 \,\mathbf{R}\, q_2, q_1 11 \,\mathbf{R}\, q_3, q_2 11 \,\mathbf{L}\, q_1, q_2 00 \,\mathbf{R}\, q_3\}$$

We may now complete the proof of part (*b*) of Theorem 4.6.4.

Let **Z** be a Turing machine. By Theorem 4.5.3, there is a simulating machine **Z**′ with an alphabet of two symbols 0 and 1. By the preceding lemma there is a machine **C** in quintuple formulation on an alphabet consisting of 0 and 1 equivalent to **Z**′ and hence which simulates **Z**.

Relabel the states of **C** such that the index of the auxiliary of the initial i.d. is 1. Continue to call this machine **C**. We now proceed to show how a Post machine **W** may be constructed equivalent to **C**.

Recall that **W** will be an ordered list (ordered on the indices of the q symbols) of pairs. Let Q be the states of **C**. The first pair of **W** is $Q_1(7)$. We next arrange that each ordered pair of quintuples $q_i 0 s \,\mathbf{M}\, q_l$ and $q_i 1 s' \,\mathbf{M}'\, q_l'$ corresponds to ten pairs of **W** (where s, s', **M**, **M**′ are 0 or 1, 0 or 1, **R** or **L**, **R** or **L**, respectively) as below. First, we have

$$q_i \to Q_{10(i-1)+2+j} \qquad j = 0, \ldots, 9 \tag{1}$$

For example, corresponding to q_4 we have $Q_{32}, Q_{33}, \ldots, Q_{41}$. Second, completing the construction of pairs, where $j = x \to y$ means if $j = x$ then the second member of the pair is y:

$$\begin{aligned}
j &= 0 \to s \\
j &= 1 \to \mathbf{M} \\
j &= 2 \to (10(l-1)+7) \\
j &= 3 \to 1 \\
j &= 4 \to (10(l-1)+2) \\
j &= 5 \to s' \\
j &= 6 \to \mathbf{M}' \\
j &= 7 \to (10(l'-1)+7) \\
j &= 8 \to 1 \\
j &= 9 \to (10(l'-1)+2)
\end{aligned}$$

For example, corresponding to $q_4 01\,\mathbf{R}\,q_5$, $q_4 11\,\mathbf{L}\,q_4$ we have the Post machine list of pairs:

$Q_{32}1$	$Q_{37}1$
$Q_{33}\mathbf{R}$	$Q_{38}\mathbf{L}$
$Q_{34}(47)$	$Q_{39}(37)$
$Q_{35}1$	$Q_{40}1$
$Q_{36}(42)$	$Q_{41}(32)$

This completes the construction.

Now consider the quintuple $q_i 0s\,\mathbf{M}\,q_l$. If $i = 1$, then the **W** machine list is:

$Q_1(7)$	$Q_4(10(l-1)+7)$
$Q_2 s$	$Q_5 1$
$Q_3\mathbf{M}$	$Q_6(10(l-1)+2)$

Since **C** is, by the given quintuple, scanning a 0 in state q_1, **W** is also scanning a 0. So $Q_1(7)$ is followed by print s, and move **M**. Next **C** goes into state q_l. By the preceding correspondence (1) this should lead to

$$Q_{10(l-1)+2}$$

if **C** scans 0 in q_l, or $Q_{10(l-1)+7}$ if **C** scans 1 in q_l. But these are precisely the operations specified for states Q_6 and Q_4, respectively. Similarly, the result holds for all quintuples of **C**. Q.E.D.

EXERCISES 4.6

1. Define a Post machine as a semi-thue system.

2. Explain how a proof may terminate w.r.t. a Post machine. (*Hint*: Compare formal programs, Section 3.2.) In view of this explanation, interpret our requirements concerning quintuple construction from quadruples for undefined quadruples.

3. Design a Post machine for addition, using the Davis tally convention (cf. Footnote 10, Section 4.3). First, design a Turing machine in quadruple form, then proceed as in the proof of Lemma 4.6.8.

4. Is it possible to define Post-like machines for an alphabet with *more* than two symbols?

5. Provide a reasonable definition for isomorphism of two Turing machines $\mathbf{Z}_1$ and $\mathbf{Z}_2$, and give necessary and sufficient conditions for relabeling auxiliaries so as to "preserve" a Turing machine behavior. (*Hint*: Consider a Turing machine, say in quadruple form, to consist of two mappings $f\colon S \times Q \to Q$ and $g\colon S \times Q \to S \cup \{\mathbf{R}, \mathbf{L}\}$. Both machines are to have the same pure alphabet S. The isomorphism is then to be a one–one mapping on $Q_{\mathbf{Z}_1}$ onto $Q_{\mathbf{Z}_2}$).

6. $\mathbf{Z}_1$ and $\mathbf{Z}_2$ are *strongly equivalent* if every proof in one system is identical to a proof in the other, for the same axiom instances, except possibly for indices on the auxiliary symbols. In other words, the deleted words $d(w)$ yield identical proof sequences. Are such machines isomorphic? If so, give a proof. If not, give a counterexample.

4.7 HISTORICAL AND BIBLIOGRAPHICAL REMARKS

The Turing machine was invented by A. M. Turing [1936] as a device for proving the unsolvability of certain problems in logic. Interest in such machines as devices comparable to actual digital computers is recent, probably not earlier than 1945. In fact, if a stored-program computer has available an infinite amount of tape, it is equivalent to a Universal machine; and hence under this assumption, all the results as to computable classes of functions and unsolvability problems apply to actual machines. Our proof of the computability of recursive functions is similar to one in Shepherdson and Sturgis [1964], but was developed independently by the author. The discussion of recursively enumerable predicates and unsolvability problems is largely a survey of the first few chapters of Davis [1958]. The proof of the sufficiency of binary Turing machines is Shannon's [1956]. The formulation of Post machines [1936] is due to C. Y. Lee [1960], and the proof of equivalence between Turing machines in our sense and Post machines is an adaptation of a similar one by Lee. Post machines further limited so as not to be able to erase (that is, print 0) were studied by H. Wang [1957], who showed that even such a severely limited computer can calculate the partial recursive functions. Wang's machine is a model of a computer with punched paper tape. The Universal Turing machine used was developed at the Lincoln Laboratories of M.I.T. by Clark [1956].

CHAPTER 5

Finite Transducers

5.0 Introduction. With the exception of encoding, decoding, and switching networks, the simplest automaton with input and output is the sequential machine or finite transducer. Although we will postpone discussion of the capabilities of these machines until Chapter 7, it is convenient to think of them as limited Turing machines: finite transducers move only right (or left) w.r.t. tape, and they operate by scanning a symbol, overprinting, moving right, etc. Usually, however, one thinks of a transducer as having sequences of symbols injected into it and as emitting sequences which are functions of the input sequence and the memory structure of the machine.

At any rate, we return to the Turing machine analogy: by omitting, say, a move left we deprive the machine of using its past input or output and hence limit its memory. So a finite transducer has just that memory provided by its finite set of internal states. By this seemingly minor change in operability, we descend from machines that can compute any recursive function to machines that can essentially only *add*; as far as arithmetic is concerned multiplication is beyond their range.

Finite transducers are simple enough to be amenable to fairly sophisticated mathematical treatment. On the other hand, the infinite transducers of Chapter 4 are not—all of the problems there are combinatorial in character and none of them, at the present state of development of the science, seem to benefit from the use of modern algebra.

If we follow the suggestion above for viewing them as unidirectional Turing machines, and think of sequential machines as sets of quadruples, then there are no quadruples included of the form $q_i s_j \mathbf{L} q_l$ provided the machines move right only. If we adopt the convention that any sequential machine accepts its input symbols in sequence, always moving right w.r.t. the sequence, accepting input to the right and ejecting output to the left, we may think of it as a set of quadruples of the form $q_i s_j s_k q_l$. Since no two quadruples by Definition 4.1.7 have the same determinant $q_i s_j$, it follows that such a collection is simply a way of writing a *pair of functions*. In fact, the quadruple relates to each pair q_is_j a symbol s_k and an auxiliary q_l, thus determining two functions on (a subset of) $Q \times S$ with co-domain O and Q.[1,2] These functions are the output and next state or transition functions, respectively.

The output function is a somewhat complicated object since its co-domain need not be all (or, according to Footnote 1, even a part) of S. Nevertheless, properties of a machine which depend on the output such as machine behavior and equivalence are still more tractable than is the case with Turing machines. We are able to form equivalence classes of states, in terms of equal output given any input, and then use elementary mathematical concepts about equivalence relations together with some arithmetic and logic to prove the existence and uniqueness of minimal machines. We can also obtain a decision procedure for equivalence. All of this is a slight gain in sophistication over the methods at hand for dealing with Turing machines. The development of these ideas is taken up in Sections 5.1 and 5.2 with some additional very basic material given in Section 5.3.

Moreover, in dealing with structural properties and classes of sequential machines we may attend to the transition function only. If the transition function is "extended" to sequences—that is, if we widen its domain to S^*—then from the function $M: Q \times S^* \to Q$ so obtained, we may derive for each $x \in S^*$ a function $\varphi_x: Q \to Q$. The set of these functions constitutes a semigroup and, for certain transducers, a group. It turns out that many interesting structural properties of transducers (or of the detectors of Chapter 7) may be studied algebraically. Alternatively, the semigroup of an automaton alluded to previously may be viewed as a system of equivalence classes (called a quotient semigroup) of elements of S^* determined by a certain relation: x is equivalent to y if it sends the automaton into the same target state from the state q as y does. The quotient semigroup and the semigroup of functions φ are isomorphic, and so the algebraic approach may be made in at least two ways. A large amount of research is going into the study of automata from the semigroup point of view; we shall treat the most elementary aspects in Section 5.4 where, among other things, we give an algorithm for determining the semigroups.

A different approach to structure, due to Hartmanis, hinges upon *lattices of partitions* of transducer states. In terms of systems of partitions of states of a certain special kind (to be introduced below) it is possible to

[1] It is customary to think of the automaton's alphabet as having an input part S and a possibly overlapping output part O. If so, as above, one function takes $Q \times S$ into O.

[2] Of course, the same can be done with Turing machines except the one co-domain would be $S \cup \{L, R\}$ rather than O above. However, in this case, the trivial change in viewpoint does not lead anywhere.

study the structure of transducers as made up of *submachines* connected in parallel, cascade, or having certain loop or cycle properties. Such questions are considered in Section 5.5 after a review of some of the elementary facts about lattices beyond those already mentioned in Section 1.3.

In Section 5.6 we shall return to the use of semigroups in studying structure and will derive an important theorem due to Krohn and Rhodes.

5.1 FINITE TRANSDUCERS AND ASSOCIATED SYSTEMS

We shall use the same alphabet and notations as in Definition 4.1.1.

Definition 5.1.1. A *finite transducer* or *sequential machine* is a semi-thue System $\mathbf{T} = \langle A, \mathscr{B}, \mathscr{A}, \mathscr{P}\rangle$, where the alphabet A consists of two not necessarily disjoint subalphabets S and O and a subset of auxiliaries disjoint from S and O. As in the case of Turing machines we use

$$S = \{s_0, s_1, \ldots, s_m, \#\} \qquad Q = \{q_0, q_1, \ldots, q_n\}$$

and also

$$O = \{o_0, o_1, \ldots, o_r\}$$

The notation S^* for the words on $S - \{\#\}$, x, y, etc., as any words in S^*, s, q, s', q', etc., for arbitrary elements of A, is the same as before. Also P, R range over $\mathscr{B}$ in the listing of productions.

The axiom $\mathscr{A}$ is of the form $q_i x\#$, $x \neq \Lambda$.

$\mathscr{P}$ is a set of rules of the following types:

1. (*a*) $Pq_i s_j R \to P o_k q_l R$
   (*b*) $Pq_i\# \to P$

2. There is exactly one production of type *a* for each pair $q_i s_j \in Q \times (S - \{\#\})$ and one of type *b* for each q_i.

3. Nothing is a production unless its being so follows from 1 and 2.

The definitions of proof, theorem, and terminal theorem are the same as Definitions 3.3.3, 3.3.5, and 3.3.7. A finite transducer is obviously *monogenic* or *deterministic*.

Corollary 5.1.2. Every terminal theorem of a finite transducer is of the form P, where P is a word on O.

Proof is trivial.

EXAMPLE 1. The student should review at this point the example at the end of Section 3.0.

EXAMPLE 2. $S = \{2, 3, 4, 5\}$, $O = \{0, 1\}$, $Q = \{q_0, q_1\}$. The single axiom is of the form $q_0 x 2\#$. The productions are the ten that follow.

(i)	$Pq_02R \to P0q_0R$	(vi)	$Pq_13R \to P0q_1R$
(ii)	$Pq_03R \to P1q_0R$	(vii)	$Pq_14R \to P0q_1R$
(iii)	$Pq_04R \to P1q_0R$	(viii)	$Pq_15R \to P1q_1R$
(iv)	$Pq_05R \to P0q_1R$	(ix)	$Pq_0\# \to P$
(v)	$Pq_12R \to P1q_0R$	(x)	$Pq_1\# \to P$

If we interpret 2 to mean the pair (0, 0), 3 the pair (0, 1), 4 the pair (1, 0), and 5 the pair (1, 1), then this transducer can be seen to be a full serial binary adder. Suppose we have the summands

$$\begin{array}{c} 01101 \\ 11001 \end{array}$$

By the foregoing interpretation this is the word of pairs

$$(0, 1)(1, 1)(1, 0)(0, 0)(1, 1) = 35425$$

Since the convention in writing numerals is to put the least significant digit (the beginning of a word) to the right, in order to accommodate the convention that our machines move right, we write 52453. The axiom is, then, $q_0524532\#$. It is now easy to verify that the terminal theorem is 011001, which according to numeralwise conventions is 100110.

From now on we will call any x an *input word*, any s an *input*, and any word on the alphabet O an *output word*. Each o is an *output*. Each auxiliary symbol is an *internal state*.

Definition 5.1.3. Given a finite transducer **T**, an *associated transducer system*, also labeled **T**, is a quintuple $\langle S, Q, M, N, O\rangle$, where S, Q, and O are finite nonempty alphabets as in the semi-thue formulation and M and N are functions constructed as follows: $M\colon Q \times S \to Q$, where $M(q_i, s_j) = q_l$ iff there exists a production $Pq_is_jR \to Po_kq_lR$, for some o_k, in **T**; $N\colon Q \times S \to O$, where $N(q_i, s_j) = o_k$ iff there exists a production $Pq_is_jR \to Po_kq_lR$, for some q_l in **T**.

M is called the *next state* or transition function and N is the *output* function.

EXAMPLE 3. The M and N functions derived from the productions for Example 2 are given in Table 5.1.1.

TABLE 5.1.1

q \ s	M: 2	M: 3	M: 4	M: 5	N: 2	N: 3	N: 4	N: 5
q_0	q_0	q_0	q_0	q_1	0	1	1	0
q_1	q_0	q_1	q_1	q_1	1	0	0	1

Any transducer can be viewed essentially as a device for processing input words and ejecting output words. Since the input is processed symbol by symbol, where each symbol read is "forgotten," it is natural to think of a transducer as the realization of a function of sequences. That is to say, if O^* is the set of words on O, we think of transducers as embodying the function $G\colon S^* \to O^*$. This is one reason for now extending M and N to sequences.

Definition 5.1.4. For all x and s

$$\begin{aligned}
&(a)\quad M(q_i, xs_j) = M(M(q_i, x), s_j)\\
&(b)\quad N(q_i, xs_j) = N(M(q_i, x), s_j)\\
&(c)\quad G(q_i, s_{i_1}s_{i_2}\cdots s_{i_k})\\
&\qquad = N(q_i, s_{i_1})N(q_i, s_{i_1}s_{i_2})\cdots N(q_i, s_{i_1}s_{i_2}\cdots s_{i_k}) \qquad \text{for } k \geqslant 1
\end{aligned}$$

Thus M and N as extended are functions of sequences into Q and O respectively. The G function is from words to words. When several transducers are being discussed, we will use the notation $\mathbf{T}_a$, $\mathbf{T}_b$, M_a, M_b, etc.

EXAMPLE 4. Suppose M and N are functions associated with a transducer $\mathbf{T}$ as in Table 5.1.2.

TABLE 5.1.2

q \ s	M: s_0	M: s_1	M: s_2	N: s_0	N: s_1	N: s_2
q_0	q_1	q_0	q_1	o_0	o_1	o_1
q_1	q_1	q_1	q_1	o_1	o_0	o_0

Let $x = s_1s_0s_0s_1s_2$. Computing the output function G starting in state q_0, we have:

$$\begin{aligned}
G(q_0, s_1s_0s_0s_1s_2) &= N(q_0, s_1)N(q_0, s_1s_0)N(q_0, s_1s_0s_0)\\
&\quad\ N(q_0, s_1s_0s_0s_1)N(q_0, s_1s_0s_0s_1s_2)\\
&= N(q_0, s_1)N(M(q_0, s_1), s_0)N(M(q_0, s_1s_0), s_0)\\
&\quad\ N(M(q_0, s_1s_0s_0), s_1)N(M(q_0, s_1s_0s_0s_1), s_2)\\
&= N(q_0, s_1)N(M(q_0, s_1), s_0)N(M(M(q_0, s_1), s_0), s_0)\\
&\quad\ N(M(M(M(q_0, s_1), s_0), s_0), s_1)\\
&\quad\ N(M(M(M(M(q_0, s_1), s_0), s_0), s_1), s_2)\\
&= o_1o_0o_1o_0o_0
\end{aligned}$$

Notice that it is possible for $N(q_i, x) = N(q_i, y)$, $x, y \in S^* - \{\Lambda\}$, whereas $G(q_i, x) \neq G(q_i, y)$. In this example,

$$N(q_0, s_0s_0) = o_1 = N(q_0, s_2s_0)$$

whereas $G(q_0, s_0s_0) = o_0o_1$, and $G(q_0, s_2s_0) = o_1o_1$; that is, the outputs at the end of an input sequence can be the same without the output sequences being the same.[3]

Definition 5.1.5. The *transition diagram* of a transducer **T** is a directed linear graph (see Definition 4.1.8) in which there is a node for every symbol Q; each node is labeled by the symbol with which it is associated; for each ordered pair (q_i, q_l) such that $Pq_is_jR \rightarrow Po_kq_lR$ there is a directed branch from q_i to q_l, and each branch so determined is labeled by the pair (s_j, o_k).

Thus the transition diagram for the adder of Example 2 is shown in Fig. 5.1.1.

Definition 5.1.6. Given two transducer systems $\mathbf{T}_a = \langle S, Q_a, M_a, N_a, O\rangle$ and $\mathbf{T}_b = \langle S, Q_b, M_b, N_b, O\rangle$, not necessarily different. Two states $q \in Q_a$ and $q' \in Q_b$ are *equivalent*, written $q \equiv q'$, iff $N_a(q, x) = N_b(q', x)$ for every word x. Two states are equivalent iff they produce the same output for every input word.

We will now state and prove three theorems which are basic to the whole study of the structural properties of finite transducers.

Theorem 5.1.7. For any q, x, y,

$$M(q, xy) = M(M(q, x), y) \qquad \text{and} \qquad N(q, xy) = N(M(q, x), y)$$

Proof. By induction on the length of y, $l(y)$, let $y = s$; then

$$M(q, xs) = M(M(q, x), s)$$

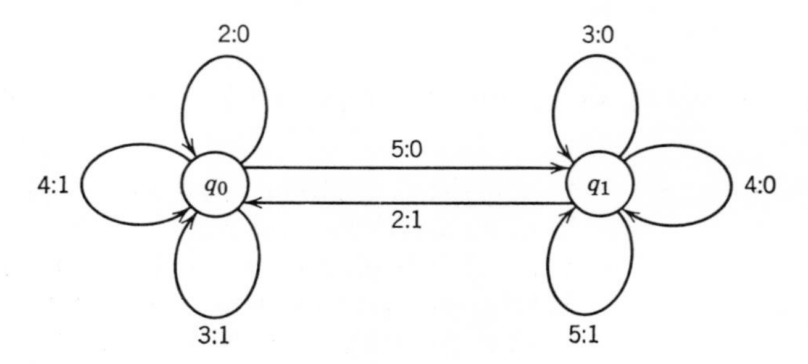

Fig. 5.1.1

[3] One might ask why we bother about the N function at all since we are really interested in *word* to *word* mappings. An answer is that if $N(q_i, x) = N(q_i, y)$ for every x and y, then G and N are equivalent functions in a sense explained in Theorem 5.1.9. Since most uses of N arise in this way and since N is easier to manipulate, we find it useful. See Exercise 2 below for another possible pair of functions like M and G (Ginsburg [1962]).

by Definition 5.1.4*a*. The induction hypothesis is

$$M(q, xy) = M(M(q, x), y)$$

Then we have

$$M(q, xys) = M(M(q, xy), s)$$

by the definition again; whereas

$$\begin{aligned} M(M(q, xy), s) &= M(M(M(q, x), y), s) \\ &= M(M(q, x), ys) \end{aligned}$$

using the induction hypothesis and the definition once more. The second part is to be proved in the Exercises. Q.E.D.

Theorem 5.1.8. If $q_i \equiv q_j$, then for every x, $M(q_i, x) \equiv M(q_j, x)$.

Proof. Since $q_i \equiv q_j$, $N(q_i, xy) = N(q_j, xy)$ for arbitrary word xy by Definition 5.1.6. Hence, by the theorem just proved, we have

$$N(M(q_i, x), y) = N(M(q_j, x), y)$$

for arbitrary y. Since there is nothing special about this y, the definition applies again, from which $M(q_i, x) \equiv M(q_j, x)$ follows. Q.E.D.

In later sections we will call an equivalence relation (such as $\equiv$) which is preserved under the transition function M a congruence relation [see Exercises 5.1(13) and Section 1.3].

Theorem 5.1.9. $G(q_i, x) = G(q_j, x)$ for every x iff $N(q_i, x) = N(q_j, x)$ for every x, that is, iff $q_i \equiv q_j$.

Proof. For the student.

EXERCISES 5.1

1. Verify the performance of the adder of Example 2 for the axiom $q_0 244532\#$.

2. Consider the two functions

$$(a) \quad \delta(q_i, s_{i_1} s_{i_2} \cdots s_{i_k}) = \delta(q_{i_k}, s_{i_k})$$

where

$$q_i = q_{i_1}, \quad q_{i_{j+1}} = \delta(q_{i_j}, s_{i_j}) \qquad \text{and} \quad \delta(q_i, s_j) = M(q_i, s_j)$$

$$(b) \quad \lambda(q_i, s_{i_1} s_{i_2} \cdots s_{i_k}) = \lambda(q_i, s_{i_1}) \lambda[\delta(q_i, s_{i_1}), s_{i_2} \cdots s_{i_k}]$$

where

$$\lambda(q, s) = N(q, s)$$

Prove that when M and N are extended to sequences $\delta = M$ and $\lambda = G$.

3. Write a definition of production types for finite transducers which, unlike our Definition 5.1.1, uses only productions of the forms used in 4.1.1 for the definition of Turing machines.

4. Given a function table for M and N for some **T**, provide an algorithm for deriving **T** as a semi-thue system.

5. Prove that if two rows (corresponding to states q_i and q_j) in a function table for a transducer are unlike in the N part, then $q_i \neq q_j$.

6. Prove that if rows q_i and q_j are the same in both the M and N parts, then $q_i \equiv q_j$. Is the converse true?

7. Construct a transition diagram for a transducer with pure alphabets $S = \{(0, 0), (0, 1), (1, 0), (1, 1)\}$ and $O = \{0, 1\}$ which performs binary proper subtraction. An input word $(1, 0)(1, 1)(0, 1)(0, 1)(1, 1)$ may as in Definition 3.1.1 be interpreted to mean (11001, 01111).

8. Using the result of Exercise 7, define the M and N functions for the subtractor.

9. Using the result of Exercise 8, formulate a semi-thue subtractor in a manner analogous to Example 2 and with the same symbolic conventions.

10. Complete the proof of Theorem 5.1.7.

11. Prove Theorem 5.1.9.

12. Do any other changes have to be made in Definition 5.1.1 in order to lift the restriction $x \neq \Lambda$ on the axiom?

13. Prove that $\equiv$ is an equivalence relation (see Section 1.1).

14. Prove that $G(q_i, x)$ is the output sequence of an associated transducer system given the input x iff $w = G(q_i, x)$ is a terminal theorem from the axiom $q_i x\#$.

5.2 REDUCED TRANSDUCERS

In this section, we prove the existence of transducers with the fewest possible states equivalent to a given one **T** and we also show how to test two transducers for equivalence. By the constructive nature of the treatment, we provide decision procedures for minimality and equivalence. The reader will probably be familiar with the discussion of reduced machines and the grouping of states into equivalence classes as related to the process of "merging" states.

Definition 5.2.1. Let $\mathbf{T}_a = \langle S, Q_a, M_a, N_a, O\rangle$ and $\mathbf{T}_b = \langle S, Q_b, M_b, N_b, O\rangle$ be transducers with the same pure input and output alphabets. $\mathbf{T}_a$ and $\mathbf{T}_b$ are *equivalent*, written $\mathbf{T}_a \equiv \mathbf{T}_b$, iff for all $q_a \in Q_a$ there exists a $q_b \in Q_b$ such that $q_a \equiv q_b$, and for all $q_b \in Q_b$ there exists $q_a \in Q_a$ such that $q_a \equiv q_b$.

Corollary 5.2.2. The relation $\equiv$ between two states or two transducers is an equivalence relation.

We have represented two equivalent transducers having the same alphabets but different auxiliaries in Tables 5.2.1*a* and 5.2.1*b*.

TABLE 5.2.1*a*

T

$q \backslash s$	M s_0	s_1	s_2	s_3	N s_0	s_1	s_2	s_3
q_0	q_0	q_3	q_2	q_4	o_0	o_1	o_0	o_1
q_1	q_1	q_2	q_3	q_4	o_1	o_0	o_1	o_0
q_2	q_2	q_3	q_2	q_4	o_0	o_1	o_0	o_1
q_3	q_4	q_1	q_1	q_1	o_0	o_1	o_1	o_1
q_4	q_4	q_3	q_0	q_2	o_0	o_1	o_0	o_1

TABLE 5.2.1*b*

T′

$q' \backslash s$	M' s_0	s_1	s_2	s_3	N' s_0	s_1	s_2	s_3
q_0'	q_0'	q_2'	q_0'	q_0'	o_0	o_1	o_0	o_1
q_1'	q_1'	q_0'	q_2'	q_0'	o_1	o_0	o_1	o_0
q_2'	q_0'	q_1'	q_1'	q_1'	o_0	o_1	o_1	o_1

We see that q_0' in $\mathbf{T}'$ is equivalent to q_0, q_2, and q_4 in $\mathbf{T}$; q_1' in $\mathbf{T}'$ is equivalent to q_1 in $\mathbf{T}$; and q_2' in $\mathbf{T}'$ to q_3 in $\mathbf{T}$. So the definition holds and $\mathbf{T} \equiv \mathbf{T}'$. Note that the N and N' parts of the tables are the same for the correspondence indicated above. But this is only a necessary condition for equivalence [see Exercise 5.1(6)].

As discussed in Section 1.1, every equivalence relation induces a partition on a set of objects, in this instance a family of equivalence classes of states. We denote, in conformity with the earlier notation, the set of states equivalent to q as $[q]$.

$$[q] = \{q' \mid q' \equiv q\}$$

Corollary 5.2.3a. $[q] = [q'] \Leftrightarrow q \equiv q'$.

Definition 5.2.3. A transducer $\mathbf{T}$ is *reduced* iff $q_i \equiv q_j$ implies $q_i = q_j$ for all states $q_i, q_j \in Q$.

That is, a reduced automaton of this kind has states which are equivalent to themselves and no others. There are no two distinct equivalent states in reduced machines.

Theorem 5.2.4. For each transducer $\mathbf{T}_a$ and set of states Q_a, there exists an equivalent transducer $\mathbf{T}_b$ with states Q_b such that $Q_b \subseteq Q_a$ and $\mathbf{T}_b$ is reduced.

Proof. First we show how to construct $\mathbf{T}_b$. Let Q_a be partitioned into a set of equivalence classes $[q]$. Next define the set function σ on the partition so that $\sigma[q] = q'$, where q' is an arbitrary fixed element of $[q]$, called a *representative*. Obviously $q' \equiv q$ in $\mathbf{T}_a$. Now Q_b, the set of states of $\mathbf{T}_b$, is the set of all such q':

$$Q_b = \{q' \mid (\exists q)(q \in Q_a \wedge \sigma[q] = q')\}$$

Let $S_b = S_a$ and $O_b = O_a$ be the input and output alphabets of $\mathbf{T}_b$, where, of course, S_a and O_a are the alphabets given with $\mathbf{T}_a$.

Completing the construction, the functions M_b and N_b are defined in terms of M_a and N_a, respectively, as follows:

$$M_b(q', s) = \sigma[M_a(q', s)] \tag{1a}$$

and

$$N_b(q', s) = N_a(q', s) \tag{1b}$$

This definition is meaningful since $q' \in Q_a$ as well as $q' \in Q_b$. Call this new transducer $\mathbf{T}_b = \langle S, Q_b, M_b, N_b, O \rangle$. By construction we already have proved $Q_b \subseteq Q_a$.

To show that $\mathbf{T}_a \equiv \mathbf{T}_b$ we must prove, according to Definitions 5.2.1 and 5.1.6, that for every $q \in Q_a$ there is a $q' \in Q_b$ such that $N_a(q, x) = N_b(q', x)$ for any word x, and conversely. However, we have no guarantee yet that the transition function M_b is *well-defined* (compare Section 1.3) in the sense that its value for any x is independent of the particular q' which we happen to have picked as representative of $[q]$. So we must prove

$$\sigma[M_a(q, x)] = M_b(q', x) \qquad \text{for all } x \tag{2}$$

If $x = s$, then since $q \equiv q'$ in $\mathbf{T}_a$, by Theorem 5.1.8 we have $M_a(q, s) \equiv M_a(q', s)$. From Corollary 5.2.3*a*, it follows that $[M_a(q, s)] = [M_a(q', s)]$ and hence that

$$\sigma[M_a(q, s)] = \sigma[M_a(q', s)] \tag{3}$$

Using (1) with (3),

$$\sigma[M_a(q, s)] = M_b(q', s) \tag{4}$$

To continue the induction, assume that

$$\sigma[M_a(q, x)] = M_b(q', x) \tag{5}$$

Then

$$\begin{aligned}\sigma[M_a(q, xs)] &= \sigma[M_a(M_a(q, x), s)] \\ &= \sigma[M_a(\sigma[M_a(q, x)], s)]\end{aligned}$$

using Theorem 5.1.8 and Corollary 5.2.3*a*; also

$$\sigma[M_a(q, xs)] = \sigma[M_a(M_b(q', x), s)]$$

by the induction hypothesis. Using (1a) and Theorem 5.1.7, this yields

$$\sigma[M_a(q, xs)] = M_b(q', xs) \tag{6}$$

This completes the induction and proves (2).

In order to show $\mathbf{T}_a \equiv \mathbf{T}_b$, we have at once

$$\begin{aligned} N_a(q, xs) &= N_a(M_a(q, x), s) \\ &= N_a(\sigma[M_a(q, x)], s) \\ &= N_b(\sigma[M_a(q, x)], s) \\ &= N_b(M_b(q', x), s) \\ &= N_b(q', xs) \end{aligned} \tag{7}$$

Thus for any $q \in Q_a$ there is $q' \in Q_b$, namely $q' = \sigma[q]$, such that (7) holds. Conversely, for any $q' \in Q_b$ there is a $q \in Q_a$, namely any one of the $[q]$ such that (7) holds. Thus $\mathbf{T}_a \equiv \mathbf{T}_b$.

Finally, we show $\mathbf{T}$ is reduced: for every $q_i', q_j' \in Q_b, q_i' \equiv q_j' \Rightarrow q_i' = q_j'$. Assume $q_i' \neq q_j'$. Then by definition, $\sigma[q_i] \neq \sigma[q_j], q_i, q_j \in Q_a$. Therefore, $[q_i] \neq [q_j]$ and by Corollary 5.2.3*a*, $q_i \not\equiv q_j$. But by (7), $q_i \equiv q_i'$ and $q_j \equiv q_j'$. Therefore, $q_i' \not\equiv q_j'$. Q.E.D.

Not only is $\mathbf{T}_b$ reduced, but it is unique—there is exactly *one* reduced equivalent form of a finite transducer, except possibly for relabeling of states. Thus $\mathbf{T}_b$ is unique to within an isomorphism, as we now establish.

Definition 5.2.5. Given transducers $\mathbf{T}_a$ and $\mathbf{T}_b$ with common alphabets S and O, a function $\varphi: Q_a \to Q_b$ is a *transducer homomorphism* iff

$$\varphi(M_a(q, s)) = M_b(\varphi(q), s)$$

and

$$N_a(q, s) = N_b(\varphi(q), s)$$

If φ is one–one and onto, it is an *isomorphism*, and $\mathbf{T}_a$ and $\mathbf{T}_b$ are *isomorphic*.

This definition says in effect that a homomorphic mapping of transducer states "preserves" the next state relation and yields identical outputs for the related machines.

Theorem 5.2.6. If $\mathbf{T}_a$ and $\mathbf{T}_b$ are reduced and $\mathbf{T}_a \equiv \mathbf{T}_b$, then they are isomorphic.

Proof. By hypothesis, for every $q \in Q_a$ there exists a $q' \in Q_b$ such that $q \equiv q'$. Since $\mathbf{T}_b$ is reduced, q' is unique. Conversely, for every $q' \in Q_b$ there is exactly one $q \in Q_a$. So the function defined by

$$\varphi(q) = q' \Leftrightarrow (\forall x)(N_a(q, x) = N_b(q', x))$$

is a one–one correspondence from Q_a onto Q_b. If $l(x) = 1$, $N_a(q, s) = N_b(\varphi(q), s)$, immediately.

It remains to show that

$$\varphi(M_a(q, s)) = M_b(\varphi(q), s) \tag{11}$$

as required by Definition 5.2.5.

Since $q \equiv q' \equiv \varphi(q)$, it follows by Theorem 5.1.8 that

$$M_a(q, s) \equiv M_b(\varphi(q), s)$$

and trivially,

$$M_a(q, s) \equiv \varphi(M_a(q, s))$$

Therefore

$$\varphi(M_a(q, s)) \equiv M_b(\varphi(q), s)$$

and, by the assumption that $\mathbf{T}_a$ and $\mathbf{T}_b$ are reduced, (11) follows. Q.E.D.

The remaining problem to be considered in this section is the solvability of the equivalence problem for two states and for two transducers. From the solution of this problem, it will also follow that there is an algorithm for determining reduced machines.

Definition 5.2.7. $q_i \equiv q_j(k)$ means that $N(q_i, x) = N(q_j, x)$ for all x such that $l(x) \leq k$.

In this case we also say that q_i and q_j are k-equivalent and that

$$[q_i]_k = \{q_j \mid q_i \equiv q_j(k)\}$$

is a k-equivalence class. Obviously, k-equivalence is an equivalence relation.

Corollary 5.2.8. If $q_i \equiv q_j(k + 1)$, then $q_i \equiv q_j(k)$; and if $q_i \equiv q_j$, then $q_i \equiv q_j(k)$.

Proof is immediate.

Theorem 5.2.9. Given $\mathbf{T}$ and Q, assume that for all $q_i, q_j \in Q$, $q_i \equiv q_j(1)$. It then follows that $q_i \equiv q_j$ for every q_i, q_j.

Proof. Use Theorem 5.1.7.

In the following discussion let us assume a fixed $\mathbf{T}$ and Q.

Definition 5.2.10. $[\equiv k]$ denotes the partition on Q determined by a k-equivalence relation. Equivalently,

$$[\equiv k] = \bigcup_{q \in Q} \{[q]_k\}$$

REMARK. Evidently, $[\equiv k] = [\equiv h]$ is true iff $q_i \equiv q_j(k)$ iff $q_i \equiv q_j(h)$ is true; $[\equiv]$ will be used for the equivalence partition.

Theorem 5.2.11. For every integer k, $[\equiv k] = [\equiv]$ iff $[\equiv k + 1] = [\equiv k]$.

Proof. The truth that $[\equiv k] = [\equiv]$ implies $[\equiv k + 1] = [\equiv k]$ is immediate from the definitions and Corollary 5.2.8.

Conversely, assume that $[\equiv k] \neq [\equiv]$. By the Remark following Definition 5.2.10, there exist q_i, q_j such that $q_i \equiv q_j(k)$ while $q_i \not\equiv q_j$. Let m be the least k such that $q_i \not\equiv q_j(k)$. By Corollary 5.2.8, $m > k$. If $m = k + 1$, we will have proved $q_i \not\equiv q_j(k + 1)$, and therefore (since $q_i \equiv q_j(k)$, by the Remark following Definition 5.2.10), $[\equiv k + 1] \neq [k]$, thus establishing the converse.

The other case is that $m > k + 1$. Now let x be a word such that $l(x) = m$, $x = zy$, $l(y) = k + 1$, and $l(z) = m - k - 1$. Since m was selected to be the least integer satisfying $q_i \not\equiv q_j(k)$, it follows that

$$N(q_i, zy) \neq N(q_j, zy) \tag{12}$$

Hence for $q_i' = M(q_i, z)$ and $q_j' = M(q_j, z)$, by using Theorem 5.1.7,

$$N(q_i', y) \neq N(q_j', y) \tag{13}$$

Since $l(y) = k + 1$, q_i' and q_j' are $k + 1$-inequivalent; that is, $q_i' \not\equiv q_j'(k + 1)$.

On the other hand, suppose that $l(y) \leq k$. Then we also have that $l(x) < m$. Since m was the least integer violating k-equivalence, we must conclude that

$$N(q_i, zy) = N(q_j, zy)$$

From this it follows easily that $q_i' \equiv q_j'(k)$, by using Theorem 5.1.7 again. In sum, we have found q_i', q_j' such that $q_i' \not\equiv q_j'(k + 1)$ while $q_i' \equiv q_j'(k)$, from which it follows that $[\equiv k] \neq [\equiv k + 1]$. Q.E.D.

The foregoing theorem may be interpreted in the following useful way. If we have some way of testing whether every pair of states is equivalent for words of length k, then we have a way to establish equivalence classes of all k-equivalent states. This yields the partition $[\equiv k]$. If, moreover, this partition is stable for words of length $k + 1$, that is, if $[\equiv k] = [\equiv k + 1]$, then (and only then), the theorem tells us, equivalence in general is the same as k-equivalence.

Thus we may begin the description of an algorithm for construction of a reduced transducer, and *a fortiori*, for testing the equivalence of any two states of a transducer. If we begin with the table of **T** for M and N, and if $N(q_i, s) = N(q_j, s)$ for every q_i, q_j, and s, then it follows that $q_i \equiv q_j(1)$ by Definition 5.2.7; and by Theorem 5.2.9, $q_i \equiv q_j$ for all $q_i, q_j \in Q$. In this case, we complete the algorithm by selecting a representative q and have a trivial, one-state machine.

If for every distinct q_i, q_j, there is an s such that $N(q_i, s) \neq N(q_j, s)$, then by the definition of reduction (5.2.3) we are done.

If states q_i and q_j are equivalent for every s, then $q_i \equiv q_j(1)$. Using Definition 5.2.7, we form the partition $[\equiv 1]$. So far, this process is effective. In formal terms the problem of deciding 1-equivalence is decidable.

Proceeding inductively, if there is an effective way of obtaining $[\equiv k + 1]$ from $[\equiv k]$, and if, in addition, the process terminates so that $[\equiv k + 1] = [\equiv k]$ for some integer k, then by the theorem just proved and by the construction used in Theorem 5.2.4 we will have arrived at a reduced equivalent machine. It remains therefore to show how to construct $[\equiv k + 1]$ given $[\equiv k]$ and to show that the process terminates.

Theorem 5.2.12. For states q_i, q_j, $q_i \equiv q_j(k + 1)$ iff, $q_i \equiv q_j(k)$ and for every s, $M(q_i, s) \equiv M(q_j, s)(k)$.

Proof. Since, by Corollary 5.2.8, $q_i \equiv q_j(k + 1)$ implies $q_i \equiv q_j(k)$, we need only show that

$$q_i \equiv q_j(k + 1) \Leftrightarrow M(q_i, s) \equiv M(q_j, s)(k) \tag{14}$$

By Definition 5.2.7, Theorem 5.1.7 and 5.1.8, this is the same as

$$N(q_i, sx) = N(q_j, sx) \Leftrightarrow M(q_i, s) \equiv M(q_j, s)(k) \tag{15}$$

where $l(sx) = k + 1$. Q.E.D.

EXAMPLE 1. Suppose $Q = \{q_0, q_1, q_2, q_3, q_4, q_5\}$ and that $[\equiv k]$ is

$$\{\{q_0, q_4\}, \{q_1, q_3, q_4\}, \{q_5\}\} \tag{16}$$

By the theorem no states are $k + 1$-equivalent unless they already appear in the same class of the partition. From the M table for the transducer, calculate $M(q_0, s)$ and $M(q_4, s)$. If both are elements of the same equivalence class in (16), then q_0 and q_4 are $k + 1$-equivalent. If they are not, $\{q_0, q_4\}$ breaks up into two classes $\{q_0\}$ and $\{q_4\}$. When this calculation is made for all pairs in each class, $[\equiv k + 1]$ is the result.

Theorem 5.2.13. If $[\equiv k] \neq [\equiv]$, then the number of classes in $[\equiv k]$ is greater than or equal to $k + 1$.

Proof. Let $k = 1$. From Theorem 5.2.9 if $[\equiv 1] \neq [\equiv]$, then there are at least two distinct states q_i, q_j such that $q_i \neq q_j(1)$. Hence there are at least two classes in $[\equiv 1]$, that is, $K([\equiv 1]) \geq k + 1$. For the induction step, assume that $[\equiv k] \neq [\equiv]$ implies $K([\equiv k]) \geq k + 1$. We must show that $[\equiv k + 1] \neq [\equiv]$ implies $K([\equiv k + 1]) \geq k + 2$.

Therefore, to prove this latter implication assume $[\equiv k + 1] \neq [\equiv]$. Then obviously $[\equiv k] \neq [\equiv]$. It follows by the induction hypothesis that

$K([\equiv k]) \geq k + 1$. By Theorem 5.2.11, it also follows that $[\equiv k] \neq [\equiv k + 1]$, and by the Remark after Definition 5.2.10, that there are states q_i, q_j such that $q_i \equiv q_j(k)$ while $q_i \not\equiv q_j(k + 1)$. Finally, by Theorem 5.2.12, $M(q_i, s) \not\equiv M(q_j, s)(k)$, and hence $[\equiv k + 1]$ has more equivalence classes than $[\equiv k]$. Therefore $K([\equiv k + 1]) \geq k + 2$. Q.E.D.

Theorem 5.2.14. Suppose a transducer **T** has $n > 1$ states; there exists an integer $k \leq n - 1$ such that $[\equiv k] = [\equiv]$.

Proof. By Theorem 5.2.13, if the number of n-equivalence classes is less than $n + 1$, then $[\equiv n] = [\equiv]$. In an n-state transducer there can be at most n equivalence classes, so $K([\equiv n]) < n + 1$. However, this bound, as asserted in the theorem, can be lowered.

From the foregoing, we know there exists an m (n, at any rate) such that $[\equiv m] = [\equiv]$. Let k be the least of these m. Clearly, $k \geq 1$. If $k = 1$, then $n > 1$ by hypothesis, $k \leq n - 1$, and the theorem is proved.

If $k > 1$, then either $k > n - 1$ or $k \leq n - 1$. We will see that the first alternative is impossible. Since k is the least m such that $[\equiv m] = [\equiv]$, it follows that $[\equiv k - 1] \neq [\equiv]$. Thus by Theorem 5.2.13, the number of classes in $[\equiv k - 1]$ is at least k. Now, assuming that $k > n - 1$, this implies there are at least n equivalence classes in $[\equiv k - 1]$. However, it is impossible that there be more than n equivalence classes in $[\equiv k]$, since **T** has only n states. Hence, $[\equiv k - 1] = [\equiv k]$, by Theorem 5.2.12. Hence using Theorem 5.2.11, we have, letting k be $k - 1$, that $[\equiv k - 1] = [\equiv]$, a contradiction. Q.E.D.

Corollary 5.2.15. Suppose **T** has n states and that there are states q_i, q_j such that $q_i \not\equiv q_j$. There exists a word x of at most length $n - 1$ such that $N(q_i, x) \neq N(q_j, x)$.

This completes the discussion of a decidable method for finding reduced transducers and for checking equivalence of states. The same procedure, essentially, may be used to test two transducers $\mathbf{T}_a$ and $\mathbf{T}_b$ for equivalence.

EXERCISES 5.2

1. A transducer, which counts on the sequence 0, 2, 4, 6, 1, 3, 5, 7, 0, etc., emits an output of 1 immediately *before* it advances to an even count, and only then. The counter is stepped by an input signal $x = 1$. Prove that the reduced form has 8 states.

2. Prove that if $\mathbf{T}_a$ and $\mathbf{T}_b$ are two transducers with the same input and output alphabets and with n_a and n_b internal states, respectively, then $q_a \not\equiv q_b$ implies $q_a \not\equiv q_b(n_a + n_b - 1)$. *Hint*: Construct the *direct sum* of $\mathbf{T}_a$ and $\mathbf{T}_b$ by "pasting" together their M and N tables with auxiliary symbols labeled so as to preserve their identity with $\mathbf{T}_a$ or $\mathbf{T}_b$ as the case may be. (See Definition 5.4.16.)

3. Provide a modified form of the reduction algorithm for checking the equivalence of two transducers.

4. Prove that the transducers of Tables 5.2.1*a* and 5.2.1*b* are equivalent.

5. Prove Corollary 5.2.8.

6. Prove Theorem 5.2.9.

7. Two transducers $\mathbf{T}_a$ and $\mathbf{T}_b$ are equivalent w.r.t. the nonempty subsets Q_a' and Q_b' of Q_a and Q_b iff for every $q \in Q_a'$ there exists an equivalent state $q' \in Q_b'$, and conversely.

Show that if φ is an isomorphism between $\mathbf{T}_a$ and $\mathbf{T}_b$ and if $Q_a' \subseteq Q_a$ and Q_b' is the range of $q \in Q_a'$ under φ, then $\mathbf{T}_a$ and $\mathbf{T}_b$ are equivalent w.r.t. Q_a' and Q_b'.

8. If $\mathbf{T}_a$ and $\mathbf{T}_b$ are equivalent and $K(Q_a) = K(Q_b)$, then $\mathbf{T}_a$ and $\mathbf{T}_b$ are isomorphic. If this statement is true, provide a proof. If it is not, construct a counterexample.

9. Show that the reduced form $\mathbf{T}_b$ of $\mathbf{T}_a$ is a homomorphic image of $\mathbf{T}_a$.

10. Show that if φ is a homomorphism of $\mathbf{T}_a$ onto $\mathbf{T}_b$, then $\mathbf{T}_a \equiv \mathbf{T}_b$.

5.3 SOME SPECIAL CLASSES OF TRANSDUCERS

From this point on, in studying finite transducers it will be convenient to permit null inputs so that the restriction $x \neq \Lambda$ on the axiom scheme of Definition 5.1.1 is removed [Exercise 5.1(12)]. We also permit null outputs and use Λ for the null word on O. Extending M and N to sequences, we have, in place of Definition 5.1.4, for a given $\mathbf{T}$:

$$\begin{aligned} M(q_i, \Lambda) &= q_i \\ M(q_i, xs_j) &= M(M(q_i, x), s_j) \\ N(q_i, \Lambda) &= \Lambda \\ N(q_i, xs) &= N(M(q_i, x), s) \\ G(q_i, \Lambda) &= \Lambda \\ G(q_i, s_{i_1}s_{i_2}\cdots s_{i_k}) &= N(q_i, s_{i_1})N(q_i, s_{i_1}s_{i_2})\cdots N(q_i, s_{i_1}s_{i_2}\cdots s_{i_k}) \end{aligned}$$

In practice, we commonly use sequential machines with distinguished initial states. For example, the various counters used in the control of the memory cycle of a digital computer are reset to zero at the beginning of each cycle. We will now discuss such instances within our present model.

Definition 5.3.1. A *finite transducer with an initial state* is a system like that of Definition 5.1.1, except the axiom is of the form $q_0x\#$; the auxiliary symbol q_0 is called the *initial state.*

Considered as an associated system (cf. Definition 5.1.3), a transducer with an initial state is a sextuple $\langle S, Q, q_0, M, N, O\rangle$ where, again, S and O are finite nonempty sets of symbols, Q is a set of states, and M and N are as specified at the beginning of this section.

Although the basic definitions and Theorems 5.1.7 to 5.1.9 for initial-state machines are the same as those for the more general case, the counterpart of Definition 5.2.1 is simpler.

Definition 5.3.2. Let $\mathbf{T}_a = \langle S, Q_a, q_0, M_a, N_a, O\rangle$ and
$$\mathbf{T}_b = \langle S, Q_b, q_0', M_b, N_b, O\rangle$$

$\mathbf{T}_a$ and $\mathbf{T}_b$ are *equivalent* iff $q_0 \equiv q_0'$. As before, we write $\mathbf{T}_a \equiv \mathbf{T}_b$.
As a corollary of Theorem 5.2.4 we have the following theorem.

Theorem 5.3.3. For each initial-state finite transducer $\mathbf{T}_a$ and set of states Q_a, there exists an equivalent initial-state transducer $\mathbf{T}_b$ with states Q_b such that $Q_b \subseteq Q_a$ and $\mathbf{T}_b$ is reduced.

This theorem is almost word for word identical with Theorem 5.2.4. In constructing Q_b, we let $q_0' = \sigma[q_0]$. Then, using result (7) of Section 5.2 we have as an immediate instance the relation $q_0 \equiv q_0'$. Since we are now permitting use of the null word Λ, the inductions used in Theorem 5.2.4 must be rewritten using $l(x) = 0$ as basis in each step. This task is left to the student.

Reduced initial-state machines, as we shall now see, are not yet *minimal* in regard to the number of internal states. Unlike machines without initial states, it is possible for our new transducers to have inactive states which the system will never enter from the initial state. In this context, consider the following.

In Fig. 5.3.1, there is a finite transducer which, if held to be an instance of Definition 5.1.1 (or 5.1.3) is already reduced according to the standard

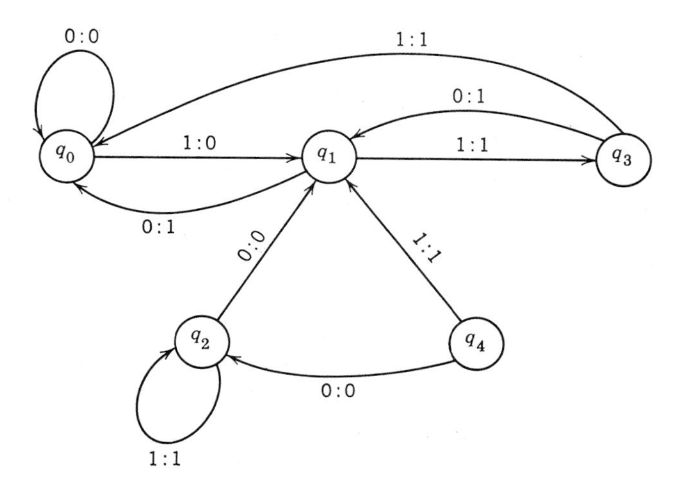

Fig. 5.3.1

of Definition 5.2.3. The student may verify this fact using the algorithm presented in Section 5.2.

Alternatively, let us now consider Fig. 5.3.1 as an initial-state machine satisfying Definition 5.3.1. Inspection shows that if one always starts in state q_0 (which we are taking here as the initial state), then there is no word x such that $M(q_0, x) = q_2$, and there is no x such that $M(q_0, x) = q_4$. Hence in an obvious sense q_2 and q_4 are superfluous, and the machine would behave in identically the same way if one were to design it without either state. Evidently, Fig. 5.3.1 is not a minimal machine in the natural sense of having the fewest possible states, if it is considered as a transducer with initial state. To take care of this special situation, we introduce the following definitions.

Definition 5.3.4. A finite transducer $\mathbf{T}$ with initial state is *connected* iff for every state q of $\mathbf{T}$ there is a word x such that $M(q_0, x) = q$. Every state of a connected transducer is said to be *accessible*.

Theorem 5.3.5. If $\mathbf{T}_a$ is connected, its reduced equivalent form $\mathbf{T}_b$ is also connected. Connectedness is preserved under reduction.

Proof. Using the notation of Definition 5.3.2, we have, to start with, that every state $q \in Q_a$ is accessible from q_0 since $\mathbf{T}_a$ is connected. Let $q \equiv q'$, $q' \in Q_b$. We must show that there exists a word x such that $M_b(q_0', x) = q'$.

By Theorem 5.3.3, $q' \in Q_a$; so by the hypothesis there is an x such that $M_a(q_0, x) = q'$. Since $\sigma[q'] = q'$ by construction (compare the construction of Q_b in Theorem 5.2.4), it follows at once that $\sigma[M_a(q_0, x)] = q'$; and by (2) of Theorem 5.2.4 we obtain $M_b(q_0', x) = q'$. Q.E.D.

We now may define minimality, keeping in mind the natural criterion we alluded to in discussing Example 1.

Definition 5.3.6. A finite transducer $\mathbf{T}$ with initial state is *minimal* iff it is connected and reduced.

Inasmuch as we already have a procedure for reduction, and connectivity is preserved under reduction, all we lack for obtaining minimality is a procedure for finding a connected machine equivalent to a given transducer. Such a procedure is provided for by an elementary application of lattice theory.

Definition 5.3.7. The *connection matrix* of a labeled directed linear graph with n nodes is the $n \times n$ matrix A such that element a_{ij} of A is equal to 1 if there is a directed branch from node i to node j, or is equal to 0 otherwise.

EXAMPLE 1. Since transition diagrams are directed linear graphs, the concept of connection matrix is applicable to transducers. Thus the matrix of Fig. 5.3.1 is shown in Fig. 5.3.2. Here, we should think of subscripts i

and j for the ith row and jth column as ranging from 0 to 4, in conformity with the names of the states of the represented machine.[4]

$$A = \begin{vmatrix} 1 & 1 & 0 & 0 & 0 \\ 1 & 0 & 0 & 1 & 0 \\ 0 & 1 & 1 & 0 & 0 \\ 1 & 1 & 0 & 0 & 0 \\ 0 & 1 & 1 & 0 & 0 \end{vmatrix}$$

Fig. 5.3.2

Definition 5.3.8. A matrix A is a *lattice matrix* iff each element a_{ij} is an element of a lattice. The *join* of two $m \times n$ lattice matrices A, B, written $A \cup B$, with elements in a lattice, is the $m \times n$ matrix C such that $c_{ij} = a_{ij} \cup b_{ij}$, $a_{ij} \in A$, and $b_{ij} \in B$.

The product of an $m \times n$ matrix A and an $n \times r$ matrix B, written $A \cdot B$, is the matrix C, whose elements are

$$c_{ij} = \sum_{k=0}^{n-1} (a_{ik} \cap b_{kj}) \qquad i = 0, 1, \ldots, m - 1 \qquad \text{and} \quad j = 0, 1, \ldots, r - 1$$

(The notation $\sum$ is used here in a way analogous to that of ordinary summation, except, for instance,

$$\sum_{i=0}^{3} a_i$$

means $a_0 \cup a_1 \cup a_2 \cup a_3$; $\cap$ is the lattice meet.)

EXAMPLE 2. Given the two 2×2 matrices A_1 and A_2

$$A_1 = \begin{vmatrix} a & b \\ 0 & a \end{vmatrix} \qquad A_2 = \begin{vmatrix} a & 0 \\ 1 & b \end{vmatrix}$$

[4] A matrix is a rectangular array of objects having m rows and n columns. In the applications with which the student is most probably familiar, the objects are elements of a field (Section 1.3), and, in particular, are real or complex numbers. In our use of matrices here, the objects will be elements of a lattice and the usual operations of addition and multiplication of matrices will appear here in terms of *joins* and *meets* of matrices. Also, as implied in the text, our conventions for naming elements will be as displayed for an $(m + 1) \times (n + 1)$ array.

$$A = \begin{vmatrix} a_{00} & a_{01} & a_{02} & \cdots & a_{0n} \\ a_{10} & a_{11} & a_{12} & \cdots & a_{1n} \\ \vdots & \vdots & \vdots & & \vdots \\ a_{m0} & a_{m1} & a_{m2} & \cdots & a_{mn} \end{vmatrix}$$

with 0 and 1 the least and greatest elements of a lattice, respectively, and with a, b elements of the same lattice. Then we have

$$A_1 \cup A_2 = \begin{vmatrix} a & b \\ 0 & a \end{vmatrix} \cup \begin{vmatrix} a & 0 \\ 1 & b \end{vmatrix}$$

$$= \begin{vmatrix} a \cup a & b \cup 0 \\ 0 \cup 1 & a \cup b \end{vmatrix} = \begin{vmatrix} a & b \\ 1 & a \cup b \end{vmatrix}$$

and

$$A_1 \cdot A_2 = \begin{vmatrix} a & b \\ 0 & a \end{vmatrix} \cdot \begin{vmatrix} a & 0 \\ 1 & b \end{vmatrix}$$

$$= \begin{vmatrix} (a \cap a) \cup (b \cap 1) & (a \cap 0) \cup (b \cap b) \\ (0 \cap a) \cup (a \cap 1) & (0 \cap 0) \cup (a \cap b) \end{vmatrix} = \begin{vmatrix} a \cup b & b \\ a & a \cap b \end{vmatrix}$$

Continuing with the conventions of Definition 5.3.8, we will take the nth *power* A^n of A to be the n-fold product $A \cdot A \cdots (n \text{ times})$ of A. We will write $A \leq B$ to mean that for all $a_{ij} \in A$ and $b_{ij} \in B$, $a_{ij} \leq b_{ij}$. This *partial ordering* relation is defined only for a family of $m \times n$ lattice matrices m and n fixed. Two $m \times n$ matrices are *equal* iff $a_{ij} = b_{ij}$ for all i, j.

As we return to connection matrices, recall that an entry $a_{ij} = 1$ means node i is orientedly connected to j, and entry $a_{ij} = 0$ means it is not. A connection matrix is clearly a lattice matrix, provided we interpret joins, meets, etc., in an appropriate manner. Thus, given A_1 and A_2, we mean by the join B the matrix of elements b_{ij} such that $b_{ij} = 1$ if there is a path from i to j either in the graph corresponding to A_1 or in the graph corresponding to A_2, or in both; otherwise, $b_{ij} = 0$.

By the product B of A_1 and A_2, we mean the matrix of elements b_{ij} such that $b_{ij} = 1$ if there is a path from i to k in the graph corresponding to A_1 and from k to j in A_2 for at least one k; otherwise, $b_{ij} = 0$. The verification that the matrix elements and operations on elements interpreted in this way satisfy the lattice axioms is left to the student.

In general, the nth power of a connection matrix represents the paths of length n, if any, between every i and j.

Thus the second power of the matrix in Fig. 5.3.2 is

$$A^2 = \begin{vmatrix} 1 & 1 & 0 & 0 & 0 \\ 1 & 0 & 0 & 1 & 0 \\ 0 & 1 & 1 & 0 & 0 \\ 1 & 1 & 0 & 0 & 0 \\ 0 & 1 & 1 & 0 & 0 \end{vmatrix} \begin{vmatrix} 1 & 1 & 0 & 0 & 0 \\ 1 & 0 & 0 & 1 & 0 \\ 0 & 1 & 1 & 0 & 0 \\ 1 & 1 & 0 & 0 & 0 \\ 0 & 1 & 1 & 0 & 0 \end{vmatrix} = \begin{vmatrix} 1 & 1 & 0 & 1 & 0 \\ 1 & 1 & 0 & 0 & 0 \\ 1 & 1 & 1 & 1 & 0 \\ 1 & 1 & 0 & 1 & 0 \\ 1 & 1 & 1 & 1 & 0 \end{vmatrix}$$

With our interpretation (recalling $n = 0, 1, 2, 3, 4$) of the matrix meet, there is a "path" of length 2 from 0 to 3 (see Fig. 5.3.1); in other words, the product element

$$\begin{aligned} a_{03}^2 &= (a_{00}^1 \cap a_{03}^1) \cup (a_{01}^1 \cap a_{13}^1) \cup (a_{02}^1 \cap a_{23}^1) \cup (a_{03}^1 \cap a_{33}^1) \cup (a_{04}^1 \cap a_{43}^1) \\ &= 0 \cup 1 \cup 0 \cup 0 \cup 0 = 1 \end{aligned}$$

indicates a path from 0 to 1 to 3, that is, the word 11. Also,

$$A^1 \cup A^2 = \begin{vmatrix} 1 & 1 & 0 & 1 & 0 \\ 1 & 1 & 0 & 1 & 0 \\ 1 & 1 & 1 & 1 & 0 \\ 1 & 1 & 0 & 1 & 0 \\ 1 & 1 & 1 & 1 & 0 \end{vmatrix}$$

From our interpretation, the fact that the 13 element is 1 means there is a path of either length 1 or length 2 between 1 and 3.

Theorem 5.3.9. Let **T** be a transducer with initial state and $A_{\mathbf{T}}$ its connection matrix. **T** is connected iff there is a positive integer m such that every element a_{0j} of the matrix

$$\sum_{k=1}^{m} A_{\mathbf{T}}{}^{k} \tag{1}$$

equals 1.

Proof. If **T** is connected, then for every q_j in its set of internal states there is a (finite) word x such that $M_{q_0}(x) = q_j$. If the longest of these, y, has length $l(y) = m$, then every q_j is connected to q_0 by a word of length 1, or 2, or 3, or . . . m. Hence every $a_{0j} = 1$ is in $A_{\mathbf{T}}{}^1$ or $A_{\mathbf{T}}{}^2$ or, etc., which means in $A_{\mathbf{T}}{}^1 \cup A_{\mathbf{T}}{}^2 \cup \cdots \cup A_{\mathbf{T}}{}^m$. If, on the other hand, **T** is not connected, then there exists a state q_j such that for all x, $M_{q_0}(x) \neq q_j$ so there is *no* m such that $l(y) = m$ for some y and such that $a_{0j} = 1$ in the matrix (1). Q.E.D.

Theorem 5.3.10. If A is an $n \times n$ lattice matrix, then for every r,

$$\sum_{i=1}^{n} A^i = \sum_{i=1}^{n+r} A^i \tag{2}$$

Proof. We sketch the proof for $r = 1$, leaving it to the student to complete the proof [see Exercise 5.3(1)]. For $r = 1$, (2) becomes

$$\sum_{i=1}^{n} A^i = \sum_{i=1}^{n} A^i \cup A^{n+1} \tag{3}$$

We wish to show that every element a_{ij} of A^{n+1} is included in its corresponding i, j element of

$$\sum_{i=1}^{n} A^i$$

Then (3) will follow by Definition 5.3.8 and (18a) of Section 1.3. The i, j element of A^{n+1} is a manifold join

$$a_{ij}^{n+1} = \sum_{k_n=0}^{n-1} \sum_{k_{n-1}=0}^{n-1} \cdots \sum_{k_1=0}^{n-1} (a_{ik_1} \cap a_{k_1k_2} \cap \cdots \cap a_{k_{n-1}k_n} \cap a_{k_nj}) \quad (4)$$

Each term (manifold meet) of this element has $n + 1$ factors not all of which are distinct, as we can readily verify. Therefore for some s, either (1) $k_s = j$, or (2) $k_s = i$, or (3) $k_s = k_r$ for some r.

CASE 1. $k_s = j$. Then

$$a_{ik_1} \cap a_{k_1k_2} \cap \cdots \cap a_{k_{s-1}k_s} \cap \cdots \cap a_{k_{n-1}k_n} \cap a_{k_nj} \quad (5)$$

may be written

$$a_{ik_1} \cap a_{k_1k_2} \cap \cdots \cap a_{k_{s-1}j} \cap \cdots \cap a_{k_{n-1}k_n} \cap a_{k_nj} \quad (6)$$

Hence since in general $a \cap b \leq a$ holds for lattices, (5) is included in $a_{ik_1} \cap a_{k_1k_2} \cap \cdots \cap a_{k_{s-1}}a_j$. However, this latter term is a term of the manifold join constituting the i, j element of A^s for some $s \leq n$. Therefore by transitivity (5) is included in the i, j element of A^s.

For cases 2 and 3, we are similarly able to conclude that every term under these cases is included in the i, j element of $A^{s'}$ or $A^{s''}$ for some s' and some s'', s', $s'' \leq n$.

Each meet in the i, j element of A^{n+1} is therefore included in a term of some matrix A^r, $r \leq n$, and hence the i, j element is included in the i, j element of

$$\sum_{i=1}^{n} A^i \qquad \text{Q.E.D.}$$

Our latest theorem establishes an algorithm for connectivity. We simply take the sum of the first, second, etc., powers of the matrix $A_{\mathbf{T}}$ corresponding to a transducer of n states and examine row 0. If $\mathbf{T}$ is not connected, we may easily construct a connected transducer equivalent to $\mathbf{T}$.

Definition 5.3.11. A *subtransducer* of a machine $\mathbf{T} = \langle S, Q, M, N, O \rangle$ is a transducer $\mathbf{T}' = \langle S, Q', M', N', O' \rangle$ such that $Q' \subseteq Q$, $O' \subseteq O$, and M' and N' are functions restricted to $Q' \times S$. If $\mathbf{T}$ has initial state q_0, then $\mathbf{T}'$ also has the same initial state q_0 and $q_0 \in Q'$.

Note that a subtransducer is defined for *all* of the alphabet S. A *connected subtransducer* is, as the name implies, one such that every $q \in Q'$ is the image under M for q_0 and some x.

Corollary 5.3.12. For every transducer $\mathbf{T}$ with initial state there exists an equivalent connected subtransducer $\mathbf{T}'$.

Proof. Construct $\sum^n A_{\mathbf{T}}$. If **T** is connected, our proof is complete. If it is not, construct $\mathbf{T}'$ as follows: Q' is the set of all states q_j of Q such that $a_{0j} = 1$ in $\sum^n A_{\mathbf{T}}$. M and N are restricted to $Q' \times S$ from $Q \times S$ by examination of the transition diagram of **T**, and O' is the range of N. Q.E.D.

EXAMPLE 3. Continuing with the study of the transducer of Fig. 5.3.1, we find that the $\sum^n A$ matrix of the matrix A, Fig. 5.3.2, is

$$\begin{vmatrix} 1 & 1 & 0 & 1 & 0 \\ 1 & 1 & 0 & 1 & 0 \\ 1 & 1 & 1 & 1 & 0 \\ 1 & 1 & 0 & 1 & 0 \\ 1 & 1 & 1 & 1 & 0 \end{vmatrix}$$

Since $a_{02} = a_{04} = 0$, the transducer is not connected, as, of course, we knew all along. The M, N function table for the original machine is given in (Table 5.3.1).

TABLE 5.3.1

	M		N	
	0	1	0	1
q_0	q_0	q_1	0	0
q_1	q_0	q_3	1	1
q_2	q_1	q_2	0	1
q_3	q_1	q_0	1	1
q_4	q_2	q_1	0	1

We now delete rows for q_2 and q_4, and the transition diagram for the resulting connected subtransducer is shown in Fig. 5.3.3. Alternatively, we could just as well lop off state nodes q_2 and q_4 of Fig. 5.3.1, together with all branches coming into or out of these two states, instead of working

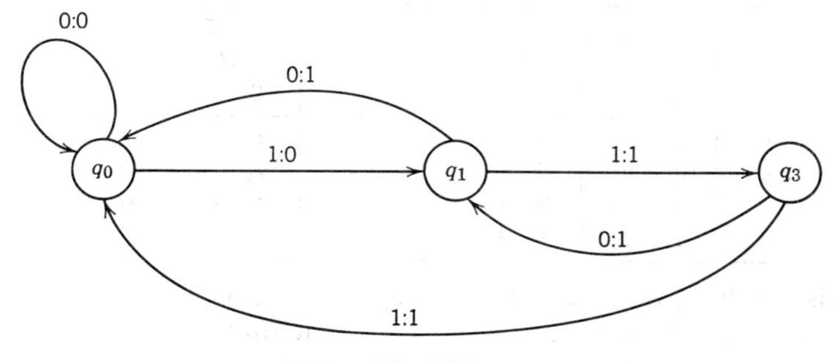

Fig. 5.3.3

with the M, N table. The resulting machine is the minimal transducer equivalent to Fig. 5.3.1.

This completes the discussion of connected transducers with initial states.

Let us suppose now that we were faced with the problem of determining whether two general transducers $\mathbf{T}_a$ and $\mathbf{T}_b$ (that is, transducers without initial states) are equivalent or not. We have a method, by Exercise 5.2(3), of deciding such issues. In effect, this procedure shows us whether for every $q_a \in Q_a$ there exists a $q_b \in Q_b$ such that every sequence applied to $\mathbf{T}_a$ gives the same output as it gives to $\mathbf{T}_b$, and conversely. But suppose someone suggests the following substitute procedure: pick any word x and inject it into $\mathbf{T}_a$ in state q_a; observe the output sequence. Next, inject x into $\mathbf{T}_b$ in state q_b; observe the output sequence. If the output is not the same as that from $\mathbf{T}_a$ try q_b'; and if this is not the same, try q_b'', etc. If eventually we were able to find a state of Q_b yielding the same output sequence, if we could do this for every $q_a \in Q_a$ and every x, and if, conversely, we could obtain the same kind of agreement from $\mathbf{T}_a$ starting with states of $\mathbf{T}_b$ and arbitrary words x, then we would want to say that in a certain sense $\mathbf{T}_a$ and $\mathbf{T}_b$ behave the same. This discussion suggests a weakened kind of equivalence (to be contrasted with the equivalence concept of Definition 5.2.1).

Definition 5.3.13. Given two transducers $\mathbf{T}_a$ and $\mathbf{T}_b$, having the same input and output alphabets, with internal states Q_a and Q_b, respectively, and functions G_a and G_b (cf. Definition 5.1.4*c*); $\mathbf{T}_a$ and $\mathbf{T}_b$ are *indistinguishable* iff for every $q_a \in Q_a$ and word x there is a $q_b \in Q_b$ such that $G_a(q_a, x) = G_b(q_b, x)$, and for every $q_b \in Q_b$ and word x there is a $q_a \in Q_a$ such that $G_a(q_a, x) = G_b(q_b, x)$.

It is perhaps clear, in view of Theorem 5.1.9, that equivalent transducers are indistinguishable, whereas it is not true that all indistinguishable ones are equivalent. Consider the two machines of Table 5.3.2.

TABLE 5.3.2

	$\mathbf{T}_a$					$\mathbf{T}_b$			
	M		N			M		N	
	0	1	0	1		0	1	0	1
q_1	q_2	q_3	1	0	q_1	q_2	q_3	1	0
q_2	q_1	q_3	0	0	q_2	q_1	q_3	0	0
q_3	q_1	q_2	0	1	q_3	q_1	q_2	0	1
q_4	q_2	q_2	1	1					

$\mathbf{T}_b$ is simply $\mathbf{T}_a$ with the q_4 row of the M-N table omitted. Obviously, for every state q_i in T_b and every x, there is a state (in fact q_i) in $\mathbf{T}_a$ such that the G functions are equal. Conversely, for every q_i ($i = 1, 2, 3$) in $\mathbf{T}_a$ and every x, there is q_i in $\mathbf{T}_b$ such that the G functions are equal. Furthermore, as is rather easily checked, if we start up $\mathbf{T}_a$ in state q_4, then for every word $0x$, $G(q_4, 0x) = G(q_1, 0x)$; and for every word $1x$, $G(q_4, 1x) = G(q_3, 1x)$. Consequently $\mathbf{T}_a$ and $\mathbf{T}_b$ are indistinguishable. On the other hand, there is no state q_i such that even $q_4 \equiv q_i$ (1) holds; consequently, $\mathbf{T}_a$ and $\mathbf{T}_b$ are not equivalent. We will now briefly study a kind of transducer for which indistinguishability and equivalence are the same.

Definition 5.3.14. A transducer $\mathbf{T}$ is *strongly connected* if for every q_i and q_j in the set of states of $\mathbf{T}$ there is an x such that $M(q_i, x) = q_j$.

This definition says that for every (ordered) pair of states there is a word carrying the transducer from the first member of the pair into the other.

EXAMPLE 4. The machine $\mathbf{T}_b$ of Table 5.3.2 is strongly connected, whereas $\mathbf{T}_a$ is not.

Corollary 5.3.15. There is a decision procedure for determining whether a given transducer is strongly connected.

The proof is left to the student by using the apparatus of connection matrices, an appropriate modification of Theorem 5.3.9, and Theorem 5.3.10.

Theorem 5.3.16. Let $\mathbf{T}_a$ be strongly connected, and let $\mathbf{T}_b$ be any transducer having the same input and output alphabets. If, for every $q_a \in Q_a$ and every word x, there is a state $q_b \in Q_b$ such that $G(q_a, x) = G(q_b, x)$, then for every $q_a \in Q_a$ there is $q_b \in Q_b$ such that $q_a \equiv q_b$.

Proof. Let q_a and x be arbitrarily chosen. Then, by the hypothesis of the theorem, there exists at least one (maybe more) $q_b \in Q_b$ such that $G(q_a, x) = G(q_b, x)$. As x is injected, $\mathbf{T}_b$ passes through states $q_b, \ldots, q_b'$. Define the set $[q_a x]$ as follows:

$$[q_a x] = \{q_b' \mid (\exists q_b)(M_b(q_b, x) = q_b' \wedge G(q_a, x) = G(q_b, x))\} \qquad (7)$$

Thus $[q_a x]$ designates a set of states q_b' of $\mathbf{T}_b$ which are the target states into which $\mathbf{T}_b$ goes from every state q_b which yields the same output with input x from $\mathbf{T}_b$ as $\mathbf{T}_a$ does from q_a. Similarly, $[q_a xy]$ designates the set of states of $\mathbf{T}_b$ associated with the extended input word xy. Since q_b exists, satisfying both $G(q_a, x) = G(q_b, x)$ and $G(q_a, xy) = G(q_b, xy)$, neither $[q_a x]$ nor $[q_a xy]$ is empty. Furthermore, since, by Definition 5.1.4, $G(q_a, xy) = G(q_b, xy)$ implies $G(q_a, x) = G(q_b, x)$, it follows that

$$0 < K[q_a xy] \leq K[q_a x]$$

as the reader may verify.

Let x_0 be a word such that $[q_a x_0]$ is the least set of states q_b' such that for every y,[5]

$$K[q_a x_0] = K[q_a x_0 y] \tag{8}$$

Since $\mathbf{T}_a$ is strongly connected, there are, for each state $q_{a_1}, q_{a_2}, \ldots, q_{a_n} \in Q_a$, words $x_1, x_2, \ldots, x_n$ such that $M_a(q_a, x_0x_1) = q_{a_1}$, $M_a(q_a, x_0x_1x_2) = q_{a_2}, \ldots, M_a(q_a, x_0x_1, \ldots, x_n) = q_{a_n}$. In general, we will write

$$M_a(q_a, x_0x_1, \ldots, x_j) = q_{a_j}$$

We will now show that there is a $q_b' \in [q_a\, x_0x_1 \cdots x_j]$ such that $q_b' \equiv q_{a_j}$, thus proving the theorem. Our technique will be to show that if $q_b' \not\equiv q_{a_j}$, then the class $[q_a\, x_0x_1 \cdots x_j]$ will contain fewer members than it would otherwise, in conflict with (8).

Suppose, then, there is a y such that $N_a(q_{a_j}, y) \neq N_b(q_b', y)$, or equivalently, by strong connectedness that

$$N_a(M_a(q_a, x_0x_1 \cdots x_j), y) \neq N_b(q_b', y) \tag{9}$$

From Theorem 5.1.9, it follows that

$$G_a(M_a(q_a, x_0x_1 \cdots x_j), y) \neq G_b(q_b', y) \tag{10}$$

By Definition (7), letting $M_b(q_b, x_0x_1 \cdots x_j) = q_b'$ and noting that

$$G_a(q_a, x_0x_1 \cdots x_j, y) = G_b(q_b, x_0x_1 \cdots x_j, y)$$

implies $G_a(M_a(q_a, x_0x_1 \cdots x_j), y) = G_b(q_b', y)$, we have

$$\begin{aligned} q_b'' \in [q_a\, x_0x_1 \cdots x_j y] \Leftrightarrow (\exists q_b')(M_b(q_b', y) = q_b'' \wedge q_b' \in [q_a\, x_0x_1 \cdots x_j] \\ \wedge\ G_a(M_a(q_a, x_0x_1 \cdots x_j), y) = G(q_b', y)) \end{aligned} \tag{11}$$

From (10) and (11) it follows that

$$q_b'' \notin [q_a\, x_0x_1 \cdots x_j y] \tag{12}$$

Consequently, $K[q_a\, x_0x_1 \cdots x_j y] < K[q_a\, x_0x_1 \cdots x_j]$; hence there is a $y' = x_1 \cdots x_j y$, where

$$K[q_a x_0] > K[q_a x_0 y']$$

contradicting (8). Q.E.D.

Corollary 5.3.17. Let $\mathbf{T}_a$ and $\mathbf{T}_b$ be strongly connected. $\mathbf{T}_a \equiv \mathbf{T}_b$ iff for every $q_a \in Q_a$ and every x there is a $q_b \in Q_b$ such that $G(q_a, x) = G(q_b, x)$ and, conversely, for every $q_b \in Q_b$ and for every x there is a $q_a \in Q_a$ such

[5] The existence of this set follows from the well-ordering principle of the integers which asserts that every subset of the integers I contains a number n such that $n \leq m$, $m \in I$.

that $G(q_a, x) = G(q_b, x)$. Hence for strongly connected machines indistinguishability and equivalence are the same.

Theorem 5.3.18. If $\mathbf{T}_a$ is strongly connected, then its reduced equivalent transducer $\mathbf{T}_b$ is also strongly connected.

The theorem states that if we apply the reduction algorithm of Section 5.2 to a strongly connected transducer, then the resulting machine will be strongly connected as well. A proof following the lines of Theorem 5.3.5 will fulfill our requirements. Alternatively (and in essence equivalently), one can show that the reduced form of any transducer is a *homomorphic image* of a given transducer; and strong connectedness is preserved under this homomorphism. The detailed formulation of these alternative proofs is left to the student.

In our work with digital devices, we sometimes deal with systems in which certain internal state and input symbol pairs are undefined for either the M or N function, or both. In engineering terminology, we say that the next state or output or both are 'don't care' states or outputs. A simple example of a transducer with undefined conditions appears in Table 5.3.3.

TABLE 5.3.3

	M		N	
	0	1	0	1
q_0	q_0	q_1	–	–
q_1	q_0	q_2	–	–
q_2	q_0	q_3	–	1
q_3	—	q_3	–	0

This machine has an output alphabet $\{0, 1\}$; the dashes (–) indicate don't care outputs and states, outputs and states which may be arbitrarily chosen. It satisfies the following design requirements. If, beginning in state q_0, there occurs in an input word x a sequence of exactly three consecutive 1's, the output is 1; if there occur sequences of fewer than three 1's, the output is irrelevant; if there occurs a sequence of four 1's, the output is 0; and from the first such occurrence of either three 1's or four 1's, we don't care what the machine does (until it is reset to q_0, of course).

By using the merging technique for machines with don't care conditions—a technique with which we suppose the student to be familiar[6]—one

[6] One may form the 1-equivalence classes, as a start for the algorithm, in a number of ways, depending on the assignment chosen for the don't care cases. In the example, we may form the 1-equivalence partitions: $\{\{q_0, q_1, q_2\}, \{q_3\}\}$; $\{\{q_1, q_2\}, \{q_0, q_3\}\}$; $\{\{q_0, q_2\}, \{q_1, q_3\}\}$; or $\{\{q_2\}, \{q_0, q_1, q_3\}\}$. In each instance, the merging process is carried out and then the simplest case often yields the reduced machine.

finds that the transducer represented above is minimal; it is connected in our technical sense and also reduced. However, in the general case one may not be so fortunate as in our happily chosen illustration. Ginsburg [1962] has shown that, under a reasonable generalization of the concept of equivalence, there are transducers (with or without initial state) which cannot be made minimal by the process of merging, even in the generalized form indicated in Footnote 6. Although an algorithm exists in principle for Ginsburg's form of the minimization problem, it is in practice quite useless.

A rather efficient procedure does exist, however, for determining minimal forms of transducers, using a somewhat different model than our basic one of Definition 5.1.1. Although a Moore machine, as the new model is termed, is of interest in its own right for many important reasons, some of which we shall examine, the present motivation in terms of the minimization problem is sufficient.

Definition 5.3.19. A *Moore transducer* or *machine* is a semi-thue system $\mathbf{T}_{\mathrm{M}} = \langle A, \mathscr{B}, \mathscr{A}, \mathscr{P} \rangle$, where $A = S \cup O \cup \{\mathbf{u}\} \cup Q$, $\mathbf{u} \notin S$, or Q, and Q, as usual, is distinct from the rest of A. The notation used is that of Definition 5.1.1 for elements of S, O, S^*, etc. The axiom $\mathscr{A}$ is of the form $q_0 x \#$, q_0 fixed. The productions $\mathscr{P}$ are characterized by the following types:

1. (*a*) $Pq_i s_j R \to P o_k q_l R$
   (*b*) $Pq_i s_j R \to P \mathbf{u} q_l R$
   (*c*) $Pq_i \# \to P$
2. At most one production of type (*a*) or type (*b*), but not both, occurs in $\mathscr{P}$ for each pair $q_i s_j$; exactly one of type (*c*), for each q_i, occurs.
3. If there is a q_l such that $P o_k q_l R$ and $P o_m q_l R$ occur on the right of any two productions, then $o_k = o_m$. Both $P o_k q_l R$ and $P \mathbf{u} q_l R$ do not occur in $\mathscr{P}$ for any q_l or any o_k.
4. Nothing is a production of $\mathscr{P}$ unless its being so follows from preceding statements 1–3.

If there is exactly one production of type (*a*) for each $q_i s_j$, then $\mathbf{T}_{\mathrm{M}}$ is *complete*, otherwise *incomplete*. It is customary to refer to incomplete Moore machines simply as *machines*. In the above statement $\mathbf{u}$ means "undefined."

REMARK. According to statement 3 of the preceding list, the "output" depends only on the "final state" q_l, rather than on the pair $q_i s_j$. This explains the main distinction between transducers in our earlier sense and Moore machines.[7] One could equally characterize a Moore machine in

[7] Transducers in our first sense are frequently termed *Mealy Machines* after the author of one of the first transducer formulations. See Section 5.7 for further discussion.

such a way as to make the output dependent on the "initial state" q_i'; here, statement 3 of our specification of $\mathscr{P}$ would read:

3′. If there exists q_i such that $P\, q_i\, s_j\, R \rightarrow Po_k q_t R$ and $Pq_i s_r R \rightarrow Po_m q_n R$, then $o_k = o_m$. Not both, etc. (as in 3).

Corollary 5.3.20. $\mathbf{T}_\mathrm{M}$ is *incomplete* iff either **u** occurs on the right side of some production or there is a pair $q_i s_j$ such that $q_i s_j$ does not appear in either a type (*a*) or a type (*b*) production.

Proof. If $\mathbf{T}_\mathrm{M}$ is incomplete, then by Definition 5.3.19 there is *not* exactly one production of type (*a*) for each pair $q_i s_j$; and by statement 2 of the conditions for $\mathscr{P}$ there is, therefore, *no* production of type (*a*) for some pair $q_i s_j$. Conversely, if **u** occurs in a production with $q_i s_j$, then $q_i s_j$ does not occur in a type (*a*) production by statement 2. Q.E.D.

Again, as in the case of finite transducers, the concepts of consequence, proof, theorem, and terminal theorem are as those in Definitions 3.3.2 to 3.3.5 and 3.3.7. Clearly a Moore system is monogenic. However, there is no companion to Corollary 5.1.2, as the reader should check for himself.

EXAMPLE 5. Let $\mathbf{T}_\mathrm{M}$ have $S = \{0, 1\}$, $O = \{0, 1, 2\}$, axiom $q_0 x\#$, and the five productions:

(i) $Pq_0 0R \rightarrow P\mathbf{u}q_0 R$
(ii) $Pq_0 1R \rightarrow P1q_1 R$
(iii) $Pq_1 0R \rightarrow P\mathbf{u}q_0 R$
(iv–v) $Pq_i\# \rightarrow P, \qquad i = 0, 1$

Now consider the axiom instance $q_0 10110\#$. From this we obtain the sequence $q_0 10110$, $1q_1 0110$, $1\mathbf{u}q_0 110$, $1\mathbf{u}1q_1 10$. Since $q_1 1$ is undefined, $1\mathbf{u}1q_1 10$ is terminal, and hence there is no output sequence determined by 10110. This illustrates one sense in which a Moore system fails to give an output: the input sequence is blocked by an undefined qs condition.

Next, consider the case $q_0 10\#$. Here we have the sequence $q_0 10$, $1q_1 0$, $1\mathbf{u}q_0$, $1\mathbf{u}$. In this case the sequence "goes through," but there are (1) no output sequence (since $\mathbf{u} \notin O$) and (2) no ultimate output (for the same reason).

This example suggests that we interpret incomplete Moore systems as giving outputs only under the following conditions.

Criterion 5.3.21. A Moore system $\mathbf{T}_\mathrm{M}$ is interpreted to *give an output* w from an axiom $q_0 x\#$ iff w is a pure terminal theorem (possibly containing occurrences of **u**) and if $w = x\sigma$, $\sigma \neq \mathbf{u}$. Furthermore, $\mathbf{T}_\mathrm{M}$ gives an *output sequence* if, in addition to the two foregoing conditions, there is no **u** occurring in w.

Definition 5.3.22. Given a Moore machine $\mathbf{T}_M$, an *associated Moore System*, also labeled $\mathbf{T}_M$, is a sextuple $\langle S, Q, q_0, M, \mathbf{n}, O\rangle$, where S, Q, and O are the sub alphabets and auxiliary alphabets of the given semi-thue system, $q_0 \in Q$, and M and $\mathbf{n}$ are constructed in the following way. If $K \subseteq Q \times S$, $M: K \rightarrow Q$ is the function where $M(q_i, s_j) = q_l$ iff either $Pq_is_jR \rightarrow Po_kq_lR$ or $Pq_is_jR \rightarrow P\mathbf{u}q_lR$ is a production of $\mathbf{T}_M$ for some symbol o_k; if $L \subseteq Q$, $\mathbf{n}: L \rightarrow O$ is the function where $\mathbf{n}(q_i) = o_k$ iff Po_kq_iR occurs in the production list of $\mathbf{T}_M$.

In analogy to the equations for M and N of Definition 5.1.4, we have a definition for words, including Λ.

Definition 5.3.23. $M(q_i, \Lambda) = q_i$

$$M(q_i, xs) = M(M(q_i, x), s)$$
$$N(q_i, \Lambda) = \mathbf{n}(q_i)$$

However,

$$N(q_i, x) = \mathbf{n}(M(q_i, x))$$

We also use the function

$$G(q_i, \Lambda) = \mathbf{n}(q_i)$$
$$G(q_i, s_{i_1}s_{i_2}\cdots s_{i_n}) = N(q_i, s_{i_1})N(q_i, s_{i_1}s_{i_2})\cdots N(q_i, s_{i_1}s_{i_2}\cdots s_{i_n})$$

Thus when we permit null inputs there may be a spurious output, provided that $\mathbf{n}(q_i)$ is defined from the semi-thue productions. It is customary to ignore this spurious output and to count the output sequence as beginning after a non-null input. The null word is introduced mainly to relate Moore machines to transducers easily (cf. Theorems 5.3.27 and 5.3.28). The G function is defined when and only when each of $N(q_i, s_{i_1}), \ldots, N(q_i, s_{i_1}s_{i_2}\cdots s_{i_n})$ is defined.

Note that N is defined for q_ix only if $M(q_i, x)$ is defined; this, in turn, holds iff when $x = s_{i_1}s_{i_2}\cdots s_{i_n}$, there exists a sequence $q_i = q_{i_1}, q_{i_2}, \ldots, q_{i_{n+1}}$ such that $M(q_{i_k}, s_{i_k}) = q_{i_{k+1}}$ exist for each $k = 1, 2, \ldots, n$.

We leave it to the student to justify this definition, using Criterion 5.3.21, and to verify the next theorem as well.

Theorem 5.3.24. The value of the function G for q_0, $s_{i_1}s_{i_2}\cdots s_{i_n}$ exists and equals $G(q_0, s_{i_1}s_{i_2}\cdots s_{i_n})$ iff there is a proof in the semi-thue system $\mathbf{T}_M$ of $w = G(q_0, s_{i_1}s_{i_2}\cdots s_{i_n})$ from $q_0s_{i_1}s_{i_2}\cdots s_{i_n}\#$ and $\mathbf{u} = o_{i_j}$ for no j. N is defined for q_0x and equals $N(q_0x)$ iff there is a proof of wo_i for q_0x and $N(q_0x) = o_i$, where $o_i \in O$.

Definition 5.3.25. Given Moore machines $\mathbf{T}_M$ and $\mathbf{T}_M'$, with internal states Q and Q', common alphabet S, O, and $q \in Q$ and $q' \in Q'$. We say that q is *equivalent* to q', written $q \equiv q'$, iff the domain of $N_M(q, x)$ equals the domain of $N_M'(q', x)$ and $N_M(q, x) = N_M'(q', x)$ for all x in that domain.

Theorem 5.3.26. If $\mathbf{T}_M$ is complete, the following statements hold true.

(*a*) For every x, y, and q,

$$M(q, xy) = M(M(q, x), y) \qquad \text{but} \quad N(q, xy) = \mathbf{n}(M(M(q, x), y))$$

(*b*) If $q_i \equiv q_j$, then $M(q_i, x) \equiv M(q_j, x)$, for every q_i, q_j.
(*c*) For every x, $G(q_i, x) = G(q_j, x)$ iff for every x

$$N(q_i, x) = N(q_j, x)$$

(*d*) There exists a complete Moore machine $\mathbf{T}_M'$ such that $Q_{\mathbf{T}_M'} \subseteq Q_{\mathbf{T}_M}$, $\mathbf{T}_M'$ is reduced (in the sense of Definition 5.2.3 but with the new meaning of $\equiv$), and $\mathbf{T}_M'$ is unique to within an isomorphism (appropriately redefined).

Note that for Moore machines we have, in analogy to Theorem 5.2.9, that 1-equivalence of all pairs q_i, q_j of states of a machine implies equivalence of all pairs. Moreover, for the reduction algorithm by "merging," one starts the usual process from the partition $[\equiv 1]$. The reduction is based on straightforward adaptations of Theorems 5.2.11, 5.2.12, 5.2.13, 5.2.14, and 5.2.15.

Statements (*a*)–(*d*) are proved almost exactly as were the companion Theorems 5.1.7, 5.1.8, and 5.1.9 for transducers, as well as Theorems 5.2.4 and 5.2.6, using the appropriate modification of the definition of isomorphism.

Before continuing with the problem of minimization of incomplete Moore machines we want to show that complete Moore machines are the same as finite transducers in the sense that they can perform the same tasks. Although we could work in the following construction with semi-thue systems, it is somewhat simpler to do so directly with the associated system.

Theorem 5.3.27. Given a finite transducer $\mathbf{T}$ with initial state q_0, there exists a complete Moore machine $\mathbf{T}_M$ with initial state q_0 such that $N(q_0, x) = N_M(q_0, x)$ for every x.

Proof. Let $\mathbf{T} = \langle S, Q, q_0, M, N, O\rangle$ and $\mathbf{T}_M = \langle S, Q_M, q_0, M_M, \mathbf{n}, O\rangle$ where

$$Q_n = (Q \times S) \cup \{q_0\} \qquad M_M((q, s), s') = (M(q, s), s')$$
$$M_M(q_0, s) = (q_0, s) \qquad \mathbf{n}(q, s) = N(q, s) \qquad \mathbf{n}(q_0) \text{ is arbitrary}$$

As a preliminary to establishing the theorem we must prove that

$$M_M(q_0, xs) = (M(q_0, x), s) \tag{13}$$

Using induction, if $l(x) = 0$, we have $M_M(q_0, s) = (q_0, s)$ by the preceding construction and $(q_0, s) = (M(q_0, \Lambda), s)$ by Definition 5.3.23. Next, assuming (13) for $l(x) \leq k$,

$$\begin{aligned} M_M(q_0xs's) &= M_M(M_M(q_0, xs'), s) \\ &= M_M((M(q_0, x), s'), s) \\ &= (M(M(q_0, x), s'), s) \\ &= (M(q_0, xs'), s) \end{aligned}$$

Finally, making use of (13) and letting $x = ys$, unless $x = \Lambda$,

$$\begin{aligned} N_M(q_0, ys) &= \mathbf{n}(M_M(q_0, ys)) \\ &= \mathbf{n}(M(q_0, y), s) \\ &= N(M(q_0, y), s) \\ &= N(q_0, ys) \end{aligned}$$

Q.E.D.

Conversely, we can prove the following theorem.

Theorem 5.3.28. Given a complete Moore machine

$$\mathbf{T}_M = \langle S, Q, q_0, M_M, \mathbf{n}, O \rangle$$

there exists a finite transducer $\mathbf{T} = \langle S, Q, q_0, M, N, O \rangle$ such that for every x, $N(q_0, x) = N_M(q_0, x)$.

Proof. Let $M = M_M$ and $N(q, s) = \mathbf{n}(M(q, s))$.

$$\begin{aligned} N(q_0, ys) &= N(M(q_0, y), s) = \mathbf{n}(M(M(q_0, y), s)) = \mathbf{n}(M_M(M_M(q_0, y), s)) \\ &= \mathbf{n}(M_M(q_0, ys)) = N_M(q_0, ys) \end{aligned}$$

Q.E.D.

As we continue with our study of incomplete Moore machines we will need the following definitions.

Definition 5.3.29. Two incomplete Moore machines $\mathbf{T}_M$ and $\mathbf{T}_M'$ are *equivalent* iff $q_0 \equiv q_0'$ where q_0 and q_0' are the initial states of $\mathbf{T}_M$ and $\mathbf{T}_M'$, respectively. As usual we write $\mathbf{T}_M \equiv \mathbf{T}_M'$.

Note that by Definition 5.3.25 the domains D and D' of $N(q_0, x)$ and $N'(q_0', x)$ must be the same, and that $N(q_0, x) = N'(q_0, x)$ for all $x \in D$.

Throughout the ensuing discussion let $\mathbf{T}_M = \langle S, Q, M, q_0, \mathbf{n}, O \rangle$ be an arbitrary incomplete machine.

Definition 5.3.30. $\mathbf{T}_M$ is *reduced* iff for every $q_i, q_j \in Q$, $q_i \equiv q_j$ implies $q_i = q_j$. $\mathbf{T}_M$ is *connected* iff for every $q \in Q$ there exists an x such that $M(q_0, x) = q$; $\mathbf{T}_M$ is *minimal* if it is both reduced and connected.

This definition, which is nearly exactly like Definition 5.3.6, is repeated here because in the present case $\equiv$ has a more general meaning. The meaning of connectedness, however, is exactly that of Definition 5.3.4.

Definition 5.3.31. A subset $Q_S \subseteq Q$ is a *sink set* of $\mathbf{T}_M$ if $\mathbf{n}(q_S)$ is undefined for all $q_S \in Q_S$, and if $M(q_S, s)$ is defined for every s and every q_S and is an element of Q_S.

EXAMPLE 6. Consider the Moore transducer of Table 5.3.4, in which the output part represents for each row q_i the output $\mathbf{n}(q_j)$ if defined, where $q_j = M(q_i, s)$. As is customary, undefined output conditions are denoted by "–" instead of the formal symbol $\mathbf{u}$ in the semi-thue formalism. Similarly, in later examples, we will use "–" for undefined cases of the function M as well.

TABLE 5.3.4

	M		$\mathbf{n}$	
	0	1		
q_0	q_1	q_1	1	1
q_1	q_2	q_0	–	0
q_2	q_2	q_3	–	–
q_3	q_3	q_2	–	–

In this example the set $\{q_2, q_3\} \subseteq Q$ is such that neither $\mathbf{n}(q_2)$ nor $\mathbf{n}(q_3)$ is defined, and moreover, $M(q_2, s)$, $M(q_3, s) \in \{q_2, q_3\}$ for the two values of s.

Definition 5.3.32. $\mathbf{T}_M$ is *transition complete* iff M is defined everywhere, that is, if $K = Q \times S$ (cf. 5.3.22).

Of course, this definition does not rule out the possibility that $\mathbf{n}$ is incomplete.

Theorem 5.3.33. For any $\mathbf{T}_M$ there exists a unique, minimal, transition complete Moore machine $\mathbf{T}_M'$ such that $\mathbf{T}_M \equiv \mathbf{T}_M'$.

Proof. Let the auxiliary symbol q_r be defined as follows. If $\mathbf{T}_M$ has a sink set $Q_S \subseteq Q$, then $q_r \in Q_S$ (that is, set $q_i = q_r$ for any choice of $q_i \in Q_S$); if $\mathbf{T}_M$ has no sink set, then $q_r \notin Q$ (that is, it is not an auxiliary of $\mathbf{T}_M$).

Consider now the machine

$$\mathbf{T}_{M^c} = \langle S, Q \cup \{q_r\}, q_0, M^c, \mathbf{n}^c, O^c \rangle$$

where $O^c = O \cup \{c\}$, c is a constant not in O, and M^c and $\mathbf{n}^c$ are defined thus:

$$\begin{aligned} M^c(q, s) &= M(q, s) && \text{if } M(q, s) \text{ is defined} \\ &= q_r && \text{otherwise} \end{aligned} \tag{14}$$

$$\begin{aligned} \mathbf{n}^c(q) &= \mathbf{n}(q) && \text{if } \mathbf{n}(q) \text{ is defined} \\ &= c && \text{otherwise} \end{aligned} \tag{15}$$

REMARK. Note that if $\mathbf{T}_M$ is incomplete, $\mathbf{T}_{M^c}$ always has a subset of states Q^c such that Q^c contain q_r (undefined cases in $\mathbf{T}_M$) and such that

$M^c(q, s) \in Q^c$ for any $q \in Q^c$. As we shall see later, Q^c is an equivalence class w.r.t. $\equiv$. So in effect the construction of $\mathbf{T}_{M^c}$ gains for us a machine which enables us to reduce all states corresponding to those for which $\mathbf{n}$ is not defined in $\mathbf{T}_M$ and which form a sink set, into one. We also remark for later use that in $\mathbf{T}_{M^c}$, $M^c(q_r, s) = q_r$ since $M(q_r, s)$ is not defined, and also that $\mathbf{n}^c(q_r) = c$.

Suppose that N is defined for (q_0, x), then we have

$$\begin{aligned} N(q_0, x) &= \mathbf{n}(M(q_0, x)) && \text{by Definition 5.3.23} \\ &= \mathbf{n}(M^c(q_0, x)) && \text{by (14)} \\ &= \mathbf{n}^c(M^c(q_0, x)) && \text{by (15)} \\ &= N^c(q_0, x) \end{aligned}$$

If, on the other hand, N is undefined for (q_0, x), then either $\mathbf{n}$ is undefined for $M(q_0, x)$ or there is a q_j in the sequence $q_0, q_1, q_2, \ldots$ such that (q_j, s), s being a symbol in x, is a pair for which M is undefined. If $\mathbf{n}$ is undefined for (q_0, x), then $\mathbf{n}^c(M(q_0, x)) = c$ by (15) above. In the other case, $M^c(q_j, s) = q_r$ by (14). Since by the conventions for constructing q_r, $M^c(q_r, s) = q_r$ for any s, and since likewise $\mathbf{n}^c(q_r) = c$, we again have $\mathbf{n}^c(M(q_0, x)) = c$.

Hence $\mathbf{T}_{M^c}$ is equivalent to $\mathbf{T}_M$ on the domain of N and has a constant output value c elsewhere. Since $\mathbf{T}_{M^c}$ is a *complete* Moore machine, by using Theorem 5.3.26(*d*), there is a unique (to within isomorphism) complete machine $\mathbf{T}'_{M^c}$ which is minimal and which is equivalent to $\mathbf{T}_{M^c}$; $\mathbf{T}_M'$, the unique, minimal, transition complete machine required by the theorem is obtained by replacing each occurrence of c in the function table for $\mathbf{n}^c$ by $\mathbf{u}$ (by "undefined"). The student may verify that $\mathbf{T}_M'$ has the properties claimed. This completes the proof. Q.E.D.

Corollary 5.3.34. Let Q' be the set of internal states of the minimal transition complete machine T_M'. The sink set Q_S' of Q' is either empty or a unit set.

Proof. Let Q'^c_S be the set of states (if there is one) of $\mathbf{T}'^c_M$ which, as in the remark following the construction of $\mathbf{T}_{M^c}$ above, satisfies $M(q^c, s) \in Q'^c_S$ and $q^c \in Q'^c_S$. If $q_i^c, q_j^c \in Q'^c_S$, then $q_i^c \equiv q_j^c(1)$, as the $\mathbf{n}$ function of both q_i^c and q_j^c is c. Assume, for the induction step, that $q_i^c \equiv q_j^c(k)$. By the Remark we have both $M(q_i^c, s) \in Q'^c_S$ and $M(q_j^c, s) \in Q'^c_S$, and therefore $M(q_i^c, s) \equiv M(q_j^c, s)$. Hence using Theorem 5.2.12 it follows that $q_i^c \equiv q_j^c$. Since $\mathbf{T}'_{M^c}$ is a reduced machine $q_i^c = q_j^c$. So Q'^c_S either is empty or contains but one element. Hence Q_S' (since $\mathbf{T}_M'$ differs from $\mathbf{T}'_{M^c}$ only in the output conditions) is also either empty or a unit set. Q.E.D.

Theorem 5.3.35. For any $\mathbf{T}_M$ there exists a unique, minimal (in general, incomplete) Moore machine $\mathbf{T}''_M$ which is equivalent to $\mathbf{T}_M$.

If $\mathbf{T_M}'$ has no sink state, let $\mathbf{T_M''}$ be $\mathbf{T_M}'$ and the theorem is proved.

If $\mathbf{T_M}'$ has a sink state q_r, let $\mathbf{T_M''}$ be like $\mathbf{T_M}'$ except for its set of internal states which will be $Q' - \{q_r\}$ and for its M table which will contain "undefined" for all occurrences of q_r in the table of $\mathbf{T_M}'$. We leave it to the student to show that $\mathbf{T_M''} \equiv \mathbf{T_M}'$ (and hence $\mathbf{T_M}$), and that $\mathbf{T_M''}$ is minimal and unique. Q.E.D

EXERCISES 5.3

1. Complete the proof of Theorem 5.3.10 for an arbitrary integer r. If A is a lattice matrix, is it true, for every n and m, that $A^n \leq A^{n+m}$? If so, give a proof; if not, give a counterexample.

2. Let $\mathbf{T}$ and $\mathbf{T}'$ be reduced, strongly connected transducers such that at least one state of $\mathbf{T}$ is equivalent to a state of $\mathbf{T}'$. Show that $\mathbf{T}$ and $\mathbf{T}'$ are isomorphic.

3. Show that every transducer has a strongly connected subtransducer.

4. Reconstruct the proofs of Theorems 5.2.4 and 5.2.6 for complete Moore machines instead of Mealy transducers.

Prove that if $\mathbf{T}$ is strongly connected so is its reduced form $\mathbf{T}'$. Do so by showing that under homomorphism strong connectedness is preserved.

5. Show that connectedness is preserved in passing from (Mealy) transducers to equivalent Moore transducers and conversely.

6. Find the minimal complete Moore machine equivalent to the transducer of Table 5.2.1*a*. Construct from the machine obtained an equivalent Mealy transducer. What can you say about preservation of reducedness in such transformations?

7. Invent an algorithm for discovering whether or not a given Moore machine has a sink set.

8. In the table below a Moore machine is given. Find the minimal form.

	M		n	
	0	1		
q_0	q_0	q_2	1	–
q_1	q_2	q_3	–	0
q_2	q_4	q_2	–	–
q_3	q_3	q_0	0	1
q_4	q_2	q_4	–	–
q_5	q_1	—	2	–

9. Complete the proof of Theorem 5.3.35.

5.4 TRANSDUCER SEMIGROUPS

In Section 5.3 we discussed several properties of transducers which depend solely on the transition function. For example, both connectedness and strong connectedness are defined in terms of the transition but not the output function. In this section, we will continue this emphasis. Since almost everything we have to say will depend only on the M function we find it convenient to abstract from the notion of a transducer to that of a transition system.

Definition 5.4.1. A *transition system* is the projection $\mathbf{T}_S = \langle S, Q, M \rangle$ of a reduced finite transducer $\mathbf{T} = \langle S, Q, M, N, O \rangle$.

One of our aims in this section is to relate the theory of automata to the theory of semigroups by way of transition systems.[8] Although the subject is getting to be an important one in the study of automata, we shall have to content ourselves here with little more than an introduction and an application to one interesting class of transducers, the permutation machines. To begin with we introduce the notion of a quotient semigroup (the student would do well to review the material on groups and semigroups in Section 1.3, at this point).

Definition 5.4.2. Given a monoid $M = \langle A, \cdot, e \rangle$ and an equivalence relation P defined on A. P is a *congruence relation* iff for all $a, b, c, d \in A$ whenever aPb, then $c \cdot a \cdot dPc \cdot b \cdot d$ (or, more perspicuously, $cadPcbd$).

As usual, we will employ the notation $[a]_P$ for the set of elements of A which are equivalent to a under an equivalence relation P.

Theorem 5.4.3. Let M be a monoid and let there be a relation P satisfying Definition 5.4.2. P determines a partition M/P, which is, in fact, a monoid and a homomorphic image of M.

Proof. See Section 1.3 and Exercise 5.4(2).

We write $\langle A/P, \cdot, [e] \rangle = M/P$, where A/P is the set of equivalence classes under P and where $[e]$ is the identity. Recall from Section 1.3 that the canonical mapping $\psi(a) = [a]$, $a \in A$, is a monoid homomorphism of M *onto* M/P since

$$\psi(a \cdot b) = [a \cdot b] = [a] \cdot [b] = \psi(a) \cdot \psi(b)$$

Thus M/P is a homomorphic image of M.

EXAMPLE 1. Let A be the set of positive integers, $\cdot$ the operation of multiplication, and $e = 1$. Then, as in Examples 17 and 18 in Section 1.1, let P be the relation of congruence modulo 3; that is, $a \equiv b$ (3), for any $a, b \in A$, iff a and b yield the same remainder $r_a = r_b$ upon division by 3.

[8] What we have to say will be applicable to the theory of finite acceptors (Chapter 7) and in a certain indirect way to finite generators (Chapter 8) as well as to transducers. What we are terming a transition system with initial state is in essential respects commonly referred to in the current literature as an "automaton." Our present usage of the latter term is, of course, generic.

P thus determines the partition consisting of the equivalence classes $\{1, 4, 7, \ldots\}$, etc., as in Example 18 of Section 1.1.

P is a congruence relation in the sense of our Definition 5.4.2, considering the set of positive integers as a semigroup under multiplication, as can be readily seen. Using Exercise 5.4(2) we can show that if $a \equiv b\,(3)$ and $a' \equiv b'\,(3)$, then $a \cdot a' \equiv b \cdot b'\,(3)$, and hence that the partition determined is, in fact, a quotient semigroup with $[a]\cdot[b] = [a \cdot b]$ the unambiguous operation.

We will now see how to construct a quotient monoid of the free monoid $\mathscr{S}$ in the generators S for any transition system. Recall that we write $\mathscr{S} = \langle S^*, \cdot, \Lambda \rangle$ (Example 1.3, (10)).

Definition 5.4.4. Suppose we have the transition system $\mathbf{T}_S = \langle S, Q, M \rangle$ and as usual $\mathscr{S}$, the free monoid on S. Let $x, y \in \mathscr{S}$. We define $x\,E\,y$ to mean that for every $q \in Q$, $M(q, x) = M(q, y)$; $x\,E\,y$ is read "x is equivalent to y mod $\mathbf{T}_S$."

It is easy to see that E is an equivalence relation, and that the interpretation is that two words on S are equivalent if they send $\mathbf{T}_S$ into the same state from any state q. But we may conclude a good deal more than this.

Corollary 5.4.5. The equivalence relation E modulo $\mathbf{T}_S$ is a congruence over S^*.

Proof is left to the student.

Corollary 5.4.6. Let $\mathbf{T}$ be a transition system and E the relation as in Definition 5.4.4. Then E determines a quotient monoid

$$\mathscr{S}/\mathbf{T}_S = \langle S^*/\mathbf{T}_S, \cdot, [\Lambda] \rangle$$

which is a homomorphic image of $\mathscr{S}$.

This corollary follows immediately from Corollary 5.4.5 and Theorem 5.4.3. As to notation, we will use, as in the early discussion $[x]$ for $\{y \mid x\,E\,y\}$ or, in other words for $\{y \mid (\forall q)(M(q, x) = M(q, y))\}$. Also we set $[x][y] = [xy]$ so that concatenation is used as the quotient monoid operator. Finally, we will use $[\Lambda]$ for the identity of $\mathbf{T}_S$ as indicated above.

Corollary 5.4.7. If $\mathbf{T}_S$ has n states, then $\mathscr{S}/\mathbf{T}_S$ has at most n^n elements and $\mathscr{S}/\mathbf{T}_S$ is a finite monoid.

Proof. For the student.

Corollary 5.4.8. Let $\mathbf{T}$ be a finite transducer and E a relation as in Definition 5.4.4. Then E determines $\mathscr{S}/\mathbf{T}$, a quotient monoid which is a homomorphic image of $\mathscr{S}$.

The quotient monoid $\mathscr{S}/\mathbf{T}$ constructed as above is frequently referred to as *the automaton* or *transducer monoid.* In order to avoid confusion with $\mathscr{S}$ we will refer to $\mathscr{S}/\mathbf{T}$, as is customary, as a *transducer semigroup* (and, in later sections, as an *acceptor semigroup* or more generally still as an *automaton semigroup*).

EXAMPLE 2. Consider the following two-state transition system (Table 5.4.1)

TABLE 5.4.1

	0	1
q_0	q_0	q_1
q_1	q_1	q_0

The transition diagram for this simple system (obtained by omitting output designation from the diagrams as defined by Definition 5.1.5) is shown in Fig. 5.4.1. Experimentation with the diagram shows that there are two classes of words of S^* determined modulo this system. These classes are very hard to describe with the equipment at our disposal. However, by proceeding intuitively, we define the class α in ordinary English as follows.

1(*a*) A word consisting of a sequence of any number of 0's is in α.

(*b*) A word consisting of any (including zero) number of 0's followed by an *even* number of 1's followed by any (including zero) number of 0's followed by an *even* number of 1's, etc., any number of times, is in α.

(*c*) Any number (including zero) of 0's followed by an *odd* number of 1's followed by any *positive* number of 0's followed by any *odd* number of 1's, etc., an *even* number of times, is in α.

2. If $x = yz$ and y and z are in α by 1a, 1b, or 1c, then x is in α.
3. x is in α only if its being so follows from 1 and 2.

β is the class of all words not in α, that is, $S^* - \alpha$; one may now verify that the system represented by Table 5.4.2 is a semigroup with the identity α and operation o given by $[x] \circ [y] = [xy]$. This semigroup is isomorphic to the additive semigroup on 0, 1 (cf. Example 1.3(3)).

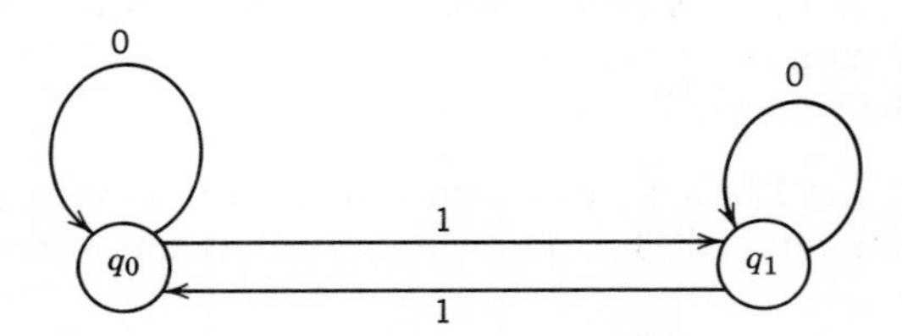

Fig. 5.4.1

TABLE 5.4.2

	α	β
α	α	β
β	β	α

As a check on the correctness of our determination of the equivalence classes of the Example 2, it is convenient to introduce a trivial variant of the transducer semigroup concept.

Definition 5.4.9. Given a transition system $\mathbf{T}_S = \langle S, Q, M \rangle$ with $x \in S^*$ as usual, define the function $\varphi_x: Q \to Q$ by $\varphi_x(q) = M(q, x)$. From this definition we have $\varphi_\Lambda(q) = q$, $\varphi_{xs}(q) = \varphi_s\varphi_x(q)$.

Clearly the set Φ of such functions is a monoid with identity φ_Λ. It is equally clear that Φ is isomorphic to $\mathscr{S}/\mathbf{T}_S$, since $\varphi_x(q) = \varphi_y(q)$ iff $M(q, x) = M(q, y)$ iff $[x] = [y]$.

Corollary 5.4.10. The monoid Φ is isomorphic to $\mathscr{S}/\mathbf{T}_S$.

Hence, alternatively, we may and indeed shall speak of Φ as the function semigroup of $\mathbf{T}_S$ or of the transducer related to $\mathbf{T}_S$. By reverting to Example 1 and observing the diagram, the reader may gain some insight if he notes that α is the class of all x such that $\varphi_x(q_i) = q_i$, for $i = 1, 0$, and that β is the class of y such that $\varphi_y(q_i) = q_j$, if $i \neq j$. We will provide an algorithm for determining the semigroup of a transition system later, beginning with Definition 5.4.18. At present let us explore some further relationships between semigroups and automata.

Theorem 5.4.11. Every finite monoid (semigroup with identity) is isomorphic to the semigroup of a transition system.

Proof. Consider any finite semigroup $F = \langle A, \circ, e \rangle$. Let $\mathbf{T}_S = \langle S, Q, M \rangle$ be a transition system such that $Q = A$, and such that S is indexed by A. For example if $A = \{0, 1, 2\}$, $S = \{s_0, s_1, s_2\}$. Define the function M as follows:

$$M(a, s_b) = a \circ b, \; a, b \in A$$

In the usual way, we construct the equivalence classes under E and thus, by Corollary 5.4.6, the semigroup $\mathscr{S}/\mathbf{T}_S$. Now let ψ be the mapping taking each $a \in A$ into the equivalence class $[s_a]$. We will show that ψ is, in fact, an isomorphism between F and $\mathscr{S}/\mathbf{T}_S$.

Assume that $[s_a] = [s_b]$. It follows that $s_a \, E \, s_b(\mathbf{T}_S)$, or in other words that $M(c, s_a) = M(c, s_b)$ for every state $c \in A$. Hence by the definition of the M function $c \circ a = c \circ b$ for all c, and in particular $e \circ a = e \circ b$. It follows that $a = b$, proving that ψ is one–one.

To show that ψ is onto we must prove that for any word $x \in S^*$ we can find $a \in A$ such that $\psi(a) = [x]$. Using induction on the length $l(x)$ of x, when $l(x) = 0$, we have $x = \Lambda$. Since $M(a, \Lambda) = a = a \circ e = M(a, s_e)$, for any a, it follows that $[\Lambda] = [s_e] = \psi(e)$. Next, if $l(x) = k + 1$, then $M(a, x) = M(a, ys_c) = M(M(a, y), s_c)$ for some symbol s_c. By induction hypothesis, there exists an element $b \in A$ such that $\psi(b) = [y]$, and since by construction $\psi(b) = [s_b]$, $[y] = [s_b]$. Hence $M(a, y) = M(a, s_b)$. Therefore $M(a, x) = M(M(a, s_b), s_c) = M(a \circ b, s_c) = (a \circ b) \circ c = a \circ (b \circ c) = M(a, s_{b \circ c})$. Hence $[x] = [s_{b \circ c}] = \psi(b \circ c)$.

Finally, by the preceding construction, $\psi(a \circ b) = [s_{a \circ b}]$ and also $\psi(a) \cdot \psi(b) = [s_a] \cdot [s_b]$. We will show that $[s_{a \circ b}] = [s_a] \cdot [s_b]$. Let $s_{a \circ b} = s_c$; then $M(d, s_c) = d \circ c = d \circ (a \circ b)$. But $d \circ (a \circ b) = (d \circ a) \circ b = M(d \circ a, s_b) = M(M(d, s_a), s_b) = M(d, s_a s_b) = M(d, s_c)$. Hence $[s_a s_b] = [s_c]$ and the desired equality is proved. Q.E.D.

As remarked by Myhill, to whom this theorem is due, the result shows that the variety of transition systems is at least as great as that of finite semigroups with identity. Oddly enough, however, it turns out that under an appropriate definition of "sameness" or isomorphism of transition systems there are instances of two nonisomorphic transition systems belonging to the same semigroup! It is easy to show that there are, in consequence, two transducers which are inequivalent (and minimal) but which share the same semigroup.

EXAMPLE 3 (McNaughton). The transition systems given in Tables 5.4.3*a* and 5.4.3*b* have the same semigroup, Table 5.4.3*c*. The semigroup (in fact,

TABLE 5.4.3*a*

	0	1
q_0	q_0	q_1
q_1	q_1	q_2
q_2	q_2	q_0

TABLE 5.4.3*b*

	0	1
q_0	q_2	q_1
q_1	q_0	q_2
q_2	q_1	q_0

TABLE 5.4.3*c*

	Λ	1	11
Λ	Λ	1	11
1	1	11	Λ
11	11	Λ	1

a group) is the semigroup of the system of Table 5.4.3*a* where we have written simply Λ for $[\Lambda]$, etc. It is an easy exercise [5.4(7) below] to see that this semigroup is isomorphic to that of Table 5.4.3*b*. Suppose we take as our definition of transition isomorphism the first part of Definition 5.2.5 where the map is of course one–one onto (cf. Definition 5.5.7), then it is easily verified that Tables 5.4.3*a* and 5.4.3*b* are nonisomorphic.

We continue with a brief treatment of the case when the semigroup of a transition system is a *group*.

Transducers are *deterministic* in the sense that for any word x and state q, $M(q, x)$ is uniquely determined. However, since it is quite possible that for two states q_i and q_j such that $q_i \neq q_j$, $M(q_i, x) = M(q_j, x)$ holds for some x, knowing the target state after an input of x does not always enable us to discover whether the transducer began in state q_i or q_j. If, on the other hand, we can go back and identify, from a target state q_k the state q_i such that $M(q_i, x) = q_k$, we say that the transducer is *backwards deterministic* or a *permutation* transducer. We will deal with this concept in terms of transition systems.

Definition 5.4.12. A system $\mathbf{T}_S$ is a *permutation transition system* if $\mathscr{S}/\mathbf{T}_S$ is a group, that is, if for every class $[x] \in \mathscr{S}/\mathbf{T}_S$ there is another class $[y]$ such that $[x][y] = [\Lambda]$. As is customary, we write $[x]^{-1}$ for $[y]$.

Corollary 5.4.13. Let $\mathbf{T}_S = \langle Q, S, M \rangle$. For every x

$$M(q_i, x) = M(q_j, x) \Rightarrow q_i = q_j$$

holds iff $\mathbf{T}_S$ is a permutation system.

Proof. For the student.

Theorem 5.4.14. Φ (cf. Definition 5.4.9) is a group iff (for each symbol $s \in S$) φ_s is a permutation.

Proof. If Φ is a group, then every element φ_s has an inverse and hence (recalling the discussion in Section 1.3) φ_s is one–one onto, that is, a permutation. Conversely, if φ_s and $\varphi_{s'}$ are permutations, so is $\varphi_s \circ \varphi_{s'}$ by Exercise 1.3(1). Hence, by induction, every element φ_x of Φ is a permutation. Therefore Φ is a group. Q.E.D.

Corollary 5.4.15. $\mathbf{T}_S$ is a permutation system iff each function φ_s is a permutation.

This follows from Theorems 5.4.14, and 5.4.10 and Definition 5.4.12.

Definition 5.4.16. Let $\mathbf{T}_a = \langle S, Q_a, M_a, N_a, O \rangle$ and $\mathbf{T}_b = \langle S, Q_b, M_b, N_b, O \rangle$ be transducers. The *direct sum* $\mathbf{T} = \mathbf{T}_a + \mathbf{T}_b$ is the transducer

$$\mathbf{T} = \langle S, Q, M, N, O \rangle$$

where Q, M, and N are constructed as follows:

$$Q = (Q_a \times \{a\}) \cup (Q_b \times \{b\})$$

where a, b are new symbols such that $a, b \notin Q_a$, $a, b \notin Q_b$;

$$M((q, a), s) = (M_a(q, s), a) \qquad q \in Q_a$$
$$M((q, b), s) = (M_b(q, s), b) \qquad q \in Q_b$$
$$N((q, a), s) = N_a(q, s) \qquad q \in Q_a$$

and

$$N((q, b), s) = N_b(q, s) \qquad q \in Q_b$$

From the definition, it should be apparent that the subsets of Q deriving from Q_a and Q_b are disjoint, and also that we could easily simplify the notation by making some new distinct auxiliary symbols correspond to each distinct pair (q, a) and (q, b) of Q, and, by using this simplification, we could rewrite the M and N functions using the foregoing relations. In the following theorem we will suppose that the concept direct sum has been extended in the natural way to any number n of transducers so that we may discuss, for instance, the direct sum $\mathbf{T}_1 + \mathbf{T}_2 + \cdots + \mathbf{T}_n = \mathbf{T}$. In such a case, the special symbols "a" and "b" used in Definition 5.4.16 become $a_1, a_2, \ldots, a_n$. Thus (q, a_j) will be the element derived from a state q of the jth transducer $\mathbf{T}_j$.

Theorem 5.4.17. Every permutation transducer $\mathbf{T}$ is isomorphic to the direct sum of strongly connected permutation transducers, or else is strongly connected.

Proof. Let $q_i, q_j \in Q$. Now define $q_i \sim q_j$ to mean that for some x, $\varphi_x(q_i) = q_j$. Since $\mathbf{T}$ is a permutation machine, it follows that $\sim$ is an equivalence relation: $\varphi_\Lambda(q) = q$, so $q \sim q$; if $q_i \sim q_j$, then $\varphi_x(q_i) = q_j$ for some x, and since φ_x is one–one onto, there is a y such that $\varphi_y(q_j) = q_i$, and hence $q_j \sim q_i$; finally, if $q_i \sim q_j$ and $q_j \sim q_k$, then for some x $\varphi_x(q_i) = q_j$ and for some y $\varphi_y(q_j) = q_k$, so that $\varphi_y\varphi_x(q_i) = \varphi_{xy}(q_i) = q_k$, and hence $q_i \sim q_k$.

As $\sim$ is an equivalence relation, it partitions Q into equivalence classes Q_j. Now if $\mathbf{T} = \langle S, Q, M, N, O\rangle$, then, using each class Q_j, we may construct transducers $\mathbf{T}_j = \langle S, Q_j, M_j, N_j, O_j\rangle$, where $O_j \subseteq O$ and $M_j(q_j, s) = M(q_j, s)$ and similarly for N_j.

Now since every state q_j of Q_j is equivalent under $\sim$ to $q_{j'} \in Q$, we have at once that for some x $\varphi_x(q_j) = q_{j'}$, or $M_j(q_j, x) = q_{j'}$. Hence by Definition 5.3.14, each $\mathbf{T}_j$ is strongly connected.

Since $\sim$ determines a partition, the direct sum of the transducers $\mathbf{T}_j$ has as many states as $\mathbf{T}$ itself. In other words, $K(Q) = K[\bigcup_j Q_j]$. Consequently, the function $\psi(q) = (q, a_j)$ is a one–one correspondence onto the direct sum machine. That ψ is an isomorphism is a routine and trivial verification. Q.E.D.

For use in later sections (especially Section 5.6), it is worthwhile to find a practical algorithm to obtain the semigroup of an automaton. Such a procedure can be developed by using the idea of a linear graph (cf. Footnote 4, Section 4.1). Recall that such an object is a collection of *nodes* and *branches*—that is, elements of a set joined with pairs of the elements.

Definition 5.4.18. Suppose $A = \{a_1, a_2, \ldots, a_m\}$ is a collection of nodes. A sequence of branches $(a_{i_1}, a_{i_2}), (a_{i_2}, a_{i_3}), \ldots, (a_{i_{n-1}}, a_{i_n})$ is a *path*, provided that $i_j \neq i_k$ for $1 < j, k \leq n$, and $i_1 \neq i_2$. The path is a *loop* iff $i_1 = i_n$. A graph is *connected* iff there is a path between every pair of nodes. A *tree* is a connected graph without loops.

Definition 5.4.19. Consider a node a such that $(a, a_{i_1}), (a, a_{i_2}), \ldots, (a, a_{i_p})$ are distinct branches; then a has *out* degree p. Similarly, if there are branches $(a_{i_1}, a), (a_{i_2}, a), \ldots, (a_{i_p}, a)$, then a has *in* degree p; a is a *root* iff it has in degree 0 [that is, there are no branches (a_{i_j}, a)]; a is a *leaf* if it has out degree 0. A tree is *rooted* if it has exactly one root.

REMARK. As in the case of transition diagrams one may think of the branch out of a into a' (a, a') as an arrow.

Definition 5.4.20. The *height* of a node a in a rooted tree with root r is the length of the path $(r, a_{i_1}), (a_{i_1}, a\ ), \ldots, (a_{i_n}, a)$. The kth *row* of a tree is the set of nodes of height k.

Definition 5.4.21. A *congruence tree* for a transition system $\mathbf{T}_S = \langle S, Q, M \rangle$ is a rooted tree such that

(a) the root has out degree $K(S) = m$;
(b) every other node has out degree m unless it is a leaf;
(c) the leftmost branch "growing" from (out of) each node is labeled s_0, the second left is labeled s_1, etc., to s_{m-1}, $s_i \in S$;
(d) the root is labeled by the ordered n-tuple $(q_0, q_1, \ldots, q_{n-1})$, $q_j \in Q$;
(e) proceeding on inductively, if
 (i) the kth row has been labeled,
 (ii) a is a node in that row labeled $(q_{i_0}, \ldots, q_{i_{n-1}}) = \overleftarrow{q}$,
 (iii) $\overleftarrow{q}$ is *not* the label of a node in any row with height less than k,
 (iv) $\overleftarrow{q}$ is not the label of any node in row k to the left of a,
 (v) (a, a') is in the graph and is labeled s_i,
then label the node a' in $k + 1$ by the n-tuple $(M(q_{i_0}, s_i), \ldots, M(q_{i_{n-1}}, s_i))$;
(f) no node or branch is labeled except under (c) to (e).

EXAMPLE 3. Given the transition system

	0	1	2
q_0	q_1	q_1	q_0
q_1	q_1	q_0	q_1
q_2	q_2	q_0	q_2

The congruence tree for this system will be such that every node which is not a leaf will have growing from it three branches; one labelled 0, the next from the left 1, etc., in accordance with Definition 5.4.21(a) and (b). Thus the tree may be drawn as in the Fig. 5.4.2. This indicates the shape of

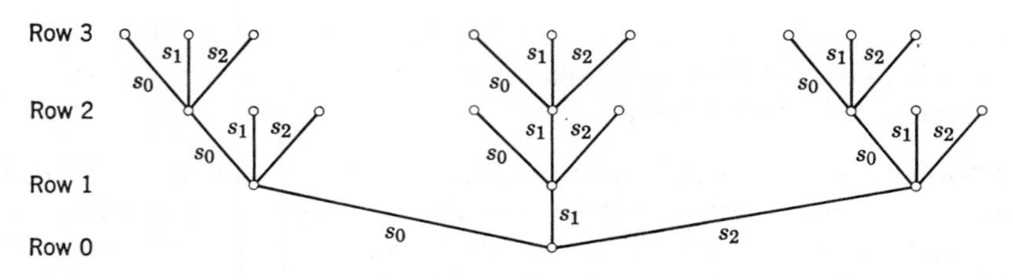

Fig. 5.4.2

the tree we want, although the indicated leaves at rows 2 and 3 are schematic—we do not know when to terminate at a node without actually using the algorithm provided for by (*d*) and (*e*) of Definition 5.4.21. So let us perform this step next.

In Fig. 5.4.3 the root is labeled (0, 1, 2) for (q_0, q_1, q_2), and the first row nodes are labeled directly, using the M function table. Next, consider the node (1, 1, 2). This will have three labeled branches growing out of it, and the target nodes will be labeled $(M(q_1, 0), M(q_1, 0), M(q_2, 0))$, $(M(q_1, 1), M(q_1, 1), M(q_2, 1))$, and $(M(q_1, 2), M(q_1, 2), M(q_2, 2))$, respectively. Figure 5.4.4 is obtained from these labels, again using the M table. Similarly, further branches are grown from the node (1, 0, 0) of Fig. 5.4.3; but none is grown from node (0, 1, 2) of the figure, since such a branch would violate (*e*), (iii), of Definition 5.4.21. Similarly, continuing with Fig. 5.4.4, only node (0, 0, 0) grows a branch. It is obvious that every path from the root leads to a leaf—the tree is finite. The student can verify this fact himself by using Corollary 5.4.7 in the context of the following informal discussion.

Note that in the completed tree (Fig. 5.4.5) each path from the root up to a node represents a function φ of the semigroup Φ of the example. Thus, $\varphi_1\varphi_1\varphi_0 = \varphi_{011}$, where 011 denotes a path from the root to the second leaf in the third row, is a function from (0, 1, 2) to (1, 1, 1); that is, $\varphi_{011}(0) = 1$, $\varphi_{011}(1) = 1$, and $\varphi_{011}(2) = 1$, a constant function. Also note that $\varphi_{011} = \varphi_{010} = \varphi_{10} = \varphi_{100} = \varphi_{110}$. Alternatively, using the isomorphic

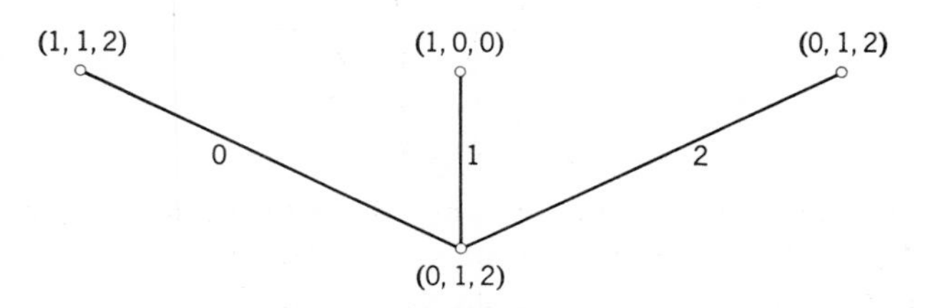

Fig. 5.4.3

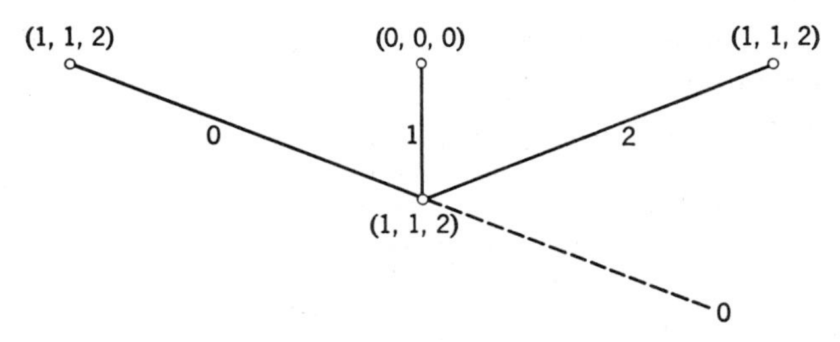

Fig. 5.4.4

semigroup $\mathscr{S}/\mathbf{T}_S$, each path denotes a word in an equivalence class. So in the same subexample, 011 is an element of a congruence class of which all members x satisfy $M(q_0, x) = q_1$, $M(q_1, x) = q_1$, and $M(q_2, x) = q_1$. It follows from the construction of congruence trees that every element of $\mathscr{S}/\mathbf{T}_S$ (or of Φ) is represented by such a tree.

To construct the multiplication table of $\mathscr{S}/\mathbf{T}_S$ we first impose an order on the nodes of the congruence tree. This order is by row height within the tree and by row position within each row from the left. Then the list of words of branch labels denoting paths from $(q_0, \ldots, q_{n-1})$ to any node $(q_{i_0}, \ldots, q_{i_{n-1}})$ is ordered by the order of $(q_{i_0}, \ldots, q_{i_{n-1}})$. This list of words is the *lexicographical* ordering of the words occurring in the tree. Note that if x and y are in the list, then x precedes y iff x precedes y in the usual lexicographical ordering of S^*: 0, 1, 2, ..., 00, 01, 02, ..., 10, 11, 12, ..., 20, 21, 22, ...

The next step is to construct a *tableau* of all of the semigroup elements represented in the tree. Thus the words taking (0, 1, 2) into (1, 1, 1) are to

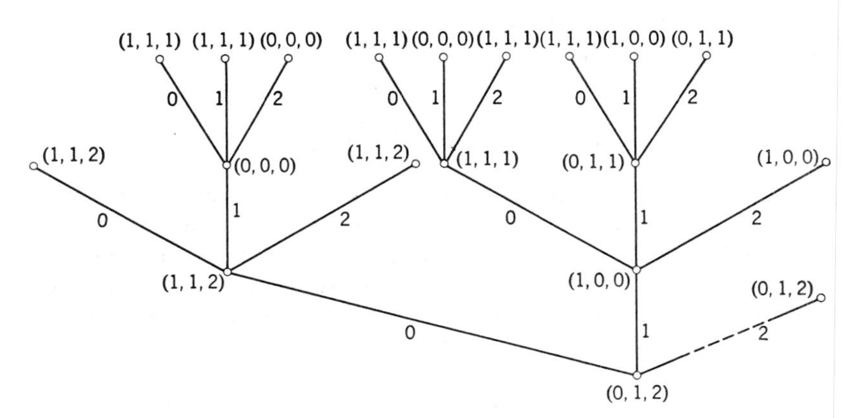

Fig. 5.4.5

be listed in lexicographical order. A convenient format to be used is given below in terms of this example.

TABLE 5.4.4

(0 1 2)	→ (1 1 2):	0, 00, 02
	→ (1 0 0):	1, 12, 111
	→ (0 1 2):	Λ, 2
	→ (0 0 0):	01, 012, 101
	→ (1 1 1):	10, 010, 011, 100, 102, 110
	→ (0 1 1):	11, 112

It is also convenient to write the information in Table 5.4.4 as a list of relations where, as above, "x" stands for "$[x]$":

TABLE 5.4.5

$0 = 00 = 02$
$1 = 12 = 111$
$\Lambda = 2$
$01 = 012 = 101$
$10 = 010 = 011 = 100 = 102 = 110$
$11 = 112$

Evidently $\mathscr{S}/\mathbf{T}_S$ for this example has six elements. Picking the six lexicographically first words of each class as representatives, that is, letting $x' = \sigma[x]$, x' being lexicographically first, we may write Table 5.4.6 for $\mathscr{S}/\mathbf{T}_S$ in the form.

TABLE 5.4.6

	Λ	0	1	01	10	11
Λ	Λ	0	1	01	10	11
0	0	0	01	01	10	10
1	1	10	11	01	10	1
01	01	10	10	01	10	01
10	10	10	01	01	10	10
11	11	10	1	01	10	11

Some explanation is required here as to the manner of computation of the elements of Table 5.4.6. We make use of Table 5.4.4 (or 5.4.5) together with the fact that the relation determining the classes is a congruence relation (Definition 5.4.2); thus suppose we were interested in discovering of which class in Table 5.4.5 the word 1022110 is a member. We know that

$$x \, E \, y \Rightarrow xz \, E \, yz \tag{1}$$

If $\boldsymbol{u} = wv$ and $w \neq \Lambda$, call w a *proper head* of $\boldsymbol{u}$ ($v = \Lambda$ is possible). Now scan 1022110 for the longest proper head x appearing in Table 5.4.5.

This is $x = 102$. Let y be the lexicographically earliest word in the same class as x. If 1022110 is xz and if y (in this case) is 01, then by (1) yz is 012110. Using the same process again we may replace the head 012 by 01 in 012110 yielding 01110. Another such replacement yields 1010, and then finally 010 and 10. Thus $1022110 \in [10]$. In Table 5.4.6, the entry $10 \cdot 10 = 1010 = 010 = 10$; similarly for the others.

It follows from the manner of construction of the congruence tree that every word $x \in S^*$ can be classified by use of the relations as exemplified in Table 5.4.5.

The verification of this fact is left to the student.

Theorem 5.4.22. The congruence tree of $\mathbf{T}_S$ effectively determines the semigroup $\mathscr{S}/\mathbf{T}_S$ of $\mathbf{T}_S$.

Notice that the representative words in the example do not include any occurrences of 2, which is, nevertheless, a symbol of S. This suggests that there is a transition system with the same semigroup on a smaller alphabet. Thus there is no necessary similarity of behavior among the transition systems having the same semigroup; the question of behavior and the relation of it to semigroup structure will be taken up in connection with acceptors in Chapter 7.

EXERCISES 5.4

1. A transition system with initial state is a quadruple $\langle S, Q, q_0, M\rangle$. Let the relation R on S^* be defined as $x\,R\,y$ iff $M(q_0, x) = M(q_0, y)$. (a) prove that R is an equivalence relation; (b) prove that $x\,R\,y$ implies that for all $z \in S^*$, $xz\,R\,yz$; (c) show by counterexample that R is not a congruence relation; (d) show by counterexample that the partition determined by R is not necessarily a semigroup with identity.

2. If f is any mapping on $A \times A$ into A, then an equivalence relation R on A is a congruence relation iff for all $a, b, c, d \in A$, $a\,R\,b \wedge c\,R\,d \Rightarrow f(a, c)\,R\,f(b, d)$. Show that if f is concatenation ($f(a, c) = ac$), then our Definition 5.4.2 is equivalent to the above definition of congruence.

3. Prove the Theorems (a) 5.4.5; (b) 5.4.7; (c) 5.4.10.

4. Prove Corollary 5.4.13.

5. Construct a Moore transducer whose semigroup is isomorphic to the group of transformations of a rectangle.

6. Given a finite alphabet A, write a definition of "lexicographical order" w.r.t. elements of A^* which does not make use of the notion of a tree, that is, of a linear graph. Any "natural" lexicographical order will do.

7. Given the cyclic group[9] of order three (that is, with three elements). Using the method of Theorem 5.4.11, construct a transition system with

[9] A cyclic group is one all the elements of which are equal to a power of some *one* generator.

semigroup isomorphic to the given group. Independently find another transition system with fewer input symbols (with two, in fact) which has the same group as semigroup.

8. Making use of the tree idea, develop an alternative to the matrix algorithm of Section 5.3 for deciding the connectedness of a transducer.

5.5 THE LATTICE OF TRANSITION SYSTEMS

Throughout Chapter 5 we have been developing various properties of transducers which depend, in one way or another, on the concept of equivalence relation. In Section 5.2 we found, for instance, that a reduced (complete) machine is in fact determined by the relation $\equiv$. In Section 5.4, on the other hand, we discussed a certain congruence relation E on S^* induced by a transition system. E, furthermore, gave rise to a certain semigroup of equivalence classes of S^*, a semigroup which we have seen to be useful in studying structural properties of transducers (that is, transition systems).

In Section 5.5 we will again take up the study of equivalence classes of states, but this time with the purpose of understanding the decomposition of transducers into systems of independently operating subtransducers.

In order to understand the problem of decomposition, consider the "black box" representation of a transducer in Fig. 5.5.1. If this machine begins in state q and has an input s, it emits an output o and transits to state q, for example. The "wire" marked with an arrow indicates the fact that the state q of the machine is a function of the previous state and the input.

A parallel transducer is depicted in Fig. 5.5.2. In this case the component machine $\mathbf{T}_a$ begins in the initial state q_{a_0}, while $\mathbf{T}_b$ begins in q_{b_0}. Let us assume that when an input s is injected, $\mathbf{T}_a$ goes into q_{a_1} and *simultaneously* $\mathbf{T}_b$ goes into q_{b_1}.[10] We may think of the transducer which is composed of $\mathbf{T}_a$ and $\mathbf{T}_b$, thus in parallel, as passing from the state denoted by the pair

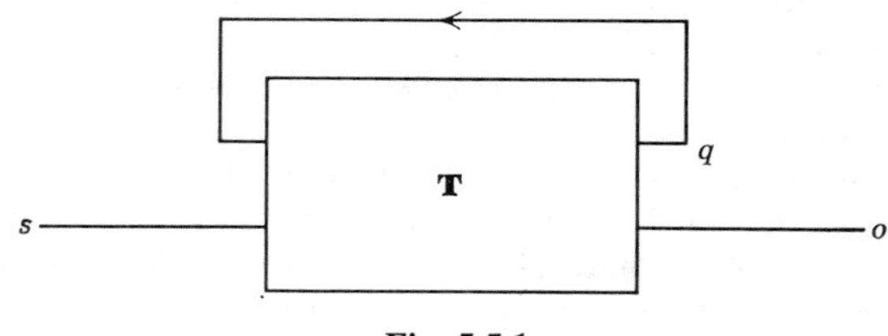

Fig. 5.5.1

[10] In this and the following illustration we assume that $\mathbf{T}_a$ and $\mathbf{T}_b$ are synchronous in the sense that the sequences of states are indexed the same.

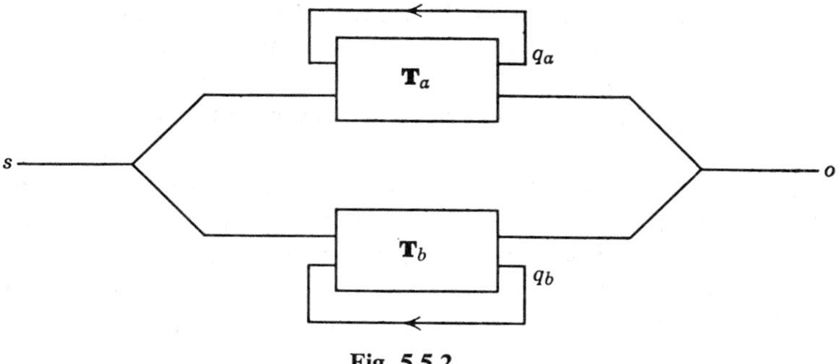

Fig. 5.5.2

(q_{a_0}, q_{b_0}) into the state (q_{a_1}, q_{b_1}) upon receipt of s. The output o is emitted as a function of s and the pair (q_{a_0}, q_{b_0}).

Similarly, consider a *cascade* transducer as in Fig. 5.5.3. Note that the output of $\mathbf{T}_a$ is the *input* to $\mathbf{T}_b$. This is expressed as in the diagram by the relation $o_a = s_b$. In this case $\mathbf{T}_a$ and $\mathbf{T}_b$ start in q_{a_0} and q_{b_0}, and when s_a is injected q_{a_0} goes to q_{a_1}, and o_a is emitted in accordance with the relation $N_a(q_{a_0}, s_a) = o_a$. Simultaneously, o_a serves as input to $\mathbf{T}_b$, so we have $N_b(q_{b_0}, s_b) = N_b(q_{b_0}, o_a) = o_b$. Moreover, as q_{a_0} passes to q_{a_1}, q_{b_0} passes to q_{b_1}, that is, $M_b(q_{b_0}, s_b) = M_b(q_{b_0}, o_a) = q_{b_1}$. As in the instance of the parallel composition, the cascade composite transducer has states (q_a, q_b).

Of course n-fold parallel or cascade compositions are possible. Besides, research workers in this field have considered fairly general compositions of parallel, cascade, and even feedback structures. However, we shall here limit ourselves to the parallel case. In Section 5.6 we shall also include serial compositions.

Our problem, then, is to characterize those transducers which are amenable to decomposition in the parallel sense of Fig. 5.5.2. This question is equivalent to finding necessary and sufficient conditions for a given transducer to be isomorphic to a system of component machines in parallel. The desired solution to the problem is to be found in the study of a certain relation between transducers having initial states and certain partitions on S^*. Thus the theoretical aim (which is possibly of more

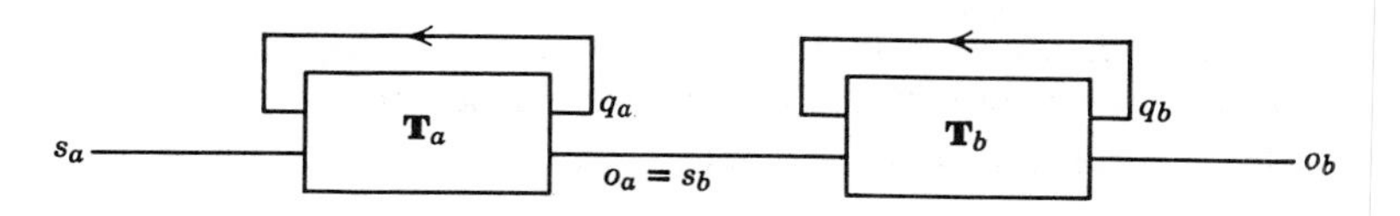

Fig. 5.5.3

importance than the application to decomposition) will be to show that the set of all transducers on a fixed alphabet S forms a partially ordered system with the relation of *transition homomorphism* (cf. Definitions 5.2.5 and 5.5.7) as the ordering relation. Furthermore, we are about to see that this system of systems is a *lattice* isomorphic to the lattice of partitions of S^* w.r.t. the relation R of Exercise 5.5.4(1). Finally, our proposed application will be that a transducer is decomposable into parallel systems iff it is isomorphic to the lattice meet of two other transducers of a certain description in the (aforementioned) lattice of transition systems. (The reader, if troubled, should reread the later portions of Section 1.3.) In this discussion (as we did in Section 5.4) we will use only the next-state function, and hence all of our discussion will develop in terms of transition systems. Indeed, our classification of transducers by certain structural relationships will be in terms of the M function alone. Further, the application of our findings to transducers will remain on an informal basis. One of these applications will be to the problem of economical sequential circuit synthesis (in Chapter 6). The reader may find it of motivational value to read Sections 6.0 and 6.1 next, and then return to this section.

Everything further we have to say in this section will be about connected transition systems with initial states. These are the quadruples $\mathbf{T}_S = \langle S, Q, q_0, M \rangle$ (Definition 5.4.1) with S fixed throughout the inquiry. The theory we are about to discuss considers transition systems where Q may be any nonempty (including infinite) set. Clearly no such system is a part of an automaton, yet the decomposition results will hold for the finite case. We shall indicate the significance of the finiteness requirement for automata theory in Section 7.1.

We begin by recalling Example 23, Section 1.3, that the collection of partitions on a set of objects constitutes a lattice. This will follow directly from the construction in the next paragraph together with Definitions 5.5.1 and 5.5.2.

If $\leq$ is the lattice partial ordering relation and P_1, P_2 any two partitions, then $P_1 \leq P_2$ means that every class of P_1 is contained in some class of P_2.[11] Also if $\cap$ is the lattice meet, then $P_1 \cap P_2$ is characterized as follows:

a and b are in the same class of $P_1 \cap P_2$ iff a and b are in the same class in both P_1 and P_2. In order to define the lattice join for partitions we need a further conceptual apparatus.

Definition 5.5.1. Given a family of sets $A_1, \ldots, A_n$, A_i and A_l are *chain connected* in the family iff there exists a sequence of sets $A_{i_1}, A_{i_2}, \ldots, A_{i_k}$ such that $A_i = A_{i_1}$, $A_l = A_{i_k}$, and for $j = 1, 2, \ldots, k-1$, $A_{i_j} \bigcap A_{i_{j+1}} \neq \varnothing$.

[11] Throughout this section we consistently use "class" to mean "equivalence class."

Definition 5.5.2. Let P be the union of the partitions P_1 and P_2; then $P_1 \cup P_2$, the *join* of P_1 and P_2, is the set of all classes $[a]$ such that $[a]$ is the union of chain connected classes of P.

EXAMPLE 1. Let $A = \{a, b, c, d, e\}$ and suppose $P_1 = \{\{a, b\}, \{c\}, \{d, e\}\}$, $P_2 = \{\{a, e, c\}, \{b, d\}\}$, and $P_3 = \{\{a\}, \{b\}, \{d\}, \{c, e\}\}$; then

$$P_1 \cap P_2 = \{\{a\}, \{b\}, \{c\}, \{d\}, \{e\}\} = 0 \tag{1}$$

$$P_1 \cup P_2 = \{\{a, b, c, d, e\}\} = 1 \tag{2}$$

and

$$P_3 \leq P_2 \leq P_1 \cup P_2 \tag{3}$$

also

$$P_2 \cap P_3 = P_3 \tag{4a}$$

$$P_2 \cup P_3 = P_2 \tag{4b}$$

Expressions (4a) and (4b), in line with (18) of Section 1.3 are what we should expect from (3). Note that the greatest or 1 element of the lattice is the partition whose sole class is A. Hereafter we will use I instead of 1 for the special lattice of partitions (or equivalence relations); 0 is the partition consisting exactly of the unit sets of A, and is the least element.

In Section 1.1 we noted a certain duality between partitions and equivalence relations. Corresponding to every partition there is such a relation and *vice versa*. It is convenient to use relations in some contexts and partitions in others, although one concept would be sufficient. Thus we will use symbols R_1, R_2, etc., for equivalence relations and P_1, P_2, etc., for the corresponding partitions. Moreover, we will use $[\alpha]_{R_i}$ with an appropriate variable α to denote the equivalence class of elements the same as α under R_i.

To use relations we need the analogs of the lattice operations and relations for partitions. Thus if R_1 and R_2 are two equivalence relations, then $R_1 \leq R_2$ has the set-theoretic meaning of inclusion of one set (of pairs) in another, while the meet $R_1 \cap R_2$ is set intersection. As in the case of partitions, the join is slightly complicated.

Definition 5.5.3. If R_1 and R_2 are equivalence relations on A, the join $R_1 \cup R_2$ is the least equivalence relation containing R_1 and R_2. $R_1 \cup R_2$ is called the *transitive closure* of R_1 and R_2.

Definition 5.5.3 states that $R_1 \cup R_2$ consists of all pairs in R_1 or in R_2, or those which can be obtained from such pairs by repeated use of the transitivity rule.

REMARK. If R_1 and R_2 are equivalence relations so are $R_1 \cup R_2$ and $R_1 \cap R_2$.

EXAMPLE 2. R_1, R_2, and R_3 correspond to the respectively indexed partitions of Example 1. Thus

$$R_1 = \{(a, a), (a, b), (b, a), (b, b), (c, c), (d, d), (d, e), (e, d), (e, e)\}$$
$$R_2 = \{(a, a), (a, e), (a, c), (e, a), (e, c), (e, e), (c, a), (c, e), (c, c), (b, b), (b, d), (d, b), (d, d)\}$$
$$R_3 = \{(a, a), (b, b), (d, d), (c, c), (c, e), (e, c), (e, e)\}$$

Hence

$$R_1 \cap R_2 = \{(a, a), (b, b), (c, c), (d, d), (e, e)\}$$

which is simply the set-theoretic intersection of R_1 and R_2. Now we will study the construction of $R_1 \cup R_2$. It will consist of every pair in either R_1 or R_2 together with pairs obtained by transitivity. For example $(a, b) \in R_1$ and $(b, d) \in R_2$; and although $(a, d) \notin R_1, R_2$, it is an element in $R_1 \cup R_2$ since by transitivity (a, b) and (b, d) imply (a, d). Proceeding in this fashion, the reader will find that $R_1 \cup R_2$, as should be expected from the facts of Example 1, is the *universal* relation. We will denote this relation by I. Similarly the *identity* relation, which is exemplified by $R_1 \cap R_2$ above, is denoted by 0. *Caution*: $0 \neq \varnothing$.

Recall the general definition of a congruence relation w.r.t. a two variable function (binary operation) as given in Exercise 2 of Section 5.4. If f is a function on $A \times A$ into A, then R is a congruence iff

$$a\,R\,b \wedge c\,R\,d \Rightarrow f(a, c)\,R\,f(b, d) \tag{5}$$

Similarly, if g is a function of one variable (a singulary operator), then R is a congruence iff

$$a\,R\,b \Rightarrow g(a)\,R\,g(b) \tag{6}$$

We will speak of partitions corresponding to congruence relations as *congruence partitions* or, alternatively, as partitions with the *substitution property*. First we show that congruency is preserved under lattice operations. We give the proof for an arbitrary set with 1-ary function as above. The extension to any n-ary function is easy.

Theorem 5.5.4. Given a set A and $g: A \to A$. If R_1 and R_2 are congruences on A w.r.t. g, then $R_1 \cap R_2$ and $R_1 \cup R_2$ are also congruences.

Proof. Assume $a(R_1 \cap R_2)b$. By definition $a\,R_1\,b$ and $a\,R_2\,b$. Thus by hypothesis $g(a)\,R_1\,g(b)$ and $g(a)\,R_2\,g(b)$. Hence $(g(a), g(b))$ is in $R_1 \cap R_2$, that is, $g(a)(R_1 \cap R_2)g(b)$.

Now assume $a(R_1 \cup R_2)b$. If $a\,R_i\,b$ ($i = 1$ or 2), then $g(a)\,R_i\,g(b)$ by hypothesis. Since $R_i \leq R_1 \cup R_2$, $g(a)(R_1 \cup R_2)g(b)$. Suppose, on the other hand, that $a(R_1 \cup R_2)b$ arises because $a\,R_i\,c_1$, $c_1\,R_i\,c_2, \ldots, c_m\,R_i\,b$. Then we have $g(a)\,R_i\,g(c_1)$, $g(c_1)\,R_i\,g(c_2)$, etc., and owing to the inclusion stated above, $g(a)(R_1 \cup R_2)g(c_1)$, $g(c_1)(R_1 \cup R_2)g(c_2)$, etc. Finally, from the fact that $R_1 \cup R_2$ is an equivalence relation we have that $g(a)(R_1 \cup R_2)g(b)$.

Q.E.D.

In the case of transition systems, we are interested in congruence relations on sets of states. Thus in conformity with (6) we will say that R is a congruence on Q, for some system $\mathbf{T}_S$, iff

$$q\, R\, q' \Rightarrow (\forall s)(M(q, s)\; R\; M(q', s))$$

In words, R is a congruence only if the *next states* of equivalent states are still equivalent.[12]

EXAMPLE 3. The relation $\equiv$ of Section 5.1 is a congruence by Theorem 5.1.8. The relations $\equiv (k)$ are not congruences, however.

EXAMPLE 4. In the transducer in Table 5.5.1, the partition

$$P_1 = \{\{q_0, q_1, q_2\}, \{q_3, q_4, q_5\}\}$$

has the substitution property.

TABLE 5.5.1

	M		N	
	0	1	0	1
q_0	q_3	q_2	0	2
q_1	q_5	q_2	2	2
q_2	q_4	q_1	1	1
q_3	q_1	q_4	1	1
q_4	q_0	q_3	0	0
q_5	q_2	q_3	2	2

To check this fact, note that q_0, q_1, and q_2 all go into the partition of equivalent states q_3, q_5, q_4 under input 0 and into the partition consisting of themselves under 1. This is similarly true for q_3, q_4, and q_5. Formally $q_0\; R_1\; q_1 \Rightarrow M(q_0, 0)\; R_1\; M(q_1, 0)$, etc. Next we discover by experimentation with the table that $P_2 = \{\{q_0, q_5\}, \{q_1, q_4\}, \{q_2, q_3\}\}$ also has the substitution property. By Theorem 5.5.4, which was just proved, it follows that $R_1 \cap R_2$

[12] Strictly speaking, congruences with respect to 2-ary functions are such on the cartesian product $A \times A$ of a set A with itself and not w.r.t. functions such as M, whose domain is $Q \times S$. However, in view of Definition 5.4.9 we may take $M(q, s)\; R\; M(q', s)$ to mean $\varphi_s(q)\; R\; \varphi_s(q')$. Then $q\; R\; q'$ implies $(\forall s)(M(q, s)\; R\; M(q', s))$ iff $\varphi_s(q)\; R\; \varphi_s(q')$ for every function φ_s. Thus the congruence here is so w.r.t. singulary functions as in (6).

In a similar vein some writers complain that h in Definition 5.5.7 should not be considered as a homomorphism. However, the formulation

$$h(q_{a_0}) = q_{b_0}$$
$$h(\varphi_s(q_a)) = \varphi_s(h(q_a)) \quad \text{for every } s$$

is clearly immune from criticism.

(or $P_1 \cap P_2$) is also a congruence, but is the trivial one $R_1 \cap R_2 = 0$. Also $R_1 \cup R_2 = I$.

Fortunately, as the student may already have observed, there is an algorithm for determining partitions with the substitution property, or, equivalently, for congruence relation. Since every transition system has a finite set of states Q, there is only a finite number of partitions to check.[13] Any candidate for the substitution property may then be tested as in Example 4 by checking whether pairs of equivalent states go into equivalent pairs under the M function. Also pairs of partitions which have the property generate other pairs by the meet and join operations.

Another operation on relations, besides the meet and join, which will be of use later, is the Peirce product.

Definition 5.5.5. The *Peirce product* of any two relations R_1, R_2 over the set A is

$$R_1 \mid R_2 = \{(a, b) \mid (\exists c)(a\, R_1\, c \wedge c\, R_2\, b)\}$$

where a, b, c are understood to be in A.

EXAMPLE 5. $A = \{1, 2, 3\}$; R_1 is $<$ and R_2 is $>$. Then

$$R_1 \mid R_2 = \{(1, 1), (1, 2), (2, 1), (2, 2)\}$$

The student should also verify the following expressions. $R_1 \mid R_2 \neq R_2 \mid R_1$ (Peirce product is not commutative); $(R_1 \mid R_2) \mid R_3 = R_1 \mid (R_2 \mid R_3)$, (the product is associative); $R_1 \mid R_2 \cup R_2 \mid R_1 = \mathrm{I}$; $R_1 \mid R_2 \cap R_2 \mid R_1 = \{(2, 2)\}$. Finally, note should be taken of the fact that R_1 and R_2 can be equivalence relations without $R_1 \mid R_2$ being so.

We also record here a theorem for future reference.

Theorem 5.5.6. For any equivalence relations R_1 and R_2

$$R_1 \mid R_2 = R_2 \mid R_1 \Leftrightarrow R_1 \mid R_2 = R_1 \cup R_2$$

Thus a necessary and sufficient condition that R_1 and R_2 commute is that the Peirce product equal the join of R_1 and R_2.

Proof. If $R_1 \mid R_2 = R_1 \cup R_2$, then since $R_1 \mid R_2$ is symmetric

$$R_1 \mid R_2 = R_2 \mid R_1$$

[13] The number of partitions $H(n)$ of a set with n objects may be determined recursively as follows.

$$H(0) = 1$$

$$H(n+1) = \sum_{r=0}^{n} \binom{n}{r} H(r)$$

where

$$\binom{n}{r} = \frac{n!}{r!(n-r)!}$$

Conversely, assume $a(R_1 \cup R_2)b$. By the definition of the join (5.5.3) either (i) $a\ R_1\ b$, (ii) $a\ R_2\ b$, or (iii) there are $c_1, \cdots, c_j$ such that $a\ R_{i_1}\ c_1 \wedge c_1\ R_{i_2}\ c_2 \wedge \cdots \wedge c_j\ R_{i_j}\ b$, $i_k = 1, 2$.

CASE (i).
$$a\ R_1\ b \Rightarrow a\ R_1\ b \wedge b\ R_2\ b$$

since R_2 is an equivalence relation. Hence,

$$a\ R_1\ b \Rightarrow (\exists c)(a\ R_1\ c \wedge c\ R_2\ b) \tag{7}$$

CASE (ii). This is similar to Case (i),

$$a\ R_2\ b \Rightarrow (\exists c)(a\ R_2\ c \wedge c\ R_1\ b) \tag{8}$$

CASE (iii).

$$a\ R_{i_1}\ c_1 \wedge c_1\ R_{i_2}\ c_2 \wedge \cdots \wedge c_{ij}\ R_i\ b \Rightarrow a\ R_i | R_i | \cdots R_i\ b$$

By the given commutativity and associativity of $|$, we obtain either (7) or (8). Hence $a(R_1 \cup R_2)b$ implies $aR_1 \mid R_2b$ or $aR_2 \mid R_1b$. And, trivially, $aR_1 \mid R_2b$ implies $a(R_1 \cup R_2)b$. From these facts, by a simple logical argument which we leave to the student, the theorem follows. Q.E.D.

We next modify the notion of transducer homomorphism (see Definition 3.2.5) for transition systems with initial states.

Definition 5.5.7. Let $\mathbf{T}_{\mathrm{S}_a} = \langle S, Q_a, q_{a_0}, M_a \rangle$ and $\mathbf{T}_{\mathrm{S}_b} = \langle S, Q_b, q_{b_0}, M_b \rangle$ be two transition systems. The mapping $h: Q_a \to Q_b$ is a *transition homomorphism* iff

1. $h(q_{a_0}) = q_{b_0}$
2. $h(M_a(q_a, s)) = M_b(h(q_a), s)$ for all s

Furthermore, if h is one–one and onto, it is a *transition isomorphism.*

Corollary 5.5.8. The following properties of transition homomorphism follow directly from the definition.

(*a*) Clause 2 of 5.5.7 may be replaced by

$$h(M_a(q_a, x)) = M_b(h(q_a), x) \qquad \text{for all } x$$

(*b*) There is at most *one* onto homomorphism between any $\mathbf{T}_{\mathrm{S}_a}$ and $\mathbf{T}_{\mathrm{S}_b}$.

(*c*) There is a decision procedure for determining whether any map h is a transition homomorphism.

Theorem 5.5.9. Let $\mathbf{T}_{\mathrm{S}_a}$ and $\mathbf{T}_{\mathrm{S}_b}$ be systems as in Definition 5.5.7. Any homomorphism h induces a congruence relation R_h on the domain Q_a of h. This relation is specified by

$$q_a\ R_h\ q_a' \Leftrightarrow h(q_a) = h(q_a')$$

Proof. Assume $q_a \; R_h \; q_a'$; then, by the above

$$\begin{aligned} h(q_a) = h(q_a') &\Rightarrow M_b(h(q_a), s) = M_b(h(q_a'), s) \\ &\Leftrightarrow h(M_a(q_a, s)) = h(M_a(q_a', s)) \\ &\Leftrightarrow M_a(q_a, s) \; R_h \; M_a(q_a', s) \end{aligned}$$

Q.E.D.

Somewhat reminiscent of Corollary 5.4.6 in which we indicated the determination of a quotient monoid under the special congruence E, we now have the *quotient transition system* $\mathbf{T}_S/R$ determined by any congruence R on the states of $\mathbf{T}_S$.

Theorem 5.5.10. Let $\mathbf{T}_S = \langle S, Q, q_0, M \rangle$ be a transition system and R a congruence relation on Q. R determines the *quotient transition system* $\mathbf{T}_S/R$.

Proof. $\mathbf{T}_S/R = \langle S, Q/R, [q_0]_R, M/R \rangle$

where

$$Q/R = \{[q]_R \mid q \in Q\}$$

and

$$M/R([q]_R, s) = [M(q, s)]_R$$

It is sufficient to show that the latter relation is independent of the choice of $q' \in [q]_R$; hence we set $M/R([q']_R, s) = [M(q', s)]_R$. But since R is a congruence, $q \; R \; q' \Rightarrow M(q, s) \; R \; M(q', s)$, and consequently $[M(q', s)]_R = [M(q, s)]_R$.

Moreover, the canonical mapping given by $h(q) = [q]_R$ is a transition homomorphism.

Q.E.D.

EXAMPLE 6. Consider once more the relation $\equiv$ of Section 5.2; since it is a congruence relation it yields, except for the σ function, the transducer $\mathbf{T}_b$ of that section.

The proof of 5.5.10, except for notation, is the same as that of (3) in 5.2.

EXAMPLE 7. The partition P_1 of Example 4 has the substitution property. Hence $\mathbf{T}_S/R_1 = \langle S, Q/R_1, [q_0]_{R_1}, M/R_1 \rangle$ is the quotient transition system of $\mathbf{T}_S = \langle S, Q, q_0, M \rangle$ displayed by the M part of Table 5.5.1. The table for $\mathbf{T}_S/R_1$ is Table 5.5.2.

TABLE 5.5.2

$\mathbf{T}_S/R_1$

	0	1
$[q_0]_{R_1}$	$[q_3]_{R_1}$	$[q_0]_{R_1}$
$[q_3]_{R_1}$	$[q_0]_{R_1}$	$[q_3]_{R_1}$

Definition 5.5.11. A system $\mathbf{T}_S = \langle S, Q, q_0, M \rangle$ where Q is no longer necessarily finite, is a *free transition system* if the function h mapping q_0 into q_0' of any system $\mathbf{T}_S' = \langle S, Q', q_0', M' \rangle$ can be extended to a homomorphism of $\mathbf{T}_S$ onto $\mathbf{T}_S'$.

Corollary 5.5.12. A *free* transition system (on the alphabet S) is unique to within an isomorphism.

Proof. For the student.

Now let $\mathscr{S} = \langle S^*, \Lambda, \cdot \rangle$ be as usual the free monoid on S. Then $\mathbf{T}_{S\mathscr{S}} = \langle S, S^*, \Lambda, M_{\mathscr{S}} \rangle$ is an infinite transition system (which is a creation not stemming in any way from Definition 5.4.1) in which S is the alphabet, S^* the set of states, Λ the initial state and $M_{\mathscr{S}}: S^* \times S \to S^*$ where $M_{\mathscr{S}}(x, s) = xs$. Hence we also have $M_{\mathscr{S}}(x, ys) = x(ys) = (xy)s = M_{\mathscr{S}}(xy, s) = M_{\mathscr{S}}(M_{\mathscr{S}}(x, y), s)$.

We will use $\mathbf{T}_{S\mathscr{S}}$, its property of being a free system, and Theorem 5.5.9 to show the existence of a set of right invariant equivalence relations on S^*. We will then show that this set constitutes a partially ordered system isomorphic to the set of transition systems over S ordered by homomorphism.

Theorem 5.5.13. $\mathbf{T}_{S\mathscr{S}}$ *is the free transition system on S.*

Proof. Consider any system $\mathbf{T}_S = \langle S, Q, q_0, M \rangle$ and let $h(\Lambda) = q_0$. Next extend h to sequences by $h(x) = M(q_0, x)$. Thus h is a map from the states of $\mathbf{T}_{S\mathscr{S}}$ *onto* states of $\mathbf{T}_S$ as may be seen in the following way. Since $\mathbf{T}_S$ is by our general assumption a connected system, there must exist x such that $M(q_0, x) = q$ exists for all $q \in Q$. Hence in any case $h^{-1}(q)$ exists. Next,

$$h(M_{\mathscr{S}}(x, s)) = h(xs) = M(q_0, xs) = M(M(q_0, x), s) = M(h(x), s)$$

which together with Corollary 5.5.12 proves the theorem. Q.E.D.

Definition 5.5.14. An equivalence relation R on A is *right invariant* w.r.t. a 2-ary function $f: A \times A \to A$ if for any $c \in A$, $a\,R\,b \Rightarrow f(a, c)\,R\,f(b, c)$.

EXAMPLE 8. The relation R of Exercise 5.4(1) is right invariant on S^* w.r.t. concatenation.

Theorem 5.5.15. Any congruence relation of $\mathbf{T}_{S\mathscr{S}}$ is right invariant on S^*, and conversely.

Proof. Suppose R is such that for states $x, y \in S^*$

$$x\,R\,y \Rightarrow (\forall s)(M_{\mathscr{S}}(x, s)\,R\,M_{\mathscr{S}}(y, s))$$

But then also

$$M_{\mathscr{S}}(x, z)\,R\,M_{\mathscr{S}}(y, z) \Rightarrow M_{\mathscr{S}}(M_{\mathscr{S}}(x, z), s)\,R\,M_{\mathscr{S}}(M_{\mathscr{S}}(y, z), s)$$

So by induction we have: $x\,R\,y \Rightarrow (\forall z)(M_{\mathscr{S}}(x, z)\,R\,M_{\mathscr{S}}(y, z))$. By the definition of the function $M_{\mathscr{S}}$ this yields $x\,R\,y \Rightarrow (\forall z)(xz\,R\,yz)$. And therefore by Definition 5.5.14 R is right invariant on S^*. Q.E.D.

By Theorem 5.5.9 a homomorphism induces a congruence relation on its domain. Hence for arbitrary $\mathbf{T}_S$, the homomorphism $h: \mathbf{T}_{S\mathscr{S}} \to \mathbf{T}_S$

induces a congruence on $\mathbf{T}_{S_{\mathscr{S}}}$. By Theorem 5.5.15, this relation will be a right invariance relation on S^*. We will call this relation (for arbitrary $\mathbf{T}_S$), R_h. Corresponding to $\mathbf{T}_{S_\alpha}$ we have R_{h_α}.

REMARK 5.5.16. Hence $x\ R_h\ y$ iff $h(x) = h(y)$ iff $M(q_0, x) = M(q_0, y)$ iff $(\forall z)(xz\ R_h\ yz)$. Thus, whereas the relation $(\forall q)(M(q, x) = M(q, y))$ defines a congruence relation on S^* (see Definition 5.4.4 and Corollary 5.4.5), $M(q_0, x) = M(q_0, y)$ defines a right invariance relation on S^*.

Theorem 5.5.17. The collection $\mathscr{P}$ of partitions under the right invariance relations R_{h_α} on S^* constitutes a lattice.

Proof. Define the function g_z on S^* by $g_z(x) = xz$.[14] Then $x\ R_{h_\alpha}\ y \Rightarrow g_z(x)\ R_{h_\alpha}\ g_z(y)$ for all z. We may next straightforwardly apply the method of Theorem 5.5.4 to show that if R_{h_a} and R_{h_b} are right invariant, so are $R_{h_a} \cup R_{h_b}$ and $R_{h_a} \cap R_{h_b}$. Consequently the set of all such relations, or equivalently of the determined partitions, constitutes a lattice. Q.E.D.

Theorem 5.5.18. There is a homomorphism ψ from $\mathbf{T}_{S_a}$ onto $\mathbf{T}_{S_b}$ iff $R_{h_a} \leq R_{h_b}$, where R_{h_a} and R_{h_b} are congruence relations induced on S^* by the homomorphisms h_a: $\mathbf{T}_{S_{\mathscr{S}}} \to \mathbf{T}_{S_a}$ and h_b: $\mathbf{T}_{S_{\mathscr{S}}} \to \mathbf{T}_{S_b}$.

Proof. Assume ψ: $\mathbf{T}_{S_a} \to \mathbf{T}_{S_b}$ and that we have given h_a and h_b as in the statement of the theorem. Note that h_b is unique by Corollary 5.5.8(*b*). Hence $\psi h_a = h_b$, since ψh_a is onto the states of $\mathbf{T}_{S_b}$ which by the assumption is the co-domain of ψ. Consequently,

$$\begin{aligned} x\ R_{h_a}\ y \Leftrightarrow h_a(x) = h_a(y) &\Rightarrow \psi(h_a(x)) = \psi(h_a(y)) \\ &\Leftrightarrow h_b(x) = h_b(y) \\ &\Leftrightarrow x\ R_{h_b}\ y \end{aligned} \tag{9}$$

Since x and y are arbitrary words, we have

$$(\forall x)(\forall y)(x\ R_{h_a}\ y \Rightarrow x\ R_{h_b}\ y) \tag{10}$$

and thus $R_{h_a} \leq R_{h_b}$ by definition of the partial ordering relation $\leq$.

Conversely, assume $R_{h_a} \leq R_{h_b}$ and again assume that h_a and h_b are homomorphisms on the free system onto $\mathbf{T}_{S_a}$ and $\mathbf{T}_{S_b}$, respectively.

By (9) and (10), $h_a(x) = h_a(y) \Rightarrow h_b(x) = h_b(y)$; hence a mapping from Q_a *onto* Q_b is possible. Let ψ be the function given by $\psi(h_a(x)) = h_b(x)$. Since h_a is onto, ψ has (as it should) all states of $\mathbf{T}_{S_a}$ as its domain. We must next prove that ψ is an onto homomorphism [Corollary 5.5.(8*a*)]; that is, we show

$$\psi(M_a(q_a, x)) = M_b(\psi(q_a), x) \tag{11}$$

[14] Called the right translation of S^* by z.

where q_a is an arbitrary member of Q_a. Since $\mathbf{T}_{\mathrm{S}_a}$ is connected, we have for some y

$$\begin{aligned}\psi(M_a(q_a, x) &= \psi(M_a(M_a(q_{a_0}, y), x))\\ &= \psi(M_a(q_{a_0}\, yx))\\ &= \psi(h_a(yx))\\ &= h_b(yx)\\ &= M_b(h_b(y), x) \qquad \text{by various steps}\\ &= M_b(\psi(h_a(y), x)\\ &= M_b(\psi(M_a(q_{a_0}, y), x)\\ &= M_b(\psi(q_a), x)\end{aligned}$$

This proves (11). ψ is onto since h_b is onto, and the theorem is proved. Q.E.D.

Corollary 5.5.19. The homomorphism ψ of Theorem 5.5.18 is an isomorphism iff $R_{h_a} = R_{h_b}$.

Definition 5.5.20. The set of all transition systems which are mutually isomorphic (Definition 5.5.7) is an *isomorphism type.* We will also speak of any representative, that is, any arbitrarily selected member of this set, as an isomorphism type.

Corollary 5.5.21. The family $\mathscr{T}_{\mathrm{S}}$ of isomorphism types of connected transition systems on an alphabet S is a partially ordered set with homomorphism the partial ordering relation.

Lemma 5.5.22. For any congruence R on $\mathbf{T}_{\mathrm{S}_{\mathscr{S}}}$ (cf. Theorem 5.5.10),

$$R_{\mathbf{T}_{\mathrm{S}_{\mathscr{S}}}/R} = R \tag{12}$$

Expression (12) states that the congruence induced on S^* by a quotient system $\mathbf{T}_{\mathrm{S}_{\mathscr{S}}}/R$ is R itself.

Proof. The canonical mapping $\psi(x) = [x]_R$, $x \in S^*$, is a homomorphism ψ between $\mathbf{T}_{\mathrm{S}_{\mathscr{S}}}$ and $\mathbf{T}_{\mathrm{S}_{\mathscr{S}}}/R$ (Theorem 5.5.10). Hence

$$\begin{aligned}xR_{\mathbf{T}_{\mathrm{S}_{\mathscr{S}}}/R}\,y &\Leftrightarrow \psi(x) = \psi(y)\\ &\Leftrightarrow [x]_R = [y]_R \Leftrightarrow xRy\end{aligned}$$

Q.E.D.

Lemma 5.5.23. If $\mathbf{T}_{\mathrm{S}}$ is any transition system, R_h the congruence induced by the homomorphism h of $\mathbf{T}_{\mathrm{S}_{\mathscr{S}}}$ onto $\mathbf{T}_{\mathrm{S}}$, then $\mathbf{T}_{\mathrm{S}}$ is isomorphic to $\mathbf{T}_{\mathrm{S}_{\mathscr{S}}}/R_h$.

Proof. From (12) we have at once that

$$R_{\mathbf{T}_{\mathrm{S}_{\mathscr{S}}}/R_h} = R_h$$

From Corollary 5.5.19 the desired result then follows. Q.E.D.

Definition 5.5.24. Let α and β be partial orderings. Two partially ordered systems $\langle A, \alpha\rangle$, $\langle B, \beta\rangle$ are *order isomorphic* iff there exists a function φ

such that φ is a one–one correspondence between A and B such that for all $a, b \in A$

$$a\alpha b \Leftrightarrow \varphi(a)\beta\varphi(b)$$

Theorem 5.5.25. The family $\mathcal{T}_S$ of isomorphism types partially ordered by homomorphism is order isomorphic to the family of partitions $\mathcal{P}$ under the right invariance relations R_h on S^*.

Proof. Theorems 5.5.8(b) and 5.5.15 and Lemmata 5.5.22 and 5.5.23 establish a one–one correspondence between the elements of $\mathcal{T}_S$ and those of $\mathcal{P}$; this is the mapping of the isomorphism type $\mathbf{T}_S$ one–one onto R_h. By Theorem 5.5.18 this mapping is an order isomorphism. Q.E.D.

Since by Theorem 5.5.17 $\mathcal{P}$ is a lattice, we can now construct lattice operations on $\mathcal{T}_S$. We let ψ be the one–one correspondence established by Theorem 5.5.25. Then we have,

$$\psi(\mathbf{T}_S) = R_h = \psi(\mathbf{T}_{S\mathcal{S}}/R_h)$$

and

$$\psi^{-1}(R) = \mathbf{T}_{S\mathcal{S}}/R$$

Also

$$\psi^{-1}\psi(\mathbf{T}_S) = \mathbf{T}_{S\mathcal{S}}/R_h$$

which is transition isomorphic to $\mathbf{T}_S$; and

$$\psi\psi^{-1}(R) = R$$

Finally, we define the *lattice meet* and *join* over transition systems by

$$\mathbf{T}_{S_a} \cap \mathbf{T}_{S_b} = \psi^{-1}(\psi(\mathbf{T}_{S_a}) \cap \psi(\mathbf{T}_{S_b})) \tag{12a}$$

$$\mathbf{T}_{S_a} \cup \mathbf{T}_{S_b} = \psi^{-1}(\psi(\mathbf{T}_{S_a}) \cup \psi(\mathbf{T}_{S_b})) \tag{12b}$$

The preceding construction proves Theorem 5.5.26.

Theorem 5.5.26. The family $\mathcal{T}_S$ of isomorphism types of transition systems is a lattice with meet and join as in (12a) and (12b).

We have now shown by means of the last two theorems that the theory of transition systems is essentially the theory of right invariance relations on a set of words, and, moreover, that the collection of such systems (isomorphism types of such systems) is partially ordered w.r.t. the relation of homomorphism and that the meet and join of any two transition systems exist. We are now going to study the meet operation on transition systems with special consideration of the problem of characterizing those systems decomposable into constituent systems operating in parallel.

Definition 5.5.27. The *direct product* $\mathbf{T}_S = \mathbf{T}_{S_a} \times \mathbf{T}_{S_b}$ of connected systems $\mathbf{T}_{S_a} = \langle S, Q_a, q_{a_0}, M_a \rangle$ and $\mathbf{T}_{S_b} = \langle S, Q_b, q_{b_0}, M_b \rangle$ is the transition system $\langle S, Q_a \times Q_b, (q_{a_0}, q_{b_0}), M_a \times M_b \rangle$

where

$$M_a \times M_b((q_a, q_b), s) = (M_a(q_a, s), M_b(q_b, s))$$

EXAMPLE 8. Two transition systems $\mathbf{T}_{S_a}$ and $\mathbf{T}_{S_b}$ are shown in Tables 5.5.3 and 5.5.4.

TABLE 5.5.3

$\mathbf{T}_{S_a}$

	0	1
q_{a_0}	q_{a_1}	q_{a_0}
q_{a_1}	q_{a_1}	q_{a_2}
q_{a_2}	q_{a_0}	q_{a_3}
q_{a_3}	q_{a_1}	q_{a_2}

TABLE 5.5.4

$\mathbf{T}_{S_b}$

	0	1
q_{b_0}	q_{b_2}	q_{b_1}
q_{b_1}	q_{b_0}	q_{b_2}
q_{b_2}	q_{b_2}	q_{b_1}

The direct product $\mathbf{T}_{S_a} \times \mathbf{T}_{S_b}$ appears in Table 5.5.5.

TABLE 5.5.5

$\mathbf{T}_{S_a} \times \mathbf{T}_{S_b}$

	0	1
(q_{a_0}, q_{b_0})	(q_{a_1}, q_{b_2})	(q_{a_0}, q_{b_1})
(q_{a_0}, q_{b_1})	(q_{a_1}, q_{b_0})	(q_{a_0}, q_{b_2})
(q_{a_0}, q_{b_2})	(q_{a_1}, q_{b_2})	(q_{a_0}, q_{b_1})
(q_{a_1}, q_{b_0})	(q_{a_1}, q_{b_2})	(q_{a_2}, q_{b_1})
(q_{a_1}, q_{b_1})	(q_{a_1}, q_{b_0})	(q_{a_2}, q_{b_2})
(q_{a_1}, q_{b_2})	(q_{a_1}, q_{b_2})	(q_{a_2}, q_{b_1})
(q_{a_2}, q_{b_0})	(q_{a_0}, q_{b_2})	(q_{a_3}, q_{b_1})
(q_{a_2}, q_{b_1})	(q_{a_0}, q_{b_0})	(q_{a_3}, q_{b_2})
(q_{a_2}, q_{b_2})	(q_{a_0}, q_{b_2})	(q_{a_3}, q_{b_1})
(q_{a_3}, q_{b_0})	(q_{a_1}, q_{b_2})	(q_{a_2}, q_{b_1})
(q_{a_3}, q_{b_1})	(q_{a_1}, q_{b_0})	(q_{a_2}, q_{b_2})
(q_{a_3}, q_{b_2})	(q_{a_1}, q_{b_2})	(q_{a_2}, q_{b_1})

Note that the state (q_{a_1}, q_{b_1}), along with some others, is not accessible from (q_{a_0}, q_{b_0}) and consequently that $\mathbf{T}_{S_a} \times \mathbf{T}_{S_b}$ is not connected. Thus the connectivity of two ingredient systems does not imply that of the direct product.

Definition 5.5.28. A *subdirect product* of

$$\mathbf{T}_{S_a} \times \mathbf{T}_{S_b} = \langle S, Q_a \times Q_b, (q_{a_0}, q_{b_0}), M_a \times M_b \rangle$$

is a system $\langle S, Q', (q_{a_0}, q_{b_0}), M' \rangle$ such that $Q' \subseteq Q_a \times Q_b$ and M' is $M_a \times M_b$ restricted to $Q' \times S$.

Definition 5.5.29. The *connected direct product* of $\mathbf{T}_{S_a}$ and $\mathbf{T}_{S_b}$, written $\mathbf{T}_{S_a} \boldsymbol{\times} \mathbf{T}_{S_b}$, is the subdirect product of $\mathbf{T}_{S_a} \times \mathbf{T}_{S_b}$ such that Q' is

$$\{(q_a, q_b) \mid (\exists x)(M_a \times M_b((q_{a_0}, q_{b_0}), x) = (q_a, q_b))\}$$

and $M_a \times M_b$ is restricted to Q'. We also will write $Q_a \times Q_b$ for Q' and $M_a \times M_b$ for the appropriately restricted transition function.

If we return temporarily to our intended application to parallel machines, it should be clear from the introductory discussion that if a connected transducer is the composition of two component machines in parallel, then it is (or is isomorphic to) a connected direct product system. Next, we show that the connected direct product is precisely the meet operation for the lattice of transition systems.

Lemma 5.5.30. Let $R_{h_{a \times b}}$ denote the right invariance relation induced on S^* by the homomorphism $h: \mathbf{T}_{\mathbf{S}_{\mathscr{S}}} \to \mathbf{T}_{\mathbf{S}_a} \times \mathbf{T}_{\mathbf{S}_b}$. Then

$$R_{h_{a \times b}} = R_{h_a} \cap R_{h_b}$$

Proof. The homomorphism h is given by

$$\begin{aligned} h(\Lambda) &= (q_{a_0}, q_{b_0}) \\ h(x) &= M_a \times M_b((q_{a_0}, q_{b_0}), x) \end{aligned} \tag{13}$$

By Theorem 5.5.9

$$x \; R_{h_{a \times b}} \; y \Leftrightarrow h(x) = h(y)$$

Hence, by a few steps, using (13), Definition 5.5.27 and Theorem 5.5.9 again, and recalling (Section 1.1) that pairs are equal iff they are componentwise equal

$$x \; R_{h_{a \times b}} \; y \Leftrightarrow x \; R_{h_a} \; y \wedge x \; R_{h_b} \; y$$

The theorem then follows by the definition of $\cap$. Q.E.D.

Theorem 5.5.31. $\mathbf{T}_{\mathbf{S}_a} \times \mathbf{T}_{\mathbf{S}_b}$ is isomorphic to $\mathbf{T}_{\mathbf{S}_a} \cap \mathbf{T}_{\mathbf{S}_b}$.

The theorem follows directly from Lemma 5.5.30 and Corollary 5.5.19 using $R_{h_{a \times b}} = R_{h_a} \cap R_{h_b}$. Q.E.D.

We will now proceed with the discussion of the remaining conditions for parallel decomposition.

Theorem 5.5.32. Let $\mathbf{T}_\mathbf{S} = \langle S, Q, q_0, M \rangle$ be a connected transition system and let R_1 and R_2 be two congruence relations on Q. Then

$$\mathbf{T}_\mathbf{S}/R_1 \times \mathbf{T}_\mathbf{S}/R_2$$

is isomorphic to

$$\mathbf{T}_\mathbf{S}/(R_1 \cap R_2)$$

Proof. Recall, from Theorem 5.5.8, that

$$\mathbf{T}_\mathbf{S}/R_i = \langle S, Q/R_i, [q_0]_{R_i}, M/R_i \rangle \qquad i = 1, 2$$

Then $\mathbf{T}_S/R_1 \times \mathbf{T}_S/R_2$ is the subdirect product

$$\langle S, Q/R_1 \times Q/R_2, ([q_0]_{R_1}, [q_0]_{R_2}), M/R_1 \times M/R_2 \rangle$$

To complete the proof we need the following lemma.

Lemma 5.5.33. $([q]_{R_1}, [q']_{R_2}) \in Q/R_1 \times Q/R_2 \Leftrightarrow [q]_{R_1} \cap [q']_{R_2} \neq \varnothing$, for every $q, q' \in Q$.

Proof. Suppose that $[q]_{R_1} \cap [q']_{R_2} \neq \varnothing$. Then there is a $q'' \in [q]_{R_1} \cap [q']_{R_2}$, and since $\mathbf{T}_S$ is by assumption connected, there is an x such that $M(q_0, x) = q''$. From the first of the two foregoing assumptions, it follows trivially that

$$[q'']_{R_1} = [q]_{R_1} \quad \text{and} \quad [q'']_{R_2} = [q']_{R_2} \tag{14}$$

Now we have

$$\begin{aligned} &M/R_1 \times M/R_2(([q_0]_{R_1}, [q_0]_{R_2}), x) && \text{(15a)}\\ &\quad = (M/R_1([q_0]_{R_1}, x), M/R_2([q_0]_{R_2}, x)) \\ &\quad = ([M(q_0, x)]_{R_1}, [M(q_0, x)]_{R_2}) \quad \text{by 5.5.10} \\ &\quad = ([q'']_{R_1}, [q'']_{R_2}) && \text{(15b)}\\ &\quad = ([q]_{R_1}, [q']_{R_2}) \quad \text{by (14)} && \text{(15c)} \end{aligned}$$

For the proof from left to right: if $([q_1]_{R_1}, [q']_{R_2}) \in Q/R_1 \times Q/R_2$, then since the product system is connected, the equation (15c) holds for some x; since the pairs (15b) and (15c) are equal iff the components are equal, (14) holds. Therefore, since $q'' \in [q]_{R_1}$ and $q'' \in [q']_{R_2}$, $[q]_{R_1} \cap [q']_{R_2}$ is nonempty.

Q.E.D.

Returning to the main theorem, we define the function φ *on* $Q/R_1 \times Q/R_2$

$$\varphi\colon Q/R_1 \times Q/R_2 \to Q/(R_1 \cap R_2)$$

by $\varphi([q]_{R_1}, [q]_{R_2}) = [q]_{R_1 \cap R_2}$. By the foregoing lemma, with $q' = q$, to every nonempty set $[q]_{R_1} \cap [q]_{R_2}$, there corresponds a pair

$$([q]_{R_1}, [q]_{R_2}) \in Q/R_1 \times Q/R_2$$

Therefore since, by the definition of the meet relation, $[q]_{R_1} \cap [q]_{R_2} = [q]_{R_1 \cap R_2}$, it follows that φ is onto. Also, φ is one–one since $[q]_{R_1 \cap R_2} = [q']_{R_1 \cap R_2}$ is true iff $[q]_{R_1} = [q']_{R_1}$ and $[q]_{R_2} = [q']_{R_2}$. Finally, using the definitions of quotient systems and of direct products,

$$\begin{aligned} &\varphi(M/R_1 \times M/R_2(([q]_{R_1}, [q]_{R_2}), x)) \\ &\quad = \varphi(M/R_1([q]_{R_1}, x), M/R_2([q]_{R_2}, x)) \\ &\quad = \varphi([M(q, x)]_{R_1}, [M(q, x)]_{R_2}) \\ &\quad = [M(q, x)]_{R_1 \cap R_2} \\ &\quad = M/(R_1 \cap R_2)([q]_{R_1 \cap R_2}, x) \\ &\quad = M/(R_1 \cap R_2)(\varphi([q]_{R_1}, [q]_{R_2}), x) \end{aligned}$$

which shows that φ is a homomorphism. Q.E.D.

Corollary 5.5.34. Let $\mathbf{T}_S$, R_1, and R_2 be as given in Theorem 5.5.32. Then, $\mathbf{T}_S/R_1 \times \mathbf{T}_S/R_2$ is isomorphic to $\mathbf{T}_S$ iff $R_1 \cap R_2 = 0$.

Proof. If $R_1 \cap R_2 = 0$, then (Definition 5.5.2) the equivalence relation consists solely of identity pairs (q, q); that is, each class $[q]_{R_1 \cap R_2}$ is a unit class. It follows that the quotient system $\mathbf{T}_S/(R_1 \cap R_2)$ is just (to within isomorphism) $\mathbf{T}_S$ itself. Q.E.D.

The next definition and corollary provide a necessary and sufficient condition for dispensing with connected direct products.

Corollary 5.5.35. Let $\mathbf{T}_S$, R_1, and R_2 be as given in Theorem 5.5.32. Then $\mathbf{T}_S/R_1 \times \mathbf{T}_S/R_2$ is isomorphic to $\mathbf{T}_S/(R_1 \cap R_2)$ iff $R_1 \mid R_2 = \mathrm{I}$.

Proof. Since $\mathbf{T}_S$ is connected $\mathbf{T}_S/(R_1 \cap R_2)$ is also connected; for $\mathbf{T}_S/R_1 \cap R_2$ is a homomorphic image of $\mathbf{T}_S$ (Theorem 5.5.10), and homomorphism preserves connectivity. Therefore by the assumed isomorphism $\mathbf{T}_S/R_1 \times \mathbf{T}_S/R_2$ is also connected. By Lemma 5.5.33, $[q]_{R_1} \cap [q']_{R_2} \neq \varnothing$, for any $q, q' \in Q$. However, if the intersections of all pairs of equivalence classes under R_1 and R_2 are nonempty, it follows by the definition of transitive closure that $R_1 \cup R_2 = \mathrm{I}$; and, as may be readily verified (see Exercise 13), $qR_1 \mid R_2q' \Leftrightarrow qR_2 \mid R_1q'$. But by Theorem 5.5.6 these latter two conditions are equivalent to the condition $R_1 \mid R_2 = \mathrm{I}$. The converse follows by a reverse argument. Q.E.D.

We obtain Corollary 5.5.36 as an immediate consequence of the foregoing theorems and corollaries.

Corollary 5.5.36. Let $\mathbf{T}_S$, R_1, and R_2 be as given in Theorem 5.5.32. Then $\mathbf{T}_S/R_1 \times \mathbf{T}_S/R_2$ is isomorphic to $\mathbf{T}$ iff the following conditions hold:

$$R_1 \cup R_2 = \mathrm{I}$$
$$R_1 \cap R_2 = 0$$
$$R_1 \mid R_2 = R_2 \mid R_1$$

This completes the theoretical part of the discussion of this subsection. Let us now illustrate these results with an example.

Definition 5.5.37. A transducer $\mathbf{T}$ with initial state is decomposable into two parallel operating machines iff $\mathbf{T}_S$, the transition system corresponding to $\mathbf{T}$, is isomorphic to the direct product $\mathbf{T}_S/R_1 \times \mathbf{T}_S/R_2$ of quotient systems $\mathbf{T}_S/R_1$ and $\mathbf{T}_S/R_2$ under the congruences R_1 and R_2.

From Corollary 5.5.36 it now follows that $\mathbf{T}$ is decomposable iff $R_1 \cup R_2 = \mathrm{I}$, $R_1 \cap R_2 = 0$, and $R_1 \mid R_2 = R_2 \mid R_1$.

EXAMPLE 4 (*Continued*). The partitions $P_1 = \{\{q_0, q_1, q_2\}, \{q_3, q_4, q_5\}\}$ and $P_2 = \{\{q_0, q_5\}, \{q_1, q_4\}, \{q_2, q_3\}\}$ both have the substitution property, as we have previously seen. Also, $P_1 \cup P_2 = \mathrm{I}$ and $P_1 \cap P_2 = 0$. Furthermore, $R_1 \mid R_2 = R_2 \mid R_1$, which can be confirmed by observing that $R_1 \mid R_2 = \mathrm{I}$, and by using Theorem 5.5.6; thus $\mathbf{T}$ is decomposable.

The next step is to construct the two quotient machines $\mathbf{T}_S/R_1$ and $\mathbf{T}_S/R_2$. These appear in Table 5.5.6, where we use $q_0 = [q_0]_{R_1}$, $q_3 = [q_3]_{R_1}$, $q_5 = [q_5]_{R_2}$, $q_4 = [q_4]_{R_2}$, and $q_2 = [q_2]_{R_2}$ for convenience.

TABLE 5.5.6

$\mathbf{T}_S/R_1$	0	1
q_0	q_3	q_0
q_3	q_0	q_3

$\mathbf{T}_S/R_2$	0	1
q_2	q_4	q_4
q_4	q_5	q_2
q_5	q_2	q_2

Except for the abbreviated notation, $\mathbf{T}_S/R_1$ is, of course, precisely Example 7.

We continue with $\mathbf{T}_S/R_1 \times \mathbf{T}_S/R_2$, which appears in Table 5.5.7

TABLE 5.5.7

		$\mathbf{T}_S/R_1 \times \mathbf{T}_S/R_2$ 0	1
(2)	(q_0, q_2)	(q_3, q_4)	(q_0, q_4)
(1)	(q_0, q_4)	(q_3, q_5)	(q_0, q_2)
(0)	(q_0, q_5)	(q_3, q_2)	(q_0, q_2)
(3)	(q_3, q_2)	(q_0, q_4)	(q_3, q_4)
(4)	(q_3, q_4)	(q_0, q_5)	(q_3, q_2)
(5)	(q_3, q_5)	(q_0, q_2)	(q_3, q_2)

As theory assures us, this system is isomorphic to the transition part of the transducer of Example 4; the correspondence is, in fact, Table 5.5.8

TABLE 5.5.8

$q_0 \leftrightarrow (q_0, q_5)$	$q_3 \leftrightarrow (q_3, q_2)$
$q_1 \leftrightarrow (q_0, q_4)$	$q_4 \leftrightarrow (q_3, q_4)$
$q_2 \leftrightarrow (q_0, q_2)$	$q_5 \leftrightarrow (q_3, q_5)$

To recover the transducer, now represented in parallel form, we use Table 5.5.8 and the N function of Table 5.5.1. The parallel decomposed machine is then as in Table 5.5.9.

TABLE 5.5.9

	M		N	
	0	1	0	1
(q_0, q_5)	(q_3, q_2)	(q_0, q_2)	0	2
(q_0, q_4)	(q_3, q_5)	(q_0, q_2)	2	2
(q_0, q_2)	(q_3, q_4)	(q_0, q_4)	1	1
(q_3, q_2)	(q_0, q_4)	(q_3, q_4)	1	1
(q_3, q_4)	(q_0, q_5)	(q_3, q_2)	0	0
(q_3, q_5)	(q_0, q_2)	(q_3, q_2)	2	2

EXERCISES 5.5

1. Two transition systems, $\mathbf{T}_{\mathbf{S}_a}$ and $\mathbf{T}_{\mathbf{S}_b}$ are shown.

$\mathbf{T}_{\mathbf{S}_a}$

	0	1
q_0	q_0	q_1
q_1	q_2	q_3
q_2	q_2	q_2
q_3	q_3	q_3

$\mathbf{T}_{\mathbf{S}_b}$

	0	1
q_0	q_3	q_1
q_1	q_1	q_2
q_2	q_3	q_3
q_3	q_3	q_3

(*a*) Determine R_{h_a} and R_{h_b}. Describe in words, using the style of Example 2 in Section 5.4.

(*b*) Determine whether $R_{h_a} \cap R_{h_b}$ is empty or not.

(*c*) Describe the construction of $\mathbf{T}_{\mathbf{S}_{\mathscr{S}}}/R_{h_a}$.

(*d*) Given $P_1 = \{\{q_0\}, \{q_1, q_2, q_3\}\}$, construct $T_{\mathbf{S}_a}/P_1$. Is the result a *bona fide* quotient machine?

(*e*) Similarly given $P_2 = \{\{q_0, q_3\}, \{q_1, q_2\}\}$, what about $\mathbf{T}_{\mathbf{S}_b}/P_2$?

(*f*) Construct $T_{\mathbf{S}_a} \cap \mathbf{T}_{\mathbf{S}_b}$.

2. Determine the lattice of partitions on $\{a, b, c, d\}$.

3. Verify the assertions made in Example 5.

4. Complete the proof of Theorem 5.5.6.

5. Prove Corollary 5.5.8.

6. Complete the proof of Theorem 5.5.10.

7. Prove Corollary 5.5.12.

8. Making use of the fact that any connected transition system with initial state on S is a homomorphic image of the free system $\mathbf{T}_{\mathbf{S}_{\mathscr{S}}}$, *prove* $M(q, xs) = M(M(q, x), s)$.

9. Show that the functions g_z of Theorem 5.5.17 constitute a monoid isomorphic to $\mathscr{S}$ (Cayley's theorem for monoids).

10. Show that there is a homomorphism of $\mathbf{T}_{\mathbf{S}_a}$ onto $\mathbf{T}_{\mathbf{S}_b}$ iff

$$\mathbf{T}_{\mathbf{S}_a} \cap \mathbf{T}_{\mathbf{S}_b} = \mathbf{T}_{\mathbf{S}_a}$$

11. Characterize the 1 and 0 elements of the lattice of transition systems on S. What is the cardinality of this system? Does the cardinality depend on S?

12. Verify that connectedness is preserved under transition homomorphism (cf. Exercise 5.3(4).)

13. Prove that $[q]_{R_1} \cap [q']_{R_2} \neq \varnothing$ implies $R_1 \cup R_2 = \mathrm{I}$ and $R_1|R_2 = R_2|R_1$ (cf. Corollary 5.5.35).

14. Under certain conditions R_1 and R_2 commute w.r.t. the Peirce product. Define a companion property for partitions P_1 and P_2. (This property is usually termed "permutability.")

15. Explain that the theory of parallel decomposition as developed in the text applies to either Moore or Mealy transducers (for instance, Example 4).

16. Decompose the following transducer into parallel systems as in Example 4 (the q-symbols have been omitted for ease of reading and writing; thus, in the M part of the table, $i = q_i$). As indicated $S = \{0, 1, 2, 3\}$ and $O = \{0, 1\}$.

q	0	1	2	3	0	1	2	3
0	1	2	8	5	0	1	1	0
1	0	1	6	3	1	0	0	1
2	2	2	7	4	1	1	0	0
3	4	2	5	8	1	0	0	1
4	3	1	3	6	0	1	1	0
5	5	2	4	7	0	0	0	0
6	1	8	2	2	1	0	1	0
7	0	7	0	0	1	0	0	1
8	2	8	1	1	0	0	1	0

17. Develop an algorithm for determining partitions with the substitution property over Q for transition systems.

18. Supply the missing details for the proof of Lemma 5.5.30.

5.6 LOOP-FREE STRUCTURES

In Section 5.5 we found necessary and sufficient conditions for the parallel decomposition of transducers by using the criterion that a transducer is parallel decomposable provided that it is isomorphic to a certain direct product machine. If we drop the requirement that our transducers be connected—thus also renouncing our interest in the lattice-theoretic treatment of transition systems—it is possible to obtain far less restrictive results about machine structure. We are going to take up a more general approach in two stages. First, we demand only isomorphism to a subtransition system of a direct product; second, we will require only that a transition system, to be decomposed, be the homomorphic image of a certain subtransition system. In each of the two stages of the discussion we shall also treat serial decomposition. In Chapter 6 we shall indicate applications to switching circuits.

As in Section 5.5, we concentrate on transition systems, all of which are complete but not necessarily connected. Hence it is reasonable to dispense with initial states, and we will do so thus reverting to the systems of Section 5.4. We also use just condition 2 of Definition 5.5.7 as our definition of transition homomorphism, foregoing, then, 5.5.8(b). We can still use 5.5.9 intact, but must modify 5.5.10 by deleting reference to initial states.

The first result we need is an immediate consequence of Theorems 5.5.9 and 5.5.10 as modified (homomorphism theorem for transition systems).

Theorem 5.6.1. If there is a homomorphism h of $\mathbf{T}_{S_a}$ onto $\mathbf{T}_{S_b}$, then $\mathbf{T}_{S_a}/R_h$ is isomorphic to $\mathbf{T}_{S_b}$.

Proof. The isomorphism is given by $\psi([q]_{R_h}) = h(q)$. Q.E.D.

Definition 5.6.2. A *subtransition system* of $\mathbf{T}_S = \langle S, Q, M\rangle$ is a system $\mathbf{T}_S' = \langle S, Q', M'\rangle$ where $Q' \subseteq Q$ and M' is M restricted to $Q' \times S$.

Definition 5.6.3. A transition system $\mathbf{T}_{S_b}$ *realizes* $\mathbf{T}_{S_a}$ iff $\mathbf{T}_{S_a}$ is isomorphic to a subtransition system of $\mathbf{T}_{S_b}$.

Using Definition 5.5.27 with omission of the initial state and the reference to connectedness, we next define parallel connections.

Definition 5.6.4. The *parallel connection* of $\mathbf{T}_{S_a}$ and $\mathbf{T}_{S_b}$ is the direct product $\mathbf{T}_{S_a} \times \mathbf{T}_{S_b}$.

Theorem 5.6.5. $\mathbf{T}_S$ can be realized by a parallel connection of two transition systems, each with fewer states than $\mathbf{T}_S$, iff there exist two congruence relations R_1, R_2 on Q such that $R_1, R_2 \neq \mathrm{I}$, $R_1, R_2 \neq 0$, and $R_1 \cap R_2 = 0$.

Proof. We have to prove that $\mathbf{T}_S$ is isomorphic to a subsystem of some direct product $\mathbf{T}_{S_a} \times \mathbf{T}_{S_b}$ iff there are nontrivial relations R_1, R_2 such that $R_1 \cap R_2 = 0$. (The restriction to nontrivial relations has been made to avoid the case where a machine counts as its own decomposition.) Assume that $\mathbf{T}_S$ is isomorphic under φ to $\mathbf{T}_S' \subseteq \mathbf{T}_{S_a} \times \mathbf{T}_{S_b}$; then *define* the maps h_1 and h_2 on Q as follows:

$$h_1(q) = q_a \Leftrightarrow \varphi(q) = (q_a, q_b)$$

and

$$h_2(q) = q_b \Leftrightarrow \varphi(q) = (q_a, q_b)$$

It is clear that h_1 and h_2 are homomorphisms. Furthermore, by 5.5.9, they induce congruences R_1 and R_2, respectively, on Q. By Theorem 5.6.1 the quotient systems $\mathbf{T}_S/R_1$ and $\mathbf{T}_S/R_2$ are isomorphic to the image systems under h_1 and h_2. Hence $\mathbf{T}_S$ is isomorphic to a subsystem of $\mathbf{T}_S/R_1 \times \mathbf{T}_S/R_2$. Now if $[q]_{R_1}$ and $[q]_{R_2}$ are any classes in P_1 and P_2 having more than one element in common, then $h_1(q) = q_a$, $h_1(q') = q_a$, $h_2(q) = q_b$, and $h_2(q') = q_b$ all hold. But then φ is no longer an isomorphism. Hence $R_1 \cap R_2 = 0$.

Conversely, if $R_1 \cap R_2 = 0$, let φ be the one–one onto map $\varphi: Q' \to Q$ given by $\varphi([q]_{R_1}, [q]_{R_2}) = q$, where $Q' = \{([q]_{R_1}, [q]_{R_2}) \mid q \in Q\}$.

It is easy to verify that

$$\varphi(M'(([q]_{R_1}, [q]_{R_2}), s) = M(\varphi([q]_{R_1}, [q]_{R_2}), s)$$

Hence φ is an isomorphism, and

$$\mathbf{T}_S' = \langle S, Q', M' \rangle$$

is a subtransition system of $\mathbf{T}_S/R_1 \times \mathbf{T}_S/R_2$. Q.E.D.

EXAMPLE 1. The transition system $\mathbf{T}_S$ of Table 5.6.1 possesses two congruence partitions

$$P_1 = \{\{q_0, q_1, q_2\}, \{q_3, q_4\}\}$$

and

$$P_2 = \{\{q_0, q_3\}, \{q_1, q_4\}, \{q_2\}\}$$

TABLE 5.6.1

	0	1
q_0	q_0	q_4
q_1	q_1	q_4
q_2	q_2	q_3
q_3	q_3	q_4
q_4	q_4	q_4

such that $P_1 \cap P_2 = 0$. Using Theorem 5.6.5,

$$\{([q_0]_1, [q_0]_2), ([q_0]_1, [q_1]_2), \ldots, ([q_3]_1, [q_2]_2)\}$$

is the set of states of a transition system isomorphic to that of Table 5.6.1. Furthermore, this new system is a subsystem of $\mathbf{T}_S/R_1 \times \mathbf{T}_S/R_2$. Note that $\mathbf{T}_S$ is "badly" disconnected.

Definition 5.6.6. The *serial connection* of two transition systems $\mathbf{T}_{S_a} = \langle S_a, Q_a, M_a \rangle$ and $\mathbf{T}_{S_b} = \langle S_b, Q_b, M_b \rangle$ is

$$\mathbf{T}_S = \langle S_a, Q_a \times Q_b, M \rangle$$

where $S_b = Q_a \times S_a$ and M is given by

$$M((q_a, q_b), s) = (M_a(q_a, s), M_b(q_b, (q_a, s)))$$

In this definition, which formalizes for transition systems the concept exemplified in Fig. 5.5.3, the component automaton $\mathbf{T}_{S_b}$ has its transition function M_b defined *implicitly* in the expression for M. Note that the value of M_b is determined by the state q_b of $\mathbf{T}_{S_b}$ and by the input *pair* (q_a, s); that is, we make the input a (identity) function of the present state and input of $\mathbf{T}_{S_a}$. We could, with very slight complication, deal with full transducers and make the input of $\mathbf{T}_{S_b}$, $N_a(q_a, s)$ (as in Fig. 5.5.3). So we are sacrificing little in dealing with transition systems rather than transducers. Similar remarks, it will be recalled, can be made about the parallel case (cf. discussion of Example 4 and continuation thereof in Section 5.5).

EXAMPLE 2. In Table 5.6.2*a*, the transition system $\mathbf{T}_{S_b}$ has inputs $s_0, \ldots, s_3$.

TABLE 5.6.2*a*

$\mathbf{T}_{S_a}$

	0	1
q_0	q_0	q_1
q_1	q_0	q_0

$\mathbf{T}_{S_b}$

	s_0	s_1	s_2	s_3
q_α	q_α	q_β	q_α	q_α
q_β	q_β	q_β	q_α	q_β

We may effect a serial connection by translating S_b as follows: $s_0 \rightarrow (q_0, 0)$, $s_1 \rightarrow (q_0, 1)$, $s_2 \rightarrow (q_1, 0)$, and $s_3 \rightarrow (q_1, 1)$. Then a serial system is given by Table 5.6.2*b*.

TABLE 5.6.2*b*

	0	1
(q_0, q_α)	(q_0, q_α)	(q_1, q_β)
(q_0, q_β)	(q_0, q_β)	(q_1, q_β)
(q_1, q_α)	(q_0, q_α)	(q_0, q_α)
(q_1, q_β)	(q_0, q_α)	(q_0, q_β)

The student should calculate a few values of M to insure his understanding of the construction.

The next theorem indicates when series decompositions are possible.

Theorem 5.6.7. A transition system $\mathbf{T_S}$ can be realized by a serial connection of two transition systems, each with fewer states than $\mathbf{T_S}$, iff there exists a nontrivial congruence relation R on Q.

Proof. If $\mathbf{T_S}$ is isomorphic to a subsystem $\mathbf{T_S}'$ of a serial connection of two transition systems $\mathbf{T}_{\mathbf{S}_a}$ and $\mathbf{T}_{\mathbf{S}_b}$ then there is a one–one onto map $\varphi: Q \to Q'$ where $Q' \subseteq Q_a \times Q_b$ which satisfies

$$\varphi M(q, s) = M'(\varphi(q), s) \tag{1}$$

By Definition 5.6.6, the right side of (1) is the same as

$$M'((q_a, q_b), s) = (M_a(q_a, s), M_b(q_b, (q_a, s))) \tag{2}$$

Define h as follows:

$$h(q) = q_a \Leftrightarrow \varphi(q) = (q_a, q_b)$$

Using the left side of (1) and the right side of (2), h is seen to be a homomorphism, and as such h determines a congruence R_h on Q.

Conversely, suppose $\mathbf{T_S}$ to be given and let R be a congruence relation on Q; let h be the natural homomorphism $h(q) = [q]_R$. We are now going to construct an isomorphic image $\mathbf{T_S}'$ of $\mathbf{T_S}$ which will satisfy Definition 5.6.6. Suppose $[q]$ is the largest class in Q/R. Let A be the smallest arbitrary nonempty set such that $K(A) \cdot K(Q/R) \geq K(Q)$ and such that $K(A) \geq K([q])$. Intuitively, A is to be any set such that the cartesian product of it with Q/R will be as large as Q and such that the effect of pairing the elements of A with the classes of Q/R is to identify the elements of Q constituting Q/R. A little thought will show that these are the properties of A which will provide the desired isomorphism. Let φ be a one–one function from Q *onto* $Q' \subseteq Q/R \times A$, such that

$$\varphi(q) = (h(q), k(q))$$

(The function k is a function induced by φ: if φ associates q to $a \in A$, then $k(q) = a$.)

To achieve our goal we have to construct a transition function

$$M': (Q/R \times A') \times S \to Q/R \times A', \qquad A' \subseteq A$$

which satisfies the isomorphism condition

$$\varphi M(q, s) = M'(\varphi(q), s)$$

Since φ is one–one, $q = \varphi^{-1}([q]_R, a)$, and thus

$$\begin{aligned} M'(([q]_R, a), s) &= \varphi M(\varphi^{-1}([q]_R, a), s) \\ &= (h(M(\varphi^{-1}([q]_R, a), s)), k(M(\varphi^{-1}([q]_R, a), s))) \end{aligned} \tag{3}$$

But

$$\begin{aligned} h(M(\varphi^{-1}([q]_R, a), s)) &= M/R(h(\varphi^{-1}([q]_R, a)), s) \\ &= M/R([q]_R, s) \end{aligned} \tag{4}$$

since $\varphi^{-1}([q]_R, a) = q$ and $h(q) = [q]_R$. Moreover, *define*:

$$M''(a, ([q]_R, s)) = k(M(\varphi^{-1}([q]_R, a), s)) \tag{5}$$

From (3), (4), and (5), we now have

$$M'(([q]_R, a), s) = (M/R([q]_R, s), M''(a, ([q]_R, s))$$

This is the transition function for a serial connection $\mathbf{T}_S'$ of the two transition systems

$$\mathbf{T}_S/R = \langle S, Q/R, M/R \rangle \quad \text{and} \quad \mathbf{T}_S'' = \langle Q/R \times S, A', M'' \rangle$$ Q.E.D.

EXAMPLE 3. The system in Table 5.6.3 has an appropriate partition: $P = \{\{q_0, q_1, q_3\}, \{q_2, q_4\}\}$. For convenience, call the first class I and the second II. Now let $A = \{\alpha, \beta, \gamma\}$. Let the states of the serial machine be

TABLE 5.6.3

	0	1
q_0	q_3	q_4
q_1	q_1	q_4
q_2	q_0	q_1
q_3	q_1	q_2
q_4	q_3	q_1

$$\{(\mathrm{I}, \alpha), (\mathrm{I}, \beta), (\mathrm{I}, \gamma), (\mathrm{II}, \alpha), (\mathrm{II}, \beta)\}$$

and let φ associate q_0 to (I, α), q_1 to (I, β), etc. Then, following the discussion in the theorem, $h(Q) = \{\mathrm{I}, \mathrm{II}\} = Q/R$. The functions M/R and M'' appear in Tables 5.6.4*a* and 5.6.4*b*.

TABLE 5.6.4*a*

	M/R	
	0	1
I	I	II
II	I	I

TABLE 5.6.4*b*

	M''			
	(I, 0)	(I, 1)	(II, 0)	(II, 1)
α	γ	β	α	β
β	β	β	γ	β
γ	β	α	–	–

$\mathbf{T}_S'$ is a subtransition system of $\langle S, Q/R \times A, M' \rangle$, where M', suitably restricted, is as in Table 5.6.5. The numerals in parentheses at the extreme

TABLE 5.6.5

	M'	0	1
(0)	(I, α)	(I, γ)	(II, β)
(1)	(I, β)	(I, β)	(II, β)
(3)	(I, γ)	(I, β)	(II, α)
(2)	(II, α)	(I, α)	(I, β)
(4)	(II, β)	(I, γ)	(I, β)

left indicate the correspondence φ to the original system. As in the proof of the theorem [see definition of k and (5)], the function M'' is forced to do the correct job. For instance, to determine $M''(\alpha, (\text{I}, 0))$, we have

$$\begin{aligned} M'((\text{I}, \alpha), 0) &= (M/R(\text{I}, 0), M''(\alpha, (\text{I}, 0)) \\ &= (\text{I}, ---) \\ &= (\text{I}, \gamma) \end{aligned}$$

as required by Definition 5.6.6. Hence $M''(\alpha, (\text{I}, 0))$ is *defined* in Table 5.6.4*b* to be γ, whence the dashes in (I, ---) may be filled in.

We are now ready to enter the second stage of generalization. Our developments will show that any transition system (and *a fortiori* any transducer) can be realized (in a new, looser, sense) by interconnection of two-state systems and permutation transition systems (Definition 5.4.12). Moreover, these latter systems will be the most primitive possible in that they will be, in a certain sense to be explained, indecomposable.

Definition 5.6.8. A transition system $\mathbf{T}_{S_b}$ *realizes* $\mathbf{T}_{S_a}$ iff $\mathbf{T}_{S_a}$ is a homomorphic image of a subtransition system of $\mathbf{T}_{S_b}$.

The next definition provides a useful weakening of the partition concept.

Definition 5.6.9. Given a nonempty set A, a *set system* W is a family $\{A_1, A_2, \ldots\}$ of subsets of A such that

$$\bigcup A_i = A$$

and such that there are no i, j, $i \neq j$ such that $A_i \subseteq A_j$.

It is evident that all partitions are set systems, but not conversely.

Definition 5.6.10. If $\mathscr{A}$ is any family of subsets $\{A_1, A_2, \ldots, A_k\}$ of a finite set A, then *max* $\mathscr{A}$ is the set of all sets A_i of $\mathscr{A}$ which are included only in themselves; that is,

$$\max \mathscr{A} = \{A_i \mid A_i \in \mathscr{A} \wedge (\forall A_j)(A_j \in \mathscr{A} \wedge A_i \subseteq A_j \Rightarrow i = j)\}$$

Corollary 5.6.11. The collection $\mathscr{W}$ of set systems W of a finite set A is a lattice.

Proof. Define $W \leq W'$, $W, W' \in \mathscr{W}$, to mean the same as $P \leq P'$ for partitions. Also

$$W \cup W' = \max \{A_i \mid A_i \in W \vee A_i \in W'\}$$
$$W \cap W' = \max \{A_i \bigcap A_j \mid A_i \in W \wedge A_j \in W'\}$$

The verification that $\cup$ and $\cap$ thus defined always exist and satisfy the meanings l.u.b. and g.l.b., respectively (Section 1.3), is left to the student.

EXAMPLE 4. There are nine set systems over $A = \{a, b, c\}$, and these form a lattice with $\mathrm{I} = \{\{a, b, c\}\}$ and $0 = \{\{a\}, \{b\}, \{c\}\}$. Two of the other seven elements are $\{\{a, b\}, \{b, c\}\}$ and $\{\{a, c\}, \{b\}\}$. Moreover,

$$\{\{a, b\}, \{b, c\}\} \cup \{\{a, c\}, \{b\}\} = \max \{\{a, b\}, \{b, c\}, \{a, c\}, \{b\}\}$$
$$= \{\{a, b\}, \{b, c\}, \{a, c\}\}$$

and

$$\{\{a, b\}, \{b, c\}\} \cap \{\{a, c\}, \{b\}\} = \max \{\{a\}, \{b\}, \{c\}\} = 0 = \{\{a\}, \{b\}, \{c\}\}$$

Definition 5.6.12. If W is a set system over the set Q of states of a transition system (or, more generally of an automaton) $\mathbf{T}_S$, we say W has the *substitution property* or is a *cover* for $\mathbf{T}_S$ iff for every $Q_i \in W$ and every input s there is a $Q_j \in W$ such that the direct image $M(Q_i, s) \subseteq Q_j$.

EXAMPLE 5. For the following system $\{\{q_0, q_1\}, \{q_0, q_2\}, \{q_1, q_2\}\}$ is a cover.

	0	1
q_0	q_1	q_1
q_1	q_0	q_2
q_2	q_2	q_0

Suppose we were to construct, in analogy with quotient systems, a transition system using the sets of the cover in Example 5 as states. Inspection of the system shows that the input 0 would take $\{q_0, q_1\}$ into itself, 1 would take $\{q_0, q_1\}$ into $\{q_1, q_2\}$, etc. Abbreviating the sets of the system by Q_0, Q_1, and Q_2, we may obtain the following transition system

	0	1
Q_0	Q_0	Q_1
Q_1	Q_2	Q_2
Q_2	Q_1	Q_0

which is isomorphic to Example 5 under the rule $q_0 \to Q_1$, $q_1 \to Q_2$, $q_2 \to Q_0$.

As the next example shows, however, the property of being an isomorphic image is an accident of Example 5.

EXAMPLE 6.

	0	1	2
q_0	q_1	q_1	q_3
q_1	q_2	q_1	q_2
q_2	q_3	q_2	q_3
q_3	q_0	q_3	q_3

Here we have a cover $\{Q_0, Q_1, Q_2, Q_3\}$ where $Q_0 = \{q_0, q_1, q_2\}$, $Q_1 = \{q_0, q_1, q_3\}$, $Q_2 = \{q_0, q_2, q_3\}$, and $Q_3 = \{q_1, q_2, q_3\}$. It is easy to see that when the input is 0, $M(Q_0, 0) \subseteq Q_3$, $M(Q_1, 0) \subseteq Q_0$, etc. However, under input 1, *both* $M(Q_0, 1) \subseteq Q_0$ *and* $M(Q_1, 0) \subseteq Q_0$ hold true. If we were to try to build a system in analogy with Example 5, we would have to choose the next state in this case arbitrarily—either as Q_0 or Q_3. A possible outcome, as the student should check for himself, is in Table 5.6.6. Evidently this system is not isomorphic to the original (hence not even onto homomorphic, since the state sets are equipotent).

However, what at first sight may appear to be a limitation to the use of set-system construction as opposed to quotient systems can be turned to advantage. Note that in Table 5.6.6 each of the inputs in effect either

TABLE 5.6.6

	0	1	2
Q_0	Q_3	Q_3	Q_2
Q_1	Q_0	Q_3	Q_2
Q_2	Q_1	Q_3	Q_2
Q_3	Q_2	Q_3	Q_2

permutes the states of the machine or *resets* the states—that is, acts, in the latter case, like a constant function. We shall soon see that all transition systems can be realized by interconnections of systems in which inputs either permute or reset, and this fact will help us greatly in the search for primitive automata. Before taking up this possibility, however, we need two preliminary results.

Theorem 5.6.13. Let W be a cover for $\mathbf{T_S} = \langle S, Q, M\rangle$ such that $K(W) = k$ and $K(Q') = l$, where Q' is the largest set in W. Then $\mathbf{T_S}$ can be realized by a serial connection of a k-state and l-state transition system.

Proof. Let $\mathbf{T}_{\mathbf{S}_a} = \langle S, W, M_a\rangle$ where

$$M_a(Q_i, s) = Q_j$$

iff there is a sequence of states $Q_{i_1}, \ldots, Q_{i_k}$ such that $Q_j = Q_{i_1}$, and $M(Q_i, s) \subseteq Q_{i_l}$ for $1 \leq l \leq k$. (Less formally, the value of $M_a(Q_i, s)$ is either Q_j, or if $M(Q_i, s)$ is a subset of more than one set Q_{i_l}, then the value of M_a is assigned to be the first in some listing of the Q_{i_l}.) $\mathbf{T}_{\mathbf{S}_a}$ has k states. Next, exactly as in the proof of Theorem 5.6.7, let A be a set with l states. Let φ be a function from $W \times A$ *onto* Q such that $\varphi(Q_i, \alpha) = q$,

$q \in Q_i$, $\alpha \in A$. Any one of the possible choices of q from Q_i will suffice, a different one for each α, provided that the function is onto. Let $\mathbf{T_S}'$ be $\langle S, W \times A, M' \rangle$ where

$$M'((Q_i, \alpha), s) = (M_a(Q_i, s), M_b(\alpha, (Q_i, s)))$$

The transition function M_b of the serially attached system

$$\mathbf{T}_{\mathbf{S}_b} = \langle W \times S, A, M_b \rangle$$

is determined to ensure that, if the next state of $\mathbf{T}_{\mathbf{S}_a}$ is $M_a(Q_i, s) = Q_j$, and if $M(q, s) = q'$, then we may choose $M_b(\alpha, (Q_i, s)) = \beta$ so that $\varphi(Q_j, \beta) = q'$. It follows from this construction that φ is a homomorphism.

Q.E.D.

Theorem 5.6.14. Let W and W' be covers for $\mathbf{T_S}$ such that $K(W) = k$ and $K(W') = l$; and such that $W \cap W' = 0$. Then $\mathbf{T_S}$ can be realized by a parallel connection of a k-state and an l-state transition system.

Proof. For the student.

In the next step of the development we begin using the semigroup Φ associated to a transition system (Section 5.4). The elements φ_s (or equivalently $[s]_E$), where the index s is an element of S, are generators of the semigroup, since for any element φ_x, x is a concatenation of basic symbols. We saw that φ_s may be a permutation and even that every φ_s may be such, in which case the semigroup is a group. We will be particularly interested, in the remainder of this section, in permutation elements of Φ and in *constant* elements. Moreover, we shall (as is customary), refer to "permuting inputs" s where φ_s is a permutation. We shall also speak of constant inputs s where φ_s is a constant function. Such inputs are also called *reset* inputs.

Definition 5.6.14a. A transition system $\mathbf{T_S}$ is *permutation-reset* iff each input either permutes the states of $\mathbf{T_S}$ or resets the states to one state.

EXAMPLE 6 (*Continued*). Table 5.6.6 is a permutation-reset system. φ_0 is a permutation and φ_1 and φ_2 are constant functions; that is, 1 and 2 reset the system to Q_3 and Q_2, respectively.

Theorem 5.6.15. Let $W = \max(2^Q - \{Q\})$ where Q is the set of states of $\mathbf{T_S}$ and 2^Q is its power set. Then W is a cover; moreover, W determines a permutation-reset transition system.

Proof. W consists of exactly the n, $n - 1$ element mutually noninclusive subsets of Q, where $K(Q) = n$. Hence for any s and $Q_i \in W$, $M(Q_i, s) \subseteq Q_j \in W$ for some j. Therefore W is a cover by Definition 5.6.12. Now, just as in Theorem 5.6.13, construct $\langle S, W, M_a \rangle$ where $M_a(Q_i, s) = Q_j$ if $M(Q_i, s) \subseteq Q_j$ and Q_j is either the only such set in which the direct image is included, or is one of many. If φ_s permutes Q, then $M(Q, s) = Q$. For any $Q_i \in W$, $M_a(Q_i, s)$ must then be *equal* to some $Q_j \in W$. For if $M_a(Q_i, s)$ were a *subset* of Q_j, then (since φ_s is a permutation) $\varphi_s^{-1}(Q_j)$

would be a subset of Q_i, contrary to the fact that W is a set system. Since $\varphi_s(Q_i) = Q_j$ implies $\varphi_s^{-1}(Q_j) = Q_i$, φ_s permutes W.

If φ_x does not permute the states Q of $\mathbf{T}_S$, then there are $q_i, q_j \in Q$ such that $M(q_i, s) = M(q_j, s)$. By the definition of W, it follows that there is a $Q_j \in W$ which has as elements *all* the images under s. So we choose $M_a(Q_i, s) = Q_j$ for all Q_i; in this manner, φ_s is a constant function on W. Hence $\langle S, W, M_a \rangle$ is a permutation-reset machine. Q.E.D.

Theorem 5.6.16. Every transition system can be realized by a serial connection of permutation-reset systems.[15]

Proof. The theorem follows by induction from Theorems 5.6.13 and 5.6.15, noting that every two-state transition system is trivially permutation-reset.

EXAMPLE 7. We illustrate Theorem 5.6.16 by determining W as in Theorem 5.6.15 and then using Theorem 5.6.13 to determine a serially connected automaton.

TABLE 5.6.7

$\mathbf{T}_S$

	0	1
q_0	q_0	q_2
q_1	q_2	q_1
q_2	q_1	q_1

$W = \{\{q_0, q_1\}, \{q_0, q_2\}, \{q_1, q_2\}\}$. Hence $\mathbf{T}_{S_a} = \langle S, W, M_a \rangle$ is given by Table 5.6.8, where $Q_0 = \{q_0, q_1\}$, $Q_1 = \{q_0, q_2\}$, and $Q_2 = \{q_1, q_2\}$. This

TABLE 5.6.8

	0	1
Q_0	Q_1	Q_2
Q_1	Q_0	Q_2
Q_2	Q_2	Q_2

follows the construction used in Theorem 5.6.15. In order to use Theorem 5.6.13, we need a transition system with $l = 2 = K(Q_i)$ states to put in series with $\mathbf{T}_{S_a}$. Let ψ: $W \times A \to Q$ be the function required by Theorem 5.6.13 and here given by Table 5.6.9.

TABLE 5.6.9

	α	β
Q_0	q_0	q_1
Q_1	q_0	q_2
Q_2	q_1	q_2

[15] Although theorems 5.6.13, 5.6.15, and 5.6.16 are correct, the induction step in theorem 5.6.16 presents considerable difficulties. The construction using only the maximal cover will not always suffice. This was pointed out by A. Ginzburg, and did not come to my attention until after this book was in press.

In effect, this function allows the system we are aiming to construct to "tell" in what state of a set Q_i the original system $\mathbf{T}_S$ exists.

Next, the transition function of the tandem machine

$$\mathbf{T}_{S_b} = \langle W \times S, A, M_b \rangle$$

is given by Table 5.6.10,

TABLE 5.6.10

	M_b					
	$(Q_0, 0)$	$(Q_0, 1)$	$(Q_1, 0)$	$(Q_1, 1)$	$(Q_2, 0)$	$(Q_2, 1)$
α	α	β	α	β	β	α
β	α	α	β	α	α	α

As an instance, $M_b(\alpha, (Q_1, 0))$ is constructed, following Theorem 5.6.13, by (i) finding that in Table 5.6.8, the state determined by $(Q_1, 0)$ is Q_0; (ii) finding, in Table 5.6.9, that q_0 is determined by (Q_0, α); (iii) finding in Table 5.6.7, that the next state from q_0 under 0 is q_0; and (iv) then using Table 5.6.9 again to determine the appropriate next state under M_b to be α (that is, $\psi(Q_0, \alpha) = q_0$). $\mathbf{T}_S'$ is then constructed, using Definition 5.6.6.

For the next theorem, recall that a *permutation* system is one whose semigroup is a group (Definition 5.4.12). A *reset* transition system is one whose semigroup consists of constant functions and the identity function.

Theorem 5.6.17. Every permutation-reset transition system $\mathbf{T}_S$ can be realized by a serial connection of a permutation and a reset machine.

Proof. Let $\mathbf{T}_S$ be $\langle S, Q, M \rangle$ and let $s_1, \ldots, s_l$ be permutation inputs and $r_1, \ldots, r_k$ be reset inputs. Let $\mathbf{T}_{S_a} = \langle S, \Phi, M_a \rangle$ where Φ is the group of permutations generated by $\varphi_{s_1}, \ldots, \varphi_{s_l}$ (this group exists, by Theorem 5.4.14); and where $M_a\colon \Phi \times S \to \Phi$ is given by

$$M_a(\varphi_x, s_i) = \varphi_{xs_i} \qquad i = 1, \ldots, l, \tag{6}$$

and

$$M_a(\varphi_x, r_j) = \varphi_x \qquad j = 1, \ldots, k \tag{7}$$

$\mathbf{T}_{S_a}$ is evidently a permutation system since the r's act as identity functions on Φ and the s's as permutations (since if $\varphi_x \neq \varphi_y$, then $\varphi_{xs_i} \neq \varphi_{ys_i}$ by cancellation).

Next, let $\mathbf{T}_{S_b} = \langle \Phi \times S, Q, M_b \rangle$, where

$$M_b(q, (\varphi_x, s_i)) = q \qquad \text{(identity)} \tag{8}$$

and

$$M_b(q, (\varphi_x, r_j)) = \varphi_x^{-1}(q') \qquad \text{(reset)} \tag{9}$$

where $M(q, r_j) = q'$, for all q in the original system $\mathbf{T}_S$.

The serial system $\mathbf{T}_S' = \langle S, \Phi \times Q, M' \rangle$ is now constructed with M' being

$$M'((\varphi_x, q), s) = (M_a(\varphi_x, s), M_b(q, (\varphi_x, s)))$$

in the usual way. To show that $\mathbf{T}_S'$ realizes $\mathbf{T}_S$, let $\psi: \Phi \times Q \to Q$ be given by $\psi(\varphi_x, q) = \varphi_x(q)$. We must show that ψ is a homomorphism, that is

$$\psi(M'(\varphi_x, q), s) = M(\psi(\varphi_x, q), s) \tag{10}$$

Let us first show this to be true in the case of a permutation input s. We have

$$\begin{aligned}\psi(M'(\varphi_x, q), s) &= \psi(M_a(\varphi_x, s), M_b(q, (\varphi_x, s))) \\ &= \psi(\varphi_{xs}, q)\end{aligned}$$

using (6) and (8),

$$= \varphi_{xs}(q)$$

by the definition of ψ. Similarly,

$$M(\psi(\varphi_x, q), s) = \varphi_s(\psi(\varphi_x, q))$$

by Definition 5.4.9,

$$= \varphi_s(\varphi_x(q)) = \varphi_{xs}(q)$$

Thus (10) is satisfied. Suppose, second, that s is a reset input, then we have

$$\begin{aligned}\psi(M'(\varphi_x, q), s) &= \psi(\varphi_x, \varphi_x^{-1}(q')) = \varphi_x\varphi_x^{-1}(q') \\ &= \varphi_\Lambda(q') = q'\end{aligned}$$

Simliarly, $M(\psi(\varphi_x, q), s) = q'$, and (10) is again satisfied. Thus ψ is a homomorphism onto $\mathbf{T}_S$ and therefore $\mathbf{T}_S'$ realizes $\mathbf{T}_S$. Q.E.D.

EXAMPLE 7 (*Continued*). The serial system $\mathbf{T}_S'$ of the example is a connection of two permutation-reset systems. In illustration of Theorem 5.6.17, we will now further decompose $\mathbf{T}_{S_a}$ (Table 5.6.8) into a series connection of a permutation and a reset transition system. For convenience, let $Q_i = q_i$; then the system to be decomposed is Table 5.6.11,

TABLE 5.6.11

	0	1
q_0	q_1	q_2
q_1	q_0	q_2
q_2	q_2	q_2

with 0 a permuting input and 1 a reset. Using the algorithm of Section 5.4 for determining the semigroup of a transition system we find (recalling that the semigroup elements are given by $\varphi_x(q) = M(q, x)$), Table 5.6.12.

TABLE 5.6.12

	φ_Λ	φ_0	φ_1
φ_Λ	φ_Λ	φ_0	φ_1
φ_0	φ_0	φ_Λ	φ_1
φ_1	φ_1	φ_1	φ_1

The subgroup of this semigroup, generated by φ_0, is $\Phi = \langle\{\varphi_\Lambda, \varphi_0\}, \cdot, \varphi_\Lambda\rangle$; from this the first serial component $\mathbf{T}_{S_a} = \langle S, \{\varphi_\Lambda, \varphi_0\}, M_a\rangle$ has transition Table 5.6.13. This table is obtained using (6), (7), and the semigroup multiplication table. For example, $M_a(\varphi_0, 0) = \varphi_{00} = \varphi_0\varphi_0 = \varphi_\Lambda$, while $M_a(\varphi_0, 1) = \varphi_0$ by (7). This is a permutation automaton.

TABLE 5.6.13

	0	1
φ_Λ	φ_0	φ_Λ
φ_0	φ_Λ	φ_0

$\mathbf{T}_{S_b} = \langle\Phi \times S, Q, M_b\rangle$ is given by Table 5.6.14, using (8) and (9). This is a reset system as desired. It is left as an exercise to hook up the serial realization using Theorem 5.6.17.

TABLE 5.6.14

	$(\varphi_\Lambda, 0)$	$(\varphi_\Lambda, 1)$	$(\varphi_0, 0)$	$(\varphi_1, 1)$
q_0	q_0	q_2	q_0	q_2
q_1	q_1	q_2	q_1	q_2
q_2	q_2	q_2	q_2	q_2

There are two further kinds of loop-free decomposition which we will consider. The one is fairly complicated, and will take us on an excursion into group theory. The other is trivial. For the easy one, we have the following lemma.

Lemma 5.6.18. Every reset transition system can be realized by a series or parallel connection of two-state systems.

Proof. For the student.

We now have immediately the following theorem.

Theorem 5.6.19. Every transition system can be realized by a series-parallel connection of permutation systems and two-state systems.

Definition 5.6.20. A group G is *simple* if it has only trivial homomorphisms (that is, if every homomorphic image of G is just an identity element).

The result which we desire is that all the permutation systems arising as in Theorem 5.6.19 be serially indecomposable in the sense that their semigroups are simple groups. In a certain sense a transition system which has been decomposed into a series-parallel connection of two-state systems and systems whose groups are simple (Theorem 5.6.42) will have been decomposed as far as possible—at least by the present methods. However, other kinds of decomposition still may apply to a transition system with associated simple groups (see Exercises 5.6). Hence with some misgivings we talk about "simple" transition systems in the following sense.

Definition 5.6.21. $\mathbf{T}_S$ is *simple* iff Φ_s is a simple group.

Our method of approach now will be reminiscent of Theorem 5.6.17. We use groups themselves as the states of transition systems. Furthermore, we will decompose such groups into certain subgroups in a manner analogous to the use of partitions or covers over states in obtaining state set decompositions. As usual, then, the key idea is that of a congruence relation. Thus we are led naturally to the study of quotient systems, in this instance, quotient groups.

Homomorphisms, as noted in Section 1.3, in general induce congruence relations on the set of elements of a semigroup or monoid. This is also true of groups. Suppose R is the relation induced by a homomorphism h and suppose P is the corresponding partition. It is an easy exercise to show that the classes $[u]_R$ under R comprise a group. One shows that (*a*) the group operation given by $[u]_R \cdot [y]_R = [u \cdot v]_R$ is well-defined; (*b*) every $[u]_R$ has an inverse; and (*c*) there is an identity $[e]_R$. Hence P is a group, and is known as a *quotient group*. Unfortunately this somewhat abstract approach to the subject is barren—it really does not give us for our purpose certain useful information which is intrinsic in the comparatively rich structure of groups. To probe somewhat more deeply, then, let us first focus our attention on $[e]_R$. (The notation in the following will be in a more traditional vein.)

Definition 5.6.22. Let $G = \langle A, \circ, e \rangle$ and $G' = \langle A', \cdot, i \rangle$, and let $\psi: A \to A'$ be a homomorphism. The set

$$K = \{u \mid u \in A \wedge \psi(u) = i\}$$

is the *kernel* of ψ.

Since homomorphisms map identities into identities, K is precisely $[e]$. We will now see that K is a subgroup of G of a very important kind.

Definition 5.6.23. A subgroup (cf. Section 1.3) N of a group G is *normal* iff for every $u \in G$ and $n \in N$, $unu^{-1} \in N$.

Theorem 5.6.24. If ψ is a homomorphism of G and G' as in Definition 5.6.22, then K is a normal subgroup of G.

Proof. First we prove that K is a group. Since for any $u, v \in K$, $\psi(u) = \psi(v) = i$, and since ψ is a homomorphism, we have at once that $\psi(u \circ v) =$

i; hence K is closed. By the subgroup theorem in Section 1.3, we need only show that $u \in K$ implies $u^{-1} \in K$. Since $\psi(u) = i$, $(\psi(u))^{-1} = i^{-1} = i = \psi(u^{-1})$ by the fact proved in Section 1.3 that homomorphisms map inverses into inverses.

To show that K is normal, assume that $u \in K$ and hence that $\psi(u) = i$. For any $g \in G$, $\psi(g) \cdot (\psi(g))^{-1} = i$. Recalling again that $(\psi(g))^{-1} = \psi(g^{-1})$,

$$\begin{aligned}\psi(g) \cdot \psi(g^{-1}) &= \psi(g) \cdot i \cdot \psi(g^{-1}) = \psi(g) \cdot \psi(u) \cdot \psi(g^{-1}) \\ &= \psi(g \circ u \circ g^{-1}) = i\end{aligned}$$

because ψ is a homomorphism. Hence $g \circ u \circ g^{-1} = gug^{-1} \in K$, and thus K is normal. Q.E.D.

Corollary 5.6.25. A group G is simple iff it has no nontrivial (that is, neither e nor G) normal subgroup.

We could now go on at once to the proof of the main result, but we pause to develop some elementary ideas which are of use in computing subgroups, and which also afford a somewhat richer insight into quotient groups, as mentioned just before Definition 5.6.22. We assume in the following text that the groups discussed are finite. Then to show that a set $H \subseteq G$ is a subgroup, we need only show closure (see Exercises 5.6).

Using the notation $uuu \cdots (m \text{ times}) = u^m$, $u^0 = e$, the identity, and $(u^{-1})^m = u^{-m}$ we note that the exponent laws $u^n u^m = u^{n+m}$ and $(u^n)^m = u^{nm}$ hold. We will also refer to positive, negative, and zero *powers* of an element u.

Definition 5.6.26. The *order* of u is the smallest positive m such that $u^m = e$. G is a *cyclic group* iff there is a $u \in G$ such that every $v \in G$ is equal to some positive power of u, that is, $v = u^m$, for some m.

Corollary 5.6.27. (*a*) The set of positive powers of u up to the order of u is a subgroup of G. (*b*) If G is cyclic, so are all of its subgroups.

Proof. For the student.

Theorem 5.6.28. The system of subgroups of G (including G and e) is a lattice.

Proof. The partial ordering relation is set inclusion. The g.l.b. of two subgroups H and H' is $H \bigcap H'$, the set intersection of the sets of elements of H and H' with operation $\cdot$ of G and the identity e of G. The l.u.b., written $H \bigcup H'$, is the smallest subgroup consisting of the union of the elements of H, of H', and of all powers, positive and negative, of these elements. It is left to the student to complete the proof—namely that the g.l.b. and the l.u.b. always exist and are also subgroups.

Definition 5.6.29. The *product* of two subgroups H and K of G is

$$HK = \{uv \mid u \in H \wedge v \in K\}$$

Theorem 5.6.30. HK is a subgroup of G iff $HK = KH$.

Proof. Assume that $HK = KH$. All we have to do is show closure of HK. Suppose $uv \in HK$ and $u'v' \in HK$. Also we have $vu' \in KH$. Since $HK = KH$, there are u'', v'' such that $vu' = u''v''$. Hence

$$\begin{aligned}(uv)(u'v') &= u(vu')v' = u(u''v'')v' \\ &= (uu'')\cdot(v''v') \in HK\end{aligned}$$

Conversely, if HK is a subgroup, then, if $vu \in KH$, we also know that $(u^{-1}v^{-1})^{-1} \in HK$ since $vu = (u^{-1}v^{-1})^{-1}$ [by Exercise 1.3(2)]. Hence $KH \subseteq HK$. Hence by the same kind of argument $HK \subseteq KH$. Q.E.D.

Corollary 5.6.31. If G is an abelian group [(6e) of Section 1.3], then $HK = KH$.

Proof. If a group is abelian so are its subgroups.

Theorem 5.6.32. If G is cyclic, then it is abelian.

Proof. Trivial.

Definition 5.6.33. The *order* of a group, $o(G)$ is the cardinal number of A. We also write $o(u)$ for the order of the subgroup of powers of u (Corollary 5.6.27, Clause *a*).

Definition 5.6.34. Let H be a subgroup of G, and let $a \in G$ be some fixed element. Then

$$Ha = \{ua \mid u \in H\}$$

is termed a *right co-set* of H. Similarly,

$$aH = \{au \mid u \in H\}$$

is a *left co-set*.

Theorem 5.6.35. $Ha = \{u \mid u \in G \wedge au^{-1} \in H\}$.

Proof. We note, first, that the pairs (u, v) which satisfy $uv^{-1} \in H$ constitute an equivalence relation R over G. Consequently, the set on the right side of the equality is the set of $u \in G$ equivalent to a, that is, $[a]_R$.

Assume for any $u \in H$ that $ua \in Ha$. Since H is a subgroup,

$$u^{-1} = eu^{-1} = (aa^{-1})u^{-1} = a(a^{-1}u^{-1}) = a(ua)^{-1} \in H$$

Hence $ua \in [a]_R$ by the construction of $[a]_R$. Conversely, if $u \in [a]_R$, then $au^{-1} \in H$; but then, $au^{-1} = (ua^{-1})^{-1} \in H$ also, and thus $ua^{-1} \in H$. However, by Definition 5.6.34 $(ua^{-1})a \in Ha$. So $u \in Ha$. Q.E.D.

Thus the family of right (left) co-sets of H is a partition of the elements of G. It is clear that the classes in this partition are equipotent, since for two co-sets Ha and Hb, the rule which associates, for any $u \in H$, ua to ub is onto. Also, if $u'b = ub$, by cancellation $u' = u$ and hence, $u'a = ua$. Thus the rule is one–one. Since every element of G is in some right co-set and since the co-sets are distinct, and equipotent, if there are k co-sets (the index of H in G) in the partition, $o(G) = k \cdot o(H)$, (recall $H = He$ is in the family). This is the famous theorem of Lagrange and is expressed as follows.

Theorem 5.6.36. If G is finite, then the order of every subgroup divides the order of G.

The fragment of group theory given in Definitions, Corollaries, and Theorems 5.6.26 to 5.6.36 should be of considerable help to the student in determining the subgroups of a group. Since all of the groups of concern are finite, the problem of eliciting all of the subgroups is effectively solvable, but application of the foregoing results will make the procedure more or less practical in addition. We leave it to the student to develop his own algorithms. It is convenient to start with the subgroups which are asserted to exist by Corollary 5.6.27 and then use lattice properties and Theorem 5.6.30. Lagrange's theorem can be used to rule out subgroups of certain sizes and to obviate the search altogether in the case of groups of prime order.

How do we identify the normality property? This is important, since we want to use normal subgroups (cf. Theorem 5.6.24) to construct quotient systems which, in turn, are to be ingredients of series connections of transition systems. The following theorem is the main criterion.

Theorem 5.6.37. N is normal iff every right co-set of N is a left co-set of N, and conversely; the two partitions (families of left and right co-sets) are equal.

Proof. $un \in uN$. But $un = un(u^{-1}u) = (unu^{-1})u \in Nu$, because owing to the fact that N is normal, $unu^{-1} \in N$; similarly for the other way around.

Conversely, suppose Nu is a right co-set and is equal to some left co-set vN. Now $u \in Nu$ since $e \in N$ and $eu = u$. Hence $u \in vN$. Since co-sets are equivalence classes it must be that $uN = vN$. Thus $uN = Nu$. Finally suppose $m \in N$. Since $uN = Nu$, there exists an $n \in N$ such that $um = nu$. But then $umu^{-1} = nuu^{-1} = n \in N$. Therefore, N is normal. Q.E.D.

A further test is afforded by the next theorem.

Theorem 5.6.38. N is normal iff the family of right (left) co-sets of N is closed under the subgroup product (Definition 5.6.29).

Proof. Suppose that $numv \in NuNv$, $n, m \in N$. But then

$$numv = numev = numu^{-1}uv = nm'uv \in Nuv$$

for N is normal by hypothesis, and hence $m' = umu^{-1} \in N$ and by closure $nm' \in N$.

Conversely, suppose closure, that is, that $NuNv = Nuv$. Then

$$NuN = NuNe = Nue = Nu$$

and

$$NuN = eNuN = euN = uN$$

Hence $Nu = uN$ and by Theorem 5.6.37 it follows that N is normal. Q.E.D.

Theorem 5.6.39. If $G = \langle A, \circ, e\rangle$ and N is normal in G, let A/N denote the set of right co-sets of N in G. Let $\cdot$ be the subgroup product of Definition 5.6.29. Then $G/N = \langle A/N, \cdot, N\rangle$ is a group. G/N is called the *quotient group* of G by N.

Proof. For the student.

To close the circle of ideas presented following Definition 5.6.21, the student should see that the classes $[u]_R$ determined by a homomorphism are precisely the right co-sets of N, N being the kernel of the homomorphism. He should also observe that the subgroup product w.r.t. right co-sets is precisely the usual product of equivalence classes.

Corollary 5.6.40. G/N is a homomorphic image of G.

Proof. Obvious.

The following theorem takes us at once to the desired application to automata.

Theorem 5.6.41. Let $\mathbf{T}_S$ be a permutation transition system with its semigroup Φ_S being nonsimple. Let Ψ be a normal sub-group of Φ_S. Then $\mathbf{T}_S$ can be realized by the serial connection of transition systems $\mathbf{T}_{S_a}$ and $\mathbf{T}_{S_b}$ such that (i) Φ_{S_a} is isomorphic to Φ_S/Ψ; (ii) Φ_{S_b} is isomorphic to Ψ.

Proof. Let $\mathbf{T}_S = \langle S, Q, M\rangle$. Let $\mathbf{T}_{S_a} = \langle S, \Phi', M_a\rangle$ where Φ' is a set of representatives, called *leaders*, of the right co-sets $\Psi\varphi$. (Recall that we use the notation φ, φ_s, etc., for elements of transition-system semigroups). Define

$$M_a(\varphi'_x, s) = \varphi'_{xs} \tag{11}$$

where $\varphi'_x \in \Phi'$ and $s \in S$.

Next, let $\mathbf{T}_{S_b} = \langle \Phi' \times S, Q, M_b\rangle$, where

$$M_b(q, (\varphi'_x, s)) = (M_a(\varphi'_x, s)^{-1} \cdot \varphi_{xs})(q) \tag{12}$$

Here $\varphi'_x \in \Phi'$, a leader, while $\varphi_{xs} \in \Phi_s$ and the multiplication indicated on the right side of (12) is the semigroup operation.

Finally the serial system is $\mathbf{T}_S' = \langle S, \Phi' \times Q, M'\rangle$ where as usual

$$\begin{aligned} M'((\varphi_x', q), s) &= (M_a(\varphi'_x, s), M_b(q, (\varphi'_x, s))) \\ &= (M_a(\varphi'_x, s), (M_a(\varphi'_x, s)^{-1} \cdot \varphi_{xs})(q)) \end{aligned} \tag{13}$$

The purpose of this rather complicated construction will come out in the discussion of the example following this proof.

To show the required homomorphism let $\chi: \Phi' \times Q \to Q$ be specified by $\chi(\varphi_x', q) = M(q, x) = \varphi_x'(q)$. This map is surely onto since every $q \in Q$ is an image of itself under $M(q, \Lambda) = \varphi_\Lambda'(q)$. Now we have

$$\begin{aligned}\chi M'((\varphi_x', q), s) &= \chi(M_a(\varphi_x', s), (M_a(\varphi_x', s)^{-1} \cdot \varphi_{xs})(q)) \\ &= \chi(\varphi_{xs}', \varphi_{xs}'^{-1} \cdot \varphi_{xs}(q))\end{aligned}$$

using just (11); by the construction of χ, we have

$$\begin{aligned}\chi(\varphi_{xs}', \varphi_{xs}'^{-1} \cdot \varphi_{xs}(q)) &= \varphi_{xs}' \cdot \varphi_{xs}'^{-1} \cdot \varphi_{xs}(q) \\ &= M(q, xs)\end{aligned}$$

But also,

$$M(\chi(\varphi_x', q), s) = M(M(q, x), s) = M(q, xs)$$

This proves that χ is a homomorphism. The easy verifications of (i) and (ii) are for the student. Q.E.D.

The construction used in Theorem 5.6.41 always leads to a serial connection of permutation automata by (i) and (ii). If any such machine has a nonsimple group for its semigroup, the construction may be used again. The process must surely end, as all groups concerned are finite and since the order of each composite subgroup is less than that of the group itself. Hence, using Theorems 5.6.41 and 5.6.19, the following theorem is obtained.

Theorem 5.6.42. (Krohn-Rhodes). Every transition system can be realized by a series-parallel connection of transition systems which are either simple or two-state.

EXAMPLE 8. In this example we will use the semigroup $\mathscr{S}/\mathbf{T}_S$ rather than the function semigroup Φ_S, as we did in Example 7. This is for notational convenience and allows us to avoid the somewhat confusing conventions $\varphi_s\varphi_{s'} = \varphi_{s's}$ and $\varphi_s\varphi_{xs'} = \varphi_{xs's}$. Consider the system in Table 5.6.15.

TABLE 5.6.15

	0	1	2
q_0	q_0	q_1	q_1
q_1	q_1	q_0	q_2
q_2	q_2	q_2	q_0

Inspection shows this to be a permutation system. Its semigroup $\mathscr{S}/\mathbf{T}_S$ is the symmetric group of order 6 given by Table 5.6.16. (In this table $[x]$ is written simply x, as in Section 5.4.)

TABLE 5.6.16

	Λ	1	2	12	21	22
Λ	Λ	1	2	12	21	22
1	1	Λ	12	2	22	21
2	2	21	22	1	12	Λ
12	12	22	21	Λ	2	1
21	21	2	1	22	Λ	12
22	22	12	Λ	21	1	2

The following tableau, on which Table 5.6.16 is based, is built up by the methods of Section 5.4.

$$\begin{aligned} \Lambda &= 0 = 11 = 222 \\ 21 &= 122 = 210 \\ 1 &= 10 = 212 \\ 2 &= 20 = 211 \\ 22 &= 121 = 220 \\ 12 &= 120 = 221 \end{aligned} \tag{14}$$

By Lagrange's theorem (5.6.36), if there are any subgroups, they must be of order 2 or 3. Inspection shows the group is not cyclic. However $2^3 = \Lambda$. Hence by Corollary 5.6.27(a), $2^0 = \Lambda = 2^3$, 2^1, 2^2 is a subgroup. It appears in Table 5.6.17. Three other subgroups obtained in the same way

TABLE 5.6.17

$H_1 =$

	Λ	2	22
Λ	Λ	2	22
2	2	22	Λ
22	22	Λ	2

are shown in Table 5.6.18.

TABLE 5.6.18

H_2

	Λ	1
Λ	Λ	1
1	1	Λ

H_3

	Λ	21
Λ	Λ	21
21	21	Λ

H_4

	Λ	12
Λ	Λ	12
12	12	Λ

Simple calculations show that $H_iH_j \neq H_jH_i$ for $i, j = 2, 3, 4, \ldots$. However, $H_1 \cdot H_2 = G = H_2 \cdot H_1$. But we gain nothing new.

Continuing, $H_1 \cap H_i$, $i = 2, 3, 4$ is Λ (the 0 group in lattice terminology). $H_2 \cup H_3 = G$, etc. Evidently H_1 to H_4 are the only subgroups. None of H_2 to H_4 are normal, as is easily checked.

On the other hand the index of H_1 is $\frac{6}{3} = 2$. Therefore there are two right (left) co-sets to examine.

$H_1 = \{\Lambda, 2, 22\}$	$H_1 = \{\Lambda, 2, 22\}$
$H_1 1 = \{1, 21, 12\}$	$1H_1 = \{1, 12, 21\}$
Right	Left

By Theorem 5.6.37, H_1 is normal since the partitions are the same. To verify this, note that $H_1 \cdot H_1 1 = H_1 1$, etc. So the family of right co-sets is closed under subgroup product and hence again we see that H_1 is normal (Theorem 5.6.38).

By 5.6.39, H_1 determines a quotient group $G/H_1 = \langle\{H_1, H_1 1\}, \cdot, H_1\rangle$. For later use in applying Theorem 5.6.41 we use the isomorphic group of co-set leaders or representatives $\langle\{\Lambda', 1'\}, \cdot, \Lambda'\rangle$. Note that at this point we have made two abstractions: Λ, 1, 2, etc. of Table 5.6.16 are, in fact, representatives of the equivalence classes of $\mathcal{S}/\mathbf{T}_S$ according to the tableau (14); now, furthermore, Λ' is a representative of another equivalence class under H_1—the right co-sets of H_1 in $\mathcal{S}/\mathbf{T}_S$. The quotient system to be used in the series construction is Table 5.6.19.

TABLE 5.6.19

	Λ'	$1'$
Λ'	Λ'	$1'$
$1'$	$1'$	Λ'

Using 5.6.41, $\mathbf{T}_{S_a} = \langle\{0, 1, 2\}, \{\Lambda', 1'\}, M_a\rangle$ where M_a is represented in Table 5.6.20. $\mathbf{T}_{S_b} = \langle\{\Lambda', 1'\} \times \{0, 1, 2\}, Q, M_b\rangle$ where M_b is represented

TABLE 5.6.20

	0	1	2
Λ'	Λ'	$1'$	Λ'
$1'$	$1'$	Λ'	$1'$

in Table 5.6.21. This table is computed by (12) with the aid of the original

TABLE 5.6.21

	$(\Lambda', 0)$	$(\Lambda', 1)$	$(\Lambda', 2)$	$(1', 0)$	$(1', 1)$	$(1', 2)$
q_0	q_0	q_0	q_1	q_0	q_0	q_2
q_1	q_1	q_1	q_2	q_1	q_1	q_0
q_2	q_2	q_2	q_0	q_2	q_2	q_1

M function of Table 5.6.15 and of the tableau (14). For example, $M_b(q_2, (1', 2))$ is computed thus:

$$M_a(1', 2) = 1' = 1'^{-1}$$

then $M(q_2, 22) = M(M(q_2, 2), 2) = q_1$.

Finally, $\mathbf{T}_S' = \langle S, \{\Lambda', 1'\} \times Q, M' \rangle$ with M' being as in Table 5.6.22. The mapping χ is indicated by the column of q's to the left, and may be verified to be a homomorphism by comparison of Tables 5.6.22 and 5.6.15.

TABLE 5.6.22

		0	1	2
(q_0)	(Λ', q_0)	(Λ', q_0)	$(1', q_0)$	(Λ', q_1)
(q_1)	(Λ', q_1)	(Λ', q_1)	$(1', q_1)$	(Λ', q_2)
(q_2)	(Λ', q_2)	(Λ', q_2)	$(1', q_2)$	(Λ', q_0)
(q_1)	$(1', q_0)$	$(1', q_0)$	(Λ', q_0)	$(1', q_2)$
(q_0)	$(1', q_1)$	$(1', q_1)$	(Λ', q_1)	$(1', q_0)$
(q_2)	$(1', q_2)$	$(1', q_2)$	(Λ', q_2)	$(1', q_1)$

It is an easy matter for the student to verify that the semigroup of $\mathbf{T}_{S_a}$ is isomorphic to the quotient group under H_1 and that the semigroup of $\mathbf{T}_{S_b}$ is isomorphic to H_1 itself.

EXERCISES 5.6

1. Complete the proof of Theorem 5.6.1.

2. Extend Theorem 5.6.7 to complete Moore machines, introducing the appropriate new concept of realization.

3. Complete the proof of Corollary 5.6.11.

4. Prove Theorem 5.6.14.

5. Apply the procedures of this section to the total decomposition of the transition system appearing below to a series-parallel connection of simple and two-state systems.

	0	1	2
q_0	q_1	q_2	q_1
q_1	q_2	q_1	q_3
q_2	q_0	q_0	q_0
q_3	q_2	q_0	q_2

6. Give an example of a *simple* transition system which is decomposable in the sense of Theorem 5.6.7.

7. Show that there is a transition system having the group of integers mod 6 as its semigroup, which has a serial decomposition depending on a congruence relation on states, and such that this serial system is isomorphic to a serial decomposition depending on the normal subgroup construction.

8. Show that if G is finite, G' is a subgroup of G iff G' is closed.

9. Prove Corollary 5.6.27; prove Theorem 5.6.32.

10. Prove Theorem 5.6.39.

5.7 HISTORICAL AND BIBLIOGRAPHICAL REMARKS

Essentially, the idea of a finite transducer goes back to McCulloch and Pitts [1943], although they studied the special case of certain logical models of nerve networks. The formulation used in Definition 5.1.3 is due jointly to Huffman [1954], Mealy [1955] and Kleene [1956]; that of Definition 5.3.22 is due to Moore [1956]; there are intimations of the idea in Keister, et al. [1951]. The observation that finite transducers are the same as unidirectional Turing machines is Lee's [1960].

The theory of reduction of Section 5.2 should be jointly attributed to Huffman, Mealy, and Moore, while most of the material in Section 5.3 up to Definition 5.3.29 is due both to Moore and to Burks and Wang [1957]. The present exposition in Sections 5.2 and 5.3 follows the excellent formulations in Elgot [1959]. The treatment of incomplete machines is derived from Elgot and Rutledge [1964].

The approach to transducer semigroups of Section 3.4 is Myhill's [1963*a*]. The idea of a permutation machine, however, goes back to Burks and Wang [1957]. The semigroup algorithm is new and is based on a suggestion due to Mr. R. E. Lover.

The study of what we have termed transition systems originated with Rabin and Scott [1959], but in connection with acceptors (cf. Chapter 7) rather than transducers.[16] The subject matter presented in Section 5.5 is a development of the Rabin-Scott approach by Büchi and Wright [1960], while the general form of argument used here follows Thatcher [1963]. The results on parallel decomposition, based directly on Birkhoff's [1935, 1948], are Hartmanis' [1960].

Theorem 5.6.42 is essentially the principal result of a paper by Krohn and Rhodes [1963]. The method using covers, permutation, and reset machines, and the normal subgroup construction is due to Zeiger [1964]. In our exposition we have also made use of Hartmanis and Stearns [1966] and Karp [1965], who have discussed various aspects of decomposition. Related work, in automaton groups, not discussed here, is listed in the Bibliography, notably that by Weeg [1962] and Fleck [1962]. Important contributions to decomposition have been made by Yoeli [1961; 1963a, b].

[16] The expression "transition system" as used by us is Büchi's term [1960] for an equivalent idea. Thatcher uses "transition system" for what is, in essence, a non-deterministic acceptor (Chapter 7).

CHAPTER 6

Transducer Nets

6.0 Introduction. The formal study of automata is prompted by certain problems in the use and design of digital computer and control devices and, as indicated in the preface, by a desire to understand other discrete state devices such as nerve networks. We will now investigate, therefore, specializations of the formal finite transducer model in the direction of actual physical devices. Our study in this section will be of transducer nets, that is, of the interconnections of idealized switching or "decision" elements, which correspond to formal transducers. We will also briefly consider networks of idealized nerve cells.[1] Thus in this section we will move still further away from the really basic questions, considered in earlier chapters, concerning the behavior of automata and the formal nature of effective processes in general. However, we will return to these questions in Chapters 7 and 8.

Since 1950 people in the field of transducer nets and switching have worked on a large number of problems from a large number of quite diverse points of view. In this introductory treatment it is not possible to consider all such problems or viewpoints. The policy adopted here is to concentrate on problems of minimization. This concentration seems to be typical of most of the work in this department of the theory of automata. Thus, except for the quite general and basic material in Section 6.1 dealing with net definitions and correspondence to formal transducers, we will be concerned with two problems: the state assignment and minimal switching net problems.

The first problem arises in the following way. Suppose we have at hand certain switching and memory devices such as and-gates, flip-flops, etc.; however, these are not necessarily two-state or binary in character, but

[1] We will use "net" in the sense of logical systems of decision elements (cf. Definition 6.1.5). "Circuit" on the other hand refers to physical arrangements of hardware elements. Circuits as such are studied in engineering and are outside the scope of automata theory.

m-ary for some fixed m. Suppose further it is desired to design a sequential circuit of a certain description. Now assuming we have a formal description of the requirements of the desired circuit in terms of the M and N functions of an associated transducer system **T**, and assuming further that the number of states of **T** is greater than m, how do we realize M and N in an efficient way using the given switching and memory devices? As the reader already knows, the states of **T** are *coded* in terms of the states (call them $0, 1, \ldots, m - 1$) of the available switches. Depending on the logical structure of the available switches, each such possible encodement leads to a net with a distinctive structure; however, all such nets are behaviorally equivalent—they all realize the N function exactly. The assignment problem is, given T and m, to choose in advance that code assignment which leads to an efficient design. Although this problem is trivial in the theoretical sense that only a finite number[2] of cases need be examined in confrontation with a simplicity criterion, the practical problem is appalling. There are

$$\frac{(m^n)!}{(m^n - r)!} \tag{1}$$

possible assignments where m^n is the least power of m greater than or equal to r, and r is the number of states of **T**. We will see that if our simplicity criterion is to reduce the dependency of the coded states on coded states in the realization of $M: Q \times S \to Q$, then a good solution to the problem is attainable by using the concept of congruence partitions discussed in Section 5.5. Thus we trade off the problem of examining the number of code assignments given by (1) for that of examining the number of partitions as given in footnote 13 of Section 5.5. For physical as well as logical reasons we will discuss this problem only for the case where $m = 2$.

The switching net minimization problem can be expressed as follows. Given switching elements of a certain description and a one-state finite transducer **T**, find a realization of **T** using the least number of switching elements. The reader will no doubt be familiar with the fact that for the usual two-state elements and for unilateral relay circuits this corresponds to the problem of minimizing the number of occurrences of variables in the logical representation of the switching circuit. For gating-type elements, on the other hand, the aim is to minimize connectives, that is, and's, or's, nand's, nor's, or whatever, occurring in the logical representation.

We will examine only the single output case, and hasten to remark that this problem is also theoretically trivial. That there exists a recursive procedure for producing all of the minimal versions of a switching net equivalent to a given net (in the sense that it realizes an equivalent formula

[2] That is, the problem of finding the best assignment is solvable.

of the propositional calculus, or the same boolean function—cf. Section 3.2) may be verified briefly as follows. The set of all formulas of the propositional calculus using the connectives $\wedge$, $\vee$, $\neg$ (let us say) of length less than k is finite. Hence this set can be recursively obtained. By employing an appropriate modification of Theorem 3.2.11 (for the set of connectives we are now presupposing) together with Theorem 3.2.7, we obtain a decision procedure for testing whether any formula is equivalent to any other. These two steps yield a finite set of simpler formulas equivalent to the given one; so there is again a finite number to examine for the absolutely simplest.

Needless to say such an approach is practically impossible. Instead, the usual procedure is to study sequences of operations on formulas which preserve equivalence and yield shorter forms. Another procedure, quite analogous to the methods alluded to for the state assignment problem, is to find certain *partitions* on the set of argument values of the truth function (boolean function) corresponding to the formula. The aim here is to find simple component functions of which the given function is the composite. We will examine both mentioned approaches, but only in the easiest case which is that of single output nets.

6.1 BINARY TRANSDUCER NETS

In order to simplify the discussion as much as possible without sacrificing anything of importance, we will assume that the finite transducers under discussion have initial states and are complete but not necessarily connected. In addition we will assume that the physical devices used are capable of assuming either one or the other, but not both, of two states. Thus the alphabets of our nets, including the inputs they can accept and outputs they eject, as well as the sets of internal states will contain but two distinct elements. Conventionally, we choose the set $\{0, 1\}$ with the additional but inessential understanding that 1 is "high" or "positive" and 0 is "low" or "negative." We will now approach the idea of a binary transducer net in several easy steps.

Definition 6.1.1. Let $\mathbf{T} = \langle Q, S, q_0, M, N, O\rangle$ and let m, n, and r be integers satisfying $\log_2 K(Q) \leq n$, $\log_2 K(S) \leq m$, and $\log_2 K(O) \leq r$; let there be one–one maps from Q, S, O into the set of n-tuples, the set of m-tuples, and the set of r-tuples, respectively, on $\{0, 1\}$. A *coded form* of $\mathbf{T}$ is the system $\mathbf{T}_B = \langle Q', S', q_0', M', N', O'\rangle$ where Q' is a set of n-tuples comprising the range of the one–one map from Q; and similarly for S', O'; q_0' is the m-tuple of 0's, the initial state; M' and N' are functions given by those tables which are the result of replacing each q by its corresponding n-tuple, each s by its corresponding m-tuple, and each o by its corresponding r-tuple in the tables for M and N of $\mathbf{T}$.

It is clear from the manner of construction that **T** and $\mathbf{T}_B$ are isomorphic, since each k-tuple ($k = m, n, r$) may be taken as a distinct object, and hence are equivalent (see exercises).

EXAMPLE 1. A coded form of the automaton of Table 5.2.1a may be obtained by using the correspondences

$q_0 \leftrightarrow 000$ (initial state) $\quad s_0 \leftrightarrow 00$
$q_1 \leftrightarrow 001$ $\quad s_1 \leftrightarrow 01$
$q_2 \leftrightarrow 010$ $\quad s_2 \leftrightarrow 10$
$q_3 \leftrightarrow 111$ $\quad s_3 \leftrightarrow 11$
$q_4 \leftrightarrow 100$ $\quad o_i \leftrightarrow i \quad i = 0, 1$

Thus Table 6.1.1 defines the new coded form.

TABLE 6.1.1

q' \ s'	M' 00	01	10	11	N' 00	01	10	11
000	000	111	010	100	0	1	0	1
001	001	010	111	100	1	0	1	0
010	010	111	010	100	0	1	0	1
111	100	001	001	001	0	1	1	1
100	100	111	000	010	0	1	0	1

In this example, $K(Q) = 5$, and $n = 3$ happens to be the least integer greater than or equal to $\log_2 5$. There is nothing in our requirements, however, to preclude using any greater n, although in general the least n tends to lead to the simplest nets. Similar remarks apply to m and r.

Now let $x_1, \ldots, x_m$, $y_1, \ldots, y_n$, and $z_1, \ldots, z_r$ be binary variables. We will call these *input*, *state*, and *output* variables respectively. The variable state of a coded transducer will be designated $(y_1, \ldots, y_n)$ or, in tables by $y_1 y_2 \cdots y_n$ and similarly for variable inputs and outputs.

Continuing Example 1 with $q' = (y_1, y_2, y_3)$, $s' = (x_1, x_2)$ and $0' = z_1$, we have Table 6.1.2. Here it is understood that the values of the M' function are the states (y_1, y_2, y_3) and those of the N' function are outputs z_1.

TABLE 6.1.2

	M' x_1x_2				N' x_1x_2			
$y_1y_2y_3$	00	01	10	11	00	01	10	11
000	000	111	010	100	0	1	0	1
001	001	010	111	100	1	0	1	0
010	010	111	010	100	0	1	0	1
111	100	001	001	001	0	1	1	1
100	100	111	000	010	0	1	0	1

It follows, from our constructions and from Section 1.3, that each component y_j of an n-tuple in the interior of the M' table is a boolean function (or by Theorem 3.2.13, a truth function) of $m + n$ variables, and moreover that each component z_k of an r-tuple in the N' table is also a function of $m + n$ variables. Thus we have

$$y_j \Leftrightarrow M_j(x_1, \ldots, x_m, y_1, \ldots, y_n) \qquad j = 1, \ldots, n$$

and (1)

$$z_k \Leftrightarrow N_k(x_1, \ldots, x_n, y_1, \ldots, y_n) \qquad k = 1, \ldots, r$$

In this fashion M' and N' are represented by the sequences of truth functions $M_1, \ldots, M_n$ and $N_1, \ldots, N_m$.

Using the results reviewed in Section 1.3, let us determine y_3 of our running example as a function M_3 of the variables y_1, y_2, y_3 and x_1, x_2. By Exercise 1.3(19) and Table 6.1.2, we see that there are eight cases in which M_3 has the value 1; this leads to a canonical form with eight terms. In accordance with Definition 3.2.12, and the isomorphism between free boolean algebras and propositional calculi interpreted as truth functional logics, we call this form the *complete disjunctive normal form.* Using the simplified notation (customary in the study of switching circuits) $\vee$ for or, juxtaposition for and ($\wedge$), $^-$ for not ($\neg$), we obtain the following form:

$$\begin{aligned} y_3 \Leftrightarrow\ & \bar{x}_1\bar{x}_2\bar{y}_1\bar{y}_2y_3 \vee \bar{x}_1x_2\bar{y}_1\bar{y}_2\bar{y}_3 \vee \bar{x}_1x_2\bar{y}_1y_2\bar{y}_3 \vee \bar{x}_1x_2y_1y_2y_3 \\ & \vee \bar{x}_1x_2y_1\bar{y}_2\bar{y}_3 \vee x_1\bar{x}_2\bar{y}_1\bar{y}_2y_3 \vee x_1\bar{x}_2y_1y_2y_3 \vee x_1x_2y_1y_2y_3 \end{aligned}$$

Similarly z_1 will be the value of a truth function represented by an eleven-term disjunction; and similarly again for y_1 and y_2.

The next step in our approach to nets is to introduce synchronization. We may say that equations (1) represent the *asynchronous* case of coded transducers. The several components of the n-tuple $(y_1, \ldots, y_n)$, for example, may all be computed independently. In particular, this means that in a physical realization the automaton might pass through unwanted states when transiting to a legitimate next state. Suppose the transducer of Table 6.1.2 is in state 000 and receives an input of 01. The next state, by M', is 111. If $\mathbf{T}_B$ realized $y_3 = 1 = M_3(0, 1, 0, 0, 0)$, while lagging in doing y_1 and y_2, it would be in state 001, for a moment, with spurious 0 output. As the reader presumably knows, such a situation may be avoided by special design considerations (for which a theory of the asynchronous case is developing) or by requiring that all next state transitions be "clocked"; our treatment will be limited to the "clocked" synchronous case (cf. footnote 10, Section 5.5).

Definition 6.1.2. A *coded synchronous transducer* is a coded transducer in which each variable $x_1, \ldots, x_n$, $y_1, \ldots, y_n$, $z_1, \ldots, z_n$ ranges over sets of functions of the nonnegative integers with the co-domain 0,1. A synchronous transducer is represented by the equivalences

$$y_j(0) \equiv 0, \tag{2a}$$

$$y_j(t+1) \equiv M_j(x_1(t), \ldots, x_m(t), y_1(t), \ldots, y_n(t)) \qquad j = 1, \ldots, n \tag{2b}$$

$$z_k(t) \equiv N_k(x_1(t), \ldots, x_m(t), y_1(t), \ldots, y_n(t)) \qquad k = 1, \ldots, r \tag{3}$$

where $t = 0, 1, 2, \ldots$, and where we have used $\equiv$ for $\Leftrightarrow$ to emphasize a shift to the synchronous case.

It is clear that a synchronous transducer is still equivalent to the associated transducer system from which it derives.

The values of the variables interpreted as in Definition 6.1.2 are propositional functions, a *propositional function* being a mapping from any domain whatsoever into $\{0, 1\}$. At any time t, each M_j and N_k is a truth function of the x_i and y_j. Equivalence (2a) states that for $t = 0$, each y_j is a propositional function with value 0, so that at "time" 0, $\mathbf{T}_B$ is in its initial state. Clearly by (2b) each integer or "instant of time" determines an input m-tuple and a state n-tuple which by the sequence of functions M_j determines the next state n-tuple at $t + 1$. Suppose we have the input sequence (0, 0) (0, 1) (0, 1) (1, 0). Using the convention of Definition 3.1.1, we may write this sequence of pairs (0001, 0110). This determines the two propositional functions $x_1(0) = 0$, $x_1(1) = 0$, $x_1(2) = 0$, $x_1(3) = 1$, and $x_2(0) = 0$, $x_2(1) = 1$, $x_2(2) = 1$, $x_2(3) = 0$, which make explicit the fact that (0001, 0110) is a pair of input *sequences*. Since $y_j(0) = 0$ for each j, (2a) and (2b) define the functions y_j recursively, relative to the given functions x_1 and x_2. In general, each y_j will be a different function depending on the input (see exercises). Although expressions such as (2) and (3) indicate truth functional equivalences in the sense of Definition 3.2.9, we will refer to them as equations.

In the following definition, we will assume that $t = 0, 1, 2$, etc., are discrete instants of *time*.

Definition 6.1.3. A *decision element* is an object consisting of a central *body*, exactly one attached finite length wire called an *output*, and any number of attached finite length wires called *inputs*. At each instant every input and the output have a *value* 1 or 0, and the output value is a *truth function* of the input values.

Note that, according to Definition 6.1.3, the output of a decision element is a truth function of the input at any time t. It follows that decision elements develop outputs instantaneously, which is of course an idealization of actual hardware elements used in computers or occurring in nerve networks.

We will restrict our discussion, since our purpose is not to duplicate the more or less standard available material on switching circuits, to *and*, *or*, and *not* decision elements. An *and* element is an element with two inputs such that the output is (has the value) 1 at time t iff both of the inputs are 1 at time t. Similarly, we may define the *or* and *not* elements.

Definition 6.1.4. A *delay element* is an object consisting of a central *body*, exactly one attached finite wire called an *input*, and exactly one such wire called an *output*. Inputs and outputs have *values* of either 0 or 1. The output has value 1 at time $t + 1$ iff the input has value 1 at time t.

Figure 6.1.1 displays the diagrammatic conventions we will adopt for decision and delay elements.

Definition 6.1.5. A *transducer net* is an assemblage of decision elements determined inductively as follows.

1. Any decisio ı or delay element is a *net*.

2*a*. If $\mathbf{N}_1$ and $\mathbf{N}_2$ are distinct nets, the first with output z and the second with an input x, the result of identifying the wires z and x is a *net*.

2*b*. If **N** is a net with a delay element having output y, and an input x which is not an output, then the result of identifying x and y is a *net*.

2*c*. If **N** is a net containing inputs x_1 and x_2 which are not outputs, then the result of identifying x_1 and x_2 is a *net*.

2*d*. If $\mathbf{N}_1$ and $\mathbf{N}_2$ are distinct (that is, no identified wires) nets, then $\mathbf{N}_1$ and $\mathbf{N}_2$ taken together coṇstitute a single *net*.

3. If **N** is a net, its being so follows from 1 and 2.

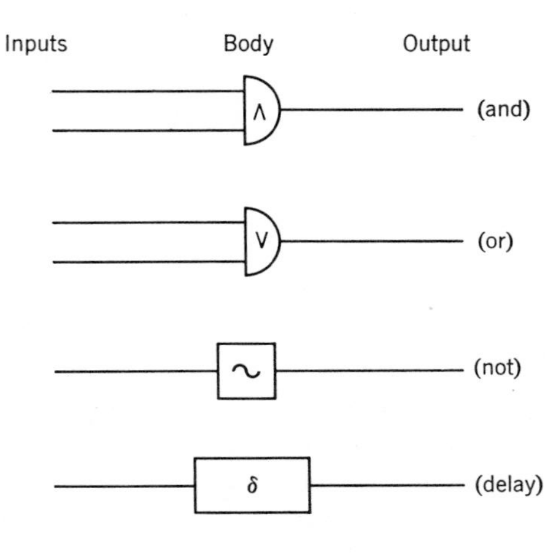

Fig. 6.1.1

REMARK. Any set of decision elements satisfying Definition 6.1.5 will have a set of inputs which are not identified with any outputs and a set of outputs which are not identified with any inputs. Such inputs and outputs are *net inputs* and *net outputs*. Each net output determines a unique *subnet* of a net **N**, which subnet has some or all of the net inputs of **N**. We will not try to formalize this idea but will nevertheless use it freely in the following text.

Assume that the n delay elements are indexed $1, \ldots, n$ and that the m inputs and r outputs are similarly indexed.

Definition 6.1.6. A *labeled binary net* is a net with m net inputs and r net outputs, m, r integers, such that the ith input has associated to it the variable x_i, $i = 1, \ldots, m$, the kth output has associated to it the variable z_k, $k = 1, \ldots, r$, and the jth delay element output has associated to it the variable y_j, $j = 1, \ldots, n$.

EXAMPLE 2. The *and* net of Fig. 6.1.1 is labeled as in Fig. 6.1.2. This decision element is a labeled net by the last two definitions. Since all wires are 0 or 1 at time t, we have $x_1(t) = 0, 1$, etc. Thus, by our developments here, x_1 is ambiguously the name of a wire and a propositional function and so are x_2 and z_1. By the definition of $\wedge$ and Definition 6.1.3 we have for arbitrary t

$$z_1(t) \equiv (x_1(t) \wedge x_2(t)) \equiv (x_1(t)x_2(t))$$

EXAMPLE 3. Figure 6.1.3 shows a net and its manner of formation according to each clause of Definition 6.1.5. Dotted rectangles are used to demarcate nets, and the letter in the northeast corner of each rectangle indicates the clause used to combine components. The use of clauses 1, $2a$, and $2b$ are shown; an application of $2c$ would result from, for example, the identification of the lower two inputs; and an application of $2d$ would result from the juxtaposition of Fig. 6.1.3 with a similar net but with no wire identification.

EXAMPLE 4. If we label the net of Fig. 6.1.3 in accordance with Definition 6.1.6, calling the two net inputs to the *and* element x_1 and x_2, the net

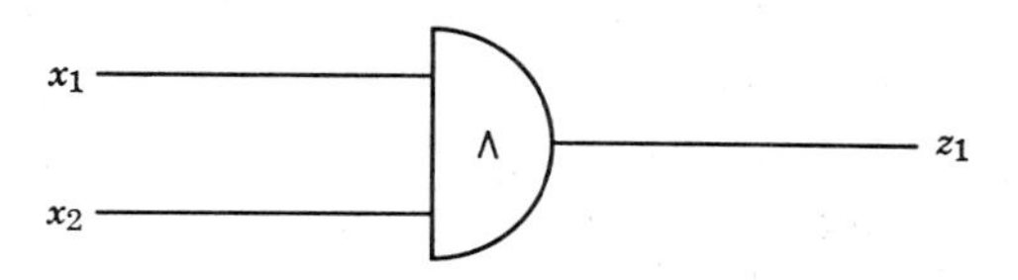

Fig. 6.1.2

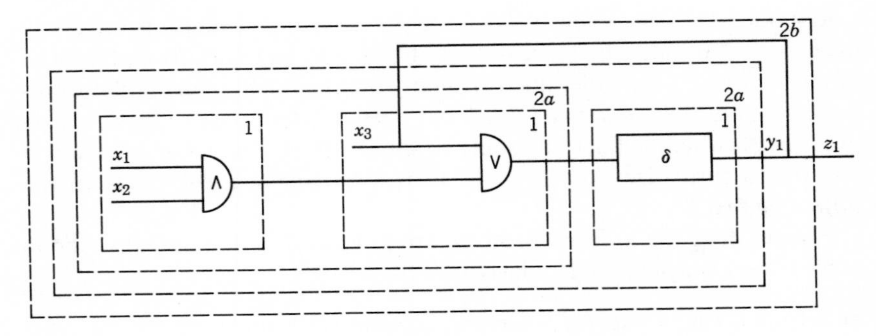

Fig. 6.1.3

input to the *or* element x_3, the net output z_1, and the delay output y_1, we have the following equivalences:

$$y_1(t + 1) \equiv x_1(t)x_2(t) \lor x_3(t) \tag{4a}$$

$$z_1(t) \equiv y_1(t) \tag{4b}$$

It is useful in the analysis of nets to label inputs to delays as well as outputs. We will label the jth delay input u_j. Thus, in (4a)

$$u_1(t) \equiv x_1(t)x_2(t) \lor x_3(t) \tag{5}$$

Equivalences (4) and (5) suggest use of the *delay operator* which is defined by the relation

$$\delta u_j(t) \equiv y_j(t) \tag{6}$$

Thus y at t is the same as u at t, delayed by δ.

The foregoing illustrations suggest a certain equivalence between nets and synchronous transducers, or more precisely speaking, an equivalence between nets and transducer equations of the form (2)–(3). In the usual mathematical terminology we say that nets *realize* functions and that equations *represent* them. In the case of truth functions, we know from switching theory that switching nets (and, or, not nets without delays) realize truth functions, and that propositional calculus formulas using $\land$, $\lor$, and $^{-}$ represent all such truth functions. Definition 6.1.7 is justified by the remark (following Definition 6.1.5) to the effect that net outputs uniquely determine subnets.

Definition 6.1.7. (*a*) Given any output u (not necessarily a *net* output) except a delay output, we say that a propositional function F of time is *realized by u* iff $F(t) \equiv u(t)$, for all t. If u is a delay element output then F is *realized by u* iff $F(t) \equiv u(t + 1)$, for all t. (*b*) The *functions realized by N* are precisely those functions realized by net outputs and delay outputs. (*c*) Given a net **N** and a synchronous transducer $\mathbf{T}_N$, **N** and $\mathbf{T}_N$ are *equivalent* iff the functions realized by **N** are precisely the functions represented by $\mathbf{T}_N$.

Lemma 6.1.8. Any net **N** without delays is equivalent to some finite set of formulas of the propositional calculus, and conversely, any such set is equivalent to some net.

Proof. Since **N** has no delays, every output and net output value by our definition of decision element is a truth function (a propositional function of 0, 1) of input values. By Exercise 3.2(7), every such function can be represented by $^{-}$ and $\wedge$, hence by $^{-}$, $\wedge$, and $\vee$. The student should now complete the proof by induction using Definitions 6.1.3 and 6.1.5 as well as the appropriate definition of "formula" (cf. Definition 3.2.1 and adapt for present connectives).

Theorem 6.1.9. Every net **N** is equivalent to some transducer $\mathbf{T}_N$ and conversely every transducer is equivalent to some net.

Proof. If **N** has no delays but has inputs $x_1, \ldots, x_m$ and outputs $z_1, \ldots, z_r$, then by Lemma 6.1.8 and Definition 6.1.5, there exist r formulas of the propositional calculus equivalent to **N**.

$$z_k \equiv f_k(x_1, \ldots, x_m) \qquad k \equiv 1, \ldots, r$$

For arbitrary t_0,

$$z_k(t_0) \equiv f_k(x_1(t_0), \ldots, x_m(t_0))$$

is also true by substitution. Now let y_1 be the constant function given by $y_1(t) \equiv 0$. Then

$$\begin{aligned} y_1(0) &\equiv 0 \\ y_1(t_0 + 1) &\equiv 0 \\ z_k(t_0) &\equiv f_k(x_1(t_0), \ldots, x_m(t_0)) \wedge \overline{y_1(t_0)} \\ &\equiv N_k(x_1(t_0), \ldots, x_m(t_0), y_1(t_0)) \end{aligned}$$

These equations define a synchronous transducer.

Suppose now that **N** has n delay elements. By Definition 6.1.5 the input to each delay element u (is identified with) is the output of a net (perhaps just a wire—see Exercise 10) without delays whose inputs are $v_1, \ldots, v_s$, where $s \leq m + n$ and each v is a net input or a delay output y. Consequently,

$$u_j \equiv g_j(v_1, \ldots, v_s) \tag{7}$$

If $s = m + n$, then, of course, g_j is simply M_j and $v_1, \ldots, v_s$ are, except for order, precisely $x_1, \ldots, x_m, y_1, \ldots, y_n$. If $s < m + n$, then for each x and y

not occurring in the s-tuple $v_1, \ldots, v_s$, conjoin the disjunctions $x \vee \bar{x}$ and $y \vee \bar{y}$ thus:

$$\begin{aligned} u_j &\equiv g_j(v_1, \ldots, v_s)(x \vee \bar{x})(y \vee \bar{y}) \\ &\equiv M_j(x_1, \ldots, x_m, y_1, \ldots, y_n) \end{aligned} \tag{8}$$

The equivalence of (7) and (8) holds by truth tables. With a few steps we have (2), assuming that all net delay elements are 0 at time 0.

Conversely, assume a synchronous transducer $\mathbf{T}_N$ is given by equivalences of the form (2) and (3); then by switching theory (Lemma 6.1.8) every z_k is realized by a net for any arbitrary instant of time. Now for each y_j identify a delay element δ_j with labeled output y_j. Count each y_j together with the x_i as the inputs to a net feeding u_j for each j, where as previously the u_j are delay inputs. Again, each u_j is realized by a net, according to the results of switching theory, since u_j is identified with the output of a net without delays. Q.E.D.

Under certain idealizations which we will confer on neurons or nerve cells, it is possible to show that nerve networks are also finite transducers. The reader is advised to examine references mentioned in Section 6.4 for discussion of the conditions under which the standard idealizations which we are to employ are or are not adequate for understanding neurological behavior.

Definition 6.1.10. A *neuron* consists of a *soma* (body) and one or more *axons* (wires) leading to *endbulbs*. Each endbulb is *excitatory* or *inhibitory* but not both.

Definition 6.1.11. (*a*) A *nerve net* is an assemblage of neurons determined inductively as follows.

1. Any single neuron is a *nerve net*.
2. If $\mathbf{N}_1$ and $\mathbf{N}_2$ are any (not necessarily distinct) nets, then the result of *impinging* an endbulb of $\mathbf{N}_1$ onto, at most, one soma of $\mathbf{N}_2$ is a *nerve net*.
3. A nerve net is so only if its existence follows from clauses 1–2.

(*b*) The point of impingement of an endbulb on a soma is a *synapse*.

(*c*) A neuron on which no endbulb impinges is an *input neuron* to a net, and all other neurons are *inner neurons*.

In the next definition, we characterize the behavior of neurons as a part of our idealized conception. As in the case of transducer nets we interpret the nonnegative integers as instants of time. Each neuron, as will be noted in Definition 6.1.12, fires at a certain time $t + k$ only if it was excited at an earlier time t (t, k are integers); k is called the *lag* time in the response of the neuron to excitation. After a neuron fires, there is a certain time, called the *refractory* period, during which it is unresponsive to stimuli. We make the assumption that our instants 0, 1, 2, ... are clocked in such a way that the time between instants is greater than the refractory time of the net neurons having the greatest such time. We will also assume that $k = 1$ for all neurons.

Definition 6.1.12. Each neuron of a net at time t either *fires* (has value 1) or *not-fires* (has value 0). If **N** is an inner neuron, it has associated with it a *threshold* which is a positive integer θ such that **N** fires at $t + 1$ iff the number of excitatory endbulbs impinging on **N** is at least θ and at least θ of the neurons to which these endbulbs belong fire at time t and none of the inhibitory endbulbs impinging on **N** belong to neurons which fire at time t.

Corollary 6.1.13. The firing of a neuron **N** at time $t + 1$ is a truth function of the neurons whose endbulbs impinge on **N** and which fire at t.

Proof. By Definition 6.1.12, if y is an excitatory endbulb of **N**, then $y(t + 1)$ is equivalent to a truth function of $x_1(t), \ldots, x_m(t)$, $x_1, \ldots, x_m$ being input neurons relative to y, and in particular is represented by a disjunctive normal form in the sense of Definition 3.2.12. Q.E.D.

EXAMPLE 5. Suppose **N** has threshold 3, 4 excitatory inputs, and 2 inhibitory inputs; then we have

$$y(t + 1) \equiv x_1(t)x_2(t)x_3(t)\overline{x_5(t)}\,\overline{x_6(t)} \vee x_1(t)x_2(t)x_4(t)\overline{x_5(t)}\,\overline{x_6(t)} \vee \cdots \vee x_2(t)x_3(t)x_4(t)\overline{x_5(t)}\,\overline{x_6(t)}$$

Here we easily see that y at $t + 1$ is a truth function of the x_i at t, which is represented in disjunctive normal form. It is presumed here that x_1, x_2, x_3, and x_4 are excitatory while x_5, x_6 are inhibitory.

In order to picture neurons, the following diagrams are useful. We use circles to represent somata (for inner neurons only), exiting-to-the-right lines for axons, black arrowheads for excitatory endbulbs and white arrowheads for inhibitors; thresholds are denoted by numerals in the interior of the soma. In analogy with Definition 6.1.6, we have *labeled* nets in which each endbulb of the ith input neuron (assuming some appropriate indexing scheme) is labelled x_i if it is an excitatory endbulb and $\bar{x}_i$ otherwise, while similarly the endbulbs of inner neurons are labeled y_j or $\bar{y}_j$. These conventions are shown in Fig. 6.1.4. As seen in the figure, we do not depict somata of input neurons. Without loss of generality we assume, as in the case of transducer nets, that the m inputs are each 0 or 1 at time 0 and that any such event is caused by an external source, perhaps another nerve network.

By Definition 6.1.11(a) a nerve net will have endbulbs which do not impinge on any soma of other neurons. Such endbulbs are *outputs* of the

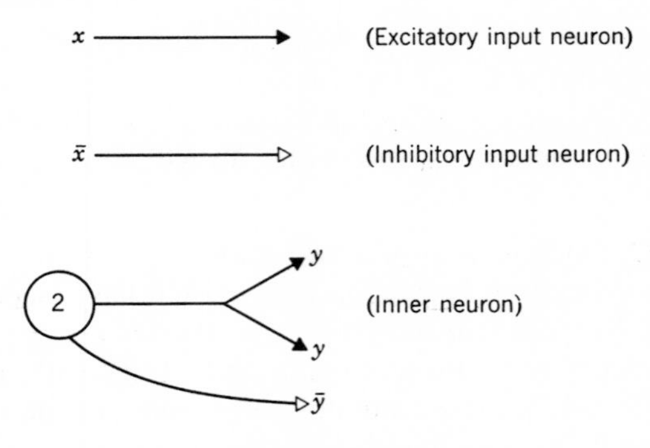

Fig. 6.1.4

net. In a labeled net these r outputs are labeled z_k, $k = 0, 1, \ldots, r$. Thus in Fig. 6.1.5, z_1 is an output; z_1 fires at time $t + 1$ iff x_1 does not fire at time t or x_2 does not fire at time t; and x_1 does not fire at time t or x_3 does not fire at time t; etc. Using the notation for propositional functions of time as for transducer nets, we have, for Fig. 6.1.5,

$$x_1(t + 1) \equiv (\overline{x_1(t)} \vee \overline{x_2(t)})\,(\overline{x_2(t)} \vee \overline{x_3(t)})\,\overline{x_1(t)} \vee \overline{x_3(\mathrm{t})})$$

EXAMPLE 6. Now let us consider a slightly more complicated example which corresponds to a flip-flop with an inverter on the output (Fig. 6.1.6). By our conventions, we have

$$z_1(t + 1) \equiv \overline{y_1(t)}$$
$$y_1(t + 1) \equiv (x_1(t) \vee y_1(t))\overline{x_2(t)}$$

or

$$z_1(t + 2) \equiv \overline{(x_1(t) \vee y_1(t))\overline{\overline{x_2(t)}}}$$

which except for the time lag performs the same logical function as the transducer net shown in Fig. 6.1.7. In the following theorem we use the terminology of Definition 6.1.7 for transducer nets.

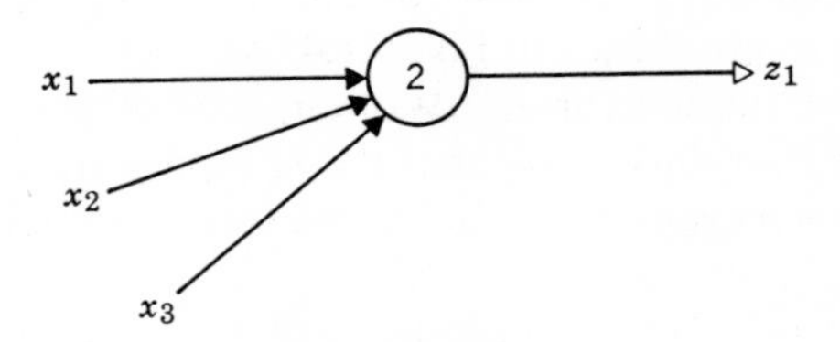

Fig. 6.1.5

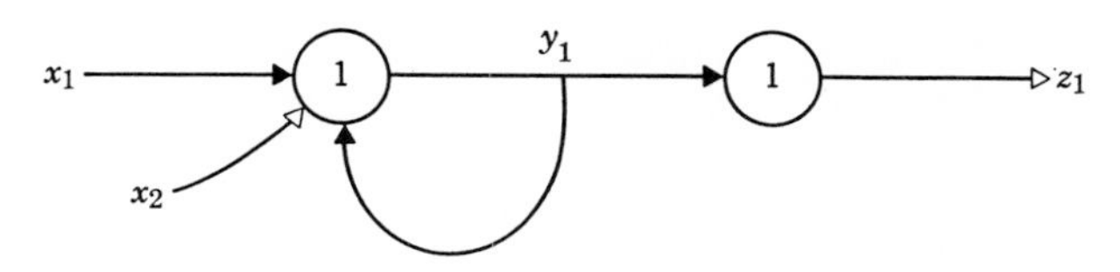

Fig. 6.1.6

Theorem 6.1.14. Every nerve net is equivalent to some transducer equations of the form (2), (3).

Proof. Assume **N** is a labeled net with m inputs and with n inner neurons. It follows directly from the manner of the formation of **N** that for every $j, j = 1, \ldots, n$

$$y_j(t + 1) \equiv f_j(x_1(t), \ldots, x_m(t), y_1(t), \ldots, y_n(t))$$

where f_j is a truth function. Also, if we label the outputs z_k, since each output axon is the axon of an inner neuron, by Definition 6.1.11(c), we have trivially

$$z_k(t) \equiv y_k(t) \qquad k = 1, \ldots, r \qquad \text{Q.E.D.}$$

It is perhaps evident to the student that the converse of Theorem 6.1.14 does not hold true. A counterexample is any combinational switching circuit which, by clause 1 of Definition 6.1.5 and equations (2) with $y(t) \equiv 0$ (alternatively with $y(t) \equiv 1$), is a transducer. No such equation as

$$z(t) \equiv h(x(t), y(t))$$

with h a truth function, can be realized by a nerve net, owing to the time lag. That is, we might have

$$z(t + 1) \equiv h'(x(t), y(t))$$

as the equation of a nerve net, but not necessarily $z(t + 1) \equiv z(t)$. It is not even possible that we can realize every truth function with a time lag of 1 as in the case of h' above. But we *can* show that we can get by with a time lag of at most 2.

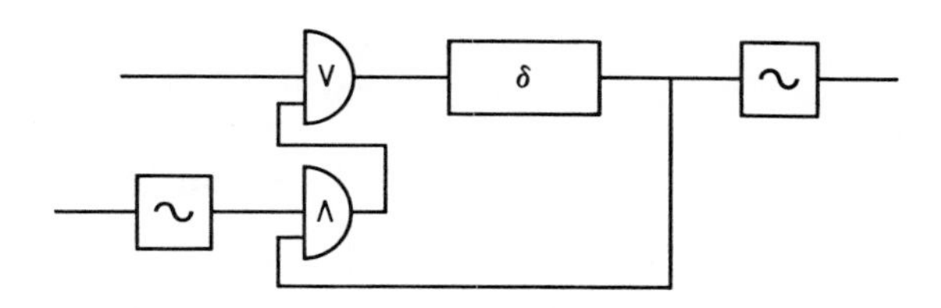

Fig. 6.1.7

Theorem 6.1.15. For every synchronous transducer $\mathbf{T}_B$ there exists a nerve net **N** such that, except for time lag, **N** is equivalent to $\mathbf{T}_B$. This lag can be kept to at most 2.

Proof. We assume that all inner neurons are quiescent at time 0, so that (2a) is satisfied. The transducer $\mathbf{T}_B$ is, in addition, described by equations (2b). Suppose for given j we have

$$y_j(t + 1) \equiv M_j(x_1(t), \ldots, x_m(t), y_1(t), \ldots, y_n(t))$$

By Section 1.3 and Definition 3.2.12, M_j can be written in complete disjunctive normal form (formally counting each propositional function $x_i(t)$ or $y_j(t)$ as a variable x_i or y_j). Since there are $m + n$ variables, there are at most 2^{m+n} terms in this normal form. Suppose α is a term with k of the variables $x_1, \ldots, x_m, y_1, \ldots, y_n$ not negated. Suppose $k = 0$, then

$$\alpha \equiv \bar{x}_1\bar{x}_2 \cdots \bar{x}_m\bar{y}_1\bar{y}_2 \cdots \bar{y}_n \tag{9}$$

By our definitions there is no neuron which is directly equivalent to (9) since all neurons have a positive integral threshold. However, by truth tables (9) is the same as

$$\alpha \equiv \overline{x_1 \vee x_2 \vee \cdots \vee x_m \vee y_1 \vee y_2 \vee \cdots \vee y_n} \tag{10}$$

Equivalence (10) can be obtained by a neuron with $m + n$ excitatory inputs, a threshold of $\theta = 1$, and an inhibitory endbulb. This neuron is quiescent at $t + 1$ iff either x_1 or $\cdots$ or y_n fires at t, and has the desired behavior except for a lag of 1. If $k > 0$, there is a neuron with threshold k, on which there impinge k excitatory endbulbs and $m + n - k$ inhibitory ones; this is equivalent to α except for a lag of 1. This is possible by Definition 6.1.10 which puts no restriction on the number of inputs to **N**. Hence every term α is obtained by a neuron with lag 1. Finally, the full function M_j may be realized by impinging the endbulbs of the neurons constructed by the preceding process onto the soma of a threshold 1 neuron. The endbulb of this neuron fires (is 1) at $t + 2$ iff $y_j(t + 1)$.

Similarly, each output function N_k can be realized by a nerve net whose output at $t + 2$ equals $z_k(t)$. Q.E.D.

EXERCISES 6.1

1. Extend the concept of transducer isomorphism (Definition 5.2.5) to automata with unequal input and output alphabets. Now justify the claim made in the text that a coded form of **T** is equivalent to **T**. What if the coded form represents input and output symbols of **T** "serially by bit"? Do we still have isomorphism? Equivalence?

2. Show that every finite transducer with one state ($K(Q) = 1$) is equivalent to a combinational switching circuit. Alternatively, show that every nontrivial finite transducer has at least two internal states.

3. If a function h of nonnegative integers is definable from the initial functions $f_1, \ldots, f_l$ by using substitution and primitive recursion, we say that h is primitive recursive *relative to* $f_1, \ldots, f_l$. Show that a synchronous transducer as given by equations (2) and (3) is relative primitive recursive. (*Hint:* Begin by assuming that Q for any transducer is a finite, nonempty set of *integers*. Justify the assumption. Also use, after establishing a proof, the fact that the function $\sigma_i(n)$ on the integers to the ith digit of the binary representation of n is primitive recursive.)

4. Determine whether, in fact, the alleged transducer net (Fig. 6.1.8) is one. If it is, give a demonstration using the technique of Fig. 6.1.3. If it is not, explain which rule(s) of Definition 6.1.5 is (are) broken, write the equations, and examine for contradictions (Definition 3.2.2). Explain the relationship between ill-formed nets and contradictions.

5. Complete the demonstration of Lemma 6.1.8.

6. Construct a nerve network equivalent in the sense of Theorem 6.1.15 to the transducer net of Fig. 3.0.2.

7. The output of every logic or delay decision element of a net is called a *junction*. We know that at any time t any junction has the value 0 or 1. Moreover we say that any such junction is *input independent* in case it changes its values from instant to instant, independently of the values of the input functions x_i. Such a junction is the value, therefore, of a function independent of input. Prove that such a function f realized by a junction of a net n is *ultimately periodic*: there exist integers x and y such that for every n, $f(t + nx + y) = f(t + y)$. (*Hint:* See Burks and Wright [1953].)

8. Using the result of Exercise 3, prove there are primitive recursive functions not realized by any transducer net.

9. The neurons used in nerve nets may be defined in such a way that the neuron N fires at $t + 1$ iff the *difference* between the number of excitatory and the number of inhibitory endbulbs which impinge on N and which belong to neurons which fire at time t is greater than or equal to θ. (*a*) Find, using this convention, a nerve net equivalent to Fig. 6.1.6. (*b*) Sketch a new proof of Theorem 6.1.14. (*c*) Does Theorem 6.1.15 still hold? If so give a proof, if not provide a counterexample.

10. Design a nerve net which "learns" in the following simplified sense. L has a stimulus input, a conditioning input, and a disabling input. L responds

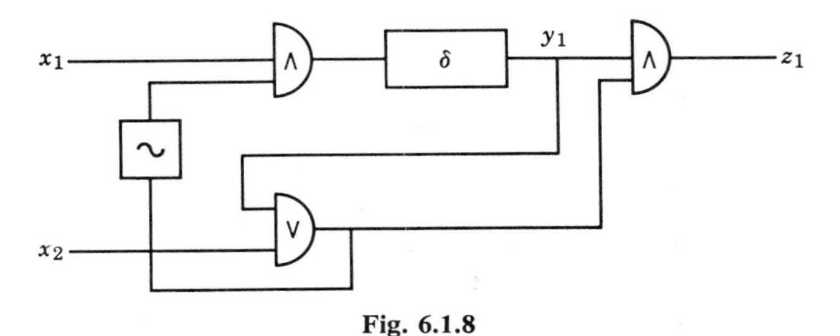

Fig. 6.1.8

to a stimulus by firing, but it does not respond to the conditioning input unless the latter input has been fired at least three consecutive instants during which the stimulus has also fired; thereafter the conditioner also causes a response. The disabler "unlearns" the net and "overrides" both the stimulus and the conditioner. Design with the shortest possible lag time.

11. Is a single (input-output) wire a "net" in our sense?

6.2 STATE ASSIGNMENTS

It is now our task to take up the first of the problems introduced in Section 6.0. We recall that the aim here is to pick binary encodements of the states of a transducer **T** in such a way as to reduce the dependency of state elements on state elements. More concisely stated, we would like to find assignments such that each y_j in (2b) of Section 6.1 is defined for as *few* of $y_1, \ldots, y_n$ as possible. This tends to lead to economical net logic.

EXAMPLE 1. Table 6.2.1 shows the transition system part of a finite transducer **T** with states named $q_i = i$ as in Exercise 5.5.16. In the next

TABLE 6.2.1

q \ s	**T** 0	1
0	1	2
1	5	4
2	4	0
3	0	3
4	3	4
5	0	5

two tables we have shown coded forms of **T**. In the first case, Table 6.2.2*a*, we have simply used the 3-bit binary equivalent of 0–5, while in the second case we chose with an eye to more economical logic.

TABLE 6.2.2*a*

			$\mathbf{T}_B$ $x_1 \equiv 0$			$x_1 \equiv 1$		
y_1	y_2	y_3	y_1	y_2	y_3	y_1	y_2	y_3
0	0	0	0	0	1	0	1	0
0	0	1	1	0	1	1	0	0
0	1	0	1	0	0	0	0	0
0	1	1	0	0	0	0	1	1
1	0	0	0	1	1	1	0	0
1	0	1	0	0	0	1	0	1

TABLE 6.2.2b

$\mathbf{T}_B'$

			$x_1 \equiv 0$			$x_1 \equiv 1$		
y_1	y_2	y_3	y_1	y_2	y_3	y_1	y_2	y_3
0	0	0	0	1	0	0	0	1
0	1	0	1	0	1	0	1	1
0	0	1	0	1	1	0	0	0
1	0	0	0	0	0	1	0	0
0	1	1	1	0	0	0	1	1
1	0	1	0	0	0	1	0	1

Each of the tables represents y_1, y_2, and y_3 as truth functions of themselves and x. As is customary, we will write

$$y_j \equiv M_j(x_1, \ldots, x_m, y_1, \ldots, y_n)$$

as an abbreviation of

$$y_j(t + 1) \equiv M_j(x_1(t), \ldots, x_m(t), y_1(t), \ldots, y_n(t))$$

keeping in mind that each of the x's and y's are propositional functions of time and that y_j depends on the other variable functions at the immediately past instant.

The "next state" equations for the version $\mathbf{T}_B$ of $\mathbf{T}$, in disjunctive normal form after some simplifications (as will be explained in 6.3), are as follows:

$$y_1 \equiv \bar{y}_1\bar{y}_2y_3 \vee \bar{x}_1y_2\bar{y}_3 \vee x_1y_1 \tag{1a}$$

$$y_2 \equiv \bar{x}_1y_1\bar{y}_3 \vee x_1\bar{y}_1\bar{y}_2\bar{y}_3 \vee x_1y_2y_3 \tag{1b}$$

$$y_3 \equiv \bar{x}_1\bar{y}_1\bar{y}_2 \vee \bar{x}_1\bar{y}_2\bar{y}_3 \vee x_1y_2y_3 \vee x_1y_1y_3 \tag{1c}$$

Similarly, for $\mathbf{T}_B'$ we have

$$y_1 \equiv \bar{x}_1y_2 \vee x_1y_1 \tag{2a}$$

$$y_2 \equiv \bar{x}_1\bar{y}_1\bar{y}_2 \vee x_1y_2 \tag{2b}$$

$$y_3 \equiv y_2\bar{y}_3 \vee \bar{x}_1\bar{y}_1\bar{y}_2y_3 \vee x_1\bar{y}_1\bar{y}_3 \vee x_1y_2 \vee x_1y_1y_3 \tag{2c}$$

Equations (2a) and (2b) are simpler than (1a) and (1b) by any conceivable criterion. Note that y_1 and y_2 in (2) depend only on themselves and each other (together with the input x_1) while y_3 depends on all variables. The reader should note that $P = \{\{0, 2\}, \{1, 4\}, \{3, 5\}\}$ is a congruence partition of the states Q of $\mathbf{T}$ and that in the coded form $\mathbf{T}_B'$ of $\mathbf{T}$, states in the same equivalence class of Q have the two leftmost bits of their encodement in common. Thus $0 \leftrightarrow 000$ and $2 \leftrightarrow 001$, and the leftmost two bits are 00 in each case.

Theorem 6.2.1. Let $\mathbf{T}$ be a finite transducer (with or without initial state), and let $\mathbf{T}_B$ be a coded transducer equivalent to $\mathbf{T}$ such that each state is coded by an n-tuple $y_1, y_2, \ldots, y_n$. If the first k variables $1 \leq k < n$ are each functions of the inputs and the first k variables,[3] then there exists a congruence partition R on Q such that q_i is R-equivalent to q_j iff the encodements of q_i and q_j agree in the first k bit positions.

Proof. Note that in the theorem the condition for the existence of a congruence partition says that

$$y_j \equiv M_j(x_1, \ldots, x_m, y_1, \ldots, y_k) \qquad j = 1, \ldots, k \tag{3}$$

while of course

$$y_{j'} \equiv M_{j'}(x_1, \ldots, x_m, y_1, \ldots, y_n) \qquad j' = k + 1, \ldots, n$$

is possible. Continuing with the proof, it is obvious that all states q which agree in the first k bits of their encodements form an equivalence class, and hence that k determines a partition. Now assume that $q_i R q_j$ where R is the equivalence determined as in the statement of the theorem. Then $y_1, \ldots, y_k$ are common bits in the codes for q_i and q_j. Therefore by (3) each y_j in the code for the next state will be the same for q_i as for q_j. Hence, for arbitrary input x, $M(q_i, x)\ R\ M(q_j, x)$ which shows the congruence property [item (6) of Section 5.5]. Q.E.D.

As a kind of converse we state the following theorem. In the statement and proof we mean by $\{r\}$ the least integer greater than or equal to r, r being any real number; and we let $n \geq \{\log_2 K(Q)\}$, where $K(Q)$ is as usual the cardinality of a set of states (cf. Definition 6.1.1). Also, $K(P)$ is the number of classes in a partition P, and if α is the largest class of P then $K(\alpha)$ is the number of elements in it (cf. Theorem 5.6.7).

Theorem 6.2.2. Let **T** be a finite transducer with $K(Q)$ states. If there is a congruence partition P such that $P \neq 0$ and $P \neq$ I, then there is a code mapping Q into binary n-tuples such that (for any code from S and O into binary sequences) if

$$n = \{\log_2 K(P)\} + \{\log_2 K(\alpha)\}$$
$$y_j \equiv M_j(x_1, \ldots, x_m, y_1, \ldots, y_k) \qquad j = 1, \ldots, k = \{\log_2 K(P)\}$$

Proof. The proof depends simply upon the observation that if P is not trivial (that is, 0 or I) it takes $\{\log_2 K(P)\}$ bits to distinguish the classes under P from one another and $\{\log_2 K(\alpha)\}$ to distinguish states from states

[3] The condition of the theorem is an elliptical way of saying that if the truth function M_j of (3) is simplified using "don't care" or undefined conditions, then M_j will be a truth function of just those variables indicated. We suppose that these techniques are known to the student from his course in digital systems. We will develop the theory in Section 6.3, thus justifying the present ellipsis. Throughout Section 6.2, when we talk about functional "dependence" we mean that the function depends on those variables occurring in a simplest normal form using don't cares. (We rely on the student, here, to take care to distinguish between the concept of *incomplete* transducers, and *don't care* conditions of truth functions.)

within classes. Hence at least n-tuples of bits are required. Finally the relations for y_j indicating dependence on $y_1, \ldots, y_k$ only (together with the x_i) are established by holding the first k bits in common in each n-tuple representing elements of a single equivalence class. (These could, of course, be *any* k bits so long as the distribution is the same for every member of a class and no others.) Q.E.D.

Theorems 6.2.1 and 6.2.2 are exemplified by transducer $\mathbf{T}'_B$ of Example 1. The first two variables, y_1, y_2, in the argument columns in Table 6.2.2*b*, divide the states into classes as indicated before. Inspection of the Table 6.2.2*b* shows that with input $x = 0$ elements of the same equivalence class go into the same equivalence class, and similarly for $x = 1$. Note again that in (2a) and (2b), y_1 and y_2 are computed in terms of each other and x_1. Note also that $\{\log_2 K(P)\} = 2, \{\log_2 K(\alpha)\} = 1$.

EXAMPLE 2. Let us now determine an economical assignment for the transition system:

TABLE 6.2.3

	x_1	x_2	x_3
0	2	0	5
1	4	0	5
2	4	7	1
3	2	0	5
4	4	7	3
5	0	2	6
6	2	7	1
7	0	4	6

Using the algorithm outlined in Exercises 5.5 for discovering partitions, we find (among others) the following congruence partition:

$$P_1 = \{\{0, 1, 3\}, \{2, 4, 6\}, \{5, 7\}\}$$

By Theorem 6.2.2, there is an equivalent coded transducer with $n = 4$. We assign the first two bits to distinguish among the three classes and the last two to distinguish states in a class. We also find that

$$P_2 = \{\{0, 2, 4, 7\}, \{1, 3, 5, 6\}\}$$

has the congruence property. Here, however, we find that $n = 3$ is sufficient. Specific encodements and derivations of the transducer equations are left to the student.

From Section 5.5, we recall that the system of partitions with substitution property form a lattice under $\cup$ and $\cap$. Since P_1 and P_2 have this property, they must be elements of a lattice, and so $P_1 \cup P_2$ and $P_1 \cap P_2$ are further partitions with the desired congruence property (see exercises).

Returning to Example 1, recall that in the partition $P = \{\{0, 2\}, \{1, 4\}, \{3, 5\}\}$ which was used for the coded form of Table 6.2.2*b*, y_1 and y_2 are interdependent, whereas y_3 depends on every y_j. There may be cases in which we have a happy situation wherein the first k variables (let us say) depend only on each other, and likewise the last $n - k$ depend only on each other. A moment's thought suggests that such a situation is determined by a transducer which is decomposable into parallel submachines (Corollary 5.5.36).

Since the theory has been developed in detail in Section 5.5, we proceed quite informally by Example 4 of Section 5.5.

After having obtained Table 5.5.7 for the example, it is a simple matter to establish a coding with reduced dependencies of the desired kind. We observe that it takes one bit to distinguish between the states of the quotient transition system $\mathbf{T}_S/R_1$—these states are q_0 and q_3; and it takes two bits to make the analogous distinctions for $\mathbf{T}_S/R_2$. If we associate q_0 to 0, q_3 to 1, q_2 to 10, q_4 to 01, and q_5 to 00, we then obtain Table 6.2.4.

TABLE 6.2.4

			M'						N'	
			0			1				
y_1	y_2	y_3	y_1	y_2	y_3	y_1	y_2	y_3	0	1
0	0	0	1	1	0	0	1	0	0	2
0	0	1	1	0	0	0	1	0	2	2
0	1	0	1	0	1	0	0	1	1	1
1	1	0	0	0	1	1	0	1	1	1
1	0	1	0	0	0	1	1	0	0	0
1	0	0	0	1	0	1	1	0	2	2

Here y_1 depends on y_1 alone (taking don't care conditions into account) and y_2 and y_3 depend on y_2 and y_3.

We conclude this subsection with a brief consideration of the state assignment problem as it relates to state reduction of transducers.

Definition 6.2.3. A partition P of states Q of a transducer is *output consistent* iff for every q_i and q_j in the same class, $N(q_i, s_k) = N(q_j, s_k)$ for every symbol s_k.

The partition constituted by the equivalence class $[\equiv 1]$ in the standard reduction procedure discussed in Section 5.2 is output consistent.

Corollary 6.2.4. If P_1 and P_2 are output consistent so are $P_1 \cap P_2$ and $P_1 \cup P_2$.

Proof. For the student.

The next theorem might have been introduced in Section 5.5. However, we postponed its statement because of its relevance to transducer net design. It is simply a rewording of the reduction result of Section 5.2.

Theorem 6.2.5. If a congruence partition P on the states of $\mathbf{T}$ is output consistent, then P determines the unique reduced transducer $\mathbf{T}'$ which is equivalent to $\mathbf{T}$.

Proof. For the student.

EXERCISES 6.2

1. Develop an algorithm for testing whether a nontrivial partition on a set of coded states has the substitution (congruence) property.

2. Complete Example 2 and compare the coded transducers deriving from P_1 and P_2. Determine further partitions from P_1 and P_2 and examine the corresponding coded machines.

3. Prove Corollary 6.2.4.

4. A certain counter counts *up* one on receiving an input 2 and *down* one on receiving an input 1. If there is an input of 0 the counter stays where it is. The counter is capable of going up to 7, and then if it counts up, it goes to 0 (it operates modulo 8 up or down). There is an output of 1 when the counter advances to 0 from 7. Design with an efficient state assignment using the results of this section.

5. Using Theorem 6.2.1, construct a serially composed transducer which realizes $\mathbf{T}$ of Table 6.2.1.

6. As an alternative to the methods of this section apply the methods of Section 5.6, using the Krohn-Rhodes decomposition, on Example 1 of Section 6.2. Compare complexity of the combinational logic.

6.3 MINIMAL NETS

In this section, our purpose is to develop the theory of simplifying nets. As is well known, this is in a sense the same as simplifying the expressions on the right side of equations (2) and (3) in Section 6.1 where each propositional function $x(t)$ or $y(t)$ is simply taken to be a propositional variable or letter x or y. First, we will be satisfied to find *simplest normal forms* of formulas, and later we will examine a method depending on decomposition of truth functions which leads to a simple form, not necessarily normal. (Recall Definition 3.2.12.)

It is customary to call the variables x, y, etc., *letters* and occurrences of a variable either with or without a negation sign, *literals*.[4] We will denote literals by l_1, l_2, l_3, etc., with or without primes or subscripts. Any conjunction of literals which is a conjunction of a disjunctive normal form of a formula F is called a *clause*. We will denote such clauses by the syntactic variables c_1, c_2, c_3, etc., with or without primes or subscripts. Similarly

[4] In this section, we use x, y as propositional variables instead of p, q, j, etc., to be in accord with the notation of Section 6.1. We use F with or without primes as syntactical variables for any formula.

any disjunction of literals of a conjunctive normal form of F is a *clause*; we denote such clauses by variables d_1, d_2, etc., with or without primes or subscripts. If needed for emphasis, we will call the first type of clause conjunctive and the second disjunctive. We will use D to denote arbitrary formulas in disjunctive normal form and likewise C for conjunctive normal forms.

By Theorem 3.2.10, two formulas F and F' are equivalent if they have the same truth table. For conciseness we will write $F \approx F'$. Another relation that will be useful for us is equality between formulas. F is equal to F', written $F = F'$, if F and F' are identical strings of symbols except possibly for the order of formulas in conjunctions or disjunctions.

The theory of simplification deals specifically with *formulas* of the propositional calculus (which we interpret as truth functions) themselves and not with whatever the formulas are understood to be about. Hence the questions we are considering are a part of the *syntax* of the propositional calculus. Unlike earlier discussions in Chapters 2 and 3 where we tended to deal informally with such questions, this one would lead to confusion unless we were to observe a sharp distinction between symbols and names or variables *for* symbols, formulas or names or sentences *about* formulas, and the like. Hence, looking back at the conventions just introduced, the c's and d's are *not* symbols of the propositional calculus but are part of the syntax language for studying it: they are names of certain symbols. Likewise F is a variable varying over any formulas in the technical sense of "formula." In this section, $=$ and $\approx$ are relations between *formulas*, thus $F \approx F'$ means for fixed F and F' that the formula denoted by F is equivalent to that denoted by F'. With some slight ambiguity we will also, however, use expressions such as $F \approx 1$ to mean that F has the value of 1. In the following text we also suppress $\wedge$ writing $(F \wedge F')$ simply (FF') or even FF' if there is no danger of ambiguity.

EXAMPLE 1. Consider the formula

$$x_1 \vee x_2 y_1 \vee \bar{x}_3 \tag{1}$$

The literals are x_1, x_2, y_1, and $\bar{x}_3$. Denote (1) by F. If F' is

$$(x_1 \vee x_2)(x_1 \vee y_1) \vee \bar{x}_3 \tag{2}$$

then $F \approx F'$. A disjunctive normal form of F is

$$x_1 x_1 \vee x_1 x_2 \vee x_1 y_1 \vee x_2 y_1 \vee \bar{x}_3 \tag{3}$$

Here the clauses are $x_1 x_1$, $x_1 x_2$, etc.

A conjunctive normal form of F is

$$(x_1 \vee x_2 \vee x_3)(x_1 \vee y_1 \vee \bar{x}_3) \tag{4}$$

(3) is of the form

$$c_1 \vee c_2 \vee c_3 \vee c_4 \vee c_5$$

whereas (4) is of the form

$$d_1 d_2$$

Although c_5 is (denotes) a single literal $\bar{x}_3$ we count it as a conjunction; any clause of a disjunctive normal form is a conjunction, even if it is a single literal. None of (1)–(4) are equal. But (4), for example, is equal to

$$(\bar{x}_3 \vee x_1 \vee y_1)(x_2 \vee x_1 \vee x_3) \tag{5}$$

If we denote the formula (5) by F'', then we have $F'' = F$, and, of course, $F'' \approx F$, as well.

In the ensuing discussion we again assume that the student knows how to perform algebraic manipulations in propositional calculus and that he knows how to use truth tables.

We will also assume that none of the formulas of which we seek simplest forms are tautologies or contradictions (Definition 3.2.2).

Although the reader may adopt any criterion of simplicity he wishes to (cf. Section 6.0), let us, to fix ideas, agree that of two formulas F and F' F is *simpler* than F' if it contains fewer literals.

A conjunction is *fundamental* if it contains no more than one occurrence of a letter. $x_1x_1x_2$ and $x_1\bar{x}_1x_2$ are not fundamental, whereas x_1x_2 is. Similarly, a disjunction is fundamental. In much of what follows we will discuss only conjunctions and disjunctive normal forms; however, what is stated will frequently be applicable to the dual cases, and it is left to the student to supply details.

Definition 6.3.1. Let F_1 and F_2 be fundamental formulas. F_1 *subsumes* F_2 iff every literal in F_2 is also in F_1.

EXAMPLE 2. $x_1x_3x_2\bar{x}_4$ subsumes $x_2x_1\bar{x}_4$ and also $x_3\bar{x}_4x_2x_1$. Clearly if F_1 subsumes F_2, F_2 implies F_1, but not necessarily conversely (Definition 3.2.8).

Definition 6.3.2. A fundamental conjunctive formula F_1 is a *prime implicant* of an arbitrary formula F_2 if F_1 implies F_2, and no simpler fundamental formula F_3, subsumed by F_1, implies F_2. Similarly, a fundamental disjunctive formula F_1' is a *prime implicant* of a formula F_2 if F_2 implies F_1' (or $\bar{F}_1'$ implies $\bar{F}_2$) and no simpler fundamental formula subsumed by F_1' has this property.

EXAMPLE 3. x_1x_2 is a prime implicant of $x_1x_2 \vee \bar{x}_1x_3$ since, if x_1x_2 has the value 1, then $(x_1x_2 \vee \bar{x}_1x_3)$ is 1 also. However if x_1 is 1 it does not follow that $(x_1x_2 \vee \bar{x}_1x_3)$ is 1, since we could also have x_2 with value 0, whence the formula is 0.

Theorem 6.3.4. Every simplest disjunctive (conjunctive) form $D(C)$ of F is a disjunction (conjunction) of prime implicants.

Proof. If c is a clause of D, then c implies F (why?). If c is not prime, there is a simpler c', by Definition 6.3.2, such that c' implies F. But this contradicts the hypothesis of the theorem. Q.E.D.

The following three theorems, though not in the main line of development, are interesting and useful in their own right.

Theorem 6.3.5. (*a*) If $D \approx c \vee D'$, then c implies D' iff $D \approx D'$; (*b*) if $D \approx cl \vee D'$, then c implies $l \vee D'$ iff $D \approx c \vee D'$.

This theorem is stated for disjunctive normal forms, although it holds for any formulas F and F'. The disjunctive case, however, is the useful one.

Proof of (*a*). Assume D is equivalent to $c \vee D'$. If $c \approx 0$, then $c \vee D' \approx D'$, hence $D \approx D'$. If $c \approx 1$, then $D \approx 1$ and $D' \approx 1$; hence $D \approx D'$.

The proof of (*b*) is left to the student.

Corollary 6.3.6. (*a*) If $C \approx dC'$, then $\bar{d}$ implies $\bar{C}'$ iff $C \approx C'$; (*b*) if $C \approx (d \vee l)C'$, then $\bar{d}$ implies $\overline{lC'}$ iff $C \approx dC'$.

Proof. For the student.

EXAMPLE 4. Consider $x_1x_2 \vee \bar{x}_1x_3 \vee x_2x_3$. If x_2x_3 is 1, then by truth tables $x_1x_2 \vee \bar{x}_1x_3$ is also 1. Hence the required implication holds, and $x_1x_2 \vee \bar{x}_1x_3 \vee x_2x_3$ is equivalent to the simpler form $x_1x_2 \vee \bar{x}_1x_3$. Thus Theorem 6.3.5(*a*) allows us to eliminate superfluous *clauses*, as does Corollary 6.3.6(*a*).

EXAMPLE 5. Consider $(x_1 \vee x_2)(x_1 \vee \bar{x}_2 \vee x_3)(\bar{x}_1 \vee \bar{x}_2 \vee \bar{x}_3)$. To show that the literal $\bar{x}_2$ is eliminable, we see by Corollary 6.3.6(*b*) that $\overline{x_1 \vee x_3}$ implies $\overline{\bar{x}_2(x_1 \vee x_2)(\bar{x}_1 \vee \bar{x}_2 \vee \bar{x}_3)}$. For $\overline{x_1 \vee x_3}$ to be 1, we must have x_1 with value 0 and x_3, 0. Hence, the right side of the implication, by truth tables, boils down to $\overline{\bar{x}_1x_2}$ which has the value 1. Therefore, a simpler form is $(x_1 \vee x_2)(x_1 \vee x_3)(\bar{x}_1 \vee \bar{x}_2 \vee \bar{x}_3)$. Thus Corollary 6.3.6(*b*) allows us to eliminate superfluous *literals* as does Theorem 6.3.5(*b*).

Theorem 6.3.7. If D is a simplest disjunctive form of F, then the complement C of D obtained by interchanging $\vee$ and $\wedge$ and replacing negated letters by unnegated ones and *vice versa* throughout D, is a simplest conjunctive normal form of $\bar{F}$.

Proof. By repeated use of De Morgan's theorems (Exercise 1.3.16) we find that C is a conjunctive normal form of $\bar{F}$, and the negation of every clause c of C implies $\bar{C}$. If, using Theorem 6.3.5 and Corollary 6.3.6, a clause or literal could be removed from C, then by another application of De Morgan's theorems we would have a formula D' in disjunctive normal form equivalent to $F(\approx \bar{\bar{F}})$ simpler than D. Q.E.D.

The foregoing items are used in informal minimization. The last theorem enables us to gear our procedure for discovering simplest conjunctive normal formulas to the disjunctive case, assuming there is an available algorithm for the latter; take F, negate it, find the simplest disjunctive form of $\bar{F}$, and apply Theorem 6.3.7.

We now continue with the main problem of finding an algorithm. By Theorem 6.3.4 every simplest form will consist of a disjunction of prime implicants. This suggests a two-part procedure: find the prime implicants, then find the simplest disjunction of them equivalent to the given formula F. Theorem 6.3.9 provides for what is known in switching literature as "Quine's algorithm."

Definition 6.3.8. If c is a clause of D, then c is a *completion* of a clause c' w.r.t. a formula F iff c subsumes c' and c contains occurrences of all and only letters of F without repetitions. If c is its own completion, it is said to be *developed.*

EXAMPLE 6. Suppose F is made up of x_1, x_2, x_3, and x_4. Let c' be x_1x_2; then a completion of c' is $x_1x_2x_3x_4$; another one is $x_1x_2\bar{x}_3x_4$; etc.

Theorem 6.3.9. Let D be the complete disjunctive normal form of F (Definition 3.2.12). c is a prime implicant of F iff (a) all letters of c occur in F; (b) all completions of c are developed clauses of D; (c) there is no simpler clause c' subsumed by c such that all completions of c' w.r.t. F are developed clauses of F.

Proof. (a) Suppose cl implies F, whereas l is not in F; then if $c \approx 1$, $F \approx 1$. Therefore cl is not prime.

(b) Suppose, contrary to what is to be shown, that c' is a completion of c, but not a developed clause of D. Then any assignment of truth values to the letters of c', giving it the value 1, also determines the value 1 for c, while F is 0. Hence c does not imply F. Conversely if every completion c' of c is a developed clause of D, then if $c' \approx 1$, $c \approx 1$ and $F \approx 1$; thus c implies F.

(c) Follows from the definition of prime implicant. Q.E.D.

We leave it to the student to review Quine's algorithm and to see that it is justified by Theorem 6.3.9 (see Exercises).

Another method, the method of consensus, will be established in Theorem 6.3.16 and is based on the following definitions and lemmata.

Definition 6.3.10. Let c and c' be clauses such that there is exactly one letter $\bar{l}$ which occurs in c while l occurs in c' or *vice versa*. The *consensus* of

c and c' is the conjunction which results from conjoining c and c' and deleting both l and $\bar{l}$ and any repeated literals.

Definition 6.3.11. Procedure $\mathbf{P}'$ (consensus algorithm) is as follows: If F is in disjunctive normal form, then (*a*) if c subsumes c', delete c; (*b*) adjoin, as an additional clause, the consensus of two clauses c'' and c''' unless said consensus subsumes some clause c' already in F.

Lemma 6.3.12. If F is in disjunctive normal form and c is a prime implicant of F not a clause of F, then there exist clauses c' and c'' of F such that the consensus of c' and c'' can be added to F.

Proof. Since c is a prime implicant but not a clause of F, there exists at least one clause k such that (*a*) k subsumes c (k may simply be c); (*b*) k subsumes no clause of F (since c is a prime implicant); (*c*) k contains only the letters of F (by Theorem 6.3.9); and (*d*) k is the least simple (that is, has the most occurrences of literals) of all clauses with properties (*a*)–(*c*). Now k does not contain *all* letters of F since if it did, then by property (*b*) it would follow that for every clause k' in F there would exist a letter l in k' such that $\bar{l}$ occurred in k (or $\bar{l}$ in k' and l in k). Consequently, k could not imply F; that is, every combination of truth values making $k \approx 1$ would make every clause k' of $F \approx 0$, and hence F itself 0. But this violates property (*a*) that k is an implicant. Thus there is a letter l in F but not in k. By property (*d*), the formula lk must violate some one of (*a*)–(*c*), and $\bar{l}k$ must do so also. It is easily seen that this can only be property (*b*). Hence there exist clauses c' and c'' of F subsumed by lk and $\bar{l}k$, respectively. By property (*b*) k does not subsume either one, so for lk to subsume c' and $\bar{l}k$ to subsume c'', c' must contain l and $c''\bar{l}$. Moreover, there are no other literals l' and $\bar{l}'$ in c' and c'', respectively (or *vice versa*, respectively); and so c' and c'' have a consensus, unless they are identically l and $\bar{l}$, respectively. But then F would be a tautology, contrary to our basic assumptions. Q.E.D.

Lemma 6.3.13. If F is in disjunctive normal form and c is a clause of F and not a prime implicant of F, then either there are subsuming clauses in F which can be dropped or there exist clauses c' and c'' of F such that the consensus of c' and c'' can be added to F. In other words, under the hypotheses of the theorem the rules in procedure $\mathbf{P}'$ apply.

Proof. c subsumes some prime implicant c' of F. If c' is already a clause of F, then by part (*a*) of $\mathbf{P}'$, c can be dropped. If c' is not a clause of F, then Lemma 6.3.12 applies. Q.E.D.

Lemma 6.3.14. If F is in disjunctive normal form, the result of applying $\mathbf{P}'$ to F is also in disjunctive normal form.

Proof. Trivial.

Lemma 6.3.15. The procedure **P**′ terminates.

If c is eliminated by part (a), then there exists a c' subsumed by c. Similarly, if c' is eliminated by part (a) there is a c'', subsumed by c' and hence by c; etc. Therefore, by part (b) no clause dropped by part (a) can be later added by part (b); neither can a clause in F be duplicated by part (b).

Finally, there are only finitely many clauses which part (b) can introduce since the alphabet of F is finite. Q.E.D.

Theorem 6.3.16. Procedure **P**′ applied to any F in disjunctive normal form yields the disjunction of all prime implicants of F.

The theorem follows immediately from the foregoing lemmata.

Since the consensus method is not as well known as the first method discussed, we will illustrate the procedure **P**′ with an example.

EXAMPLE 7. Let F be

$$\underset{(c_1)}{\bar{x}_1\bar{x}_2\bar{x}_3} \lor \underset{(c_2)}{x_1\bar{x}_2x_3} \lor \underset{(c_3)}{\bar{x}_1x_2} \lor \underset{(c_4)}{\bar{x}_1\bar{x}_3} \lor \underset{(c_5)}{x_2x_3} \tag{6}$$

By rule a since c_1 subsumes c_4 we have

$$\underset{(c_2)}{x_1\bar{x}_2x_3} \lor \underset{(c_3)}{\bar{x}_1x_2} \lor \underset{(c_4)}{\bar{x}_1\bar{x}_3} \lor \underset{(c_5)}{x_2x_3}$$

By rule b we add the consensus of c_2 and c_5,

$$\underset{(c_2)}{x_1\bar{x}_2x_3} \lor \underset{(c_3)}{\bar{x}_1x_2} \lor \underset{(c_4)}{\bar{x}_1\bar{x}_3} \lor \underset{(c_5)}{x_2x_3} \lor \underset{(c_6)}{x_1x_3}$$

and by rule a, c_2 subsumes c_6, so we obtain

$$\bar{x}_1x_2 \lor \bar{x}_1\bar{x}_3 \lor x_2x_3 \lor x_1x_3 \tag{7}$$

Inspection shows that any added consensus subsumes a clause already present in (7), and also that there are no subsuming clauses in (7). Hence (7) is the disjunction of all prime implicants of (6).

A third method is the method of *converting normal forms.* In this discussion any formula is *logically determinate* if it is either a tautology or a contradiction.

Definition 6.3.17. Procedure **P** is as follows:

(i) Put F in any conjunctive normal form C and delete any logically determinate clauses.

(ii) Using distributive laws, convert C into disjunctive normal form D.

(iii) Drop all logically determinate clauses from D; drop all occurrences of repeated literals within clauses, except one; drop all subsuming clauses.

Definition 6.3.17 provides, as we shall show, for the elicitation of all prime implicants of D. It also provides a procedure for conjunctive prime implicants d if in (i) to (iii) all occurrences of "conjunctive" are replaced by "disjunctive" and vice versa; and if all occurrences of "D" are replaced by "C" and vice versa.

EXAMPLE 7 (*Continued*). A conjunctive normal form of (6) is

$$(\bar{x}_1 \vee x_3)(x_1 \vee x_2 \vee \bar{x}_3) \tag{8}$$

"Multiplying out" yields

$$(\bar{x}_1 \vee x_3)x_1 \vee (\bar{x}_1 \vee x_3)x_2 \vee (x_1 \vee x_3)\bar{x}_3$$

and furthermore,

$$\bar{x}_1 x_1 \vee x_3 x_1 \vee \bar{x}_1 x_2 \vee x_3 x_2 \vee \bar{x}_1 \bar{x}_3 \vee x_3 \bar{x}_3 \tag{9}$$

In (9), $\bar{x}_1 x_1$ and $x_3 \bar{x}_3$ are logically determinate and therefore are dropped. The final result is identically (7).

We will justify procedure **P** by a general result which when specialized in a certain way, to be explained, provides for **P**.

Let $F_1, \ldots, F_m$ be any non-contradictory formulas and let $\mathscr{F}$ be their conjunction

$$\mathscr{F} = F_1 \cdots F_m$$

Let K be the set of all non-contradictory conjunctions

$$c_1 \cdots c_m$$

where c_i is a prime implicant of F_i. Furthermore, let $\mathscr{K}$ be the set of all conjunctions of prime implicants occurring in K, but such that no element of $\mathscr{K}$ subsumes an element of K. Note that $\mathscr{K} \subset K$. Using these ideas, all we need prove is that c is a prime implicant of $\mathscr{F}$ iff $c \in \mathscr{K}$.

Lemma 6.3.18. For any F, if $F \in K$, then F implies $\mathscr{F}$.

Proof. F must be a conjunction of prime implicants where c_i implies F_i. Hence $c_1 \cdots c_m$ implies $F_1 \cdots F_m = \mathscr{F}$.

Lemma 6.3.19. If a fundamental formula c implies $\mathscr{F}$, then there is some element of K which is subsumed by c.

Proof. Obvious.

Lemma 6.3.20. If c is a prime implicant of $\mathscr{F}$, then $c \in K$.

Proof. By Lemma 6.3.19 some element $c' \in K$ is subsumed by c, moreover c' implies $\mathscr{F}$ by Lemma 6.3.18. Hence $c = c'$; that is, $c \in K$.

Lemma 6.3.21. If c is a prime implicant of $\mathscr{F}$, then $c \in \mathscr{K}$.

Proof. By Lemma 6.3.20, $c \in K$. By Definition 6.3.2, it follows that $c \in \mathscr{K}$.

Lemma 6.3.22. If $c \in \mathscr{K}$, then it is a prime implicant of $\mathscr{F}$.

Proof. Since $c \in \mathscr{K}$, $c \in K$. Hence by Lemma 6.3.18, c implies $\mathscr{F}$ and by Lemma 6.3.19, c subsumes some element of K, and hence subsumes some prime implicant. Hence c, which is short as possible, subsumes itself; that is, c is a prime implicant.

Lemmata 6.3.21 and 6.3.22 lead directly to the following theorem.

Theorem 6.3.23. c is a prime implicant of $\mathscr{F}$ iff $c \in \mathscr{K}$.

Now let us recall the manner of construction of $\mathscr{K}$. If each function F_i is written as a disjunction of all its prime implicants (by any procedure), if $F_1, \ldots, F_m$ is "multiplied out," and if all logically determinate clauses, repeated literals, and subsuming clauses are dropped, each fundamental formula in the resulting disjunction is an element of $\mathscr{K}$. Hence, by the theorem, these are the prime implicants of $\mathscr{F}$.

Procedure **P** now follows by taking $\mathscr{F}$ to be a formula in conjunctive normal form. Each clause of $\mathscr{F}$ is one of the F_i of the preceding argument, and each *literal* of each F_i is a prime implicant of the F_i (trivially every literal of a disjunction is a prime implicant thereof).

This completes the discussion of the method of converting normal forms.

The second part of the minimization problem for normal formulas consists in finding a simplest disjunction of the prime implicants discovered by any one of the three procedures developed above. One method, due to Quine, is to set up a prime implicant table.

EXAMPLE 7 (*Continued*). The prime implicant table is formed by expanding F into complete disjunctive normal form. Each developed clause is used as an abscissa of the table and each prime implicant as an ordinate. For our running example, see Table 6.3.1.

TABLE 6.3.1

	$\bar{x}_1x_2x_3$	$\bar{x}_1x_2\bar{x}_3$	$\bar{x}_1\bar{x}_2\bar{x}_3$	$x_1x_2x_3$	$x_1\bar{x}_2x_3$
$\bar{x}_1x_2(c_1)$	x	x			
$\bar{x}_1\bar{x}_3(c_2)$		x	x		
$x_2x_3(c_3)$	x			x	
$x_1x_3(c_4)$				x	x

As indicated in the interior, an x is marked at every coordinate position such that the abscissa subsumes the ordinate. We say a prime implicant c *covers* a clause of the developed form iff the clause subsumes c. By inspecting the table we can pick out the least number of prime implicants such that these implicants cover every clause. This may happen in more than one way. The disjunction of all the prime implicants under any one covering selection, is a simplest normal form of F. The preceding procedure is justified by the next theorem.

Theorem 6.3.24. If D is a simplest disjunctive normal form of F, and if D' is the complete disjunctive normal form of F, then each clause of D' subsumes a clause of D.

Proof. For the student, using Theorem 6.3.4 and part *a* of Theorem 6.3.9.

Simplest disjunctions of prime implicants may be formed from Table 6.3.1 by an algebraic procedure. We name each prime implicant with a letter c_1, c_2, etc., as usual. In Table 6.3.1 the implicants are labeled parenthetically. Now the disjunction $c_1 \vee c_3$ expresses the fact that either $\bar{x}_1x_2$ or x_2x_3 may be used to cover the clause $\bar{x}_1x_2x_3$. In general, for each abscissa we write an expression of the form $A \vee B \vee C \vee \cdots$, iff A, B, etc., are subsumed by that abscissa. The conjunction of all such disjunctions represents the table completely. In the example this conjunction is

$$(c_1 \vee c_3)(c_1 \vee c_2)(c_2)(c_3 \vee c_4)(c_4)$$

which is equivalent to

$$(c_1 \vee c_3)(c_2)(c_4)$$

"Multiplying out" we obtain

$$c_1c_2c_4 \vee c_2c_3c_4 \tag{10}$$

Expression (10) says that either $c_1c_2c_4$ or $c_2c_3c_4$ covers the developed form. Hence, from Table 6.3.1, the simplest normal forms of (6) are

$$\bar{x}_1x_2 \vee \bar{x}_1\bar{x}_3 \vee x_1x_3$$

and

$$\bar{x}_1\bar{x}_3 \vee x_2x_3 \vee x_1x_3$$

An argument in full justification of this procedure is to be given by the student.

There is not space to discuss many of the contributions which have been made to the subject of net simplification. Some of these contributions receive brief mention in Section 6.4. In particular, the procedures of Mott [1960] and Gazale [1957] for skirting the laborious process of constructing a prime implicant table should be studied.

In earlier sections, we have seen examples of transducers having a number of states unequal to any power of 2. This results, as in Table 6.1.2, in undefined cases or "don't care" conditions. In that example there are no rows for states 101 or 110, and hence we say that $y_1\bar{y}_2y_3$ and $y_1y_2\bar{y}_3$ are don't care conditions. It is also possible for a coded transducer to be of such a design that certain input combinations are undefined.

A satisfactory explication of "don't care" or "never occurs" is to say that the subject condition is *always false*. Formally, a clause c is always false when $c \approx 0$.

Definition 6.3.25. A fundamental clause c of F is *redundant* if $c \approx 0$.

Note that $x_1\bar{x}_1$, for example, is not redundant since it is not fundamental.

Definition 6.3.26. D is a *weak simplest normal form* of F if there are redundant clauses $c_1, \ldots, c_k$ on the letters of F and there is no simpler normal form D' equivalent to F.

A simplest normal form of a formula F is the special case where the number of redundant clauses is zero, and a weak simplest normal form of a formula F is so under the hypotheses that a certain nonzero number of clauses is redundant.

Theorem 6.3.27. Let $c_1, \ldots, c_k$ be redundant clauses and let $l_1{}^1$, $l_2{}^1$, etc., be the literals of c_1 and F; $l_1{}^2$, $l_2{}^2$, etc., the literals of c_2 and $F; \ldots;$ and $l_1{}^k$, $l_2{}^k$, etc., the literals of c_k and F. Then the following implications are true.

$$\bar{c}_1\bar{c}_2\cdots\bar{c}_k \text{ implies } F \approx F \vee c_1 \vee c_2 \vee \cdots \vee c_k$$

and

$$\bar{c}_1\bar{c}_2\cdots\bar{c}_k \text{ implies } F \approx F \wedge (\bar{l}_1{}^1 \vee \bar{l}_2{}^1 \vee \cdots) \wedge \cdots \wedge (\bar{l}_1{}^k \vee \bar{l}_2{}^k \vee \cdots)$$

Proof. For the student.

Definition 6.3.28. A prime implicant of a formula F with redundancies is a fundamental formula c, which implies F, subsumes no simpler fundamental formula implying F, and is not redundant; similarly for prime implicants d.

Theorem 6.3.29. If $c_1, c_2, \ldots, c_k$ are all redundant with letters in F, then any weak simplest disjunctive normal form of F is a disjunction of prime implicants of $F \vee c_1 \vee \cdots \vee c_k$.

Proof. By Theorem 6.3.4 any simplest normal form of $F \vee c_1 \vee \cdots \vee c_k$ is a disjunction of prime implicants of $F \vee c_1 \vee \cdots \vee c_k$. Since $c_1, \ldots, c_k$ are redundant, by Theorem 6.3.27 and Definition 6.3.26, any weak simplest normal form of F is a disjunction of prime implicants of $F \vee c_1 \vee \cdots \vee c_k$.

It is left to the student to state and prove this theorem for the conjunctive case. Q.E.D.

REMARK. The prime implicants of F with redundancies are not the same as those of F without redundancies. For, if cll' is a prime implicant of F without redundancies then cl' *is* a prime implicant of F with redundancy $\bar{l}l'$, by the consensus method.

Working with $F \vee c_1 \vee \cdots \vee c_k$ we may derive the set of prime implicants of F with redundancies by any one of the three previously described methods, together with an additional step which, according to Definition 6.3.28, calls for the deletion of redundant clauses. A prime implicant table is then constructed with abscissas being the developed clauses of F, excluding any clause which subsumes a redundancy. Finally, a simplest set may be selected as in the case of ordinary normal forms. Note that, instead of deleting redundancies occurring in the disjunction of all the prime implicants, we may alternatively list them as tabular ordinates. Then no selection of simplest forms will include the selection of a redundancy, since none of the latter cover a clause of F.

Theorem 6.3.31. Any weak simplest normal equivalent of F is at least as simple as any normal simplest equivalent of F.

The proof is left to the student, observing that if $c_1, \ldots, c_k$ are redundant, then every prime implicant of F subsumes some prime implicant of $F \vee c_1 \vee \cdots \vee c_k$. And similarly for the conjunctive case.

EXAMPLE 8. Find a weak simplest conjunctive normal form of

$$x_1\bar{x}_3 \vee \bar{x}_2x_3$$

subject to the redundancy condition $x_2\bar{x}_3$. By Theorem 6.3.27 we know that

$$x_1\bar{x}_3 \vee \bar{x}_2x_3 \Leftrightarrow (x_1\bar{x}_3 \vee \bar{x}_2x_3)(\bar{x}_2 \vee x_3)$$

is always true. We transform the right side into conjunctive normal form, with application of the consensus procedure in mind.

$$\underset{(d_1)}{(x_1 \vee \bar{x}_2)}\underset{(d_2)}{(x_1 \vee x_3)}\underset{(d_3)}{(\bar{x}_2 \vee \bar{x}_3)}\underset{(d_4)}{(\bar{x}_2 \vee x_3)}$$

Using the consensus method, we see that the sole application thereof is to d_3 and d_4, yielding

$$(x_1 \vee \bar{x}_2)(x_1 \vee x_3)(\bar{x}_2 \vee \bar{x}_3)(\bar{x}_2 \vee x_3)\bar{x}_2$$

Eliminating all subsuming clauses, we are left with

$$(x_1 \vee x_3)\bar{x}_2$$

which is simplest. For comparison, it is easy to see that the original formula of this example is itself the simplest disjunctive normal form as well as the simplest weak disjunctive form.

All of the foregoing techniques are tied to the structure of the formulas representing truth functions, rather than to the truth functions themselves. The methods of functional decomposition, one simple case of which we shall examine, depend, in the search for simplicity, on the functions, not formulas.

A truth function (or boolean function) is decomposable under the same conditions as any other function [cf. Section 2.1(7)]. We limit our discussion here to a very special case.

Definition 6.3.32. A truth function f of n variables $x_1, \ldots, x_n$ is *simple disjunctive decomposable* if there exist functions h and g of $n - s + 1$ and s, $1 < s < n$ variables, respectively, such that[6]

$$f(x_1, \ldots, x_n) = h(g(y_1, \ldots, y_s), z_1, \ldots, z_{n-s})$$

and $y_1, \ldots, y_s, z_1, \ldots, z_{n-s}$ are the variables $x_1, \ldots, x_n$ in some order without repetitions.

EXAMPLE 9.

TABLE 6.3.2

(a)

x_1	x_2	x_3	f	i
0	0	0	0	0
0	0	1	1	1
0	1	0	1	2
0	1	1	0	3
1	0	0	1	4
1	0	1	0	5
1	1	0	0	6
1	1	1	1	7

(b)

x_1	x_2	g	j
0	0	1	0
0	1	0	1
1	0	0	2
1	1	1	3

(c)

g	x_3	h	k
0	0	1	0
0	1	0	1
1	0	0	2
1	1	1	3

In Table 6.3.2 we have f, g, and h truth functions of the variables appearing as arguments in the left-hand columns in the usual way; i, j, and k are integers used to index f, g, h so that f_i denotes the function value of f for an assignment of values to $x_1x_2x_3$, whose decimal value is i. We will often use the notation exemplified by $f = (0, 1, 1, 0, 1, 0, 0, 1)$. Also, $f_4 = 1$ means that the fourth component of the function f, represented as a vector, is 1, etc.

In this example, f is the simple disjunctive composition of g and h, when $n = 3$ and $s = 2$, $y_1 = x_1$, $y_2 = x_2$, $z_1 = x_3$; $f(x_1, x_2, x_3) = h(g(y_1, y_2), z_1)$, as the student may see for himself.

[6] In the earlier part of this section we used $\Leftrightarrow$ as a *connective* between formulas as in $x \Leftrightarrow y'$ or $\approx$ as a *relation* between formulas. Here we revert, as is customary, to use of $=$ to indicate the equality relation in the two-valued boolean algebra

$$\langle\{0, 1\}, \vee, \wedge, {}^{-}\rangle$$

of truth functions.

From Table 6.3.2 we have

$$\begin{aligned} g(x_1, x_2) &= x_1x_2 \vee \bar{x}_1\bar{x}_2 \\ h(g(x_1x_2), x_3) &= g(x_1x_2)x_3 \vee \overline{g(x_1, x_2)}\bar{x}_3 \\ &= f(x_1, x_2, x_3) \end{aligned}$$

these relations lead to the formula

$$(x_1x_2 \vee \bar{x}_1\bar{x}_2)x_3 \vee \overline{(x_1x_2 \vee \bar{x}_1\bar{x}_2)}\bar{x}_3 \tag{11}$$

The simplest disjunctive normal form is

$$\bar{x}_1\bar{x}_2x_3 \vee \bar{x}_1x_2\bar{x}_3 \vee x_1\bar{x}_2\bar{x}_3 \vee x_1x_2x_3 \tag{12}$$

which is not as simple as (11). Although we could informally simplify (12) by using distributive laws and the De Morgan laws, it would take experience and luck to discover (11). There is no known practical algorithm. On the other hand, the decomposition provides for the simple form directly. We will now develop an algorithm for determination of simple disjunctive decompositions.

According to Definition 6.3.32, there is associated with a simple disjunctive decomposable (henceforth "decomposable" for short) function a *partition* of the set of variables into $\{y_1, \ldots, y_s\}$ and $\{z_1, \ldots, z_{n-s}\}$. Such a partition may be represented by the notation $z_1, z_s, \ldots, z_{n-s} \mid y_1, y_2, \ldots, y_s$. By our conventions (given in Definition 6.3.32) concerning the variables z and y, a partition such as $x_3 \mid x_1x_2$ is the same as $x_3 \mid x_2x_1$ by permuting variables. Hence the number of possible partitions associated with $f(x_1, \ldots, x_n)$ is $2^n - (n + 2)$, which can be seen as follows. For each z in $z_1, \ldots, z_{n-s} \mid y_1, \ldots, y_s$ substitute a 0 in $x_1, \ldots, x_n$ and for each y substitute a 1 in $x_1, \ldots, x_n$. This gives 2^n binary numbers. There are n cases where $s = 1$ and two other *trivial* cases: $s = 0$, $s = n$.

Besides representing functions by vectors of 0's and 1's we also use the vectors $0 = (0, 0, 0, \ldots)$ and $1 = (1, 1, 1, \ldots)$. The complement of a vector $f = (x_1, x_2, \ldots, x_n)$, where $x_i = 0, 1$, is $\bar{f} = (\bar{x}_1, \bar{x}_2, \ldots, \bar{x}_n)$.

Corresponding to each partition $z_1, z_2, \ldots, z_{n-s} \mid y_1, y_2, \ldots, y_s$ is a *partition matrix* of 2^{n-s} rows and 2^s columns which represents $f(x_1, \ldots, x_n)$. The rows correspond to the 2^{n-s} combinations of values of $z_1, \ldots, z_{n-s}$ and the columns to the 2^s values of $y_1, \ldots, y_s$. Each matrix element is a value of the function $f(x_1, \ldots, x_n)$. For example, given $f(x_1, x_2, x_3, x_4)$ and the partition $x_2x_3 \mid x_1x_4$; here $n = 4$, $s = 2$, $z_1 = x_2$, $z_2 = x_3$, $x_1 = y_1$, and $x_4 = y_2$. The partition matrix is shown below; by using the decimal

x_2	x_3 \ x_1x_4	00	01	10	11
0	0	f_0	f_1	f_8	f_9
0	1	f_2	f_3	f_{10}	f_{11}
1	0	f_4	f_5	f_{12}	f_{13}
1	1	f_6	f_7	f_{14}	f_{15}

equivalents for combinations of argument values we may write more simply:

x_2x_3 \ x_1x_4	0	1	2	3
0	f_0	f_1	f_8	f_9
1	f_2	f_3	f_{10}	f_{11}
2	f_4	f_5	f_{12}	f_{13}
3	f_6	f_7	f_{14}	f_{15}

Specifically, the partition matrix of $f = (0, 1, 1, 0, 1, 0, 0, 1)$ for the partition $x_3 \mid x_1x_2$ of Example 9 is shown in the following.

x_3 \ x_1x_2	0	1	2	3
0	f_0	f_2	f_4	f_6
1	f_1	f_3	f_5	f_7

x_3 \ x_1x_2	0	1	2	3
0	0	1	1	0
1	1	0	0	1

Let the number of distinct rows of a partition matrix be μ and the number of distinct columns be ν. These will be referred to as the row or column *multiplicity* of the matrix.

Theorem 6.3.33. For any partition matrix M: $\nu = 2$ iff

1. $\mu \leq 4$.
2. At least one row vector g exists such that $g \neq 0, 1$.
3. The only possible row vectors are g, $\bar{g}$, 0, and 1.

Moreover, $\nu = 1$ iff $\mu \leq 2$ and each row vector is 0 or 1.

Proof. Assume $\nu = 2$. Consider the matrix M' whose rows are those of M and whose two columns α_1, α_2 are the distinct columns of M. Since M' is a matrix of 0's and 1's the only possible rows are (0, 0), (0, 1), (1, 0), and (1, 1). Since $\alpha_1 \neq \alpha_2$, at least one row vector is either (0, 1) or (1, 0) [that is, unequal to $0 = (0, 0)$ or $1 = (1, 1)$]. Obviously, rows in M are equal iff rows in M' are equal. Conversely, if $\mu \leq 4$ and only g, $\bar{g}$, 0, or 1 occur and at least one of g, $\bar{g}$ occurs, then $\nu = 2$. Similarly for the case $\nu = 1$. Q.E.D.

Theorem 6.6.34. A truth function f is simple disjunctive decomposable into functions h and g, as in Definition 6.3.32, iff the partition matrix corresponding to the partition $z_1, \ldots, z_{n-s} \mid y_1, \ldots, y_s$ has a column multiplicity $\nu \leq 2$.

Proof. Suppose

$$f(x_1, \ldots, x_n) = h(g(y_1, \ldots, y_s), z_1, \ldots, z_{n-s}) \tag{13}$$

By induction we can easily show that, for any function f (with $\sum$ meaning manifold $\cup$),

$$f(x_1, \ldots, x_n) = \sum_{j=0}^{2^{n-k+1}-1} f_j(x_1, \ldots, x_{k-1}) p_j(x_k, \ldots, x_n) \qquad (14a)$$

where $f_j(x_1, \ldots, x_{k-1}) = f(x_1, \ldots, x_{k-1}, \alpha_j)$ and α_j is an $n - k + 1$-tuple of 0's and 1's whose decimal representation is j, and where $p_j(x_k, \ldots, x_n)$ is a conjunction $\alpha_k \cdots \alpha_n$ such that any α_i is x_i if α_i has the value 1 in the binary expansion of j, or is $\bar{x}_i$ if α_i is 0 in the binary expansion of j (see exercises). In the present application, (14a) may be written

$$f(x_1, \ldots, x_n) = \sum_{j=0}^{2^{n-s}-1} f_j(y_1, \ldots, y_s) p_j(z_1, \ldots, z_{n-s}) \qquad (14b)$$

From (13) and (14b) (since h can be expanded about the variables $z_1, \ldots, z_{n-s}$),

$$f(x_1, \ldots, x_n) = \sum_{j=0}^{2^{n-s}-1} h_j(g(y_1, \ldots, y_s)) p_j(z_1, \ldots, z_{n-s}) \qquad (15)$$

Because of the uniqueness of the expansion (14a) we obtain, from (14b) and (15),

$$f_j(y_1, \ldots, y_s) = h_j(g(y_1, \ldots, y_s))$$

for all $0 \leq j \leq 2^{n-s} - 1$. Now any truth function of one variable x is known to be either x, $\bar{x}$, 0, or 1. Hence h_j is g, $\bar{g}$, 0, or 1. Therefore the partition matrix corresponding to $y_1, \ldots, y_s \mid z_1, \ldots, z_{n-s}$ has at most four distinct rows, whence $\nu \leq 2$ by Theorem 6.3.33.

Conversely, suppose f is a function with a partition matrix having the properties stated in the theorem. By Theorem 6.3.33, if $\nu = 2$ there is a nontrivial function g of s variables defined by some row R_j, $0 \leq j \leq 2^{n-s} - 1$ of the matrix. Next define a function h using Table 6.3.3. Each of the

TABLE 6.3.3

R_j	h_j	$h_{j+2^{n-s}}$
0	0	0
g	0	1
$\bar{g}$	1	0
1	1	1

possibilities, 0, g, $\bar{g}$, 1 for the matrix rows are listed under R_j, and thus R_j determines h_j. It is not hard to see that $f(x_1, \ldots, x_n) = h(g(y_1, \ldots, y_s), z_1, \ldots, z_{n-s})$ where h and g are determined in the manner indicated. If $\nu = 1$, Table 6.3.3 still permits construction of h for arbitrary g. Hence f is decomposable.

Q.E.D.

Theorem 6.3.34 provides not only necessary and sufficient conditions for the existence of partitions but also an algorithm for the construction of g and h when they do exist.

1. Construct a partition matrix; if $\nu = 1$, f is equal to a function f' of less than n variables.
2. If $\nu = 2$, there is a nontrivial row vector which defines g.
3. Define h using Table 6.3.3.

EXAMPLE 10. A truth function is given by Table 6.3.4.

TABLE 6.3.4

x_1	x_2	x_3	x_4	$f(x_1, x_2, x_3, x_4)$
0	0	0	0	0
0	0	0	1	1
0	0	1	0	1
0	0	1	1	0
0	1	0	0	1
0	1	0	1	1
0	1	1	0	0
0	1	1	1	0
1	0	0	0	0
1	0	0	1	0
1	0	1	0	1
1	0	1	1	1
1	1	0	0	0
1	1	0	1	0
1	1	1	0	1
1	1	1	1	1

Among the $2^n - (n + 2) = 10$ partitions for the function, we find the partition $x_1x_3 \mid x_2x_4$ whose matrix is such that $\nu = 2$ as below. We pick

x_1x_3 \ x_2x_4	00	01	10	11
00	0	1	1	1
01	1	0	0	0
10	0	0	0	0
11	1	1	1	1

$g = (0, 1, 1, 1)$. Then, using Table 6.3.3, we find that

$$h = (0, 1, 0, 1, 1, 0, 0, 1)$$

Hence

$$f(x_1, x_2, x_3, x_4) = h(g(x_2, x_4), x_1, x_3)$$

Tables 6.3.5 and 6.3.6 give values for g and h:

TABLE 6.3.5

x_2	x_4	$g(x_2, x_4)$
0	0	0
0	1	1
1	0	1
1	1	1

TABLE 6.3.6

g	x_1	x_3	$h(g(x_2, x_4), x_1x_3)$
0	0	0	0
0	0	1	1
0	1	0	0
0	1	1	1
1	0	0	1
1	0	1	0
1	1	0	0
1	1	1	1

The function h may be expressed as

$$\overline{g(x_2, x_4)}x_3 \vee g(x_2, x_4)(\bar{x}_1\bar{x}_3 \vee x_1x_3)$$

or

$$\overline{(x_2 \vee x_4)}x_3 \vee (x_2 \vee x_4)(\bar{x}_1\bar{x}_3 \vee x_1x_3)$$

Oddly enough, in this example a still simpler form of f is obtainable by finding a simplest disjunctive normal form and then using an obvious factorization.

$$x_3(\overline{x_2 \vee x_4} \vee x_1) \vee \bar{x}_1\bar{x}_3(x_2 \vee x_4)$$

This result is simpler by literals-count and also leads to a circuit in which the component $x_2 \vee x_4$ need be designed once, exactly as in the decomposition method.

The next two corollaries are consequences of Theorem 6.3.34.

Corollary 6.3.35. If $\nu = 2$ for the partition matrix corresponding to $z_1, \ldots, z_{n-s} \mid y_1, \ldots, y_s$, then there are two and only two disjunctive decompositions. One is given by $h(g(y_1, \ldots, y_s), z_1, \ldots, z_{n-s})$ and $g(y_1, \ldots, y_s)$, while the other is given by $h'(\overline{g(y_1, \ldots, y_s)}, z_1, \ldots, z_{n-s})$ with $h_j' = h_{j+2^{n-s}}$ and $h'_{j+2^{n-s}} = h_j$ in Table 6.3.3.

Theorem 6.3.36. If $f(x_1, \ldots, x_n)$ is decomposable into h and g, then $\overline{f(x_1, \ldots, x_n)}$ is also decomposable, and in particular is decomposable into $\bar{h}$ and g.

In practice, all of the possible partition matrices corresponding to the partition $z_1, \ldots, z_{n-s} \mid y_1, \ldots, y_s$ can be represented by *decomposition charts* which are marked according to certain conventions to be described. Take, for example, the partition $x_3x_4 \mid x_1x_2$. The decomposition chart is

x_3x_4 \ x_1x_2	0	1	2	3
0	0	4	8	12
1	1	5	9	13
2	2	6	10	14
3	3	7	11	15

where the entry "4" is, for example, written as short for f_4. Any of the 2^{2^4} functions of x_1, x_2, x_3, x_4 can be easily represented by encircling those numerals x for which $f_x = 1$. For example,

$$f(x_1, x_2, x_3, x_4) = (1\,0\,1\,0\,1\,1\,1\,0\,1\,1\,0\,0\,0\,1\,1\,1)$$

is represented below. Note that f is not decomposable by this partition, but

x_3x_4 \ x_1x_2	0	1	2	3
0	(0)	(4)	(8)	12
1	1	(5)	(9)	(13)
2	(2)	(6)	10	(14)
3	3	7	11	(15)

of course it may be for some other. Also note that the *transpose* of this matrix (in general M' is the transposed M iff $a_{ij}' = a_{ji}$, $a_{ij}' \in M'$, and $a_{ji} \in M$) represents the partition $x_1x_2 \mid x_3x_4$.

In general, theoretically we must construct all possible $2^n - n - 2$ decomposition charts for a function of n variables in order to obtain all decompositions. However, owing to the use of the transpose we can accomplish our purpose with $2^{n-1} - 1$ charts. The charts for $n = 4$ are given below as an illustration. Of these charts, the transposes of the

x_1 \ $x_2x_3x_4$	0	1	2	3	4	5	6	7
0	0	1	2	3	4	5	6	7
1	8	9	10	11	12	13	14	15

(*a*)

x_2 \ $x_1x_3x_4$	0	1	2	3	4	5	6	7
0	0	1	2	3	8	9	10	11
1	4	5	6	7	12	13	14	15

(*b*)

x_3 \ $x_1x_2x_4$	0	1	2	3	4	5	6	7
0	0	1	4	5	8	9	12	13
1	2	3	6	7	10	11	14	15

(*c*)

x_4 \ $x_1x_2x_3$	0	1	2	3	4	5	6	7
0	0	2	4	6	8	10	12	14
1	1	3	5	7	9	11	13	15

(*d*)

x_1x_2 \ x_2x_4	0	1	2	3
0	0	1	2	3
1	4	5	6	7
2	8	9	10	11
3	12	13	14	15

(*e*)

x_1x_3 \ x_2x_4	0	1	2	3
0	0	1	4	5
1	2	3	6	7
2	8	9	12	13
3	10	11	14	15

(*f*)

x_1x_4 \ x_2x_3	0	1	2	3
0	0	2	4	6
1	1	3	5	7
2	8	10	12	14
3	9	11	13	15

(*g*)

two-rowed ones do not give partitions, since they are defined nontrivially only for $s > 1$. However, the other transposes do provide further partitions and hence $2^n - n - 2 = 10$ in all.

The student can easily construct all possible charts for $n \leq 6$. Beyond functions of six variables the theory is impractical unless mechanized.

The decomposition charts provide a lengthy yet somewhat useful method for step 1 of the algorithm, and Corollary 6.3.35 and Theorem 6.3.36 provide other means for shortening the task of finding all decompositions.

EXERCISES 6.3

1. Find a simplest *conjunctive* normal form of the function of four variables

$$f = (0, 0, 0, 0, 0, 1, 0, 1, 0, 0, 0, 1, 0, 0, 0, 1)$$

(*a*) Use the method of converting normal forms.
(*b*) Use the method of Theorem 6.3.7.

2. Beginning with the developed conjunctive normal form of f, in Exercise 1, obtain an equivalent formula, as simple as possible, by using Corollary 6.3.6 exhaustively.

3. Prove part (*b*) of Theorem 6.3.5 and all of Theorem 6.3.6.

4. Write Quine's algorithm in detail (flow chart).

5. In Example 7 of the text, interchange $\wedge$ and $\vee$ and negate all literals, that is, $\bar{x}$ becomes x and x becomes $\bar{x}$. By consensus find all the conjunctive prime implicants. Compare with formula (7) in the text.

6. Prove Theorem 6.3.24.

7. Prove the assertion, "The conjunction of all such disjunctions represents the table completely" which occurs just before (10). Furthermore, justify the algebraic manipulations leading (in the two indicated steps) to formula (10).

8. Prove Theorem 6.3.27.

9. Prove Theorem 6.3.31.

10. Given the formula $\bar{x}_1 x_2 \vee x_1 \bar{x}_2 \vee \bar{x}_1 x_3 \vee x_1 \bar{x}_3$ show that the simplest disjunctive normal form with redundant clause $\bar{x}_1 \bar{x}_2$ is identically the same formula as the simplest conjunctive normal form with the same redundancy.

11. Prove the relation (14) of Section 6.3, and prove that the expansion indicated is *unique*.

12. Give an explicit proof that the method of construction of a function using Table 6.3.3 does, in fact, yield the function h such that

$$f(x_1, \ldots, x_n) = h(g(y_1, \ldots, y_s), z_1, \ldots, z_{n-s})$$

13. Prove Corollary 6.3.35 and Theorem 6.3.36.

14. Test for the decomposability of the function of Exercise 1.

15. Using decomposition techniques, find the simplest possible formulation for

$$f = (0, 0, 0, 0, 1, 0, 1, 0, 0, 0, 1, 1, 1, 0, 0, 0)$$

16. Using the techniques developed theoretically in this chapter, design a transducer net to perform as follows.

There are four inputs and an output. Two of the inputs s_1, s_2 are control inputs; the other two are signal inputs. When $(s_1, s_2) = (0, 0)$, the net outputs 0 and continues to do so as long as this control situation prevails. When $(s_1, s_2) = (1, 1)$, the net outputs 1 and continues to do so, etc. When $(s_1, s_2) = (0, 1)$, the output *adds* the signal inputs—that is, the device functions as a *full adder* as long as this control situation prevails. Finally, when $(s_1 s_2) = (1, 0)$, the device functions as a subtracter.

6.4 HISTORICAL AND BIBLIOGRAPHICAL REMARKS

The history of the analysis of switching circuits by using propositional calculus (equivalently, in this application, boolean algebra) begins with Ehrenfest's [1910] discovery of the correlation of logic expressions and switching. Shannon [1938] independently discovered the use of logic in analyzing switching networks. A study of logic nets, including delays, was made by Burks and Wright [1953] and provides much of the material for our exercises in Section 6.1. The analysis of nerve networks using logic was first made by McCulloch and Pitts [1943], although these writers used a somewhat different model from our basic transducer model. We follow the formulation of nets of Kleene [1956]. The actual correlation of sequential switching nets to binary transducers, in our sense, together with the proof of equivalence is due to Burks and Wang [1957]. Church [1959] defines automata in a certain formal system yielding directly our equivalences (2) and (3) of section 6.1 and studies various analysis and synthesis algorithms.

The use of partition theory in the state assignment problem is due to Hartmanis [1960, 1961]. The student should also consult the numerous other papers of Hartmanis which are listed in the Bibliography.

Most of the algebraic approaches to the truth functional simplification problem stem from Quine [1952], in which "Quine's algorithm" is presented. The consensus method is due to Samson and Mills [1954] but also somewhat later and independently to Quine [1955]. The converting normal forms method is Nelson's [1955a], as is the standard manner of treatment of "don't cares" [1955b]. The presentation here follows House and Rado [1965]. The procedure for selecting minimal disjunctions of prime implicants from the prime implicant table is due to Petrick [1956]. Other methods, not discussed here, which proceed without the table and requisite expansion into developed normal form, have been presented by Mott [1960] and Gazale [1957]. Modified forms of the Quine algorithm have been developed by McCluskey [1956]. Topological approaches to minimization have been studied by Roth [1959]. The literature in the field is extensive, and representative but not exhaustive items are given in the references.

The decomposition approach to truth functional minimization is Ashenhurst's [1953, 1959]. An exposition of the theory, part of which we followed closely in Section 6.3, is from Curtis [1962].

The student should be aware that the formal and algebraic approaches to finite transducers which we have adopted are not very realistic for certain applications. We have already indicated limitations of the neural net model (Arbib [1964]). For computing networks and systems there are other kinds of limitational properties such as the cycle structure (Holland

[1960]) of logic nets and reliability (von Neumann [1956], Moore and Shannon [1956], and others) not in any way reflected in our model. Again, decision elements can never be perfectly timed, and, further, the transducer model is only with considerable danger and complication applicable to the study of asynchronous computers. These questions have been studied, respectively, by Huffman [1954], Muller [1959], McNaughton [1964], and Unger [1959] among others. Actual computers, if one assumes synchronization and perfect timing of switches, can be thought of as vast interconnections of finite transducers (Burks and Copi [1956]), and the computer itself including magnetic tape units, drums, etc., in addition to the main frame—provided all these are fixed—is in a certain sense a finite transducer. From other points of view, however, a computer is less than a finite transducer (it cannot add two numbers whose encodement is beyond memory capacity); from yet another viewpoint, it can always be given longer and longer tapes, without end, and hence could transcend the limits of a finite machine. Presumably, then, despite our remarks in Section 4.0, a computer would be equivalent to a Turing machine. At any rate, the finite transducer, to model adequately the behavior, structure, error-proneness, and temporal properties of a digital computer, much less the properties such as part replaceability, etc., would have to be greatly elaborated. Iterative and/or cellular models of computers have been studied by Burks [1963], Cole [1964], Hennie [1961], Holland [1963], and von Neumann [1966]. Still other models of computers have been proposed by Elgot and Robinson [1964]. For an interesting assessment of automata theory see Wang [1965].

CHAPTER 7

Acceptors

7.0. Introduction. The problem of mechanical recognition of patterns, which is of some pressing importance in modern computer technology, can be approached in two ways. Given a collection of objects to be recognized, one can experiment with designs of hardware systems which will recognize an instance of an object as indeed being such. Or, second, one can consider an ideal machine of given powers and then study the properties of objects it can recognize. This second alternative is a proper one for a theory of automata.

In Chapter 4 we studied Turing acceptors and found that they are able to accept just the recursively enumerable sets. Thus, for example, if the set of instances of the letter-type A (with instances or tokens such as *a*, *A*, $\mathscr{A}$, A, *a*, etc.) is recursively enumerable, there is a Turing acceptor which goes into some state q if an appropriately coded instance is inscribed on tape. If the set is not recursive, however, the acceptor may loop infinitely when presented with, say, an instance of B. Similarly, if the sentences (formulas) of a language (artificial language) are recursively enumerable there is an accepting Turing machine.

We shall now study acceptors (which also turn out to be *detectors*—cf. Definition 3.3.14) which, unlike Turing machines, move only right w.r.t. tape. Thus these acceptors operate in a manner similar to that of finite transducers except for the fact that they do not print. As algebraic systems (again in analogy with the associated systems of finite transducers) finite acceptors are essentially transition systems having certain subsets of states designated as final states. We will say that a subset $\mathscr{U}$ of the set of words S^* on S is accepted, provided that a transition system in its initial state ends up in a state in the set of final states when a word of $\mathscr{U}$ is fed in.

It is intuitively clear that some sets will be accepted in this sense. For example, the set of words on $\{0, 1\}$ containing at least one occurrence of a 1 is such a set, because we can design an automaton which persists in the initial state until a 1 comes along, and which then transits to and stays in a final state. It is equally clear, on the other hand, that the set of words on $\{0, 1\}$ consisting of strings of n 0's followed by n 1's, that is, $0^n 1^n$, is not accepted by an acceptor with a finite set of internal states. Our main problem in this chapter will be to provide a precise characterization of the sets which are acceptable.

We can sense the general drift of a solution to this problem if we turn to some of the ideas already discussed in Section 5.5 relating to transition systems. All of the words x accepted by a given acceptor with final states Q' will satisfy the requirement $M(q_0, x) \in Q'$. Furthermore, all of them which satisfy this requirement will be R_h-equivalent in the sense of Section 5.5. In general there will be an equivalence class under the relation R_h for each $q' \in Q'$, though such classes need not necessarily be distinct. Hence the set of accepted words will be a union of R_h-equivalence classes. Moreover, we shall be able to characterize accepted sets in another way using a certain notation called "regular expressions" which will be so strong as to allow us to construct an acceptor, by way of an *algorithm*, given the set, and conversely.

These descriptions of accepted sets will be covered in Sections 7.1 and 7.2, together with some other related material.

The theory of finite acceptors also affords a basis for understanding the performance of finite transducers. Nothing said in Chapter 5 had much direct bearing on what sequential machines can *do*, although we alluded to the problem in Section 5.0. Similarly Chapter 6 provided little information about the behavior of transducer nets or nerve nets, but only the fact that they were both models of sequential machines.

To see the application of acceptor theory to transducers, suppose **T** is a transducer with the G function, which maps words on S into words on O, as given in Definition 5.1.4. What we want to know is: which word to word functions on S^* into O^* are equal to the G function of some transducer? It turns out that one condition (among some others) is that the function construed as a set of pairs of words must be the set of accepted words of an acceptor with two input tapes. In this way, the theory of the behavior of transducers is reducible to the theory of the capabilities of finite acceptors. These topics are discussed in Section 7.3.

Finally, in Section 7.4 we discuss the possibility of universal finite state acceptors. In analogy with the universal Turing machine the universal finite state acceptors we discuss will accept any set that is accepted by a finite state automaton of a certain class.

7.1 DEFINABILITY

Definition 7.1.1. A *finite state acceptor* is a semi-thue acceptor (Definition 3.5.12) with alphabets S and Q as usual, with a nonempty set of *final* states $Q' \subseteq Q$, at least one initial state q_0, an axiom $q_0x\#$, and productions of the form

1. $q_is_jR \to q_lR$
2. $q_i\# \to q_i$

We have omitted use of the symbol P since $P = \Lambda$ in all cases, as is easily seen. There is a rule of type 2 for each q_i.

Definition 7.1.2. A word x is *accepted* by a finite acceptor **A** if there is a terminal proof of some $q' \in Q'$ from $q_0x\#$ where q_0 is one of the initial states.

Definition 7.1.3. A finite acceptor is *monogenic* or *deterministic* if there is just one initial state q_0 and exactly one rule of type 1 for each pair $(q_i, s_j) \in Q \times S$. Otherwise, an acceptor is *polygenic* or *nondeterministic*. We will use the abbreviation n.f.s.a. for the nondeterministic acceptors and f.s.a. for the others.

EXAMPLE 1. The acceptor of Example 8 in Section 3.3 is an f.s.a. provided that we (1) specify $\{q_1, q_2, q_3, q_4\}$ as the final set, (2) delete rule 18, and (3) add rule $q_0\# \to q_0$. Note that an f.s.a., unlike the more general acceptor of Definition 3.3.12, has terminal results for all axioms $q_0x\#$. Therefore, instead of defining acceptance in terms of termination we define it here by means of the concept of final state. The student should ponder the fact that our new, more special definition will not apply generally—for example, to Turing machines.

Definition 7.1.4. Given an f.s.a. **A**, an *associated* f.s.a. (or simply f.s.a. for short since no confusion will arise) is a quintuple $\langle S, Q, q_0, M, Q' \rangle$ where S and Q are the alphabets of the f.s.a. and q_0 is the initial state. $M: Q \times S \to Q$ is given by $M(q_i, s_j) = q_l$ iff $q_is_jR \to q_lR$ is a rule of the given f.s.a.; and $Q' \subseteq Q$.

Note that, from this point of view, an f.s.a. is a finite transition system with a subset of states designated as final. M can be extended to sequences in the usual way.

Moreover, an f.s.a. may be represented by a finite transducer graph modified so as to omit output designations as in Example 2 of Section 5.4. We further modify the graph conventions by representing final states by concentric circles. Thus, returning to Example 1, we have for the f.s.a. discussed there the graph shown in Fig. 7.1.1.

Definition 7.1.5. Given an n.f.s.a., an *associated* n.f.s.a. is a quintuple $\langle S, Q, Q_0, M, Q' \rangle$ where $Q_0 \subseteq Q$ is the set of initial states, $Q' \subseteq Q$ the set of final states, and M a function on $Q \times S$ into the power set (cf. Exercise 1.2(2)), of Q, which we write $\pi(Q)$. $M(q_i, s_j) = \pi$ where $\pi \in \pi(Q)$

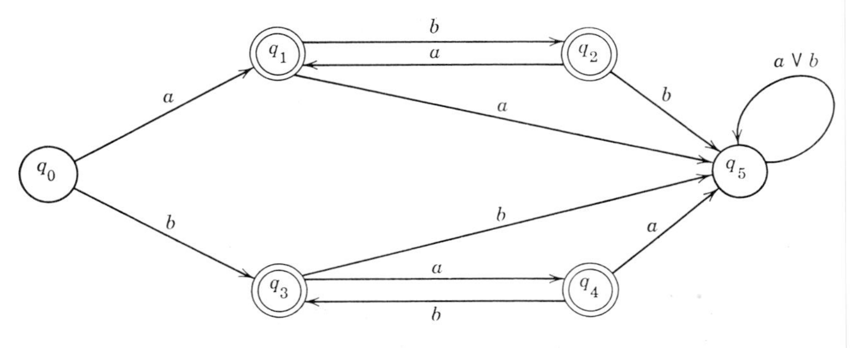

Fig. 7.1.1

iff π is the set of states q_l on the right of productions $q_i s_j R \to q_l R$ for fixed q_i, s_j.

EXAMPLE 2. Let $s = \{0, 1\}$, $Q = \{q_0, q_1, q_2\}$, $Q_0 = \{q_0, q_2\}$, $Q' = \{q_0\}$, and suppose we have the rules

1.	$q_0 0R \to q_0 R$	6.	$q_1 1R \to q_0 R$
2.	$q_0 0R \to q_2 R$	7.	$q_2 1R \to q_1 R$
3.	$q_0 1R \to q_1 R$	8.	$q_0\# \to q_0$
4.	$q_1 0R \to q_2 R$	9.	$q_1\# \to q_1$
5.	$q_1 0R \to q_1 R$	10.	$q_2\# \to q_2$

Note that this system has two productions with $q_0 0$ on the left and two with $q_1 0$. Hence by Definition 7.1.3 it is an n.f.s.a. because there are two initial states and a polygenic set of rules. It is an easy matter to verify that there are two different proofs from $q_0 0101\#$ and none at all from $q_2 0101\#$, even though q_2 is given as an initial state. There is, however, a proof of q_0 from $q_2 1001\#$. Hence both 0101 and 1001 are accepted by this n.f.s.a., according to Definition 7.1.3, but under quite unlike circumstances. The n.f.s.a.'s are more flexible than the f.s.a.'s and it takes more imagination to find proofs. Contrary to intuition, however, these nondeterministic systems are capable of processing no more than ordinary ones.

Continuing the example, the associated n.f.s.a. is the quintuple $N = \langle \{0, 1\}, \{q_0, q_1, q_2\}, \{q_0, q_2\}, M, \{q_0\} \rangle$ where M is Table 7.1.1. Here, following Definition 7.1.5, $M(q_0, 0) = \{q_0, q_2\}$, which is an element of $\pi\{q_0, q_1, q_2\}$, since $\{q_0, q_2\}$ is the set of states which occur on the right of productions with $q_0 0R$ on the left; similarly for $M(q_1, 0)$. Moreover, $M(q_2, 0) = \varnothing$ since there are no productions $q_2 0R \to x$ in the example.

Nondeterministic acceptors may be represented by graphs similar to Fig. 7.1.1, but allowing for the possibility of more than one branch labeled s_j stemming from a node q_j.

TABLE 7.1.1

$q \backslash s$	0	1
q_0	$\{q_0, q_2\}$	$\{q_1\}$
q_1	$\{q_1, q_2\}$	$\{q_0\}$
q_2	ϕ	$\{q_1\}$

Corollary 7.1.6. A word x is *accepted* by an f.s.a. iff $M(q_0, x) \in Q'$, Q' the set of final states.

This corollary follows directly from the Definitions 7.1.2, 7.1.3, and 7.1.4. The details are left to the student.

Corollary 7.1.7. A word x is *accepted* by an n.f.s.a. iff there exists a sequence of states $q_{i_0}, q_{i_1}, \ldots, q_{i_n}$ for $x = s_{i_1}s_{i_2}\cdots s_{i_n}$ such that

(*a*) $q_{i_0} \in Q_0$
(*b*) $q_{i_j} \in M(q_{i_{j-1}}, s_{i_j})$
(*c*) $q_{i_n} \in Q'$

Proof. For the student.

Definition 7.1.8. A set of words $x(\mathbf{A}) \subseteq S^*$ is *accepted* by an f.s.a. $\mathbf{A} = \langle S, Q, q_0, M, Q' \rangle$ iff $M(q_0 x) \in Q'$ for all $x \in x(\mathbf{A})$.

Similarly, a set of words $x(\mathbf{N})$ is accepted by an n.f.s.a. if each x satisfies the conditions *a–c* of Corollary 7.1.7. We postpone further discussion of nondeterministic acceptors until the next section.

Definition 7.1.9. A set $\mathscr{U} \subseteq S^*$ is definable provided that there is an f.s.a. $\mathbf{A}$ such that $\mathscr{U} = x(\mathbf{A})$.

A really precise statement of the problem we posed for ourselves in Section 7.0 is to characterize the *definable* sets.

As in Section 5.5, it will be useful and instructive here to use the transition system concept with Q being possibly any nonempty (that is, even infinite) set. We will also now introduce the notion of generalized acceptor (not to be confused with an f.s.a.), which, of course, is not an automaton (cf. Definition 3.3.10).

Definition 7.1.10. A *generalized acceptor* (g.a.) is a system

$$\mathbf{G} = \langle S, Q, q_0, M, Q' \rangle$$

which is like an f.s.a. except that Q is any nonempty set. A word $x \in S^*$ is accepted by $\mathbf{G}$ iff $M(q_0, x) \in Q'$. The set of such words is $x(\mathbf{G})$.

Several of the following theorems and definitions are expressed for the general case, and of course all of them hold for f.s.a.'s as well. Note that for generalized systems we have defined acceptance outright and cannot prove the condition of acceptance by reference to an automaton as in Corollary 7.1.6.

Definition 7.1.11. A set $\mathscr{U} \subseteq S^*$ is *definable* by a *transition system* $\mathbf{T}_S = \langle S, Q, q_0, M \rangle$ iff there is a subset $Q' \subseteq Q$ such that $\mathscr{U} = x(\mathbf{G})$ where $\mathbf{G} = \langle S, Q, q_0, M, Q' \rangle$.

In order to understand the significance of the restriction that Q be a *finite* set, let us consider a situation where Q is allowed to be an infinite set. Here, it is easy to see that any set is definable as follows. Recall the free transition system $\mathbf{T}_{S\mathscr{S}}$ (Theorem 5.5.13). Now consider *any* subset $\mathscr{V} \subseteq S^*$. $\mathscr{V}$ is definable by $\mathbf{T}_{S\mathscr{S}}$ since, using Definition 7.1.11, $\mathscr{V}$ is accepted by the system $\mathbf{G}_{\mathscr{S}} = \langle S, \mathscr{S}, \Lambda, M, \mathscr{V} \rangle$. This is true since $x \in \mathscr{V}$ iff $M(\Lambda, x) = \Lambda x = x \in \mathscr{V}$; that is, $\mathscr{V} = x(\mathbf{G})$. $\mathscr{V}$, of course, may be a nonrecursively enumerable set, so that infinite acceptors transcend Turing machines! Avoidance of this triviality leads us to consideration of only the finite sets Q in automata theory.

Although the free system $\mathbf{T}_{S\mathscr{S}}$ is not a legitimate automaton we will continue to use it as a technical device as in Section 5.5 for the facilitation of proofs. The student may, at this stage, find it useful to review the other mathematical ideas used in Sections 5.4 and 5.5, since they are to be used heavily in the following sections.

Definition 7.1.12. A g.a. is *connected* iff for any $q \in Q$ there is an x such that $M(q_0, x) = q$. A g.a. is *reduced* iff for every pair of distinct $q, q' \in Q$ there is an x such that $M(q, x) \in Q'$ iff $M(q', x) \notin Q'$ where $Q' \subseteq Q$ is the set of final states. A g.a. is *minimal* if it is connected and reduced.

REMARK. By a simple device one may easily construe an f.s.a. as a complete Moore transducer (Definitions 5.3.19 and 5.3.22), and then apply the connectivity results of Section 5.3 and Theorem 5.3.26*d* to obtain a minimal acceptor (see Exercises).

EXAMPLE 3. In Fig. 7.1.1, inspection shows that $M(q_1, x) \in \{q_1, q_2, q_3, q_4\}$ iff $M(q_4, x) \in \{q_1, q_2, q_3, q_4\}$ for all x; similarly for the pair q_2, q_3. Hence this acceptor is not reduced. The result of "merging" q_1 into q_4 and q_2 into q_3 is a minimal automaton (Fig. 7.1.2).

Definition 7.1.13. Given $\mathbf{G}_a = \langle S, Q_a, q_{a_0}, M_a, Q_a' \rangle$ and

$$\mathbf{G}_b = \langle S, Q_b, q_{b_0}, M_b, Q_b' \rangle$$

and a map $g: Q_a \to Q_b$, g is an *acceptor homomorphism* provided that

$$(a) \quad g(q_{a_0}) = q_{b_0}$$
$$(b) \quad g(M_a(q_a, s)) = M_b(g(q_a), s)$$

and

$$(c) \quad q_a \in Q_a' \Rightarrow g(q_a) \in Q_b'$$

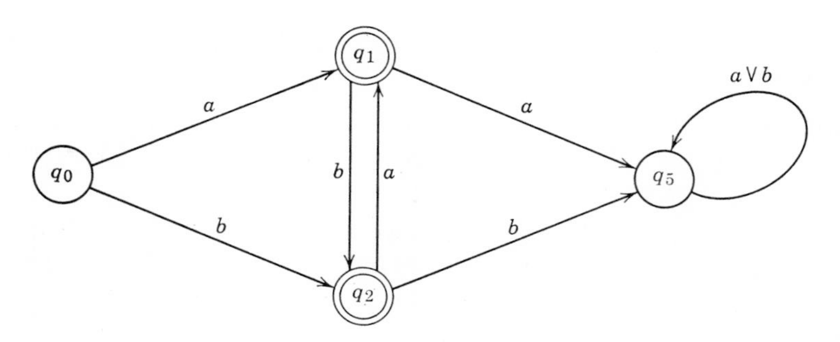

Fig. 7.1.2

If instead of c, we have

$$(c') \quad q_a \in Q_a' \Leftrightarrow g(q_a) \in Q_b'$$

g is a *strong* (acceptor) *homomorphism.*

An *isomorphism* is a one–one onto strong homomorphism.

In the next few theorems we shall discuss functions f from states to states of various automata. Recall that if f: $Q_a \rightarrow Q_b$, then by $f(Q_a')$—called the *direct* image of the subset $Q_a' \subseteq Q_a$ by f—we mean

$$\{q_b \mid q_b \in Q_b \wedge (\exists q_a)(q_a \in Q_a' \wedge q_b = f(q_a))\}$$

By $f^{-1}(Q_b')$—called the *inverse image* of the subset of $Q_b' \subseteq Q_b$ by f—we mean

$$\{q_a \mid q_a \in Q_a \wedge (\exists q_b)(q_b \in Q_b' \wedge q_b = f(q_a))\}$$

Now, if we also have the function g: $Q_b \rightarrow Q_c$, then the composition gf exists, since the range of f is included in the domain of g. In this instance, the direct image of Q_a' by gf will be a subset Q_c' of Q_c and the inverse image of Q_c', denoted by $(gf)^{-1}$, will be a subset Q_a' of Q_a. Note also that $(gf)^{-1} = f^{-1}g^{-1}$.

Theorem 7.1.14. For any transition system $\mathbf{T}_S = \langle S, Q, q_0, M \rangle$ and g.a. $\mathbf{G} = \langle S, Q, q_0, M, Q' \rangle$

$$x(\mathbf{G}) = \{x \mid x \in S^* \wedge h(x) \in Q'\} = h^{-1}(Q')$$

where h is (as in Section 5.5) the transition homomorphism (Definition 3.5.7) of $\mathbf{T}_{S\mathscr{S}}$ into $\mathbf{T}_S$.

Proof. $x \in x(\mathbf{G}) \Leftrightarrow M(q_0, x) \in Q'$
$\Leftrightarrow h(x) \in Q'$
since $h(x) = M(q_0, x)$ by Theorem 5.5.13. Q.E.D.

Theorem 7.1.15. Let $\mathbf{T}_{S_a}$ and $\mathbf{T}_{S_b}$ be connected transition systems such that there is a homomorphism g of $\mathbf{T}_{S_a}$ onto $\mathbf{T}_{S_b}$. Then if $\mathscr{V}$ is definable by $\mathbf{T}_{S_b}$, it is also definable by $\mathbf{T}_{S_a}$.

Proof. If $\mathscr{V}$ is definable by $\mathbf{T}_{S_b}$, then by Definition 7.1.11 there is a set Q_b' such that $\mathscr{V} = x(\mathbf{G}_b)$ and $\mathbf{G}_b = \langle S, Q_b, q_{b_0}, M_b, Q_b' \rangle$. Hence by 7.1.14, $\mathscr{V} = h_b^{-1}(Q_b')$. Now $h_b = gh_a$ (cf. 5.5.18) wherefore

$$h_b^{-1}(Q_b') = (gh_a)^{-1}(Q_b') = \mathscr{V}$$

But $(gh_a)^{-1} = h_a^{-1}g^{-1}$. Hence $\mathscr{V}$ is definable by $\mathbf{T}_{S_a}$; specifically;

$$\mathscr{V} = x(\mathbf{G}_a) \quad \text{and} \quad \mathbf{G}_a = \langle S, Q_a, q_{a_0}, M_a, g^{-1}(Q_b') \rangle$$

Q.E.D.

From this theorem it also follows that the free transition system $\mathbf{T}_{S_{\mathscr{S}}}$ can define any set and hence is in a natural sense a *universal* system. In Section 7.4 we take up a less trivial sense in which (finite) transition systems are universal.

Theorem 7.1.16. Let $\mathbf{G}_a$ and $\mathbf{G}_b$ be two connected acceptors. If there is a homomorphism g of $\mathbf{G}_a$ onto $\mathbf{G}_b$, then $x(\mathbf{G}_a) \subseteq x(\mathbf{G}_b)$. If g is a strong homomorphism then $x(\mathbf{G}_a) = x(\mathbf{G}_b)$.

Proof. Since $q_a \in Q_a'$ implies $g(q_a) \in Q_b'$, $Q_a' \subseteq g^{-1}(Q_b')$. Hence

$$x(\mathbf{G}_a) = h_a^{-1}(Q_a') \subseteq h_a^{-1}g^{-1}(Q_b') = h_b^{-1}(Q_b') = x(\mathbf{G}_b)$$

If $q_a \in Q_a'$ iff $g(q_a) \in Q_b'$, then $x(\mathbf{G}_a) = x(\mathbf{G}_b)$.

Alternatively, and less abstractly:

$$\begin{aligned} x \in x(\mathbf{G}_a) &\Leftrightarrow M_a(q_{a_0}, x) \in Q_a' \\ &\Rightarrow g(M_a(q_{a_0}, x)) \in Q_b' \\ &\Leftrightarrow M_b(g(q_{a_0}), x) \in Q_b' \\ &\Leftrightarrow M_b(q_{b_0}, x) \in Q_b' \\ &\Leftrightarrow x \in x(\mathbf{G}_b) \end{aligned}$$

Q.E.D.

In Exercise 4 the student is asked to prove that equality of the sets accepted by $\mathbf{G}_a$ and $\mathbf{G}_b$ implies that a homomorphism of $\mathbf{G}_a$ onto $\mathbf{G}_b$ (if there is one) is strong. Although Theorem 7.1.16 reinforced in this way yields a criterion of equivalence of connected acceptors, it is not of much use, since it is quite possible that $x(\mathbf{G}_a) = x(\mathbf{G}_b)$ whereas there is *no* homomorphic relation between the two whatsoever. Following the remark after 7.1.12, and using the familiar results about transducers, minimal equivalent f.s.a.'s will indeed be found to be strongly homomorphic (in fact isomorphic), but the method for determining equivalence is not, of course, based on prior detection of a homomorphism relation.

Definition 7.1.17. If R and R' are two equivalence relations such that $R \leq R'$, we say that R *refines* R'.

Note that any subset B of a set A trivially induces an equivalence relation, called a *dichotomy*, such that x is equivalent to y iff $x \in B \Leftrightarrow y \in B$. Thus it is meaningful in the following argument to speak of invariance relations R over S^* refining certain subsets of S^*.

For the next theorem and definition recall that R_h is the right-invariant relation given by $x\ R_h\ y$ iff $M(q_0, x) = M(q_0, y)$—cf. Theorem 5.5.15 and Remark 5.5.16.

Definition 7.1.18. An equivalence relation R over S^* is of *finite index* iff the number of equivalence classes $[x]_R$ is finite.

Note that R_h is of finite index if Q is finite, and is, in fact, no greater than the number of states Q of an automaton.

Theorem 7.1.19. If $\mathscr{U} \subseteq S^*$ is a definable set then there is a right-invariant relation R of finite index such that R refines $\mathscr{U}$.

Proof. From the hypotheses and Definition 7.1.9 there must exist an f.s.a. **A** such that $\mathscr{U} = x(\mathbf{A})$ with Q' the final states of **A**. Consider now the specific relation R_h; $x\ R_h\ y$ implies that $M(q_0, x) = M(q_0, y)$. Hence $M(q_0, x) \in Q' \Leftrightarrow M(q_0, y) \in Q'$; therefore $x \in \mathscr{U} \Leftrightarrow y \in \mathscr{U}$. Q.E.D.

It follows that $\mathscr{U}$ is the *union* of some of the equivalence classes under R_h.

We now prove the converse.

Definition 7.1.20. Let $\mathbf{G} = \langle S, Q, q_0, M, Q' \rangle$ and let R be a congruence relation over $Q \times Q$. Then $\mathbf{G}/R$ is the *quotient acceptor*

$$\langle S, Q/R, [q_0]_R, M/R, Q'/R \rangle$$

where

$$\begin{aligned} Q/R &= \{[q]_R \mid q \in Q\} \\ M/R([q]_R, s) &= [M(q, s)]_R \\ Q'/R &\subseteq Q/R \end{aligned}$$

This definition is already justified by Theorem 5.5.10, in which it is shown that M/R is well-defined.

Theorem 7.1.21. If R is a right-invariant relation of finite index over S^* which refines $\mathscr{U}$, then $\mathscr{U}$ is definable.

Proof. Consider the free transition system $\mathbf{T}_{\mathrm{S}\mathscr{S}} = \langle S, S^*, \Lambda, M_{\mathscr{S}} \rangle$. Since R is a right-invariant relation, it is a congruence on $\mathbf{T}_{\mathrm{S}\mathscr{S}}$ (by Theorem 5.5.15) and determines the homomorphic (onto) quotient system $\mathbf{T}_{\mathrm{S}\mathscr{S}}/R$ (Theorem 5.5.10, and Lemma 5.5.22) which is a *finite* transition system owing to the finiteness of R. As seen in the earlier informal argument, $\mathscr{U}$ is definable by $\mathbf{T}_{\mathrm{S}\mathscr{S}}$ with $\mathbf{G}_{\mathscr{S}}$ being the quintuple $\langle S, S^*, \Lambda, M_{\mathscr{S}}, \mathscr{U} \rangle$.

We next construct the quotient acceptor

$$\mathbf{G}_{\mathscr{S}}/R = \langle S, S^*/R, [\Lambda]_R, M_{\mathscr{S}}/R, \mathscr{U}/R\rangle$$

where $\mathscr{U}/R = \{[x]_R \mid x \in \mathscr{U}\}$. From Definition 7.1.18 we know that this is an acceptor provided that $\mathscr{U}/R$ is a well-defined subset of S^*/R. But this latter requirement follows from the theorem hypothesis: $x\,R\,y$ implies $x \in \mathscr{U} \Leftrightarrow y \in \mathscr{U}$; so $[x]_R \in \mathscr{U}/R \Leftrightarrow [y]_R \in \mathscr{U}/R$.

Let h be the homomorphism from $\mathbf{T}_{S_{\mathscr{S}}}$ onto $\mathbf{T}_{S_{\mathscr{S}}}/R$; h is a strong acceptor homomorphism from $\mathbf{G}_{\mathscr{S}}$ onto $\mathbf{G}_{\mathscr{S}}/R$ since $x \in \mathscr{U}$ iff $[x]_R \in \mathscr{U}/R$. By Theorem 7.1.16, the fact that $\mathbf{T}_{S_{\mathscr{S}}}$ is connected, and that $\mathbf{T}_{S_{\mathscr{S}}}/R$ is connected as well, (why?) it follows, finally, that $\mathscr{U} = x(\mathbf{G}_{\mathscr{S}}/R)$. $\mathscr{U}$ is definable.

Q.E.D.

Corollary 7.1.22. $\mathscr{U}$ is definable iff there is a right-invariant relation R of finite index such that R refines $\mathscr{U}$.

Theorem 7.1.23. Any right-invariant relation R of finite index over S^* has a refinement E of finite index such that E is a congruence relation.

Proof. Let $x\,E\,y$ iff $wx\,R\,wy$, for all $w \in S^*$. It is obvious from the definition that E refines R and is a congruence relation. If R is of index n, then E is of index at most n^n; that is, there are at most n classes $[xz]_R$ for each $[x]_R$.

Q.E.D.

REMARK. If R is R_h, E is precisely the relation of Definition 5.4.4.

Theorem 7.1.24. $\mathscr{U}$ is definable iff there is a congruence relation E of finite index such that E refines $\mathscr{U}$.

Proof. Immediate from Corollary 7.1.22 and Theorem 7.1.23.

EXAMPLE 4. Let $\mathscr{U}$ be the subset of S^* containing just those words on $\{0, 1\}$ containing exactly *one* occurrence of either a 0 or a 1. Hence

$$\mathscr{U} = \{0, 1, 01, 10, 001, 010, 100, 110, 101, 011, \text{etc.}\}$$

Now let R be the equivalence relation determining the set of classes in Table 7.1.2.

TABLE 7.1.2

q_0	$[\Lambda]$
q_1	[0]
q_2	[1]
q_3	[01, 010, 0100, etc., 001, 0010, 00100, etc., 0001, 00010, 000100, etc.]
q_4	[00, 000, 0000, etc.]
q_5	[10, 101, 1011, etc., 110, 1101, 11011, etc., 1110, 11101, 111011, etc.]
q_6	[11, 111, 1111, etc.]
q_7	[all words with two or more 0's and two or more 1's]

Presumably (we will accept the fact), this collection is a partition and can be determined as such by inspection. It happens that R is right-invariant as well, although at the moment this is not easy to check. Moreover, R refines $\mathscr{U}$, as the student may confirm for himself in arbitrarily selected cases. Using the method of Theorem 7.1.21, let **A** be the acceptor $\langle S, S^*/R, [\Lambda], M_{\mathscr{S}}/R, \mathscr{U}/R\rangle$ where S^*/R is the partition of Table 7.1.2, $[\Lambda]$ is the initial state as usual, $M_{\mathscr{S}}/R([x]_R, s) = [M_{\mathscr{S}}(x, s)]_R = [xs]_R$, ($M_{\mathscr{S}}$ being the transition function of the free system $\mathbf{T}_{S_{\mathscr{S}}}$), and where $\mathscr{U}/R = \{[0], [1], [01, 010, \text{etc.}, 001, 0010, 00010, \text{etc.}], [10, 101, \text{etc.}, 110, 1101, 11101, \text{etc.}]\}$. This machine is, of course, invariant under relabeling, and therefore we use the q-symbols as listed to the left in Table 7.1.2. One illustration will serve to show how the $M_{\mathscr{S}}/R = M$ function is computed. Assuming that R is well-defined, pick 00 as the representative of the class of which it is an element. Corresponding to 00 is q_4. We have

$$\begin{aligned} M(q_4, 0) &= M_{\mathscr{S}}/R([00], 0) = [M_{\mathscr{S}}(00), 0]_R \\ &= [000]_R = q_4 \end{aligned}$$

Continuing in this way, one finally obtains the f.s.a. depicted in Fig. 7.1.3; this f.s.a. accepts $\mathscr{U}$.

Although this example is illustrative, it hardly exemplifies a useful procedure for either constructing an acceptor given a definable set, or testing for definability. The following idea is more useful.

Definition 7.1.25. The *induced right-invariant* relation $R_{\mathscr{U}}$ over S^* is given by

$$xR_{\mathscr{U}}y \Leftrightarrow (\forall z)(xz \in \mathscr{U} \Leftrightarrow yz \in \mathscr{U})$$

Corollary 7.1.26. (*a*) $R_{\mathscr{U}}$ is right-invariant; (*b*) $R_{\mathscr{U}}$ refines $\mathscr{U}$; (*c*) $R_{\mathscr{U}}$ is the largest relation on S^* which refines $\mathscr{U}$.

Proof. (*a*) and (*b*) are to be proved by the student. For (*c*) assume that R is a right-invariant relation which refines $\mathscr{U}$. We have to show that $x\,R\,y$ implies $x\,R_{\mathscr{U}}\,y$. But, since right-invariant, $xz\,R\,yz$ holds and since R refines $\mathscr{U}$, $xz \in \mathscr{U} \Leftrightarrow yz \in \mathscr{U}$. Hence $x\,R_{\mathscr{U}}\,y$. Q.E.D.

Theorem 7.1.27. $\mathscr{U}$ is definable provided that $R_{\mathscr{U}}$ is of finite index, and conversely.

Proof. Immediate from Corollary 7.1.22. Note that $\mathscr{U}$ is definable by $\mathbf{G}_{\mathscr{S}}/R_{\mathscr{U}}$ with $\mathscr{U}/R_{\mathscr{U}}$ the set of final states.

Theorem 7.1.28. If $\mathscr{U}$ is definable, then $R_{\mathscr{U}}$ determines the minimal f.s.a. which accepts $\mathscr{U}$.

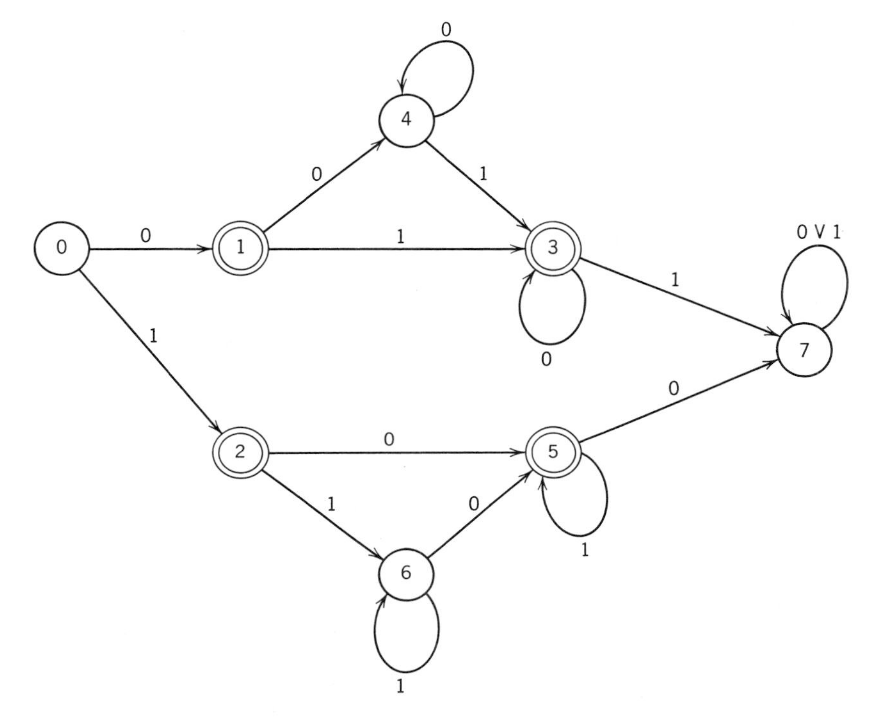

Fig. 7.1.3

Proof. If there were one with fewer states, then the number of distinct equivalence classes under R_h would be fewer than those under $R_{\mathscr{U}}$. This is contrary to Corollary 7.1.26*c*.

EXAMPLE 5. To illustrate these theorems let us take the example $S = \{0, 1\}$ and $\mathscr{U} = \{\Lambda, 1, 10, 101, 1010, 10101, \text{etc.}\}$, which is the set of all words in S^* which are equal to Λ or begin with 1 and alternate on 0 and 1. Now consider any $x, y, z \in S^*$. Then $xz \in \mathscr{U}$ if and only if $yz \in \mathscr{U}$ will hold true, for suitable z, only when the last symbol (to the right) in x is the same as it is in y. Assume the contrary and let $z = 1$, and $x = \cdots 1$ and $y = \cdots 0$, then $x\,1 = \cdots 1\,1 \notin \mathscr{U}$ whereas $y\,1 = \cdots 0\,1 \in \mathscr{U}$, provided $x, y \in \mathscr{U}$. Hence there are three classes on S^*: $\overline{\mathscr{U}}$, $\{1, 101, 10101, \text{etc.}\}$, and $\{\Lambda, 10, 1010, 101010, \text{etc.}\}$, and $\mathscr{U}$ is the union of some of them. Hence $\mathscr{U}$ is definable.

EXAMPLE 6. As an example of a set that is not definable, consider the set $\mathscr{T}$ of words on $\{0, 1\}$ such that the 1's from left to right are separated by successive multiples of 2 of 0's; that is, $\mathscr{T}$ is the collection of all x of the form $1100100001 \cdots 1000 \cdots (2k \text{ times})1$. Define $R_{\mathscr{T}}$ as in Definition

7.1.25. Now if $R_{\mathscr{T}}$ is to be of finite index, there must exist an n such that $n \neq m$ and both

$$\overbrace{1100100001\cdots1000\cdots(2m \text{ times})1}^{x}$$

and

$$\overbrace{1100100001\cdots1000\cdots(2n \text{ times})1}^{y}$$

are in the same equivalence class. Now let $z = 000\cdots(2m + 2 \text{ times})$. By the definition of $\mathscr{T}$,

$$\overbrace{1100100001\cdots1000\cdots(2m \text{ times})1}^{x}\ \overbrace{000\cdots(2m + 2 \text{ times})1}^{z}$$

is an element of $\mathscr{T}$. Since $x\ R_{\mathscr{T}}\ y$ (they are in the same equivalence class), it follows that

$$\overbrace{1100100001\cdots1000\cdots(2n \text{ times})1}^{y}\ \overbrace{000\cdots(2m + 2)1}^{z} \in \mathscr{T}$$

On the other hand, $yz \notin \mathscr{T}$, owing to its malconstruction. We have derived a contradiction, and therefore R is not of finite index. Thus $\mathscr{T}$ is not definable.

Having established the basic properties of definability, we will now explore some special cases and also prove that the family of definable sets is a boolean algebra. In the ensuing discussion, since there will be no need to use the concept of generalized acceptor, we will drop it.

We let J denote the family of definable sets: $J = \{\mathscr{U} \mid (\exists \mathbf{A})(x \in \mathscr{U} \Leftrightarrow x \in x(\mathbf{A})\}$.

Theorem 7.1.29. If $x \in S^*$, then $\{x\} \in J$.

Proof. By Theorem 7.1.25, we need show only that the appropriate right invariant relation is of finite index. The relation is given by

$$y\ R\{x\}\ z \Leftrightarrow (yw \in \{x\} \Leftrightarrow zw \in \{x\})$$

Hence y and z are in the same equivalence class in just those cases such that if y and z are initial subwords of x, then $y = z$. Thus there is an equivalence class for each initial subword of x, one class for all other words, and since x is finite in length, $R\{x\}$ is of finite index. Q.E.D.

Definition 7.1.30. The *reflection* of x, written x^{-1}, is x written backwards: if $x = s_{i_1}s_{i_2}\cdots s_{i_n}$, then $x^{-1} = s_{i_n}, s_{i_{n-1}} \ldots s_{i_1}$. $\Lambda^{-1} = \Lambda$.

Corollary 7.1.31. For every s, $s^{-1} = s$; for every x, $(x^{-1})^{-1} = x$; for every x, y, $(xy)^{-1} = y^{-1}x^{-1}$.

Theorem 7.1.32. Let $\mathscr{U}^{-1}$ be the set of reflections of the words x of $\mathscr{U}$. If $\mathscr{U} \in J$, then $\mathscr{U}^{-1} \in J$.

Proof. Assume $\mathscr{U} \in J$. Let $E_{\mathscr{U}}$ be a congruence relation (Corollary 5.4.5) as follows: $x\, E_{\mathscr{U}}\, y \Leftrightarrow (\forall z)(\forall w)(zxw \in \mathscr{U} \Leftrightarrow zyw \in \mathscr{U})$ this relation is trivially right-invariant, refines $\mathscr{U}$, and is of finite index. Now also let $E_{\mathscr{U}}{}^{-1}$ be the analogous relation w.r.t. $\mathscr{U}^{-1}$, and assume that $x\, E_{\mathscr{U}}{}^{-1}\, y$ holds. We have

$$\begin{aligned} zx^{-1}w \in \mathscr{U} &\Leftrightarrow (zx^{-1}w)^{-1} \in \mathscr{U}^{-1} \\ &\Leftrightarrow w^{-1}xz^{-1} \in \mathscr{U}^{-1} && \text{by Corollary 7.1.31} \\ &\Leftrightarrow w^{-1}yz^{-1} \in \mathscr{U}^{-1} && \text{by assumption that } x\, E^{-1}\, y, \\ &\Leftrightarrow zy^{-1}w \in \mathscr{U} \end{aligned}$$

Hence if $x\, E_{\mathscr{U}}^{-1}\, y$, then $x^{-1}\, E_{\mathscr{U}}\, y^{-1}$. Conversely, assume $x^{-1}\, E_{\mathscr{U}}\, y^{-1}$ holds.

Then

$$\begin{aligned} zxw \in \mathscr{U}^{-1} &\Leftrightarrow w^{-1}x^{-1}z^{-1} \in \mathscr{U} \\ &\Leftrightarrow w^{-1}y^{-1}z^{-1} \in \mathscr{U} \\ &\Leftrightarrow zyw \in \mathscr{U}^{-1} \end{aligned}$$

Thus we have shown $x\, E_{\mathscr{U}}{}^{-1}\, y$ iff $x^{-1}\, E_{\mathscr{U}}\, y^{-1}$. Hence since $E_{\mathscr{U}}$ is of finite index so is $E_{\mathscr{U}}{}^{-1}$. Hence $\mathscr{U}^{-1}$ is definable, that is, $\mathscr{U}^{-1} \in J$. Q.E.D.

Theorem 7.1.33. *J* is closed under complementation. If $\mathscr{U} \in J$, then $\overline{\mathscr{U}} \in J$.

Proof. If $\mathscr{U}$ is accepted by $\langle S, Q, q_0, M, Q'\rangle$, then $\overline{\mathscr{U}}$ is accepted by $\langle S, Q, q_0, M, \overline{Q}'\rangle$. Q.E.D.

Corollary 7.1.34. Every $\mathscr{U} \in J$ is recursive.

Proof. Both $\mathscr{U}$ and $\overline{\mathscr{U}}$ are recursively enumerable by Theorem 4.3.17, since f.s.a.'s are special cases of Turing acceptors. (Recall that we are saying $\mathscr{U}$ is recursive informally speaking as at the end of Chapter 2. The theorem is technically correct if $\mathscr{U}$ is the domain of an effective one–one function into integers and the range is recursive.)

Corollary 7.1.35. Every f.s.a. is a detector in the sense of Definition 3.3.14.

Proof. The partitions are $\{Q', \overline{Q}'\}$ and $\mathscr{U}, \overline{\mathscr{U}}$.

We next utilize the direct product concept (cf. Definition 5.5.27) in order to show that *J* is closed under set intersection.

Definition 7.1.36. Suppose

$$\mathbf{A}_a = \langle S, Q_a, q_{a_0}, M_a, Q_a{}'\rangle \quad \text{and} \quad \mathbf{A}_b = \langle S, Q_b, q_{b_0}, M_b, Q_b{}'\rangle$$

The *direct product* acceptor is the system

$$\mathbf{A}_a \times \mathbf{A}_b = \langle S, Q_a \times Q_b, (q_{a_0}, q_{b_0}), M_a \times M_b, Q_a' \times Q_b' \rangle$$

where $M_a \times M_b \colon S \times (Q_a \times Q_b) \to Q_a \times Q_b$ is given by

$$M_a \times M_b((q_a, q_b), s) = (M_a(q_a, s), M_b(q_b, s))$$

Clearly this *is* an acceptor by the definition, which is almost identical to Definition 5.5.27.

Theorem 7.1.37. If $\mathbf{A}_a$ and $\mathbf{A}_b$ are two f.s.a.'s then

$$x(\mathbf{A}_a \times \mathbf{A}_b) = x(\mathbf{A}_a) \bigcap x(\mathbf{A}_b)$$

Proof. It is obvious that $M_a \times M_b$ can be extended to sequences, and that since $\mathbf{A}_a \times \mathbf{A}_b$ is an f.s.a. x is accepted iff $M_a \times M_b((q_{a_0}, q_{b_0}, x) \in Q_a' \times Q_b'$, by Corollary 7.1.6. Hence x is accepted iff

$$(M_a(q_{a_0}, x), M(q_{b_0}, x)) \in Q_a' \times Q_b'$$

which by the definition of cartesian product holds iff

$$M_a(q_{a_0}, x) \in Q_a' \quad \text{and} \quad M_b(q_{b_0}, x) \in Q_b'$$

Therefore $x \in x(\mathbf{A}_a \times \mathbf{A}_b)$ iff

$$x \in x(\mathbf{A}_a) \wedge x \in x(\mathbf{A}_b); x(\mathbf{A}_a \times \mathbf{A}_b) = x(\mathbf{A}_a) \bigcap x(\mathbf{A}_b) \qquad \text{Q.E.D.}$$

Corollary 7.1.38. J is closed under intersection.

Corollary 7.1.39. J is a boolean algebra of sets of words.

Corollary 7.1.40. Any finite set of words is an accepted set.

Proof. Every finite set is a union of unit sets. So Corollary 7.1.40 follows from Corollary 7.1.39 and Theorem 7.1.29. Q.E.D.

EXERCISES 7.1

1. Two f.s.a.'s A_a and A_b are *equivalent* iff $x(A_a) = x(A_b)$. Following the Remark just after Definition 7.1.12, transform A_a and A_b into complete Moore machines $\mathbf{T}_{\mathbf{M}_a}$ and $\mathbf{T}_{\mathbf{M}_b}$. Is it true that A_a and A_b are equivalent as stated if and only if $\mathbf{T}_{\mathbf{M}_a}$ and $\mathbf{T}_{\mathbf{M}_b}$ are equivalent in the sense of Definition 5.3.25?

2. Prove Corollaries 7.1.6 and 7.1.7.

3. Construct two nonhomomorphic yet equivalent acceptors.

4. Prove that if G_a and G_b are connected and there is a homomorphism g of G_a onto G_b, then $x(G_a) = x(G_b)$ implies g is strong.

5. Prove parts a and b of Corollary 7.1.26.

6. Discuss the definability of the following sets of words (a) to (g). If a set is definable, produce a transition diagram of an acceptor (all acceptors by definition must be complete) which defines it; $S = \{0, 1\}$.

(a) The set of words containing exactly three occurrences of 1's.
(b) The set of words containing exactly three consecutive occurrences of 1's.
(c) The set of words beginning with 0 and alternating 0's and 1's.
(d) The set of words 0^m10^n (where, for example, 0^m means $000\cdots m$ times).
(e) The set of words 0^n1^n.
(f) The set of words 0^n10^n.
(g) The set of words which are powers of 2 in binary notation.
In each case verify your answer, using Theorem 7.1.27.

7. Explain how f.s.a.'s could be used as pattern recognizers of n sets of words. Assume the sets are disjoint. What if they are not disjoint? Could one use detectors as well? Explain.

8. In analogy with Definition 5.4.21 construct a tree algorithm for determining the right-invariant relation R_h of an acceptor.

7.2 REGULAR EXPRESSION ALGORITHMS

Our next question is whether there is a way of deciding if a certain automaton accepts any words at all, that is, is $x(\mathbf{A})$ empty, given $\mathbf{A}$? To understand this problem it is convenient to think of the tester as having been informed only of the number of internal states of $\mathbf{A}$, but nothing else. Theorem 7.2.1 demonstrates that he need only test a finite number of words—those whose length is less than n.

Theorem 7.2.1. Let $\mathbf{A}$ be an f.s.a with n states. $x(\mathbf{A})$ is nonempty iff $\mathbf{A}$ accepts some word x such that $l(x) < n$.

Proof. The proof from right to left is obvious. Conversely, assume that x is accepted by $\mathbf{A}$, that $l(x) \geq n$, and that $l(x) \leq l(y)$ for all $y \in x(\mathbf{A})$. We will derive a contradiction thereby, showing $l(x) < n$.

Since $l(x) \geq n$, there are non-null words y and z and a possibly null word w such that $x = yzw$ [assuming, without loss of generality, that $\mathbf{A}$ has at least two states—cf. Exercise 6.1(2)], and such that $M(q_0, y) = M(q_0, yz)$. The latter fact holds since $\mathbf{A}$ must go into some state twice when x is injected. Now, let $x' = yw$. Obviously $l(x') < l(x)$, and $M(q_0, x) = M(q_0, x')$. Thus $x' \in x(\mathbf{A})$, contradicting the statement the x is the shortest word in $x(\mathbf{A})$. Q.E.D.

Corollary 7.2.2. The emptiness problem for f.s.a. is solvable.

The next problem is whether there is an algorithm for determining if $x(\mathbf{A})$ is finite.

Theorem 7.2.3. Let $\mathbf{A}$ be an f.s.a. with n states and let $x \in x(\mathbf{A})$, $l(x) > n$. Then there exist words y, z, and w such that $x = yzw$, $z \neq \Lambda$, and for any nonnegative integer m, $yz^mw \in x(\mathbf{A})$.

Proof. As in Theorem 7.2.1, $M(q_0, y) = M(q_0, yz)$, for some y and z,

z non-null, and with $x = yzw$. Assume $M(q_0, y) = M(q_0, yz^m)$. To complete the induction,

$$\begin{aligned} M(q_0, y) &= M(q_0, yz) \\ &= M(M(q_0, y), z) \\ &= M(M(q_0, yz^m), z) \\ &= M(q_0, yz^{m+1}) \end{aligned}$$

Using this result,

$$\begin{aligned} M(q_0, x) &= M(q_0, yzw) \\ &= M(M(q_0, yz), w) \\ &= M(M(q_0, yz^m), w) \\ &= M(q_0, yz^m w) \end{aligned}$$

Q.E.D.

It follows at once that if $l(x) \geq n$, for some $x \in x(\mathbf{A})$, then $x(\mathbf{A})$ is denumerably infinite. It is also possible to show a kind of converse, namely that if $x(\mathbf{A})$ is infinite, then there is an $x \in x(\mathbf{A})$ such that $n \leq l(n) < 2n$. We omit the proof (see Rabin and Scott [1959]). The two statements provide a decision procedure which is stated in the following theorem.

***Theorem** 7.2.4.* Let $\mathbf{A}$ be an f.s.a. with n states. $x(\mathbf{A})$ is infinite iff there is an $x \in x(\mathbf{A})$ such that $n \leq l(x) < 2n$.

Our next aim is to discuss algorithms for actually constructing a finite acceptor (synthesis), given a set $\mathscr{U} \in J$, and conversely to construct a representation of the set $\mathscr{U}$ (analysis), given an automaton which accepts it. In order to achieve this end we will introduce a notation called the "regular expression language" which is very convenient for discussion of definable sets.

***Definition** 7.2.5.* Given two subsets $\mathscr{U}$ and $\mathscr{V}$ of S^*, the *complex product* $\mathscr{U} \cdot \mathscr{V}$ is

$$\mathscr{U} \cdot \mathscr{V} = \{xy \mid x \in \mathscr{U} \wedge y \in \mathscr{V}\}$$

We also write $\mathscr{U}^0$ for $\{\Lambda\}$, $\mathscr{U}^1$ for $\mathscr{U}$, $\mathscr{U}^2$ for $\mathscr{U} \cdot \mathscr{U}$, $\mathscr{U}^3$ for $\mathscr{U} \cdot \mathscr{U} \cdot \mathscr{U}$, etc.

***Definition** 7.2.6.* Given $\mathscr{U} \subseteq S^*$, the *star* of $\mathscr{U}$, written $\mathscr{U}^*$, is the infinite union of all finite powers of $\mathscr{U}$:

$$\mathscr{U}^* = \bigcup_{i=0}^{\infty} \mathscr{U}^i = \mathscr{U}^0 \cup \mathscr{U}^1 \cup \mathscr{U}^2 \cup \cdots$$

EXAMPLE 1. Suppose $\mathscr{U} = \{a, bc, ca\}$ and $\mathscr{V} = \{ba, c, cc\}$. Then,

$$\mathscr{U} \cdot \mathscr{V} = \{aba, ac, acc, bcba, bcc, bccc, caba, cac, cacc\}$$

and

$$\begin{aligned} \mathscr{U}^* &= \{\Lambda\} \cup \{a, bc, ca\} \cup \{a, bc, ca\}^2 \cup \cdots \\ &= \{\Lambda, a, bc, ca, aa, abc, aca, bca, bcbc, bcca, caa, cabc, caca, \ldots\} \end{aligned}$$

Definition 7.2.7. The *family of regular sets R* is the least set of subsets of S^* which includes the finite sets and which is closed under set union, complex product, and star. A set which is a member of this family is a *regular set.*

In order to use the next definition one must be aware of the distinction between objects, for example, sets, words, numbers, etc., and expressions denoting such objects. We are going to make a distinction between *regular sets* and the *regular expressions* which comprise a language for expressing the sets. Moreover, as stated in Section 7.0, we will produce an algorithm for constructing an f.s.a. given a set $\mathscr{U} \in J$, and the algorithm will operate on a regular expression for $\mathscr{U}$.

Definition 7.2.8. Given the alphabet S and in addition the symbols $\bigcup$, $\cdot$, $*$, $)$, $($, Λ, and $\varnothing$.

(*a*) A word consisting of any single symbol s_i, or of $\varnothing$, or of Λ standing alone is a *regular expression.*

(*b*) If α is a regular expression, then $(\alpha)^*$ is a *regular expression.*

(*c*) If α and β are regular expressions, then $(\alpha \bigcup \beta)$ and $(\alpha \cdot \beta)$ are *regular expressions.*

(*d*) An expression is regular only if its being so follows from *a*, *b*, or *c*.

Comments. Here and hereafter we use α, β, etc., as syntactical variables ranging over words of the alphabet indicated. The parentheses will be omitted wherever there is little danger of ambiguity. We will frequently write "$\alpha\beta$" instead of "$\alpha \cdot \beta$." Since this definition is inductive, it is always possible to test whether an expression is regular.

Definition 7.2.9. *Rules of Denotation.*

(a') A symbol s_i *denotes* the set $\{s_i\}$, $\varnothing$ *denotes* the empty set, Λ *denotes* $\{\Lambda\}$.

(b') If α denotes $\mathscr{U}$, then $(\alpha)^*$ denotes $\{\Lambda\} \bigcup \mathscr{U} \bigcup \mathscr{U}^2 \bigcup \cdots$.

(c') If α denotes $\mathscr{U}$ and β denotes $\mathscr{V}$, then $(\alpha \bigcup \beta)$ *denotes* $\mathscr{U} \bigcup \mathscr{V}$, and $(\alpha \cdot \beta)$ *denotes* $\mathscr{U} \cdot \mathscr{V}$.

(d') α denotes $\mathscr{U}$ only if it does so by a', b', or c'.

Comments. As is customary in the discussion of regular sets, we are using the *same* alphabet S both as our automaton alphabet and as our alphabet of language of regular expressions. A regular expression denotes both a set of words and the words of that set. This will never lead to ambiguity since each expression denotes but one set and denotes a word if and only if it is in the set. Thus "s_i" denotes $\{s_i\}$ and also s_i itself.

EXAMPLE 2. Suppose that $S = \{0, 1\}$, and consider the regular expression $((0 \cdot 1) \bigcup (1 \cdot 0)^*)^*$. That this is regular is established inductively by using Definition 7.2.8; 0 and 1 are regular by *a*; $(0 \cdot 1)$ and $(1 \cdot 0)$ are by *c*; by *b*

$(1\cdot 0)^*$ is regular, etc. Using Definition 7.2.9, a' and c', $(0\cdot 1)$ denotes $\{0\}\cdot\{1\} = \{01\}$; and similarly $(1\cdot 0)$ denotes $\{10\}$. By b', $(1\cdot 0)^*$ denotes

$$\{\Lambda\} \cup \{10\} \cup \{10\}^2 \cup \{10\}^3 \cup \cdots$$

since we already have established that $(1\cdot 0)$ denotes $\{10\}$. By c', $(0\cdot 1) \cup (1\cdot 0)^*$ denotes

$$\begin{aligned}\{01\} \cup \{\Lambda\} \cup \{10\} \cup \{10\}^2 \cup \{10\}^3 \cup \cdots \\ = \{01\} \cup \{\Lambda\} \cup \{10\} \cup \{1010\} \cup \{101010\} \cup \cdots \\ = \{\Lambda, 01, 10, 1010, 101010, \ldots\}\end{aligned}$$

Finally, $((0\cdot 1) \cup (1\cdot 0)^*)^*$ denotes, using b',

$$\begin{aligned}\{\Lambda\} \cup \{\Lambda, 01, 10, 1010, 101010, \ldots\} \\ \cup \{\Lambda, 01, 10, 1010, 101010, \ldots\}^2 \\ \cup \{\Lambda, 01, 10, 1010, 101010, \ldots\}^3 \\ = \{\Lambda, 01, 10, 1010, 101010, \ldots, 0110, 011010, \\ 01101010, 10101010, 1010101010, \ldots, \\ 010110, 01011010, \ldots, 101010101010, \ldots\}\end{aligned}$$

Corollary 7.2.10. Regular expressions denote precisely the regular sets.

Proof. For the student.

Many regular expressions are equal in that they denote the same regular set. Clearly $\alpha \cup \beta = \beta \cup \alpha$, $\alpha \cup (\beta \cup \gamma) = (\alpha \cup \beta) \cup \gamma$, $\alpha\cdot(\beta\cdot\gamma) = (\alpha\cdot\beta)\cdot\gamma$, while in general $\alpha\cdot\beta \neq \beta\cdot\alpha$.

EXAMPLE 3. A slightly more sophisticated instance is the equality

$$(\beta\cdot\alpha) \cup (\gamma\cdot\alpha) = (\beta \cup \gamma)\cdot\alpha$$

We may show this as follows. Suppose by the corollary that α denotes $\mathscr{U}$, β denotes $\mathscr{V}$, and γ denotes $\mathscr{W}$. Then

$$(\beta\cdot\alpha) \cup (\gamma\cdot\alpha)$$

denotes

$$\begin{aligned}\mathscr{V}\cdot\mathscr{U} \cup \mathscr{W}\cdot\mathscr{U} &= \{xy \mid (x \in \mathscr{V} \wedge y \in \mathscr{U}) \vee (x \in \mathscr{W} \wedge y \in \mathscr{U})\} \\ &= \{xy \mid (x \in \mathscr{V} \vee x \in \mathscr{W}) \wedge y \in \mathscr{U}\} \\ &= \{xy \mid x \in \mathscr{U} \cup \mathscr{W} \wedge y \in \mathscr{U}\} \\ &= (\mathscr{V} \cup \mathscr{W})\cdot\mathscr{U}\end{aligned}$$

which is denoted by $(\beta \cup \gamma)\cdot\alpha$.

To reinforce his understanding of the difference between a regular expression and a regular set the student should substitute some regular expression over $\{0, 1\}$ for α, β, and γ in this example and then calculate.

For further equalities and inequalities see the exercises at the end of this section.

Our next objective is to show an effective construction of nondeterministic acceptors from regular expressions. First we will need a definition.

Definition 7.2.11. An n.f.s.a. $\mathbf{N} = \langle S, Q, M, \{q_0\}, \{q_F\}\rangle$ is *simple* iff in addition to having but *one* initial state and *one* final state as indicated, it satisfies the following properties.

1. $q_0 \neq q_F$
2. $\neg(\exists x)(\exists q)(\exists Q')(Q' \subseteq Q \wedge M(q, x) = Q' \wedge q_0 \in Q')$
3. $(\forall x)(M(q_F, x) = \varnothing)$

This definition states that a simple n.f.s.a. has distinct and unique initial and final states, that q_0 is never a next state, and that q_F is never a present state—it leads nowhere. The transition diagram of a simple n.f.s.a. is such that all branches attached to q_0 lead from q_0 and all branches attached to q_F lead to q_F. We say these nodes are *extremal.*

Theorem 7.2.12. Suppose $\mathbf{N}_a = \langle S, Q_a, Q_{a_0}, M_a, Q_a'\rangle$ and $\mathbf{N}_a$ accepts $x(\mathbf{N}_a)$. Then there exists a simple n.f.s.a. $\mathbf{N}_b$ such that $x(\mathbf{N}_a) = x(\mathbf{N}_b)$.

Proof. Let $\mathbf{N}_b = \langle S, Q_b, Q_{b_0}, M_b, Q_b'\rangle$ where $Q_b = Q_a \cup \{q_{b_0}, q_F\}$; $q_{b_0}, q_F \notin Q_a$; $q_{b_0} \neq q_F$; $Q_{b_0} = \{q_{b_0}\}$; $Q_b' = \{q_F\}$; and $M_b\colon Q_b \times S \to \pi(Q_b)$ is defined in the following way.

(*a*) If $q_{a_{01}}, q_{a_{02}}, \ldots, q_{a_{0k}}$ are the initial states of $\mathbf{N}_a$, and

(i) if $M_a(q_{a_{0i}}, s) \nsubseteq Q_a'$ for all i, $1 \le i \le k$, then

$M_b(q_{b_0}, s) = M_a(q_{a_{01}}, s) \cup M_a(q_{a_{02}}, s) \cup \cdots \cup M_a(q_{a_{0k}}, s)$;

(ii) if $M_a(q_{a_{0i}}, s) \subseteq Q_a'$ for some i, $1 < i < k$, then

$M_b(q_{b_0}, s) = M_a(q_{a_{01}}, s) \cup M_a(q_{a_{02}}, s) \cup \cdots \cup M_a(q_{a_{0k}}, s) \cup \{q_F\}$;

(iii) if for some i, $q_{a_{0i}} \in Q_a'$, we set $M_b(q_{b_0}, \Lambda) = \{q_F\}$.

(*b*) For any $q \in Q_b$ excepting q_{b_0} and q_F,

(i) $M_b(q, s) = M_a(q, s)$, if $M_a(q, s) \nsubseteq Q_a'$

(ii) $M_b(q, s) = M_a(q, s) \cup \{q_F\}$ if $M_a(q, s) \subseteq Q_a'$

(*c*) $M_b(q_F, s) = \varnothing$.

$\mathbf{N}_b$ has the properties required by Definition 7.2.11: (1) is satisfied directly by the construction; (2) is satisfied since $q_{b_0} \notin Q_a$, and by (*a*) and (*b*), the value of M_b in every case is a subset of Q_a or is the union if a subset of Q_a with $\{q_F\}$; (3) is substantially (*c*). We now show equivalence. If $x \in x(\mathbf{N}_a)$, then by Corollary 7.1.7, for $x = s_{i_1}s_{i_2}\ldots s_{i_n}$ there is a sequence $q_{a_{i_0}}, q_{a_{i_1}}, \ldots, q_{a_{i_n}}$ such that $q_{a_{i_0}} \in Q_{a_0}$, $q_{a_{i_j}} \in M_a(q_{a_{i_{j-1}}}, s_{i_j})$ for all j, $1 \le j \le n$, and $q_{a_{i_n}} \in Q_a'$. To show that $x \in x(\mathbf{N}_b)$, consider the sequence $q_{b_0}, q_{a_{i_1}}, q_{a_{i_2}}, \ldots, q_{a_{i_{n-1}}}, q_F$. Each element is a state of $\mathbf{N}_b$; $q_{b_0} \in Q_{b_0}$; and $q_{a_{i_1}} \in M_b(q_{b_0}, s_{i_1})$ because $q_{a_{i_1}} \in M_a(q_{a_{i_0}}, s_{i_1})$ and $q_{a_{i_0}} =$

$q_{a_{0_i}}$ for some i by hypothesis, and then use (a) above. For other q in the sequence, $q_{a_{i_j}} \in M_b(q_{a_{i_{j-1}}}, s_{i_j})$, $1 \leq j \leq n$, by part (b). Moreover, $q_F \in M_b(q_{a_{i_{n-1}}}, s_{i_n})$ by (ii) of (b). Finally $q_F \in Q_b'$. Hence the sequence satisfies 7.1.7 and therefore $x \in x(N_b)$. By a similar use of the construction, it is easy to verify the converse. Hence $x(N_a) = x(N_b)$. Q.E.D.

EXAMPLE 4. Suppose the acceptor depicted in Fig. 7.2.1 has initial states q_{0_1} and q_{0_2}. We will construct a simple n.f.s.a. N_b in Fig. 7.2.2 with state sets

$$Q_b = Q_a \bigcup \{q_{b_0}, q_F\} \qquad Q_{b_0} = \{q_{b_0}\}, \qquad Q_b' = \{q_F\}$$

The student is invited to construct the M table for Fig. 7.2.2 and to verify that the acceptors of the two figures are equivalent.

The next theorem will provide a way of constructing an n.f.s.a. from a regular expression.

Theorem 7.2.13. If α is a regular expression, there exists an n.f.s.a. **N** such that $x(\mathbf{N})$ is the regular set denoted by α.

Proof. We proceed by showing how to obtain **N** by transition diagrams. If α is either a single symbol, or Λ, or $\varnothing$, the construction of the corresponding diagram for the automaton accepting $\{s_i\}$, $\{\Lambda\}$, or $\varnothing$ is obvious.

Suppose α is β^* and that an automaton $\mathbf{N}'$ accepts the denotation of β. Then $\mathbf{N}''$, which is the simple n.f.s.a. derived from $\mathbf{N}'$, does the same by 7.2.12. Suppose $\mathbf{N}''$ is Fig. 7.2.3, where the rectangle represents the non-

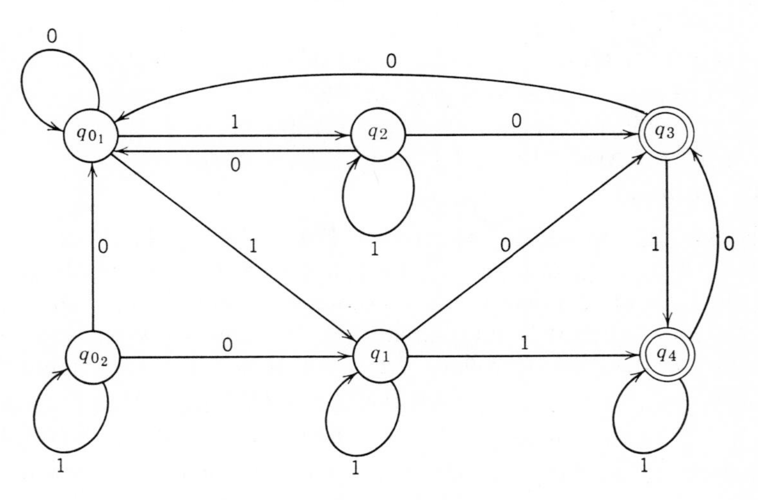

Fig. 7.2.1

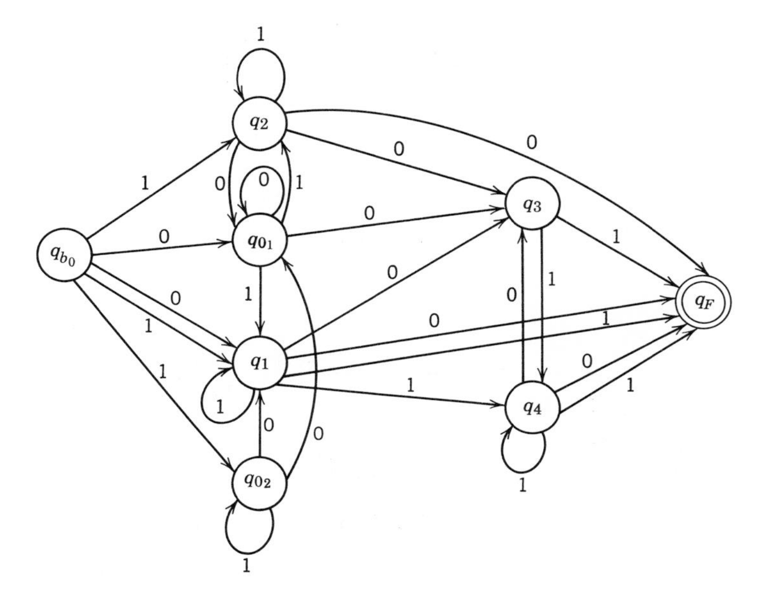

Fig. 7.2.2

extremal nodes and associated branches of the diagram of **N**″. Then **N** is Fig. 7.2.4, where q_0 and q_F have been *identified.* Obviously **N** accepts the set denoted by β^*, since if β denotes $\mathscr{U}$, **N**″ accepts $\mathscr{U}$, and **N** must accept $\{\Lambda\}$, $\mathscr{U}$, $\mathscr{U}\cdot\mathscr{U}$, etc.; **N**, here, is not simple, but this is not required by the theorem.

Continuing with the induction, suppose α is $\beta \bigcup \gamma$, and that **N**′ is simple and accepts the set denoted by β and that **N**″ is simple and accepts the set denoted by γ. Then **N** is the n.f.s.a. shown in Fig. 7.2.5, where the initial nodes of the diagrams for **N**′ and **N**″ have been identified, and similarly for the final nodes. If β denotes $\mathscr{U}$ and γ denotes $\mathscr{V}$, then **N** accepts $\mathscr{U} \bigcup \mathscr{V}$, which is the denotation of α.

Finally, suppose $\alpha = \beta\cdot\gamma$, and that **N**′ and **N**″ are simple n.f.s.a.'s accepting the sets denoted by β and γ, respectively. Then **N** is the n.f.s.a. in Fig. 7.2.6. Here, q_0 is the initial state of **N**′, $q_0{}'$ is the result of identifying

Fig. 7.2.3

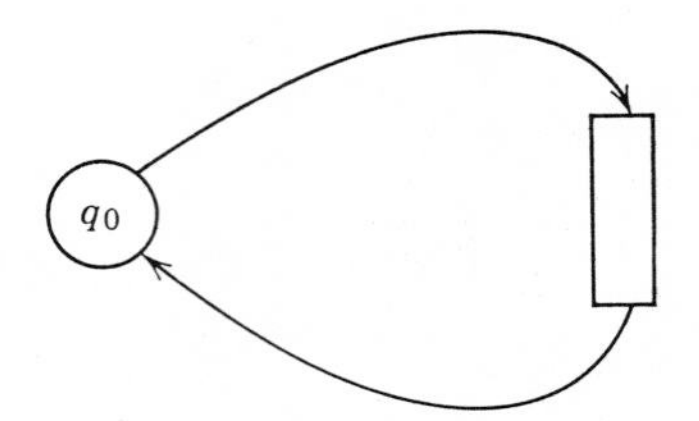

Fig. 7.2.4

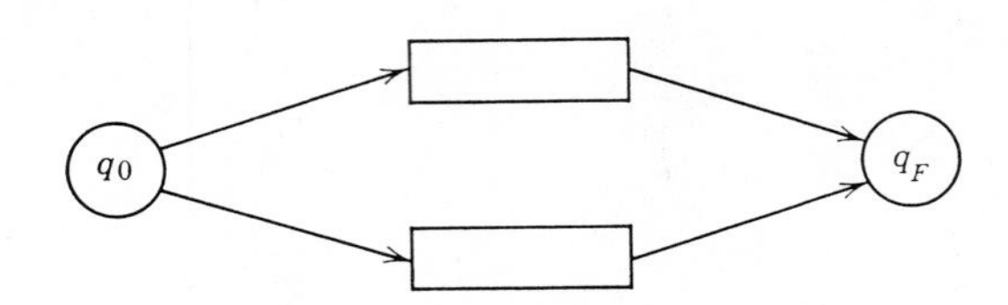

Fig. 7.2.5

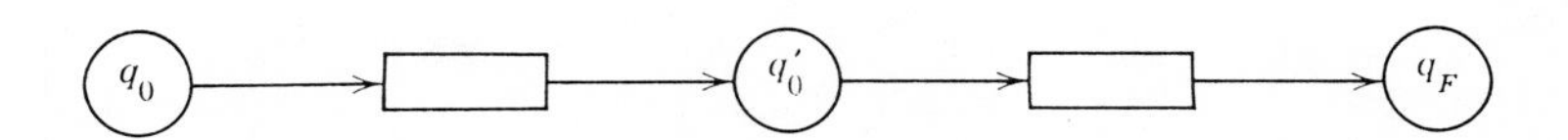

Fig. 7.2.6

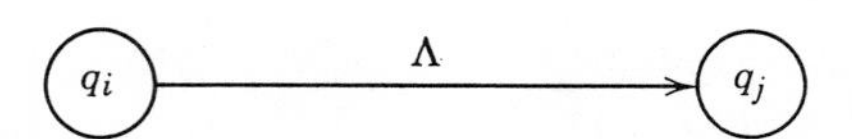

Fig. 7.2.7

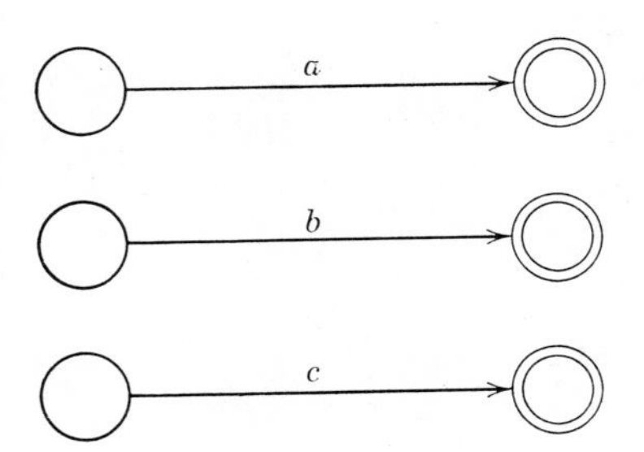

Fig. 7.2.8

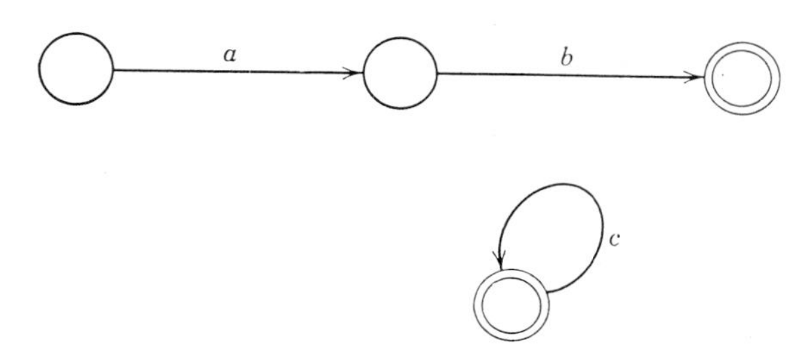

Fig. 7.2.9

the final state of $\mathbf{N}'$ with the initial state of $\mathbf{N}''$, and q_F is the final state of $\mathbf{N}''$. An easy verification as in the other cases of the induction completes the proof. Q.E.D.

REMARK. The foregoing method of construction will sometimes lead to a transition diagram containing a part like that shown in Fig. 7.2.7, owing to clause (iii) of (a) of Theorem 7.2.12. In constructing a function table for the n.f.s.a. in which such a situation occurs, the diagram exemplified in Fig. 7.2.7 is naturally interpreted to mean that if q_i is a next state under M, then so is q_j; or, if q_i is an initial state, then for all s define $M(q_i, s) = M(q_j, s)$; or both—that is, q_i may be both a next state and an initial state, since the construction does not always lead to simple automata. The steps just described are justified, since $M(q_i, \Lambda s) = M(M(q_i, \Lambda), s) = M(q_j, s)$.

We will now give an example illustrating Theorems 7.2.12 and 7.2.13 in detail.

EXAMPLE 5. $S = \{a, b, c\}$ and $\alpha = ((ab \bigcup c^*)b \bigcup a)$. First, using Theorem 7.2.13, we have the diagrams[1] of Fig. 7.2.8. To keep the diagrams

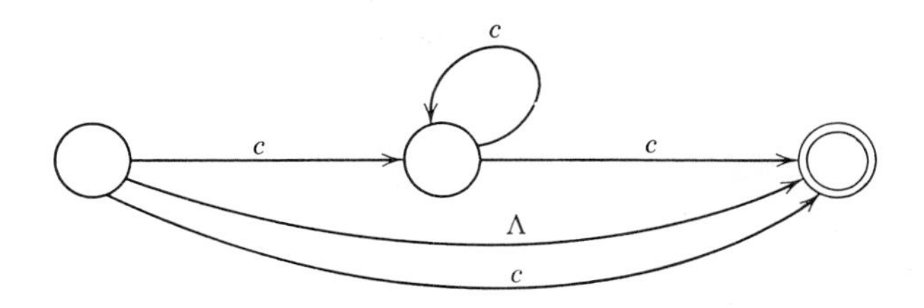

Fig. 7.2.10

[1] Each diagram is incomplete in the sense that none exhibit responses under *all* inputs. That this informal simplification leads to no trouble should be verified by the student.

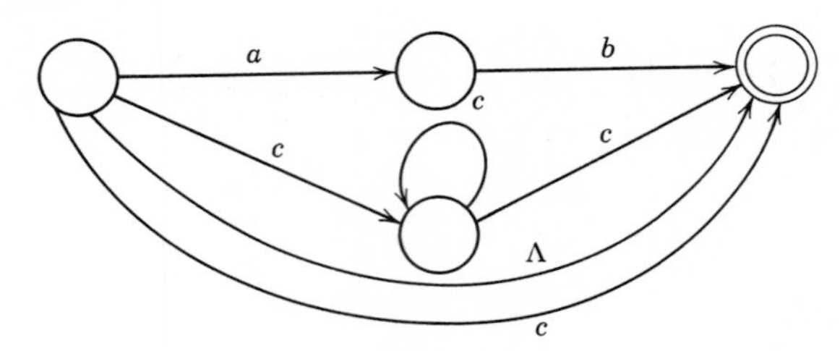

Fig. 7.2.11

uncluttered, we have omitted designations of states. In each case the left-hand node is initial and the right-hand one is final. All three are simple n.f.s.a.'s (in fact, f.s.a.'s).

Next, $a \cdot b$, and then c^* lead to Fig. 7.2.9. Now, the last automaton is not simple, so in order to apply Theorem 7.2.13 and thus obtain the machine determined by $ab \cup c^*$, we must make it simple. Using the methods of Theorem 7.2.12, we get Fig. 7.2.10. Since Fig. 7.2.10 is a simple acceptor we may combine it with Fig. 7.2.9, again using Theorem 7.2.13, to obtain the n.f.s.a. for $a \cdot b \cup c^*$. This is done (Fig. 7.2.11) by identifying the initial as well as the final nodes of the two figures. Two more steps yield the desired result, shown in Fig. 7.2.12.

Next we illustrate the remark following Theorem 7.2.13 by actually setting up a table (Table 7.2.1) for the M function of this automaton.

Note that since there is a branch labeled Λ from q_0 to q_3 in Fig. 7.2.12, and since $M(q_3, b) = \{q_4\}$, we have set $M(q_0, b) = \{q_4\}$ by the remark following Theorem 7.2.13. Table 7.2.1 is the M function for an n.f.s.a. accepting α.

So far, we have developed an algorithm for obtaining an n.f.s.a. from a regular expression. This attainment falls short of our aim, stated after Theorem 7.2.4, to synthesize an f.s.a. We are able to proceed, however, to the construction of the desired f.s.a. owing to the following remarkable fact: n.f.s.a.'s, despite their loose, nondeterministic structures, define

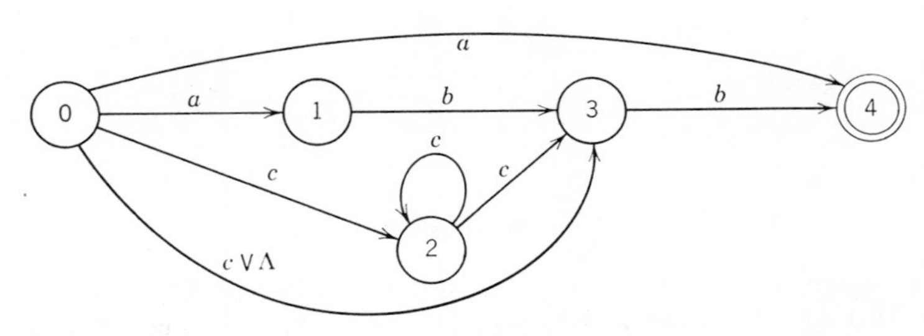

Fig. 7.2.12

TABLE 7.2.1

	a	b	c
q_0	$\{q_1, q_4\}$	$\{q_4\}$	$\{q_2, q_3\}$
q_1	$\varnothing$	$\{q_3\}$	$\varnothing$
q_2	$\varnothing$	$\varnothing$	$\{q_2, q_3\}$
q_3	$\varnothing$	$\{q_4\}$	$\varnothing$
q_4	$\varnothing$	$\varnothing$	$\varnothing$

exactly the same family of sets as the deterministic acceptors! To prove this fact, we first show how to construct a certain f.s.a., given an n.f.s.a. This construction will provide us with the second link of the desired algorithm.

Definition 7.2.14. Let $\mathbf{N} = \langle S, Q, Q_0, M, Q' \rangle$. $\mathbf{A}_N$ is the acceptor $\langle S, \pi(Q), Q_0, M_N, Q_N' \rangle$ as follows: $\pi(Q)$ is the power set of Q (of $\mathbf{N}$), so that the *states* of $\mathbf{A}_N$ are sets. $M_N: \pi(Q) \times S \to \pi(Q)$ is given by

$$M_N(\pi, s) = \bigcup_{q \in \pi} M(q,s)$$

where $\pi \in \pi(Q)$. Also

$$Q_N' = \{\pi \mid \pi \subseteq Q \wedge (\exists q)(q \in Q' \wedge q \in \pi)\}$$

Since this definition is fairly complicated, it is worthwhile to illustrate it.

EXAMPLE 6. Continuing Example 2 of Section 7.1, $\mathbf{A}_N$ for that example is given by Table 7.2.2 and the comments following it. It should be observed

TABLE 7.2.2

	0	1
$\varnothing$	$\varnothing$	$\varnothing$
$\{q_0\}$	$\{q_0, q_2\}$	$\{q_1\}$
$\{q_1\}$	$\{q_1, q_2\}$	$\{q_0\}$
$\{q_2\}$	ϕ	$\{q_1\}$
$\{q_0, q_1\}$	$\{q_0, q_1, q_2\}$	$\{q_0, q_1\}$
$\{q_0, q_2\}$	$\{q_0, q_2\}$	$\{q_1\}$
$\{q_1, q_2\}$	$\{q_1, q_2\}$	$\{q_0, q_1\}$
$\{q_0, q_1, q_2\}$	$\{q_0, q_1, q_2\}$	$\{q_0, q_1\}$

here that $\pi(Q)$ is the power set of Q including $\varnothing$; $Q_0 = \{q_0, q_2\}$; $Q_N' = \{\{q_0\}, \{q_0, q_1\}, \{q_0, q_2\}, \{q_0, q_1, q_2\}\}$—that is, it is the set of all subsets of Q which contain the final state q_0 of the original cited example. This acceptor is complete, and $\varnothing$ is defined so as to return to itself (such a state is sometimes called a "dead" state or "sink" state). Finally, to exemplify the construction of M_N, we note that $M_N(\{q_0, q_1\}, 0) = M(q_0, 0) \bigcup M(q_1, 0) = \{q_0, q_1, q_2\} = Q$.

We will illustrate Definition 7.2.14 once again after having established a certain equivalence between n.f.s.a.'s and f.s.a.'s.

Theorem 7.2.15. For every n.f.s.a. **N**, there exists an f.s.a. $\mathbf{A}_N$ such that $x(\mathbf{N}) = x(\mathbf{A}_N)$; and conversely, for every f.s.a. there exists an n.f.s.a. which accepts the same set of words.

Proof. The converse follows from the fact that an f.s.a. may be converted into an n.f.s.a. by taking the value q' of $M(q, s)$ in every case to be $\{q'\}$.

For the more significant part of the theorem, suppose we are given **N** and also $\mathbf{A}_N$ by the construction of Definition 7.2.14. We will prove that $x(\mathbf{N}) = x(\mathbf{A}_N)$. Assume that $x \in x(\mathbf{N})$ and that $x = s_{i_1}s_{i_2}\cdots s_{i_n}$. By Corollary 7.1.7, there exists a sequence of states $q_{i_0}, q_{i_1}, \ldots, q_{i_n}$ of **N** such that

$$q_{i_0} \in Q_0 \qquad q_{i_j} \in M(q_{i_{j-1}}, s_{i_j}) \qquad \text{and} \quad q_{i_n} \in Q'$$

We have to prove that $M_N(Q_0, x) \in Q_N'$. This fact will follow from the two facts that $q_{i_n} \in Q'$ and that $q_{i_n} \in M_N(Q_0, x)$, together with the definition of Q_N'.

We prove by induction that

$$q_{i_k} \in M_N(Q_0, s_{i_1}s_{i_2}\cdots s_{i_k}) \qquad 1 \leq k \leq n \tag{1}$$

Let $k = 1$. By construction

$$M_N(Q_0, s_{i_1}) = \bigcup_{q_{i_0} \in Q_0} M(q_{i_0}, s_{i_1})$$

and hence since $q_{i_0} \in Q_0$ and $q_{i_1} \in M(q_{i_0}, s_{i_1})$, it follows that

$$q_{i_1} \in M_N(Q_{01}\, s_{i_1})$$

Now assume

$$q_{i_{k-1}} \in M_N(Q_0, s_{i_1}, s_{i_2}\cdots s_{i_{k-1}}) \tag{2}$$

Let $\pi = M_N(Q_0, s_{i_1}s_{i_2}\ldots s_{i_{k-1}})$; by construction, for every $q \in Q$,

$$M_N(\pi, s_{i_k}) = \bigcup_{q \in \pi} M(q, s_{i_k}) \tag{3}$$

From (2) and (3) we have

$$M(q_{i_{k-1}}, s_{i_k}) \subseteq M_N(\pi, s_{i_k}) \tag{4}$$

and since by the theorem hypothesis $q_{i_k} \in M(q_{i_{k-1}}, s_{i_k})$, we find that $q_{i_k} \in M_N(\pi, s_{i_k})$, which proves (1). Hence, by the facts stated prior to the induction, $M_N(Q_0, x) \in Q_N'$. Thus by Corollary 7.1.6 and Definition 7.1.8, $x \in x(\mathbf{A}_N)$.

Conversely, assume that $x = s_{i_1}s_{i_2}\cdots s_{i_n} \in x(\mathbf{A}_N)$. By Corollary 7.1.6, it follows that $M_N(Q_0, x) \in Q_N'$. Now let q_{i_1} be an element of $M_N(Q_0, x)$ which is *also* in Q'. (The existence of this state follows from the definition of Q_N'). Let $\pi = M_N(Q_0, s_{i_1}s_{i_2}\cdots s_{i_{n-1}})$; then since

$$q_{i_n} \in M_N(\pi, s_{i_n}) \Leftrightarrow q_{i_n} \in \bigcup_{q \in \pi} M(q, s_{i_n})$$

there is a $q = q_{i_{n-1}} \in \pi$ such that $q_{i_n} \in M(q_{i_{n-1}}, s_{i_n})$. Similarly, let $\pi' = M_N(Q_0, s_{i_1}\cdots s_{i_{n-2}})$. Then

$$q_{i_{n-1}} \in M_N(\pi', s_{i_{n-1}}) \Leftrightarrow q_{i_{n-1}} \in \bigcup_{q \in \pi'} M(q, s_{i_{n-1}})$$

by the definition of the function M_N again, and since by the previous step $q_{i_{n-1}} \in \pi$ and $\pi = M_N(\pi', s_{i_{n-1}}), q_{i_{n-1}} \in M_N(\pi', s_{i_{n-1}})$. Hence there is a $q_{i_{n-2}} \in \pi'$ such that $q_{i_{n-1}} \in M(q_{i_{n-2}}, s_{i_{n-1}})$.

Continuing in this way for a finite number of steps, we see that (i) $q_{i_n} \in Q'$; (ii) there is a sequence $q_{i_0}, q_{i_1}, \ldots, q_{i_n}$ such that $q_{i_k} \in M(q_{i_{k-1}}, s_{i_k})$; and (iii) $q_{i_0} \in Q_0$. Hence by Corollary 7.1.7, x is accepted by the n.f.s.a. $\mathbf{N}$: $x \in x(\mathbf{N})$. Q.E.D.

EXAMPLE 5 (*Continued*). Table 7.2.1 is the transition function of an n.f.s.a. which accepts the set denoted by $((a\cdot b \cup c^*)\cdot b \cup a)$. This automaton has the set of initial states $Q_0 = \{q_0\}$ and the set of final states $Q' = \{q_4\}$ (cf. Fig. 7.2.12). Using Definition 7.2.14, we could now set up a table for M_N of an f.s.a. with designations of the elements of $\pi(Q)$ comprising the ordinates (the present states), and the elements of s the abscissas, as usual. This would be a table with $2^{K(Q)}$ rows, and in general would be wasteful—the represented f.s.a. would be badly disconnected. A simpler and much more economical procedure is the following.

1. Start rows of an M_N table with the q_i's of M becoming the $\{q_i\}$'s of M_N; that is, the unit set states of $\mathbf{A}_N$. Copy the interior of the M table for these ordinates.
2. If π is a next state in the table, and π is *not* already an ordinate of the table, add π as an ordinate.
3. Using the definition of M_N, compute the image states $M_N(\pi, s_i)$ for each i for all ordinates π. Return to step 2.

This procedure must terminate eventually (when rule 2 no longer applies), since $2^{K(Q)}$ is an integer. Table 7.2.3 shows the result of applying this algorithm to Table 7.2.1. For clarity the states (except for the inaccessible ones) of this automaton have been relabeled to the left. The

TABLE 7.2.3

		a	b	c
(0)	$\{q_0\}$	$\{q_1, q_4\}$	$\{q_4\}$	$\{q_2, q_3\}$
	$\{q_1\}$	$\varnothing$	$\{q_3\}$	$\varnothing$
	$\{q_2\}$	$\varnothing$	$\varnothing$	$\{q_2, q_3\}$
(1)	$\{q_3\}$	$\varnothing$	$\{q_4\}$	$\varnothing$
(2)	$\{q_4\}$	$\varnothing$	$\varnothing$	$\varnothing$
(3)	$\{q_1, q_4\}$	$\varnothing$	$\{q_3\}$	$\varnothing$
(4)	$\{q_2, q_3\}$	$\varnothing$	$\{q_4\}$	$\{q_2, q_3\}$
(5)	$\varnothing$	$\varnothing$	$\varnothing$	$\varnothing$

initial state is 0 and the final states are 2 and 3. The transition diagram appears in Fig. 7.2.13.

By Theorem 7.2.15 this f.s.a. accepts the set designated by

$$((a \cdot b \cup c^*) \cdot b \cup a)$$

Having found an algorithm for synthesizing an f.s.a. from a regular expression, we now turn to the opposite task of effectively analyzing a given f.s.a. in terms of regular expressions.

Definition 7.2.16. Let $q_{r_1}, \ldots, q_{r_n}$ be a sequence of the n auxiliary symbols of an f.s.a. with alphabet $\{s_1, \ldots, s_m\}$. We introduce the regular expression $\alpha_{ij}{}^k$ with $0 \leq k \leq n$ and $1 \leq i, j \leq n$ inductively as follows.

(1) $\alpha_{ij}{}^0 = \beta_1 \cup \beta_2 \cup \cdots \beta_m \cup \gamma$

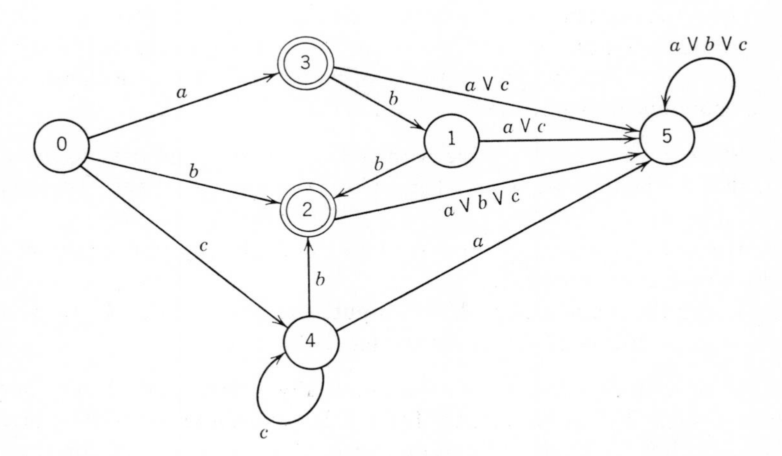

Fig. 7.2.13

where for $1 \leq g \leq m$

$$\begin{aligned} \beta_g &= s_g \quad \text{if} \quad M(q_{r_i}, s_g) = q_{r_j} \\ &= \varnothing \quad \text{if} \quad M(q_{r_i}, s_g) \neq q_{r_j} \end{aligned}$$

and

$$\begin{aligned} \gamma &= \Lambda \quad \text{if} \quad i = j \\ &= \varnothing \quad \text{if} \quad i \neq j \end{aligned}$$

(2) $\alpha_{ij}{}^k = \alpha_{ij}^{k-1} \cup \alpha_{ik}^{k-1}(\alpha_{kk}^{k-1})^* \alpha_{kj}^{k-1}$

Explanation. $\alpha_{ij}{}^k$ is a regular expression which represents the set of words taking an automaton from state q_{r_i} to q_{r_j}, given the arbitrary listing of states $q_{r_1}, \ldots, q_{r_n}$, such that the automaton passes though no states beyond q_{r_k} in the listing. Thus, using $\alpha_{ij}{}^0$ we obtain all paths from q_{r_i} to q_{r_j} which are *direct*—go through *no* (since $k = 0$) intervening states. $\alpha_{ij}{}^1$ gives all the paths from q_{r_i} to q_{r_j} which go through q_{r_1} (perhaps more than once), etc.

EXAMPLE 7. Consider the f.s.a. of Table 7.2.4.

TABLE 7.2.4.

	0	1
q_0	q_0	q_1
q_1	q_1	q_2
q_2	q_2	q_3
q_3	q_3	q_3

Given the list q_1, q_2, q_0, q_3 (that is, $r_1 = 1$, $r_2 = 2$, $r_3 = 0$, $r_4 = 3$). Using the definition, we obtain

$$\begin{aligned}
\alpha_{11}{}^0 &= 0 \cup \Lambda & \alpha_{31}{}^0 &= 1 \cup \varnothing \\
\alpha_{12}{}^0 &= 1 \cup \varnothing & \alpha_{32}{}^0 &= \varnothing \\
\alpha_{13}{}^0 &= \varnothing & \alpha_{33}{}^0 &= 0 \cup \Lambda \\
\alpha_{14}{}^0 &= \varnothing & \alpha_{34}{}^0 &= \varnothing \\
\alpha_{21}{}^0 &= \varnothing & \alpha_{41}{}^0 &= \varnothing \\
\alpha_{22}{}^0 &= 0 \cup \Lambda & \alpha_{42}{}^0 &= \varnothing \\
\alpha_{23}{}^0 &= \varnothing & \alpha_{43}{}^0 &= \varnothing \\
\alpha_{24}{}^0 &= \varnothing \cap 1 & \alpha_{44}{}^0 &= 0 \cup 1 \cup \Lambda
\end{aligned}$$

Moreover, by clause (2) of Definition 7.2.16

$$\alpha_{12}{}^2 = \alpha_{12}{}^1 \cup \alpha_{12}{}^1(\alpha_{12}{}^1)^* \alpha_{22}{}^1$$

and applying Clause (2) again

$$\alpha_{12}{}^1 = \alpha_{12}{}^0 \cup \alpha_{11}{}^0(\alpha_{11}{}^0)^* \alpha_{12}{}^0$$

and

$$\alpha_{22}{}^1 = \alpha_{22}{}^0 \cup \alpha_{21}{}^0(\alpha_{11}{}^0)^* \alpha_{12}{}^0$$

Making the backward substitutions,

$$\begin{aligned}\alpha_{12}{}^1 &= (1 \cup \varnothing) \cup ((0 \cup \Lambda)(0 \cup \Lambda)^*(1 \cup \varnothing)) \\ &= 1 \cup (0^* \cdot 1) \\ \alpha_{22}{}^1 &= (0 \cup \Lambda) \cup (\varnothing \cdot (0 \cup \Lambda)^*(1 \cup \varnothing)) = 0 \cup \Lambda\end{aligned}$$

whence

$$\begin{aligned}\alpha_{12}{}^2 &= (1 \cup 0^* \cdot 1) \cup (1 \cup 0^* \cdot 1)(0 \cup \Lambda)^*(0 \cup \Lambda) \\ &= (1 \cup 0^* \cdot 1) \cdot 0^* \qquad (5)\end{aligned}$$

(In computing these expressions we have used liberally the regular expression equations mentioned after Corollary 7.2.10, in Example 3, and Exercise 7.2(3). If the student will draw the transition diagram for Table 7.2.4, he will be able to see that the words from q_1 to q_2 are themselves represented by (5). Thus the superscript on α^2 has the meaning that the paths passing through states *up to and including* the state listed second, $q_{r_2} = q_2$, are represented; and similarly in general for the superscript k. We can now understand the following lemma).

Lemma 7.2.17. Let $q_{r_1}, \ldots, q_{r_n}$ be an arbitrary sequence of the states of an f.s.a.; $\alpha_{ij}{}^k$ denotes the set of words $x = yz$ such that $M(q_{r_i}, x) = q_{r_j}$ and such that there is no q_{i_m}, $m > k$, for which $M(q_{r_i}, y) = q_{i_m}$.

Proof. By induction on k. If $k = 0$, then by clause (1) of Definition 7.2.16, $\alpha_{ij}{}^0$ is the union of single symbols denoting words taking the f.s.a. from q_{r_i} to q_{r_j} without passing through *any* states of the given enumeration. Assume that α_{ij}^{k-1} satisfies the conditions for all i and j. To show that $\alpha_{ij}{}^k$ also satisfies the conditions, we will examine various cases. The logical possibilities are that the f.s.a. could go through state q_{i_k} zero times, once, or more than once. We will see that in each case it cannot go through any state q_{i_m}, $m > k$, thus proving the lemma.

CASE I. The f.s.a. does not enter q_{r_k}. Hence α_{ij}^{k-1} denotes the set of words in question. But then by Clause (2) of Definition 7.2.16, $\alpha_{ij}^k = \alpha_{ij}^{k-1}$, and so α_{ij}^k denotes the set of words.

CASE II. The f.s.a. passes through q_{r_k} once—that is, there is but one y such that $x = yz$, $M(q_{r_i}, x) = q_{r_j}$, and $M(q_{r_j}, y) = q_{r_k}$. Now y is denoted by α_{ik}^{k-1} and z by α_{kj}^{k-1}, by inductive assumption. Hence x is denoted by $\alpha_{ik}^{k-1}(\alpha_{kk}^{k-1})^*\alpha_{kj}^{k-1}$ (recalling the meaning of *), and, again using Clause (2) of Definition 7.2.16, x is denoted by $\alpha_{ij}{}^k$.

CASE III. The f.s.a. passes through q_{r_k} more than once. Let $x = yzw$, where y takes the f.s.a. from q_{r_i} to q_{r_k} in the case of the *first entry* into q_{r_k}; z takes the f.s.a. from q_{r_k} to q_{r_k} any finite number of times; and w takes it from q_{r_k} to q_{r_j}. By Clause (2) of Definition 7.2.16, $\alpha_{ij}{}^k$ denotes x, since α_{ik}^{k-1} denotes y, $(\alpha_{kk}^{k-1})^*$ denotes z, and α_{kj}^{k-1} denotes w.

Finally, $\alpha_{ij}{}^k$ denotes *only* the words of concern, since if there were another word it would be denoted also by α_{ij}^{k-1}, contrary to the inductive hypothesis. Q.E.D.

It is clear that $\{x \mid M(q_0, x) \in Q'\}$ is that set including all and only the words taking q_0 into q_{a_1}, or q_{a_2}, or, . . ., q_{a_m} where $Q' = \{q_{a_1}, \ldots, q_{a_m}\}$. Thus we obtain the following theorem directly.

Theorem 7.2.18. If an acceptor **A** has n states and if the set of final states is $Q' = q_{a_1}, \ldots, q_{a_m}$, then $x(\mathbf{A})$ is denoted by the regular expression

$$\alpha_{oa_1}^n \bigcup \cdots \bigcup \alpha_{oam}^n$$

Corollary 7.2.19. (Kleene). There is an algorithm for constructing an f.s.a. for a regular expression (synthesis); there is an algorithm for determining the regular expression denoting the accepted set of a given f.s.a. (analysis).

This corollary summarizes the results of 7.2.12–7.2.18.

Corollary 7.2.20. The family of definable sets J is the family of regular sets.

Proof. From Definitions 7.1.9, 7.2.7, and 7.2.8, Corollary 7.2.10, and Theorems 7.2.13, 7.2.15, and 7.2.18. Q.E.D.

Corollary 7.2.21. There exists an algorithm for deciding the equality of regular expressions.

Proof. By the synthesis result, the f.s.a.'s corresponding to α and β can be determined. The acceptors may be tested for equivalence using Exercise 7.1(1) and the equivalence algorithm developed in Chapter 5 (see in particular Exercise 5.2(3) modified for Moore machines).

EXERCISES 7.2

1. Alternatively to Theorem 7.2.1, state necessary and sufficient conditions on the structure—i.e., the M function table—of an acceptor for existence of an accepted word.

2. Construct a generator (cf. Definition 3.3.15) for generating all and only regular expressions using the alphabet $S = \{0, 1, \bigcup, \cdot, *, \Lambda, \varnothing, (,)\}$ plus needed auxiliaries.

3. Prove the following equalities; α, β, and γ are arbitrary regular expressions.

(*a*) $\phi^* = \Lambda$

(*b*) $\alpha \cdot \varnothing = \varnothing \cdot \alpha = \varnothing$

(*c*) $(\alpha \cdot \beta) \bigcup (\alpha \cdot \gamma) = \alpha \cdot (\beta \bigcup \gamma)$

(*d*) $(\alpha \bigcup \beta)^* = (\alpha^* \cdot \beta^*)^*$

4. Provide counterexamples for the following:

(*a*) $(\alpha\cdot\beta)\cap(\alpha\cdot\gamma)=\alpha\cdot(\beta\cap\gamma)$, where the regular expression language has been extended to include $\cap$ and where $\alpha\cap\beta$ is a regular expression and denotes the set intersection $\mathscr{U}\cap\mathscr{V}$, provided that α denotes $\mathscr{U}$ and β denotes $\mathscr{V}$.

(*b*) $(\alpha\cup\beta)^*=\alpha^*\cup\beta^*$.

5. Let p be a mapping from S onto T, S and T being finite, nonempty sets. From Section 1.3, we know that p can be extended to a homomorphism of $\mathscr{S}=\langle S^*,\cdot,\Lambda\rangle$ onto $\mathscr{T}=\langle T^*,\mathrm{o},\Lambda\rangle$. Show that if p so extended is restricted to a regular subset of S^*, then its range is a regular subset of T^*; that is, regularity is preserved under homomorphism.

6. Show that the following sets are regular.

(*a*) $\{xss'y \mid s, s'\in S \wedge x, y\in S^*\}$

(*b*) $\{sx \mid s\in S \wedge x\in S^*\}$

(*c*) $\{xs \mid s\in S \wedge x\in S^*\}$

7. Let $R\subseteq S\times S$ be a binary relation. A sequence $s_1, s_2, \ldots, s_n$ is an *R-sequence* iff $(s_j, s_{j+1})\in R$, for each $j<n$; 0 and 1-length sequences are included. Show that the set of all R-sequences is regular. (*Hint:* If

$$\bar{R}=S\times S-R=\{(s_1, s_1'),\ldots,(s_r, s_r')\}$$

then the set of R-sequences is S^* minus the union of all sets of sequences x, s, s', y where $(s, s')\in\bar{R}$.)

8. Prove Corollary 7.2.10.

9. Specify in detail an algorithm for deciding equality of regular expressions (Corollary 7.2.21).

10. Verify the equalities asserted for $\alpha_{12}{}^1$, $\alpha_{22}{}^1$, and $\alpha_{12}{}^2$ in Example 7.

11. Using the synthesis method presented in this section, construct f.s.a. (in the form of an M table) for the following regular expressions.

(*a*) $(1\cdot 0^*\cup 1\cdot 1)^*$

(*b*) $((a\cup b)^*\cdot(c\cup a)^*)^*\cdot a$

12. Complete the determination of the regular expression for Example 7 with q_0 as the initial state and q_1, q_2 as the set of final states. You need *not* use the sequence q_1, q_2, q_0, q_3 (as used in Example 6) for the application of Definition 7.2.16. However, you will save time if you do.

13. The *derivative* of a *regular set* $\mathscr{U}\subseteq S^*$ w.r.t. a word $x\in S^*$ is

$$\mathscr{U}'x=\{y \mid xy\in\mathscr{U}\}$$

Show that the derivative of a regular set is regular.

14. The *derivative* of a *regular expression* α w.r.t. $s\in S$ is written $D_s\alpha$. D_s is defined as follows.

$D_s s=\Lambda$

$D_s t=\varnothing$ when $t=\varnothing,\Lambda$, or s' (some $s'\in S$) and $s'\neq s$

$D_s\alpha^*=(D_s\alpha)\alpha^*$

$D_s\alpha\beta=(D_s\alpha)\beta\cup\delta(\alpha)D_s\beta$

$D_s(\alpha\cup\beta)=D_s\alpha\cup D_s\beta$

where $\delta(\alpha)=\Lambda$, if α denotes (its denoted set contains) Λ; or $\delta(\alpha)=\varnothing$ otherwise.

EXAMPLE:

$$D_0(0 \cup 10^*1) = D_0 0 \cup D_0 10^*1$$
$$= \Lambda \cup [(D_0 1)0^*1 \cup \delta(1) D_0 0^*1] = \cdots = 0^*1$$

(*a*) (i) $D_\Lambda \alpha = \alpha$

(ii) $D_{s_1 \cdots s_k} \alpha = D_{s_k}(D_{s_1 \cdots s_{k-1}} \alpha)$

Show (ii).

(*b*) Compute $D_{01}(0 \cup 10^*1)$.

(*c*) Show that if α denotes $\mathscr{U}$, then $D_x \alpha$ denotes $\mathscr{U}_x'$.

(*d*) Hence show $D_x \alpha$ is a regular expression if α is.

15. x is *accepted by a state* q of an f.s.a. iff $M(q, x) \in Q'$, the set of final states. Clearly the set of all such x is regular. Prove that if q_i accepts the set denoted by the regular expression α and q_j accepts the set denoted by β, then α and β denote the same set iff for every z $M(q_i, z) = M(q_j, z)$.

16. Suppose that $M(q_0, x) = q_i$ and $M(q_0, y) = q_j$, and that α denotes the set accepted by the f.s.a. in question. Then q_i and q_j accept the same set iff $D_x \alpha = D_y \alpha$.

From this result, prove it follows that two states of an acceptor are *distinguishable* in terms of the sets they accept iff their corresponding derivatives are distinct. Using this fact, a synthesis procedure alternative to ours following 7.2.13 can be developed. See Brzozowski [1964].

7.3 RELATIONS AND TRANSDUCER BEHAVIOR

Turing machines compute the partial recursive functions and Turing acceptors accept the recursively enumerable sets. We have also seen that finite state acceptors accept the regular sets—a subfamily of the recursive sets, assuming Gödelization, and thus a subfamily of the recursively enumerable sets. Since finite transducers are related to finite state acceptors as Turing transducers are to Turing acceptors, it seems appropriate now to inquire into the computing powers of the transducers. As suggested in Section 7.0, this problem may be approached in terms of finite state acceptors. A preliminary but also intrinsically important objective is to extend the notion of definable set to sets of word relations.

According to Definition 3.1.1, a word relation is a relation over a set of words of equal length. All of the results of the previous two sections of this chapter apply to acceptors with alphabets $S \subseteq (A^n)$, A^n being the n-fold product of a finite nonempty set with itself. Hence the concepts of regularity, definability, all of the closure properties, etc., apply to these relations—each n-tuple is, from the point of view of acceptor theory, a single symbol. Thus, reverting to the tape-oriented way of considering automata, an acceptor with such an alphabet has n one-way tapes feeding into its control box from left to right, say. These tapes all step along synchronously; in the initial state the first symbol on each tape is read, and, if when in state q_i symbol $i + 1$ is read on each tape, then the acceptor goes into q_{i+1} and shifts all tapes so that symbol $i + 2$ is scanned on each. The simultaneously scanned symbols are elements of an n-tuple.

It will at times be convenient to picture the action of an acceptor whose alphabet consists of words as previously imagined. Thus instead of writing $M(q_i, (x_1, \ldots, x_n)) = q_j$, where $(x_1, \ldots, x_n)$ is an element of an n-ary word relation we will write

$$M(q_i, \begin{matrix} x_1 \\ \vdots \\ x_n \end{matrix}) = q_j \tag{1}$$

in line with the tape orientation. Hence, modifying Definition 5.1.4, we have

$$M(q, \Lambda) = \Lambda, \qquad \text{where} \quad \Lambda = \left.\begin{matrix} \Lambda \\ \vdots \\ \Lambda \end{matrix}\right\} n \text{ times},$$

and (2)

$$M(q, \begin{matrix} x_1 s_{i_1} \\ \vdots \\ x_n s_{i_n} \end{matrix}) = M(M(q, \begin{matrix} x_1 \\ \vdots \\ x_n \end{matrix}), \begin{matrix} s_{i_1} \\ \vdots \\ s_{i_n} \end{matrix})$$

EXAMPLE 1. Consider $\{0, 1, 2\} \times \{0, 1, 2\}$. It is desired to construct an f.s.a. which will accept all words $(x, y) = \begin{matrix} x \\ y \end{matrix}$ such that if $x = s_{i_1} \ldots s_{i_n}$ and $y = s_{j_1} \ldots s_{j_n}$, then $s_{i_k} \leq s_{j_k}$, $k = 1, \ldots, n$; thus it is supposed to accept $\begin{matrix} 001 \\ 201 \end{matrix}$ but not $\begin{matrix} 122. \\ 202 \end{matrix}$

The relations we have discussed so far have the property that if $(x_1, \ldots, x_n)$ is an element, then $l(x_1) = \cdots = l(x_n)$. Suppose we set out, however, to design an acceptor for the numerical relation $\leq$. For example, we want our f.s.a. to accept (2, 5). It is clear that two adjustments are needed. (1) If we use a binary code, then we will want to write our representations of numbers from right to left—that is, with low order digits to the right. This conflicts, however, with the usual mathematical practice of writing sequences (including words) from left to right. In order not to violate either usage, we will represent numbers by both indexed *number words* and ordinary words. Thus $4_{10} = 100_2$ denotes the same number as the word 001 does. As usual, the index is the radix. The relation $\leq$ over binary words is not such that components of a pair are of equal length; $\leq$ is a subset of $(\{0, 1\}^*)^2$ and not of $(\{0, 1\}^2)^*$. The pair $\begin{matrix} 01 \\ 101 \end{matrix}$ for $2_{10} \leq 5_{10}$ contains the symbols $\begin{matrix} 0 \\ 1 \end{matrix}$, $\begin{matrix} 1 \\ 0 \end{matrix}$, and 1. Clearly, such an alphabet does not coincide with our ideas of acceptors that scan pairs (or n-tuples) only.

To take care of length discrepancies of this kind, and yet deal quite generally with relations we will use blanks. So for numerical work our base alphabet will be $S = \{0, 1\} \bigcup \{B\}$. However we always want to use just enough B's to fill out words to the same length, and no more. Thus for $2 \leq 5$ we would use $\begin{matrix} 01B \\ 101 \end{matrix}$ but not $\begin{matrix} 01BB \\ 101B \end{matrix}$. So the fundamental alphabet of n-tuples of numbers will be $(S \bigcup \{B\})^n - \{B\}^n$. For arbitrary alphabets we use A rather than $S = \{0, 1\}$.

Definition 7.3.1. An n-ary *word relation* R (with blanks) is a subset of $((A \bigcup \{B\})^n - \{B\}^n)^*$.

Definition 7.3.2. An n-ary word relation R is *length preserving* iff $R \subseteq (A^n)$.

Comment. That is, the component words are all on A and are equal in length (since otherwise B's would occur to fill out inadequacies in length).

Definition 7.3.3. An n-ary *numerical word relation* R is a subset of $((S \bigcup \{B\})^n - \{B\}^n)^*$ such that each element of each component of an n-tuple is an element of $(0 \bigcup (0 \bigcup 1)^* \cdot 1) \cdot B^*$. Equivalently,

$$R \subseteq ((0 \bigcup (0 \bigcup 1)^* \cdot 1) \cdot B^*)^n \bigcap ((S \bigcup \{B\})^n - \{B\}^n)^* = \mathcal{N}^n$$

Note that according to Definition 7.3.3 a word like $0B10$ is not a number. Note also that each component of each element is equal in length to every other one, though it is not necessary that the relation is length preserving in the sense of Definition 7.3.2. As in section 7.2 and throughout the remainder of this section we shall use the symbol "$\bigcup$" ambiguously for both itself and set-theoretic union in expressions denoting regular sets.

EXAMPLE 2. We are now able to construct an f.s.a. for $\leq$. The alphabet is $(\{0, 1, B\}^2 - \{B\}^2)^*$. The transition diagram of such an f.s.a. appears in

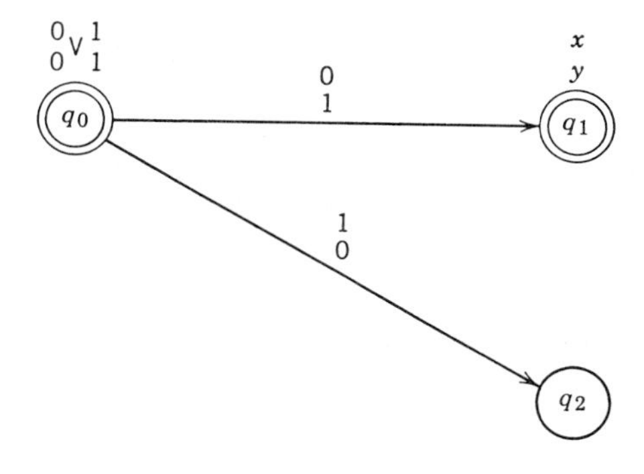

Fig. 7.3.1

Fig. 7.3.1. By Definition 7.3.3, x and y are elements of $(0 \cup (0 \cup 1)^* \cdot 1) \cdot B^*$. This acceptor defines $\leq$ since $x \leq y$ iff a 1 does not occur in x before a 1 occurs in y in the usual bit ordering.

Definition 7.3.4. An n-ary word relation R is *definable* just in case there is an f.s.a. $\mathbf{A}$ such that $\mathbf{A} = \langle (A \cup \{B\})^n - \{B\}^n, Q, q_0, M, Q' \rangle$ and $x(\mathbf{A}) = R$.

We are now almost ready to discuss closure properties of numerical relations and to characterize those relations which are definable. We need just a little more equipment.

Definition 7.3.5. Let R be an n-ary relation. The ith *component* of R is the set
$A_i = \{x_i \mid (\exists x_1) \cdots (\exists x_{i-1})(\exists x_{i+1}) \cdots (\exists x_n)\, R(x_1, \ldots, x_{i-1}, x_i, x_{i+1}, \ldots, x_n)\}$ where $1 \leq i \leq n$ and where as usual $R(x_1, \ldots, x_n) \Leftrightarrow (x_1, \ldots, x_n) \in R$.

Theorem 7.3.6. If $R \subseteq ((A \cup \{B\})^n - \{B\}^n)^*$ is regular, then the ith component A_i is regular w.r.t. the alphabet $A \cup \{B\}$, for any i.

Proof. Observe that $((A \cup \{B\})^n - \{B\}^n)^*$ is the free monoid generated by $(A \cup \{B\})^n - \{B\}^n$ with identity $\Lambda = (\Lambda, \ldots, \Lambda)$. Let φ_i be a *projection* map on the set of generators onto the ith component given by

$$\varphi_i(a_1, \ldots, a_n) = a_i$$

Extending φ_i to words using (1), we have

$$\varphi_i\begin{pmatrix} x_1 a_1 \\ \vdots \\ x_n a_n \end{pmatrix} = \varphi_i\begin{pmatrix} x_1 \\ \vdots \\ x_n \end{pmatrix} \varphi_i\begin{pmatrix} a_1 \\ \vdots \\ a_n \end{pmatrix} = x_i a_i$$

Any such φ_i is a homomorphism. Therefore if R is regular and if φ_i' is φ_i restricted to R, then the direct image of $\varphi_i'(R)$ is regular by Exercise 7.2(5). But $\varphi_i'(R) = A_i$. Q.E.D.

We will also find the following kind of converse to Exercise 7.2(5) to be useful.

Theorem 7.3.7. Let $\varphi: A \to T$ be an onto function with A and T finite. Extend φ to a homomorphism of A^* onto T^*. If $\mathscr{U} \subseteq T^*$ is regular, so is the inverse image $\varphi^{-1}(\mathscr{U}) \subseteq A^*$.

Proof. By Corollary 7.1.22 (using Corollary 7.2.20) $\mathscr{U}$ is the union of equivalence classes under some right-invariant relation R which refines $\mathscr{U}$. Now let a right-invariant relation R' be defined in $A^* \times A^*$ by

$$x\, R'\, y \Leftrightarrow \varphi(x)\, R\, \varphi(y) \qquad \varphi(x), \varphi(y) \in T^*$$

Since $[x]_{R'} = \varphi^{-1}[\varphi(x)]_R$, R' is of finite index because R is. Now from the right invariance of R we have that

$$\varphi(x)\varphi(s)\ R\ \varphi(y)\varphi(s)$$

and since φ is a homomorphism,

$$\varphi(xs)\ R\ \varphi(ys)$$

holds. Therefore, by definition $xs\ R'\ ys$, for all s. So R' is right-invariant. Finally, if $x\ R'\ y$ and $x \in \varphi^{-1}(\mathscr{U})$, then certainly $\varphi(x) \in \mathscr{U}$; but by hypothesis $\varphi(y) \in \mathscr{U}$, since $\mathscr{U}$ is definable; therefore $y \in \varphi^{-1}(\mathscr{U})$. Thus R' refines $\varphi^{-1}(\mathscr{U})$. Therefore $\varphi^{-1}(\mathscr{U})$ is definable, that is, is regular. Q.E.D.

Corollary 7.3.8. Let $R \subseteq ((A \bigcup \{B\})^n - \{B\}^n)^*$, let A_i be the ith component and let φ_i be a projection as in Theorem 7.3.6. If $\varphi_i^{-1}(A_i)$ is R and A_i is regular, then R is regular.

Proof. From Theorem 7.3.7. Q.E.D.

Corollary 7.3.9. The universal numerical n-ary relation $\mathscr{N}^n$ (Definition 7.3.3) is definable.

Proof. Every component S_i is $(0 \bigcup (0 \bigcup 1)^* \cdot 1) \cdot B^*$. Therefore, for every i $\varphi_i^{-1}(S_i)$ is regular, where φ_i is a projection, as in theorem 7.3.6, restricted to $\mathscr{N}^N$. Q.E.D.

In our brief study of recursive sets and relations, we considered unions and intersections of n-tuples, n being a fixed integer. But in addition, by way of using recursive predicates, we could in effect take unions (or intersections) of, say, an n-ary and an m-ary relation. For instance, when x, y, and z are integers

$$\{(x, y, z) \mid x + y = z \wedge x < y\}$$

is a recursive set of triples of integers. This, however, is not the same set as

$$\{(x, y) \mid x < y\} \bigcap \{(x, y, z) \mid x + y = z\}$$

since the latter set is empty. However, it is the same as

$$\{(x, y, z) \mid x < y \wedge z = z\} \bigcap \{(x, y, z) \mid x + y = z\}$$

Using a similar device of introducing dummy identities implicitly we may now show the closure of the definable numerical relations under intersection.

Theorem 7.3.10. Let $\overleftarrow{x} = x_1, \ldots, x_n$, $\overleftarrow{y} = y_1, \ldots, y_m$, and $\overleftarrow{z} = z_1, \ldots, z_p$.

Let

$$R_1 = \{(\overleftarrow{x}, \overleftarrow{y}) \mid R_1(\overleftarrow{x}, \overleftarrow{y})\}$$

and

$$R_2 = \{(\overleftarrow{y}, \overleftarrow{z}) \mid R_2\,(\overleftarrow{y}, \overleftarrow{z})\}$$

be definable $n + m$-ary and $m + p$-ary numerical relations, respectively. Then their intersection

$$R_1 \cap R_2 = \{(\overleftarrow{x}, \overleftarrow{y}, \overleftarrow{z}) \mid R_1(\overleftarrow{x}, \overleftarrow{y}) \wedge R_2(\overleftarrow{y}, \overleftarrow{z})\}$$

is a definable $n + m + p$-ary numerical relation.

Proof. Let φ_1 be a projection from $(S \cup \{B\})^{n+m+p} - \{B\}^{n+m+p}$ onto $(S \cup \{B\})^{n+m} - \{B\}^{m+n}$ and let φ_2 be a projection from the same domain onto $(S \cup \{B\})^{m+p} - \{B\}^{m+p}$. Extending φ_1 and φ_2 by Corollary 7.3.8, $\varphi_1^{-1}(R_1)$ and $\varphi_2^{-1}(R_2)$ are both definable over $(S \cup \{B\})^{n+m+p} - \{B\}^{n+m+p}$. But then $\varphi_1^{-1}(R_1) \cap \varphi_2^{-1}(R_2)$ is definable (that is, they are both on the same alphabet of $n + m + p$-tuples so that Corollary 7.1.38 applies) and is precisely $R_1 \cap R_2$ as desired. Q.E.D.

Theorem 7.3.11. If an n-ary numerical relation R is definable, so is its complement $\bar{R}$ w.r.t. $\mathcal{N}^n$.

Proof. By Corollary 7.3.9 $\mathcal{N}^n$ is definable. Moreover if R is definable, its complement w.r.t. $((S \cup \{B\})^n - \{B\}^n)^*$ is definable. But since the intersection is definable by 7.3.10 and since $\bar{R} = \mathcal{N}^n - R$, $\bar{R}$ is definable. Q.E.D.

Theorem 7.3.12. If $R(y, \overleftarrow{x})$ is a definable numerical relation, then so is $(\exists y)\, R(y, \overleftarrow{x})$.

Proof. Let φ be the projection map, again, from $((S \cup \{B\})^{n+1} - \{B\}^{n+1}$ onto $(S \cup \{B\})^n$. If $l(y)$ = number of 0's and 1's in y and $l(y) \leq l(x_i)$, $i = 1, \ldots, n$, then the direct image of $\varphi(\{(y, \overleftarrow{x}) \mid R(y, \overleftarrow{x})\})$ is precisely $\{(\overleftarrow{x}) \mid (\exists y)\, R(y, \overleftarrow{x})\}$. The completion of the proof by lifting the restriction on y is left to the reader [Exercise 7.3 (13)]. Q.E.D.

Corollary 7.3.13. The family of definable numerical relations is closed under union, intersection, complementation, and unbounded quantification.

Proof. From propositions 7.3.9, 7.3.10, 7.3.11, and 7.3.12.

To show definability of specific examples, we still need one more concept.

Definition 7.3.14. Given a word relation R', R is defined from R' by *explicit transformation* iff

$$R(x_1, \ldots, x_n) \Leftrightarrow R'(y_1, \ldots, y_k)$$

where for each i, $i = 1, \ldots, k$, either y_i is constant (that is, a word of A^*, A the alphabet) or there is a j, $j = 1, \ldots, n$, such that $y_i = x_j$.

EXAMPLE 3. $x + 1 = z$ is definable by explicit transformation from $x + y = z$; if $\Sigma(x, y, z)$ is the addition relation, then the pairs satisfying $x + 1 = z$ are precisely $\{(x, z) \mid \Sigma(x, 1, z)\}$.

Theorem 7.3.15. If R' is definable and R is its explicit transform, then R is definable.

Proof. For the Student.

We now demonstrate that the addition relation is regular. In principle it is, of course, possible to construct an acceptor (having an alphabet of 26 symbols—$\{0, 1, B\}^3 - \{B\}^3$—and having 10 states) or even to find a regular expression of triples for using a synthesis algorithm. However, neither course is easy. Instead we follow Ritchie [1962] by showing definability in an indirect way.

Theorem 7.3.16. The addition relation $\sum$ is definable.

Proof. We must show that

$$\sum = \begin{array}{c} xB^n \\ yB^m \\ x + y \end{array}$$

is definable where x, y, and $x + y$ are words on $\{0, 1\}$. Let

$$\mathbf{A}_1 = \langle \{0, 1\}^3, \{q_0, q_1, q_2\}, q_0, M, \{q_0\} \rangle$$

with M given by Table 7.3.1. Here we use $q_0 = 0$, etc. The student can

TABLE 7.3.1

	0 0 0	0 0 1	0 1 0	0 1 1	1 0 0	1 0 1	1 1 0	1 1 1
0	0	2	2	0	2	0	1	2
1	2	0	1	2	1	2	2	1
2	2	2	2	2	2	2	2	2

check for himself that the set of words on $\{0, 1\}^3$ which $\mathbf{A}_1$ accepts is

$$x(\mathbf{A}_1) = \begin{array}{c} x0^n \\ y0^m \\ x + y0^r \end{array}$$

where either n, m, or $r = 0$. Next we work on $x(\mathbf{A}_1)$ so as to eliminate the 0's tailing $x + y$ and to convert the others to B's.

Let $\mathbf{A}_2$ accept $x(\mathbf{A}_2) = (0 \cup (0 \cup 1)^* \cdot 1) \cdot B^*$. Let $\mathbf{A}_3$ accept $0 \cup (0 \cup 1)^* \cdot 1$. We will use $\mathbf{A}_2$ and $\mathbf{A}_3$ in the construction of an automaton which will accept word relations of the form

$$\begin{array}{l} xB^n \\ yB^m \\ z \end{array} \qquad (3)$$

by taking elements of $x(\mathbf{A}_2)$ and $x(\mathbf{A}_3)$ as the first two and the third components, respectively. This is accomplished by use of the projections φ_i as follows:

$$\varphi_i: \{0, 1, B\}^3 - \{B\}^3 \rightarrow \{0, 1, B\} \qquad i = 1, 2, 3$$

maps onto the ith component. Extending each φ_i to a homomorphism we know from Theorem 7.3.7 that $\varphi_1{}^{-1}(x(\mathbf{A}_2))$, $\varphi_2{}^{-1}(x(\mathbf{A}_2))$, and $\varphi_3{}^{-1}(x(\mathbf{A}_3))$ are all regular. Moreover,

$$\varphi_1{}^{-1}(x(\mathbf{A}_2)) \bigcap \varphi_2{}^{-1}(x(\mathbf{A}_2)) \bigcap \varphi_2{}^{-1}(x(\mathbf{A}_3)) \tag{4}$$

is definable by Corollary 7.3.13 and indeed is exactly the word relation (3). Call the accepting f.s.a. for this relation $\mathbf{A}_4$.

Finally, map $\{0, 1, B\}^3 - \{B\}^3$ onto $\{0, 1\}^3$ by $0 \rightarrow 0$, $1 \rightarrow 1$, and $B \rightarrow 0$. Again, the inverse image of $x(\mathbf{A}_1)$ under this map (extended to a homomorphism) is definable. Call this set $x(\mathbf{A}_5)$. Then

$$x(\mathbf{A}_4) \bigcap x(\mathbf{A}_5) = \sum$$

and is definable. Q.E.D.

Corollary 7.3.17. The initial relations (corresponding to the initial recursive functions) $x = 0$, $x + 1 = y$, and $x = x$ are definable. Moreover, $x \leq y$ and $x < y$ are definable.

Proof. Use Corollary 7.3.13, and Theorems 7.3.15, and 7.3.16.

We are now able to consider transducer computable functions, and we wish to know what functions coincide with the behavior of a finite machine. We may think of the behavior of some $\mathbf{T}$ as being either a transformation of S^* to O (the extended N function) or a transformation of S^* to O^* (G function). The first case is covered in the exercises. We now discuss in detail the second case for finite transducers in our sense. The discussion can easily be adapted to Moore machines. In the following text, we return to our earlier usage of S as an arbitrary nonempty, finite, automaton alphabet; similarly for O.

Definition 7.3.18. Let $\mathbf{T} = \langle S, Q, q_0, M, N, O\rangle$ be a finite transducer with initial state. A relation $\boldsymbol{\beta} \subseteq S^* \times O^*$ is the *behavior* of $\mathbf{T}$ iff $\boldsymbol{\beta} = G$. We also write $\boldsymbol{\beta}_T$.

REMARKS. It is clear that $\boldsymbol{\beta}_T$ is a function. Moreover, from the definition of the G function (beginning of Section 5.3), if $x = s_{i_1} \ldots s_{i_n}$ and $y = o_{i_1} \ldots o_{i_n}$, and if $(x, y) \in \boldsymbol{\beta}_T$, then $(s_{i_1} \cdots s_{i_j}, o_{i_1} \cdots o_{i_j}) \in \boldsymbol{\beta}_T$ for any j, $1 \leq j \leq n$. Finally, going back to 5.1.1, $\boldsymbol{\beta}_T$ is a *total* function.

Definition 7.3.19. Let A be any alphabet, even an alphabet of n-tuples, and let $\mathscr{U} \subseteq A^*$. The *interior* of $\mathscr{U}$ is given by

$$\operatorname{Int}(\mathscr{U}) = \{x \mid x \in \mathscr{U} \wedge (\exists w)(\exists y)(w, y \in A^* \wedge x = wy \wedge w \in \mathscr{U})\}$$

EXAMPLE 4. In the remarks immediately above, $(x, y) \in \text{Int}(\boldsymbol{\beta}_T)$ since every pair $(s_{i_1} \cdots s_{i_j}, o_{i_1} \cdots o_{i_j}) \in \boldsymbol{\beta}_T$.

Definition 7.3.20 $\mathscr{U}$ is *open* iff $\mathscr{U} = \text{Int}(\mathscr{U})$.

REMARK. If $\mathscr{U}$ is open and $wy \in \mathscr{U}$, then $w \in \mathscr{U}$. If $\mathscr{U}$ is an open relation, then it is necessarily length preserving in the sense of Definition 7.3.2.

Theorem 7.3.21. If $\boldsymbol{\beta}_T$ is the behavior of a finite transducer, then $\boldsymbol{\beta}_T$ is regular.

Proof. Assume that $\mathbf{T} = \langle S, Q, q_0, M, N, O \rangle$ and that $\boldsymbol{\beta}_T = G$. Thus $(x, y) \in \boldsymbol{\beta}_T$ iff $G(q_0, x) = y$, $x \in S^*$ and $y \in O^*$. Define a binary relation R_T in $S \times O \times Q$ as follows:

$$\begin{aligned}(s_{i_1}, o_{i_1}, q_{i_1})\ &R_T\ (s_{i_2}, o_{i_2}, q_{i_2})\\ &\Leftrightarrow M(q_{i_1}, s_{i_1}) = q_{i_2} \wedge N(q_{i_1}, s_{i_1}) = o_{i_1}\\ &\wedge N(q_{i_2}, s_{i_2}) = o_{i_2}\end{aligned}$$

Thus $(\alpha, \beta) \in R_T$ iff α is a triple representing the present input, present output, and present state of a finite transducer, whereas β represents the next input, etc.

Let $\boldsymbol{\beta}'$ be a set constructed as follows. $\alpha \in \boldsymbol{\beta}'$ iff $\alpha = \Lambda$ or α is an R_T-sequence [cf. Exercise 7.2(7)] $a_1, a_2, \ldots$ such that a_1 is a triple of the form $(s_{i_1}, N(q_0, s_{i_1}), q_0)$. Thus $\boldsymbol{\beta}' \subseteq (S \times O \times Q)^*$. Now extend the projection $\varphi(s, o, q) = (s, o)$ to sequences. The direct image $\varphi(\boldsymbol{\beta}') = \boldsymbol{\beta}$ is the behavior of $\mathbf{T}$ and is a regular binary relation since the set of R_T-sequences $\boldsymbol{\beta}'$ is regular. This assertion follows from Exercise 7.2(7) and Theorem 7.3.6. Q.E.D.

Corollary 7.3.22. If $\boldsymbol{\beta}$ is the behavior of a finite transducer, then $\boldsymbol{\beta}$ satisfies the conditions:

1. $\boldsymbol{\beta}$ is a total function.
2. $\boldsymbol{\beta}$ is an open relation.
3. $\boldsymbol{\beta}$ is regular.

This merely summarizes the remark following Definition 7.3.18, using Definition 7.3.20, and the last theorem.

The proof of the converse is quite complicated. Roughly, the idea is to assume a relation R has the properties 1–3 of the corollary. This relation will be a subset of $S^* \times O^*$ and will be functional, length preserving, open, and regular. If we code O on $\{0, 1\}$, then R will be a subset of $S^* \times (\{0, 1\}^r)^*$ for an appropriate r. Now suppose the ith component y_i in $\left(x, \begin{matrix} y_1 \\ \vdots \\ y_r \end{matrix}\right)$ is a word $y1$, y on $\{0, 1\}$, $x \in S^*$. Collect *all* the x's associated to this case and for all other cases $i = 1, \ldots, r$, and build r f.s.a.'s accepting these collections of words x. We will prove that such f.s.a.'s exist. Then, finally, a transducer which is in effect a direct product of the r f.s.a.'s is constructed, and its behavior will be precisely R. To carry out this program we need the following lemma.

Lemma 7.3.23. Suppose that $\alpha \subseteq (S \times \{0, 1\})^*$ is regular. Now let P_1 and P_0 be as follows:

$$P_1(\alpha) = \{x \mid (\exists y)(\exists w)(y, w \in \{0, 1\}^* \wedge y = w1 \wedge (x, y) \in \alpha)\}$$
$$P_0(\alpha) = \{x \mid (\exists y)(\exists w)(y, w \in \{0, 1\}^* \wedge y = w0 \wedge (x, y) \in \alpha)\}$$

Then $P_i(\alpha)$ is regular, $i = 1, 0$.

Proof. Since α is regular, both

$$(a) \quad (S \times \{0, 1\})^* \cdot (S \times \{1\}) \cap \alpha$$

and

$$(b) \quad (S \times \{0, 1\})^* \cdot (S \times \{0\}) \cap \alpha$$

are regular. With our projection techniques the first components of (a) and (b) are precisely $P_1(\alpha)$ and $P_0(\alpha)$, respectively. Q.E.D.

Theorem 7.3.24. If a relation $R \subseteq S^* \times O^*$ satisfies conditions 1 to 3 of Corollary 7.3.22, then $R = \boldsymbol{\beta}_T$ for some $\mathbf{T}$.

Proof. Code O on $\{0, 1\}$ so that each element of O is represented by an r-tuple of 0's and 1's. Then $R \subseteq (S \times \{0, 1\}^r)^*$. Let φ_i project $S \times \{0, 1\}^r$ onto the cartesian product of S and the ith component of $\{0, 1\}^r$: $\varphi_i(s, o_{j_1}, \ldots, o_{j_r}) = (s, o_{j_i})$, $i = 1, \ldots, r$. Extend φ_i to $(S \times \{0, 1\}^r)^*$. Now $\varphi_i(R)$ is regular since R is regular by Theorem 7.3.6 and, by Lemma 7.3.23, $P_1(\varphi_i(R))$ is a regular subset of S^*. Hence there is an f.s.a. $\mathbf{A}_i = \langle S, Q_i, q_{i_0}, M_i, Q_i' \rangle$ such that $x(\mathbf{A}_i) = P_1(\varphi_i(R))$, for each $i = 1, \ldots, r$.

We are now ready to construct the transducer whose behavior will be R. Let $\mathbf{T} = \langle S, Q, q_0, M, N, O \rangle$, where $O = \{0, 1\}^r$, $Q = Q_1 \times \cdots \times Q_r$, each Q_i a set of its $\mathbf{A}_i$, and where

$$M((q_1, \ldots, q_r), s) = (M_1(q_1, s), \ldots, M_r(q_r, s))$$

and

$$N((q_1, \ldots, q_r), s) = (N_1(q_1, s), \ldots, N_r(q_r, s));$$

and, finally, $N_i(q_i, s) = 1$ if $M_i(q_i, s) \in Q_i'$ and $N_i(q_i, s) = 0$ otherwise. Note that $\mathbf{T}$ is transition complete since each (in effect) component $\mathbf{A}_i$ is such that $P_1(\varphi_i(R)) \cup P_0(\varphi_i(R)) = S^*$, since R is a total function; and also $P_1(\varphi_i(R)) \cap P_0(\varphi_i(R)) = \varnothing$ since R is a function. So N is a function and hence G is. Let $\boldsymbol{\beta}_T$ be the behavior of $\mathbf{T}$. Then by Corollary 7.3.22, $\boldsymbol{\beta}_T$ is, besides being a total function, open and regular. So it remains to prove $R = \beta_T$. We will prove this in the form: if $x \in S^*$ and if $y \in O^*$ are such that $(x, y) \in R$ and if $y' \in O^*$ such that $(x, y') \in \beta_T$, then $y = y'$. We proceed by induction. Obviously $(\Lambda, \Lambda) \in R \cap \beta_T$. Assume that $(x, y) \in R \cap \beta_T$ and that $(xs, y't) \in R$. Since R is open, $(x, y') \in R$ and since R is a function, $y = y'$.

To complete the induction we must show that if $(xs, yt') \in \beta_T$, then $t' = t$.

By our various constructions,

$$\begin{aligned}(xs, yt) \in R &\Leftrightarrow (\forall_i)((xs, y_i t_i) \in \varphi_i(R))\\ &\Leftrightarrow (\forall_i)(t_i = 1 \Leftrightarrow xs \in P_1(\varphi_i(R))) \qquad i = 1, \ldots, r \qquad (5)\end{aligned}$$

On the other hand,

$$\begin{aligned}(xs, yt') \in \beta_T &\Leftrightarrow (\exists q_0, \ldots, q_{n-1})(G(q_0, xs) = yt')\\ &= yN(q_0, xs) = yN(M(q_0, x), s)\\ &= yN(q_{n-1}, s))\\ &\Leftrightarrow N(q_{n-1}, s) = t'\end{aligned}$$

But

$$N(q_{n-1}, s) = t' \Leftrightarrow (\forall_i)(t_i' = 1 \Leftrightarrow M_i(q_{i_{n-1}}, s) \in Q_i') \qquad (6)$$

However,

$$(\forall_i)(M_i(q_{i_{n-1}}, s) \in Q_i' \Leftrightarrow xs \in P_1(\varphi_i(R))) \qquad (7)$$

whence it follows from (5), (6), and (7) that $t_i = 1$ iff $t_i' = 1$ for every i, $i = 1, \ldots, r$. Therefore $t = t'$. Q.E.D.

EXAMPLE 5. To illustrate Corollary 7.3.22 and Theorem 7.3.24 and indicate the independence of the conditions 1 to 3, consider the function given by $f(1^{n+1}) = 0^n 1$ with domain $\{1\}$ and co-domain $\{0, 1\}$; f is indeed a function and is regular (why?), but is not open since, for example, $(1^n, 0^n) \notin f$. Again, the intersection of all the open sets containing f would include both pairs $(1, 0)$ and $(1, 1)$. Hence, although such a set would be regular and open [see Exercise 7.3(6)], it would not be a function. It is also possible to display a set which is functional and open but not definable (see Elgot [1959]).

EXAMPLE 6. Assuming that A is simply ordered (Section 1.3) we call $g: A^* \to A^*$ a *sorting function* if each element of the range is of the form $a_0^* a_1^* \cdots a_{m-1}^*$ where $a_i \in A$, $i = 0, \ldots, m - 1$ and $a_i \leq a_j$. There is no finite transducer whose behavior is g, because g is not open.

Definition 7.3.25. A numerical function f is *strictly computable* by a finite transducer **T** iff $f = \beta_T$.

EXAMPLE 7. The bitwise complementation function $g(x) = y$, where if $x = s_{i_1} \cdots s_{i_m}$, $y = \bar{s}_{i_1} \cdots \bar{s}_{i_m}$, $s_{i_j} \in \{0, 1\}$, $j = 1, \ldots, m$, and $^-$ being the boolean complementation operator is strictly computable. Also the pulse-dividing function (Section 3.0).

It is not hard to find extremely simple functions which are not strictly computable. If we use the numerical conventions of Definition 7.3.3 for numerical functions, not even the identity function $I(x_1, \ldots, x_n) = x_i$ is strictly computable since it is not total *wordwise*. For instance considering $I(x_1, x_2) = x_1$, the domain does not include such elements as (B, B) or $(01, BB)$ because neither B nor BB are numeral words. Yet they are obviously in $(\{0, 1, B\}^2)^*$ which is the domain of β for an appropriate transducer. However, we may get around this difficulty by dropping the totality condition. We will then say **I** is transducer computable in the sense that there is a transducer such that if the argument is fed in, the value comes out. Any function which is computable in this new sense must still be regular and open. That is, Theorem 7.3.24 (and trivially Corollary 7.3.22) hold for *incomplete* transducers (Elgot and Mezei [1965]). For such automata we will still use $\beta_T = G$ for behavior later in the text, with G being defined as in Definition 5.3.23 for Moore machines.

Unfortunately, the successor function, to take another simple case, is not open. To verify this somewhat irritating fact note that $(1B, 01)$—numerically $(1, 10)_2$—is in the function, whereas $(1, 0)$ is not. Thus the behavior of no sequential machines, even foregoing totality, is the successor function. But this too can be remedied.

Observe that the successor function S has the property that the relation R which is the union of S and all elements (x, y) such that $(xB, y1) \in S$ is an open relation. This can be easily verified by induction. If R so constructed is regular (it is), and if R is functional (it is), then R is the behavior of some transducer. Clearly then, S is in a sense computable, though not strictly so, since for every integer x appropriately coded as a number word we obtain $S(x)$ likewise as the output of a transducer. The foregoing discussion motivates the following definition.

Definition 7.3.26. A numerical word function f on n variables is *transducer computable* iff there is a **T** (with appropriate alphabet, and in general incomplete) such that

$$\beta_T = \{(x_1 B^{k_1}, \ldots, x_n B^{k_n}, yB^r) \mid (x_1 B^{k_1}, \ldots, x_n B^{k_n}, yB^r) \in f \lor (\exists s_1, \ldots, s_n, s_{n+1})((x_1 B^{k_1} s_1, \ldots, x_n B^{k_n} s_n, yB^r s_{n+1}) \in f)\} \quad k_j, r \geq 0, j = 1, \ldots, n,$$

where at least one of the s's is not a B.

In the following text we will use the notation $\mathcal{O}(R)$ for the union of R and the word prefixes as in Definition 7.3.26. $\mathcal{O}$ suggests "opening."

Theorem 7.3.27. An $n + 1$-ary numerical word relation R is transducer computable iff $\mathcal{O}(R)$ is functional, open, and regular.

Theorem 7.3.28. Addition is transducer computable.

Proof. $\sum$ is regular by Theorem 7.3.16. Let $\mathcal{O}(\sum)$ be formed by joining to $\sum$ all words (x, y, z) such that $(xB, yB, z1) \in \sum$. Then obviously $\mathcal{O}(\sum)$ is open. It is also functional, since if it were not, we would have both $(xB, yB, z1)$ and $(xB, yB, z'1)$ for $z \neq z'$ or $(xB, yB, z1)$ and (x, y, z') where $z1 = z'$, each case being impossible. Next, the regularity of $\mathcal{O}(\sum) - \sum$ can be shown by a construction similar to that for $\sum$; and since $\sum$ is regular and union preserves regularity, $\mathcal{O}(\sum)$ is regular. Q.E.D.

Lemma 7.3.29. If R is open, any explicit transform of R is open. If R is functional, its explicit transform is functional.

Proof. For the student.

Theorem 7.3.30. The successor function is transducer computable.

Proof. $\mathcal{O}(\sum)$ is open and functional, hence so is its explicit transform w.r.t. the second argument by Lemma 7.3.29; and by Theorem 7.3.15, since $\mathcal{O}(\sum)$ is regular, so is its transform. But the transform is evidently $S \bigcup R$ where R is the set obtained by deleting the tail $(B, 1)$ from words in S (see discussion just before Definition 7.3.26). Q.E.D.

Theorem 7.3.31. The Peirce product (Definition 5.5.5) of open relations is open.

Proof. Suppose R_1 and R_2 are open. Then by definition,

$$R_1 \mid R_2 = \{(x, y) \mid (\exists z)((x, z) \in R_1 \wedge (z, y) \in R_2)\}$$

for some appropriate domain of words. Since R_1 and R_2 are open, $l(x) = l(y) = l(z)$. We have to show that if $(x'x, y'y) \in R_1 \mid R_2$, then $(x', y') \in R_1 \mid R_2$. Assuming the former, there is a z such that $l(z) = l(x'x) = l(y'y)$ and $(x'x, z) \in R_1$ and $(z, y'y) \in R_2$. But then $(x', z') \in R_1$ and $(z', y') \in R_2$ for some z' by the theorem hypothesis, whence $(x', y') \in R_1$. Q.E.D.

Corollary 7.3.32. If f_1 and f_2 are numerical functions of one variable and are transducer computable, their composition $f_1 f_2$ is also transducer computable.

The theory following Definition 7.3.26 is hardly satisfactory. We have said nothing about the adequacy of that definition itself. Does it comprehend precisely the set of functions that an informed engineer, say, would maintain are computable by sequential machine? Also, Corollary 7.3.32 is very weak. Nevertheless the method of approach and the relatively powerful concepts used in this section seem to be indispensable for any one who wants to do further work in the field.

EXERCISES 7.3

1. Discuss the definability of the following numerical relations.

(*a*) $x \dot{-} y = z$ (*c*) $x \mid y$

(*b*) $x \cdot y = z$ (*d*) $x < y \Rightarrow y < x$

(*e*) $x - y$

2. Write a regular expression for the addition relation.

3. Prove Theorem 7.3.15.

4. Prove that the binary regular relations are closed under Peirce product.

5. Prove that if $\mathscr{U}$ is regular, then Int ($\mathscr{U}$) is regular.

6. Prove that the intersection of all the open sets containing a regular set is open and regular.

7. Let F be an arbitrary function from a subset of S^* into O, and let $F_x(y) = F(xy)$ if the latter is defined and be undefined otherwise. Let $\boldsymbol{\beta}_{\mathrm{M}}$ be the behavior of a (perhaps incomplete) Moore machine and let $\boldsymbol{\beta}_{\mathrm{M}} = N$. Prove there is a Moore machine whose behavior is F iff the number of distinct functions F_x, $x \in S^*$, is finite. (*Hint*: Let the set of functions F_x be Q for $\mathbf{T}_{\mathrm{M}}$ where $\mathbf{T}_{\mathrm{M}}$ is minimal.)

8. Prove Lemma 7.3.29.

9. Prove that the initial recursive functions $N(x) = 0$ and $I(x_1, \ldots, x_n) = x_i$ are finite transducer computable.

10. Prove that $x \dot{-} y$ is finite transducer computable.

11. Prove that multiplication is not finite transducer computable.

12. "Since the set of words 0^{3n} is regular and since $(0^{3n}, 0^n1^n0^n) \subseteq (S^2)^*$, by Theorem 7.3.7, $\varphi^{-1}(0^{3n})$ is regular, where φ is the projection $\varphi(x, y) = x$; so by Theorem 7.3.6 $0^n1^n0^n$ is regular, contrary to Exercise 7.1(6)." Correct this argument.

13. Complete the proof of Theorem 7.3.12. (*Hint:* Prove that if R is definable there is a definable relation S such that $(\exists y)\ R(y, \overleftarrow{x})$ iff $(\exists y)\ (S(y, \overleftarrow{x} \wedge l(y) \leq l(x_i))$ where $\overleftarrow{x} = (x_1, \ldots, x_n)$ and $i = 1, \ldots, n$.)

7.4 UNIVERSAL ACCEPTORS

At several points in this book we have noted discrepancies between the structure and behavior of automata. There are three main facts: (1) two automata can be equivalent—that is to say, of acceptors we can have $x(\mathbf{A}_1) = x(\mathbf{A}_2)$, or by Exercise 7.1(1) of initial state transducers we can have output equivalence—without there being any structural similarity relation, that is, homomorphism, between the two; (2) two transition systems can share a semigroup, yet be non-homomorphic and even possess different alphabets (cf. Section 5.4); (3) if one automaton is a homomorphic image of the other, they behave the same.

Thus if we are to discuss finite automata which will be in some appropriate sense universal we will need to do this with regard to behavioral equivalence directly, and not with regard to automaton homomorphism, which is too narrow. Nevertheless, since homomorphism implies sameness of behavior, a machine which is a homomorphic image of a number of machines would also show a kind of universality. So there are two ways of approach, a broad and a narrow, and we will try both. In either case we will limit the discussion to acceptors. It can easily be modified for transducers. The key mathematical idea is, again, the semigroup.

A universal automaton, if we understand the term in a manner consistent with Definition 7.1.11, is a transition system $\langle S, Q, q_0, M\rangle$ which can behave the same as any of a given set of f.s.a.'s. We wish, however, to broaden this idea so that the universal machine need not operate on the same alphabet as the machines simulated. In general, its alphabet will be words on the symbols (base alphabet of the systems simulated), but the words accepted will be *codings* of those accepted by the systems in the universal set.

***Definition** 7.4.1.* A *k-n* transition system is one with $K(S) = k$ and $K(Q) = n$, supposing $\mathbf{T}_S = \langle S, Q, q_0, M\rangle$.

***Definition** 7.4.2.* A transition system $\mathbf{T}_{S_a} = \langle S, Q_a, q_{a_0}, M_a\rangle$ can *simulate* an acceptor $\mathbf{A}_b = \langle S, Q_b, q_{b_0}, M_b, Q_b'\rangle$ iff there is an acceptor

$$\mathbf{A}_a = \langle S, Q_a, q_{a_0}, M_a, Q_a'\rangle$$

and a code $C\colon S^* \to S^*$ such that

$$x \in x(\mathbf{A}_b) \Leftrightarrow C(x) \in x(\mathbf{A}_a)$$

It is obvious from the definition of f.s.a. that there can be no *k-n* transition system which can simulate every acceptor, since such a system would have to have an infinite number of states. There is a trivial system of the latter kind as we have already observed, namely the free system $\mathbf{T}_{S\mathscr{S}}$; but it is of no interest. So we must always relativize a simulating system to a class of automata having some fixed number n (or less) of states.

***Definition** 7.4.3.* $\mathbf{T}_S$ is *universal* for a set of acceptors iff $\mathbf{T}_S$ can simulate every acceptor of the set.

The central idea we will use in constructing universal systems in this sense is the semigroup generator. Suppose it should turn out that any automaton semigroup can be generated by a fixed finite number of elements. Then it turns out, after some thought, that a transition system whose transition function M is the same as these generating functions should be universal. Fortunately it is true that any semigroup of functions of a finite set (for example, Q) into itself can be obtained by the composition of three functions.

Definition 7.4.4. Given a finite, nonempty set $A = \{a_0, \ldots, a_{n-1}\}$, we define three functions $\varphi_0, \varphi_1, \varphi_2$ on A into A:

$$\begin{aligned} \varphi_0(a_i) &= a_{i+1} && i < n-1 \\ \varphi_0(a_{n-1}) &= a_0 \\ \varphi_1(a_0) &= a_1 \\ \varphi_1(a_1) &= a_0 \\ \varphi_1(a_i) &= a_i && 1 < i \leq n-1 \\ \varphi_2(a_0) &= a_0 \\ \varphi_2(a_1) &= a_0 \\ \varphi_2(a_i) &= a_i && 1 < i \leq n-1 \end{aligned}$$

φ_0 is a *great permutation*, φ_1 is a *transposition*, and φ_2 is a *contraction.*

REMARK. Although we shall most often use the functions as defined, a suitable transposition function need only interchange any two elements and likewise a contraction function would be equally effective for our purposes if it contracted any two, not just a_0 and a_1.

Lemma 7.4.5. The group of permutations of n elements $\{a_0, \ldots, a_{n-1}\}$ is generated by φ_0 and φ_1.

Proof. For the student.

Theorem 7.4.6. The semigroup of functions on $A = \{a_0, \ldots, a_{n-1}\}$ into A is generated by φ_0, φ_1, and φ_2.

Proof. If an element ψ of the semigroup is a permutation, then by Lemma 7.4.5 it can be obtained from φ_0 and φ_1. Suppose it is not a permutation, and that $\{a_{i_0}, \ldots, a_{i_r}\} = A' \subseteq A$ is the largest subdomain for which ψ thus restricted is one–one. Let ψ' be a permutation such that $\psi' = \psi$ on A'. Let $\varphi_j^i(a_i) = a_j$ and $\varphi_j^i(a_k) = a_k$ for $k \neq i$. φ_j^i is a generalization of $\varphi_0{}^1 = \varphi_2$; that is to say, $\varphi_0{}^1(a_0) = a_0$ and $\varphi_0{}^1(a_1) = a_0$. By composing functions φ_j^i with ψ' we can obtain ψ as follows. Recalling that $\psi' = \psi$ over A', suppose $a_i \in A - A'$ and $a_j \in A'$ while $\psi(a_i) = \psi(a_j) = a_k$; then we have

$$(\psi'\varphi_j^i)(a_i) = \psi'(\varphi_j^i(a_i)) = \psi'(a_j) = a_k$$

So ψ is equal to the composition of ψ' with φ_j^i.

Finally, it remains to show that any function φ_j^i is reducible to products of permutations and $\varphi_0{}^1$. Let θ be a permutation such that $\theta(a_i) = a_1$ and $\theta(a_j) = a_0$. Then we have at once that

$$\varphi_j^i = \theta^{-1}\varphi_0{}^1\theta$$

Q.E.D.

Now we may construct a universal transition system whose M function, by way of the equality $M(q, x) = \varphi_x(q)$, is determined by φ_i, $i = 0, 1, 2$.

Theorem 7.4.7. There exists a universal 3-n transition system.

Proof. Let $\mathbf{T}_S{}^3 = \langle\{0, 1, 2\}, Q, q_0, M\rangle$ where $K(Q) = n$, and let M be given by Definition 7.4.4 using Definition 5.4.9 and setting $q = a$. For example, if $n = 3$ we would have Table 7.4.1. Thus φ_0, for instance, is the

TABLE 7.4.1

	0	1	2
q_0	q_1	q_1	q_0
q_1	q_2	q_0	q_0
q_2	q_0	q_2	q_2

great permutation on three letters (states). Suppose now that $\mathbf{A}_a = \langle\{s_0, s_1, s_2\}, Q_a, q_0, M_a, Q_a'\rangle$. By Theorem 7.4.6, there exists a word $x \in \{0, 1, 2\}^*$ such that

$$M_a(q, s_0) = \varphi_{s_0}(q) = \varphi_x(q) = M(q, x) \tag{1}$$

where φ_{s_0} is an element of the semigroup of $\mathbf{A}_a$ and φ_x is a product of powers of φ_0, φ_1, and φ_2. Similarly for $M_a(q, s_1)$ and $M_a(q, s_2)$. Let x_a be a word on $\{s_0, s_1, s_2\}$ and let $x_a \in x(\mathbf{A}_a)$. Then if $x_a = s_{i_1} \cdots s_{i_n}$

$$\begin{aligned} M_a(q_0, x_a) \in Q_a' &\Leftrightarrow M_a(q_0, s_{i_1} \cdots s_{i_n}) \in Q_a' \\ &\Leftrightarrow \varphi_{s_{i_1} \cdots s_{i_n}}(q_0) \in Q_a' \\ &\Leftrightarrow \varphi_{s_{i_n}} \cdots \varphi_{s_{i_1}}(q_0) \in Q_a' \\ &\Leftrightarrow \varphi_{x_n} \cdots \varphi_{x_1}(q_0) \in Q_a' \\ &\Leftrightarrow \varphi_{x_1^{-1} \cdots x_n^{-1}}(q_0) \in Q_a' \end{aligned}$$

where $\varphi_{x_j} = \varphi_{s_{i_j}}$. Let $\mathbf{A}^3 = \langle\{0, 1, 2\}, Q, q_0, M, Q_a'\rangle$ be an acceptor obtained by adding Q_a' as final states to $\mathbf{T}_S{}^3$, and let C be the appropriate coding determined by (1), taking $\{s_0, s_1, s_2\}^*$ one–one into $\{0, 1, 2\}^*$. Then, by the foregoing, x_a is accepted by $\mathbf{A}_a$ iff $C(x_a)$ is accepted by $\mathbf{A}^3$. Hence $\mathbf{T}_S{}^3$ simulates $\mathbf{A}_a$, by Definition 7.4.2, and since $\mathbf{A}_a$ is an arbitrary 3-n acceptor, $\mathbf{T}_S{}^3$ is universal for that class. Q.E.D.

An immediate generalization is given by the following corollary.

Corollary 7.4.8. For every $k \geq 3$ there is a universal k-n transition system.

The reader may wonder about the case $k = 2$ ruled out by this corollary. Unfortunately, it turns out that there is no 2-n system universal for the set of 2-n acceptors when $n \geq 3$, except in the case of permutation automata (see exercises). We will therefore be content to prove the weaker statement that for the set of 2-n machines there is a universal 2-n + 1 transition system.

Theorem 7.4.9 (Stearns). There is an $n + 1$ state binary transition system universal for the set of n state binary acceptors.

Proof. $\mathbf{T}_S^2 = \langle \{0, 1\}, Q, q_0, M \rangle$ where $Q = \{q_0, \ldots, q_n\}$ and where M is given by

$$\begin{aligned} M(q_i, 0) &= q_{i+1} && 0 \leq i \leq n - 2 \\ M(q_n, 0) &= M(q_{n-1}, 0) = q_0 && \\ M(q_0, 1) &= q_{n-2} && \\ M(q_{i+1}, 1) &= q_i && 0 \leq i \leq n - 3 \\ M(q_{n-1}, 1) &= q_n && \\ M(q_n, 1) &= q_0 && \end{aligned} \tag{2}$$

provided that $n \geq 3$. If $n = 2$ (if we are attempting to simulate the set of 2-2 automata), the relation $M(q_{i+1}, 1) = q_i$ does not apply. As an alternative to (2) write the equations in terms of the semigroup functions:

$$\begin{aligned} \varphi_0'(q_i) &= q_{i+1} && 0 \leq i \leq n - 2 \\ \varphi_0'(q_n) &= \varphi_0'(q_{n-1}) = q_0 && \\ \varphi_1'(q_0) &= q_{n-2} && \\ \varphi_1'(q_{i+1}) &= q_i && 0 \leq i \leq n - 3 \\ \varphi_1'(q_{n-1}, 1) &= q_n && \\ \varphi_1'(q_n, 1) &= q_0 && \end{aligned} \tag{3}$$

Now we will show that any function on $\{q_0, \ldots, q_{n-1}\}$ into itself is obtainable from φ_0' and φ_1' (which latter of course are functions on $\{q_0, \ldots, q_n\}$. Note, to start with, that φ_0 (of Definition 7.4.4) is given by φ_0' restricted to $\{q_0, \ldots, q_{n-1}\}$: φ_0' thus restricted is the great permutation over the required domain. Hence we need only show (Lemma 7.4.5) that any transposition is obtainable and φ_2 is obtainable as well.

By Lemma 7.4.5 the special transposition given by (see remark preceding lemma)

$$\begin{aligned} \bar{\varphi}_1(q_0) &= q_{n-1} && \\ \bar{\varphi}_1(q_{n-1}) &= q_0 && \\ \bar{\varphi}_1(q_i) &= q_i && i \neq n - 1 \neq 0 \end{aligned}$$

together with φ_0 is sufficient to generate all permutations. But $\bar{\varphi}_1$ can be had from φ_0' and φ_1' as follows:

$$\begin{aligned} \varphi_0'\varphi_1'(q_0) &= q_{n-1} \\ \varphi_0'\varphi_1'(q_{n-1}) &= q_0 \\ \varphi_0'\varphi_1'(q_i) &= q_i \end{aligned}$$

by (3). Therefore $\bar{\varphi}_1 = \varphi_0'\varphi_1'$.

Second, we can obtain the contraction function φ_2 from φ_1' together with permutations in the following way.

$$\begin{aligned}(\varphi_1')^2(q_0) &= q_{n-3}\\ (\varphi_1')^2(q_1) &= q_{n-2}\\ (\varphi_1')^2(q_i) &= q_{i-2} \qquad 2 \le i \le n-2\\ (\varphi_1')^2(q_{n-1}) &= q_0\end{aligned}$$

Thus $(\varphi_1')^2$ is a function on $\{q_0, \ldots, q_{n-1}\}$ onto $\{q_0, \ldots, q_{n-2}\}$, taking the value q_0 twice. Clearly there is a permutation ψ which can be obtained from φ_0' and $\bar{\varphi}_1$ such that $(\varphi_1')^2\psi = \varphi_2$, since φ_2 also takes on the value q_0 twice and is onto otherwise. It is left to the student to complete the proof after the pattern of Theorem 7.4.7. Q.E.D.

The foregoing results about universal systems all reduce to the fact that the maps on finite sets into themselves are definable from three primitive ones and that a simulating automaton can imitate an arbitrary semigroup element of the automaton simulated. This observation suggests the following theorem.

Theorem 7.4.10. If an acceptor $\mathbf{A}_b$ is minimal and if $\mathbf{T}_S$ simulates $\mathbf{A}_b$, then the semigroup Φ_b of $\mathbf{A}_b$ is a homomorphic image of a sub-semigroup Φ_a of $\mathbf{T}_S$.

Proof. Let $\mathbf{T}_S = \langle S_a, Q_a, q_0, M_a\rangle$ and $\mathbf{A}_b = \langle S_b, Q_b, q_0, M_b, Q_b'\rangle$. By hypothesis there is a code C and a set of final states Q_a' such that $\mathbf{A}_a = \langle S_a, Q_a, q_0, M_a, Q_a'\rangle$ and

$$x \in x(\mathbf{A}_b) \Leftrightarrow C(x) \in x(\mathbf{A}_a)$$

Let $\psi\colon \Phi_C \to \Phi_b$ be given by $\psi(\varphi^a_{C(x)}) = \varphi_x{}^b$ where $\Phi_C \subseteq \Phi_a$ and $\varphi^a \in \Phi_a$ and $\varphi^b \in \Phi_b$. We will show that

$$\varphi^a_{C(x)} = \varphi^a_{C(y)} \Rightarrow \varphi_x{}^b = \varphi_y{}^b \tag{4}$$

for any $\varphi^a_{C(x)}$, etc. Suppose that $\varphi_x{}^b \neq \varphi_y{}^b$, this is the same as

$$(\exists q)(M_b(q, x) \neq M_b(q, y))$$

Call this state q'. Since $\mathbf{A}_b$ is reduced (Definition 7.1.12), there is a word $z \in S_b{}^*$ such that

$$M_b(M_b(q', x), z) \in Q_i' \Leftrightarrow M_b(M_b(q', y), z) \notin Q_i'$$

and since $\mathbf{A}_b$ is connected, q' is accessible, so there is a w such that

$$M_b(M_b(M_b(q_0, w), x), z) \in Q_i' \Leftrightarrow M_b(M_b(M_b(q_0, w), y), z) \notin Q_i' \tag{5}$$

From (5) it follows that

$$wxz \in x(\mathbf{A}_b) \Leftrightarrow wyz \notin x(\mathbf{A}_b)$$

Since $\mathbf{T}_S$ simulates $\mathbf{A}_b$ we have,

$$C(wxz) \in x(\mathbf{A}_a) \Leftrightarrow C(wyz) \notin x(\mathbf{A}_a)$$

But C is an isomorphism, and so

$$C(w)C(x)C(z) \in x(\mathbf{A}_a) \Leftrightarrow C(w)C(y)C(z) \notin x(\mathbf{A}_a)$$

Therefore $C(x) \neq C(y)$ and $\varphi^a_{C(x)} \neq \varphi^a_{C(y)}$ proving (4). It follows immediately from (4) that

$$\psi(\varphi^a_{C(x)} \cdot \varphi^a_{C(y)}) = \psi(\varphi^a_{C(x)}) \cdot \psi(\varphi^a_{C(y)}) \qquad \text{Q.E.D.}$$

By specializing the concept same behavior to that of strong homomorphism (cf. Definition 7.1.13 and Theorem 7.1.16) we shall be able to secure somewhat more elegant results. We can actually produce a universal *acceptor* for a set of f.s.a.'s, and, moreover, unlike the cases just discussed, this new universal automaton will be able to simulate machines with fewer states. This is all accomplished by taking a universal automaton to be one into which automata of the simulated set are homomorphically mapped.

Definition 7.4.11. Given $\mathbf{T}_{S_a} = \langle S_a, Q_a, M_a \rangle$ and $\mathbf{T}_{S_b} = \langle S_b, Q_b, M_b \rangle$, a *transition homomorphism with transcription* is a pair of functions (θ, ψ), $\theta: Q_a \to Q_b$ and $\psi: S_a \to S_b{}^*$ such that

$$\theta M_a(q_a, s) = M_b(\theta(q_a), \psi(s)) \tag{6}$$

$q_a \in Q_a$ and $s \in S_a$.

Definition 7.4.12. Given $\mathbf{A}_a = \langle S_a, Q_a, q_{a_0}, M_a, Q_a' \rangle$ and

$$\mathbf{A}_b = \langle S_b, Q_b, q_{b_0}, M_b, Q_b' \rangle$$

an *acceptor homomorphism with transcription* is a pair of functions (θ, ψ), $\theta: Q_a \to Q_b$ and $\psi: S_a \to S_b{}^*$ which satisfies (6), and in addition satisfies

$$\theta(q_{a_0}) = q_{b_0} \tag{7}$$

and

$$q_a \in Q_a' \Leftrightarrow \theta(q_a) \in Q_b' \tag{8}$$

Definition 7.4.13. A transition system $\mathbf{T}_S$ is *universal* w.r.t. a *set of transition systems* iff every system of the set is homomorphic to $\mathbf{T}_S$ in the sense (6). Likewise an acceptor $\mathbf{A}$ is *universal* w.r.t. *a set of acceptors* iff every f.s.a. of the set is homomorphic to $\mathbf{A}$, in the sense of (6), (7), and (8).

Lemma 7.4.14. There is a universal transition system $\mathbf{T}_S$ w.r.t. the set of all transition systems with n or fewer states. $\mathbf{T}_S$ has 3 symbols and n states.

Proof. Let $\mathbf{T}_{S_a} = \langle S_a, Q_a, M_a \rangle$ with $K(Q_a) \leq n$. Let

$$\mathbf{T}_S = \langle \{0, 1, 2\}, Q, M \rangle$$

with $Q = \{q_0, \ldots, q_{n-1}\}$ and M given by Table 7.4.1, modified for n states (0, 1, and 2 are to act like the primitives φ_0, φ_1, and φ_2). Let $\theta: Q_a \to Q$ be given by $\theta(q_{a_i}) = q_i$ and $\psi: S_a \to \{0, 1, 2\}^*$ by $\psi(s) = x$ iff $\varphi_s{}^a = \varphi_x$

under Theorem 7.4.6. We need only show that (θ, ψ) is a homomorphism with transcription. For the demonstration note that $\varphi_x(q_{a_i}) = q_{a_k}$ iff $\varphi_x(q_i) = q_k$ owing to the definition of θ.

$$\begin{aligned} \theta(M_a(q_{a_i}, s)) &= \theta(\varphi_s^a(q_{a_i})) = \theta(\varphi_x(q_{a_i})) \\ M(\theta(q_{a_i}), \psi(s)) &= M(\theta(q_{a_i}), x) \\ &= \varphi_x(\theta(q_{a_i})) \\ &= \varphi_x(q_i) \end{aligned}$$

But by the remark above $\varphi_x(q_i) = \theta(\varphi_x(q_{a_i}))$. Q.E.D.

In the statement of the main theorem to follow, an m, r-acceptor is one with no more than m final states and no more than r nonfinal states, and with $q_0 \in Q'$, the set of final states.

Theorem 7.4.15. The set of all m, r-f.s.a.'s includes a universal f.s.a. with m final and r nonfinal states.

Proof. Follows immediately from Lemma 7.4.14 by forcing (7) and (8), letting θ map final states into final states, nonfinal states into nonfinal states, and the initial state into the initial state. Q.E.D.

There is an obvious companion theorem for the case where $q_0 \notin Q'$.

EXERCISES 7.4

1. Prove Lemma 7.4.5.

2. Is it possible to strengthen Corollary 7.4.8 to state that for every $k \geq 3$ there is a 3-n transition system? Explain.

3. If two transition systems are homomorphic $\mathbf{T}_{S_a}$ onto $\mathbf{T}_{S_b}$, then the semigroups Φ_a and Φ_b are homomorphic.

4. Show that the converse of Theorem 7.4.10 is false.

5. Supply the missing details for the proof of Theorem 7.4.15.

6. Prove that there is a 2-n transition system which is universal for the set of all 2-n acceptors whose semigroups are groups.

7.5 HISTORICAL AND BIBLIOGRAPHICAL REMARKS

The problem of the discriminatory or accepting powers of finite acceptors was first stated and solved by Kleene [1956] in terms of regular events (that is, sets). Another important early work is Medvedev [1958]. The abstract characterization of definability in terms of right-invariance is Nerode's [1958], while a companion result using congruence classes is due to Myhill. The simplified exposition of the theory plus further material on automata having multiple tapes, two-way tapes, closure properties of definable sets, and the decidability problems discussed in Section 7.2 is Rabin and Scott's [1959]. In our exposition we follow a point of view deriving from Büchi [1961] and Thatcher [1963].

The analysis and synthesis results using regular expressions are Kleene's [1956]. However, the synthesis algorithm we actually use is an adaptation of that of Ott and Feinstein [1961], which in turn goes back to Copi, Elgot, and Wright [1958]. The idea of a nondeterministic machine employed therein should be jointly attributed to Rabin and Scott and to Myhill [1957]. The simple acceptor is an invention of Elgot and Mezei [1965]. The analysis algorithm is due to McNaughton and Yamada [1960].

The material on definable relations is taken from Ritchie [1963] while the main characterization of finite transducer computability is Elgot's [1961]. The alternative way of defining behavior, as in Exercise 7.3(7), goes back to Raney [1958] but the theorem as formulated here is due to Elgot and Rutledge [1961] (cf. also Krohn and Rhodes [1963]). Very general word relations definable by n.f.s.a.'s, called transductions, have been extensively studied by Elgot and Mezei [1965].

The section on universal automata is essentially sections 3 and 4 of Myhill [1963a] which in turn uses unpublished results of R. E. Stearns. The result relating simulation to homomorphism is due to Krohn and Rhodes [1963]. Universal automata as homomorphic images of acceptors were considered by Paz [1962].

There is a large volume of material on f.s.a.'s which we have not even mentioned. Omitted material, which the student may wish to follow up for himself, concerns probabilistic automata (Rabin [1963]), the theory of definite automata (Perles, Rabin, and Shamir [1963]), error correcting automata (for example, Winograd [1964] and Harrison [1965]), and derivatives of regular expressions (Brzozowski [1964]). Keller [1961] has analyzed learning machines from the point of view of a probabilistic acceptor theory. Some of these topics were introduced in the exercises for Sections 7.1 and 7.2.

CHAPTER 8

Generators

8.0 Introduction. In recent years, many linguists have tended to view languages, including both natural and artificial languages, as the outputs of formal systems. Moreover, the systems linguists study are formal in precisely our sense and are or can be construed to be semi-thue systems. For this reason, as already indicated in Chapter 3, we regard language generators as types of automata.

The mathematically inclined student should be cautioned against the view that mathematical linguistics is the whole of linguistics. The linguistics of natural languages, if not of artificial languages such as ALGOL, is an empirical science. A grammar considered as a set of formal rules is a model of the grammar which those fluent in the language use. So a mathematical model must in the end be submitted to certain empirical tests of adequacy. The determination of such tests is, of course, the business of linguists and psychologists, not of logicians or mathematicians.

However, as builders of formal models we must be aware of certain minimal adequacy requirements. Supposing that we limit ourselves to grammar—that branch of linguistics which studies the composition of sentences from basic phrase or phrase-like materials—we can list two such requirements. If we think, for the moment, of a language as being (whatever else it is) a subset of a set of finite sequences over a base alphabet, then the model should be consistent with and in some sense explain the grammatical principles governing the construction of every possible sentence of the language. In the sort of theory we are discussing the model of a grammar is a generator (Definition 3.3.15), the sentences are the terminal theorems, and the criteria of adequacy phrased so as to be applicable to this kind of model are as follows.

For a generator to be an adequate model of a grammar of a language L, it should

(*a*) generate all and only the sentences of L.

(*b*) provide each sentence with a description of the way in which it is composed of its phrase or phraselike grammatical constituents.

Condition *a* is merely a restatement of our generalized remarks about consistency and completeness made after Definition 3.2.2. Concerning *b*, what is required is that our grammar not only turn out the sentence but provide somehow for different readings of the *same* sentence. For example,

$$\text{(she (is (a (pretty little) girl)))} \tag{1}$$

and

$$\text{(she (is (a (pretty (little girl))))} \tag{2}$$

are identical letter for letter (suppressing parenthesis) but they do not mean the same. (1) says a certain girl is pretty little, while (2) says that a certain little girl is pretty. A single sentence which is capable of two or more interpretations depending on its phrase structure, that is, depending on its possessing more than one grammatically acceptable reading is said to be *syntactically ambiguous*. It is evidently a primary empirical fact about natural languages that they are ambiguous and hence very rich in expression.

Let us examine requirement *b* more carefully. A description of the structure of a sentence should indicate both the constituent parts thereof, as in (1) and (2), and also the grammatical *kinds* of parts of which they are instances. Thus in (1) the parentheses surrounding "pretty little" might be subscripted "Adj" so that

$$(_{\text{Adj}}\ \text{pretty little})_{\text{Adj}}$$

indicates that "pretty little" is an adjective phrase. Further, if we continue this manner of description we may rewrite (1) as follows:

$$(_{\text{S}}(_{\text{P}}\ \text{she})_{\text{P}}(_{\text{VP}}(_{\text{Cop}}\ \text{is})_{\text{Cop}}(_{\text{NP}}(_{\text{Art}}\ \text{a})_{\text{Art}}(_{\text{Adj}}(_{\text{Adv}}\ \text{pretty})_{\text{Adv}}(_{\text{Adj}}\ \text{little})_{\text{Adj}})_{\text{Adj}}\ (_{\text{N}}\ \text{girl})_{\text{N}})_{\text{NP}})_{\text{VP}})_{\text{S}} \tag{1a}$$

where the interpretations of the subscripts are

S	Sentence
P	Pronoun
VP	Verb phrase
NP	Noun phrase
Cop	Copula
Art	Article
Adj	Adjective
Adv	Adverb
N	Noun

A sentence equipped with phrase-bounding labeled parentheses as in (1a) is called a *phrase marker*. Without at all attempting to go beyond an intuitive understanding to a formal definition of "phrase marker," let us rewrite the adequacy requirement *b*.

b'. provide each sentence with a phrase marker.

It is a happy circumstance that generators such that for each production $PgR \to Pg'R$, where g is a single auxiliary, automatically provide for phrase markers, and thus satisfy b'. To see this, consider the proof 1–6 of Example 10 in Section 3.3. We will use a new kind of proof which imitates that one, but which supplies phrase-marking parentheses. The new rules modify the usual productions in a very simple way (and are indeed still productions of semi-thue systems with augmented alphabet S). If w_{i+1} follows from w_i by $q_i \to g$ then w'_{i+1} is to follow from w_i' by $q_i \to ({}_i g)_i$. Thus in the example cited we have the modified proof 1′–6′.

1′. q_0
2′. $({}_0\, q_1 q_2)_0$
3′. $({}_0({}_1\, q_3 q_4)_1\, q_2)_0$
4′. $({}_0({}_1({}_3\, \text{the})_3\, q_4)_1\, q_2)_0$
5′. $({}_0({}_1({}_3\, \text{the})_3\, ({}_4\, \text{dog})_4)_1\, q_2)_0$
6′. $({}_0({}_1({}_3\, \text{the})_3\, ({}_4\, \text{dog})_4)_1\, ({}_2\, \text{ran})_2)_0$

Now let 0 be S, 1 be NP, 2 be V, 3 be Art, and 4 be N. Evidently the structure given by the proof itself supplies the phrase marker. It seems, therefore, that a generator of this kind is an adequate model in accordance with requirement b' above. It may not, however, simultaneously satisfy *a*.

Three further remarks must be made before we can get to the technical details. The first is that our auxiliary symbols, erstwhile *states* of various kinds of machines, are now *grammatical categories*. In the preceding example "q_0" corresponds to "sentence," q_1 to "noun phrase," "q_2" to "verb," "q_3" to "definite article" and "q_4" to "noun". Thus whereas the auxiliary symbols perform a memory role in acceptors (and transducers), in a generator they play a role determining the constitutive structure of what is yet to come—they are anticipatory. In other words, in acceptors or detectors auxiliaries are needed for *analyzing* structures, whereas in generators they are needed for *synthesizing* structures. We might expect these roles to be reflected in a certain complementarity of machines. This is indeed the case. Corresponding to a given class of generators we can find a class of acceptors for the same language and conversely. We already have an example of complementarity in Theorems 4.3.17 and 4.3.20. Unfortunately this complementarity is not always so "natural" as it is in the case of Turing machines. We will discuss the question of corresponding acceptors in Sections 8.2 and 8.3 for several classes of generative grammar.

The second remark is that the study of generative grammars and their languages is, from our point of view, only a subpart of the more or less formal part of one school of approach to linguistics. It is inappropriate in a book such as this to argue the merits of this school against those of any other. Suffice it to say that generators are automata, hence interesting to us, even if to no one else. Another subpart of the formal part of linguistics, and one which we neglect, concerns *transformational* grammar. This subject goes beyond generators to the study of certain transformations on phrase markers which preserve grammaticalness. Since these transformations, although they are *bona fide* functions, have so far resisted mathematical treatment, we omit discussion of them. Suffice it to say that transformations seem to enable us to account for tense, mood, voice, etc., in a simple way not easily matched by a purely generative approach. Further reference to this question is made in Section 8.4.

The third remark is that generative grammars may be so "unrealistic" as to fail to give an adequate theory of English, French, etc. It is known that even ALGOL 60, for example, is not a phrase-structure (Definition 8.1.5) language, and indeed seems to require something like transformation theory to account for the whole of it (Floyd [1962a]). On the other hand, this writer can see no compelling reason why an essentially equivalent language cannot be designed so as to be in the phrase-structure class. It is not known that English is not a phrase-structure language—that is, strictly accountable as to its grammar by generators. However this may be, it seems to us that many useful ideas for the study of language have been developed using a formal mathematical approach.

8.1 GENERATIVE GRAMMARS

We begin by refining some of the primitive generator concepts of Section 3.3, which should be reviewed.

Definition 8.1.1. A *generative grammar* is a generator

$$\mathbf{G} = \langle S \cup Q, (S \cup Q)^*, \{\#q_0\#\}, \mathscr{P} \rangle$$

where $\# \in S$, $q_0 \in Q$; $\mathscr{P}$ is a finite set of productions $PgR \to Pg'R$, $g, g' \in (S \cup Q)^*$; every $q \in Q$ occurs in some word g of a production; there are no productions $PgR \to PgR$ ($\to$ is irreflexive); no production has an inverse ($\to$ is asymmetric); $\#$ occurs in a production P iff P is of the form $P\#wR \to P\#w'R$, $Pw\#R \to Pw'\#R$, or $P\#w\#R \to P\#w'\#R$, $w, w' \in (S \cup Q - \{\#\})^*$. From now on in analogy with our notations for other automata associated systems we write simply $\mathbf{G} = \langle S, Q, q_0, \mathscr{P} \rangle$.

REMARKS. In this definition S and Q are as usual the pure and auxiliary alphabets. In mathematical linguistics it is usual to term S the *terminal* vocabulary and Q the *nonterminal.* Since every q occurs on the left of some production, if there is a terminal theorem (Definition 3.3.7) it will contain only terminal symbols. Note that this is precisely the case with Turing generators (Definition 4.3.19). The boundary marker # is used to force rewriting, if any, only at the ends of words in cases when this is desired. It necessarily occurs only at the ends of words. Every interesting grammar is polygenic, since if it were not, it would generate but *one* sentence.

From now on, in discussing generators we will drop the formality of carrying along the syntactical symbols P and R, keeping in mind that every step in a proof is to be made as if they were there. Also we allow x, y, etc. to range over $(S \cup Q)^*$. Terminal theorems are, of course, pure. The concepts sentence and language are the same as in Definition 3.3.16, which we need not repeat. We write $L(\mathbf{G})$ for the language generated by $\mathbf{G}$.

Definition 8.1.2. Two grammars $\mathbf{G}_a$ and $\mathbf{G}_b$ are *weakly equivalent* iff $L(\mathbf{G}_a) = L(\mathbf{G}_b)$.

We will not use the stronger concept of *equivalence* of grammars. Equivalence, in addition to the identity of the generated languages, requires that the grammars provide the same phrase markers. Very little is at present known about equivalence and in particular about which of the numerous weak equivalence (inequivalence) results we discuss later also hold for strong equivalence. It is easy of course to give an exact definition of equivalence using the technique of proof 1′–6′ of the Section 8.0 (cf. Definition 8.2.25).

We now characterize four families of generative grammar and correspondingly four families of languages. Following (with slight modification) the classic procedure of Chomsky [1959] we will accomplish this characterization in terms of three conditions.

CONDITION 1. If $g \to g'$ is a rule of $\mathbf{G}$, then there are words $x, y \in (S \cup Q)^*$ such that $g = xqy$, $q \in Q$, and $g' = xwy$, $w \in (S \cup Q)^* - \{\Lambda\}$.

CONDITION 2. If $g \to g'$ is a rule of $\mathbf{G}$ which satisfies Condition 1, then $x = y = \Lambda$.

CONDITION 3. If $g \to g'$ is a rule of $\mathbf{G}$ which satisfies Condition 2, then w is of the form sq or s.

Condition 3 could equally prescribe that w be of the form qs or s. Either formulation could be used in Definition 8.1.9 below [cf. Exercise 8.2(3)].

Definition 8.1.3. A grammar $\mathbf{G}$ is an *unrestricted rewriting system* or *unrestricted grammar* iff $\mathbf{G}$ does not satisfy Condition 1.

EXAMPLE 1. A Turing generator is such a grammar since the rules in general violate Condition 1. A typical Turing production provides for the replacement of a *pair qs* by other symbols; Condition 1, on the other hand, provides just for the replacement of a *single* auxiliary. Although there is nothing in the Turing rules (Definition 4.1.1) to prevent reflexive or symmetric use of $\rightarrow$, it is obvious that any such usage can be eliminated (cf. Theorem 4.6.4 and its proof).

Since by Example 1 a Turing generator is an unrestricted grammar and since by Theorem 4.3.20 every recursively enumerable set is the output of some Turing generator, it follows that every recursively enumerable set is the language of some unrestricted grammar. This fact together with Corollary 3.3.6*b* proves the following theorem.

Theorem 8.1.4. The families of Turing generators and unrestricted grammars are the same in the sense that every Turing generator **Z** is weakly equivalent to some unrestricted grammar **G** and every **G** is weakly equivalent to some **Z**. A language L is the language $L(\mathbf{G})$ of an unrestricted grammar **G** iff L is recursively enumerable.

This theorem should be understood under the liberal interpretation of "recursively enumerable" employed after Theorems 3.1.6.

An unrestricted grammar is unsatisfactory for modeling a natural language such as English (although English is surely recursively enumerable) principally because such a grammar cannot satisfy the adequacy criterion *b′*) of Section 8.0. It is easy to see that a phrase marker can be secured for each sentence of a generated language only if at most one auxiliary symbol is rewritten by any use of a production. This is the reason for Condition 1, and suggests the following definition.

Definition 8.1.5. Any grammar which satisfies any of the Conditions 1–3 is a *phrase structure grammar*. The language associated to such a grammar is a *phrase structure language.*

Definition 8.1.6. A grammar **G** is *context sensitive* iff all its rules satisfy Condition 1. If **G** is context sensitive, $L(\mathbf{G})$ is a *context sensitive language.*

EXAMPLE 2. (Chomsky). Let L be the *copy* language consisting of all sentences $xcccx$, where $x \in \{a, b\}^*$. L is not definable; that is, not regular (see exercise). L is, however, obviously recursive. So we have found a language which is not regular but yet recursive. (We will further discuss this observation below). However, L is, in fact, context sensitive as it is generated by the following grammar, where $S = \{a, b, c, \#\}$ and the Q are the roman capitals.

Axiom: $\#S\#$

R.1.	$S \rightarrow CDGF$	***R.5.***	$G \rightarrow b$
R.2.	$G \rightarrow aG$	***R.6.***	$CDa \rightarrow CEa$
R.3.	$G \rightarrow bG$	***R.7.***	$CEa \rightarrow CEAa$
R.4.	$G \rightarrow a$	***R.8.***	$CDb \rightarrow CEb$

R.9.	$CEb \to CEBb$	***R.18.***	$\alpha D \to D\alpha$
R.10.	$CEA \to AEA$	***R.19.***	$A \to a$
R.11.	$AEA \to ACA$	***R.20.***	$B \to b$
R.12.	$ACA \to ACE$	***R.21.***	$aCDFa \to aCDca$
R.13.	$CEB \to BED$	***R.22.***	$aCDFb \to aCDcb$
R.14.	$BEB \to BCB$	***R.23.***	$bCDFa \to bCDca$
R.15.	$BCB \to BCE$	***R.24.***	$bCDFb \to bCDcb$
R.16.	$E\alpha\beta \to \beta E\alpha$	***R.25.***	$CDc \to Ccc$
R.17.	$E\alpha\# \to D\alpha\#$	***R.26.***	$Ccc \to ccc$

Rules ***R.16–R.18*** use α, β as ranging over $\{a, b, F\}$ so they simply summarize 15 legal ones. It is instructive though tiresome to follow through at least one example (exercises). We avoided essentially the same copying process in proving the computability of the recursive functions via programming systems in Chapter 4. (Cf. Davis [1958] where the proof is done directly and requires a copy machine.)

Theorem 8.1.7. Every context-sensitive language L is recursive.

Proof. If $g \to g'$ is a rule of a context-sensitive grammar which generates the language L, then $g = a_1 \cdots a_m$, $g' = b_1 \cdots b_n$, where $a_i, b_j \in S \cup Q$, $i = 1, \ldots, m$, $j = 1, \ldots, n$, and $m \leq n$. The inequality holds because the rules provide only for rewriting of single auxiliary symbols. From $m \leq n$ several facts follow. (*a*) The sequence of lengths of successive lines of a proof of a sentence is monotonic increasing. (*b*) Any terminal proof has an equivalent terminal proof in which no proof elements repeat. As a consequence of (*a*) and (*b*) and the fact that every proof is a finite sequence, we have that L is recursive. For if x is a theorem and $l(x) = k$, only a finite number of proofs—those none of whose elements exceeds k in length and none of which repeat elements—need be considered. Q.E.D.

Definition 8.1.8. A grammar **G** is *context-free* iff it satisfies Condition 2. If **G** is context-free, then $L(\mathbf{G})$ is a *context-free language*.

REMARK. Since substitutions are allowed independent of context, we will delete # from S—the boundary plays no useful role in context-free grammars until we come to the problem of acceptors for their languages.

EXAMPLE 3. The boolean language in Section 3.1, Example 2, in its second formulation.

EXAMPLE 4. A subgrammar **G** of ALGOL 60, where $L(\mathbf{G})$ is the language of numbers. The alphabet is $S = \{\cdot, +, -, 0, 1, \ldots, 9, {}_{10}\}$ and the auxiliary alphabet is $Q = \{\mathrm{N}, \mathrm{D}, \overline{\mathrm{UI}}, \overline{\mathrm{DF}}, \overline{\mathrm{EP}}, \overline{\mathrm{DN}}, \overline{\mathrm{UN}}, \mathrm{I}\}$ where $q_0 = \mathrm{N}$.

The auxiliary doublets are to be regarded as logically single symbols, hence the vinculum. The interpretation (which is, of course, irrelevant to the formalism) is as follows:

$$
\begin{aligned}
N &= \text{number};\ D = \text{decimal};\ \overline{UI} = \text{unsigned integer};\\
\overline{DF} &= \text{decimal fraction};\ \overline{EP} = \text{exponent part};\\
\overline{DN} &= \text{decimal number};\ \overline{UN} = \text{unsigned number};\\
I &= \text{integer}.
\end{aligned}
$$

As is customary in the discussions of ALGOL, we reduce production rules such as

$$
\begin{aligned}
&\overline{UI} \to D\\
&\overline{UI} \to \overline{UI}D
\end{aligned}
$$

to

R.1. $\overline{UI} \to D \mid \overline{UI}D$

where | has the force of "or." There are seven more combined rules.

R.2. $I \to \overline{UI} \mid + \overline{UI} \mid - \overline{UI}$
R.3. $\overline{DF} \to \cdot\, \overline{UI}$
R.4. $\overline{EP} \to {}_{10}I$
R.5. $\overline{DN} \to \overline{UI} \mid \overline{DF} \mid \overline{UI}\,\overline{DF}$
R.6. $\overline{UN} \to \overline{DN} \mid \overline{EP} \mid \overline{DN}\,\overline{EP}$
R.7. $N \to \overline{UN} \mid + \overline{UN} \mid - \overline{UN}$
R.8. $D \to 0 \mid 1 \mid 2 \mid 3 \mid 4 \mid 5 \mid 6 \mid 7 \mid 8 \mid 9$

An example of a "sentence" is the number $-2.46_{10}67$ which in the usual mantissa-exponent notation is -2.46×10^{67}.

EXAMPLE 5. A small fragment of English. S = {is, was, a, the, pretty, little, blond, girl, child, or, but, and, she}. Q = {S, NP, VP, C, Pr, Adj, Adv, N, Art, V}. S = q_0 and means "sentence."
Interpretation of the other auxiliaries:

$\overline{NP}$ — Noun phrase
$\overline{VP}$ — Verb phrase
C — Conjunctive (and, but, etc.)
$\overline{Pr}$ — Pronoun
$\overline{Adj}$ — Adjective
$\overline{Adv}$ — Adverb
$\overline{Art}$ — Article
N — Noun
V — Verb

The rules are the following.

R.1. $S \rightarrow \overline{NP}\ \overline{VP}$
R.2. $S \rightarrow SCS$
R.3. $S \rightarrow \overline{Pr}\ \overline{VP}$
R.4. $\overline{NP} \rightarrow \overline{Art}\ \overline{Adj}\ N$
R.5. $N \rightarrow \overline{Adj}\ N$
R.6. $\overline{Adj} \rightarrow \overline{Adv}\ \overline{Adj}$
R.7. $\overline{VP} \rightarrow V\overline{NP}$
R.8. $\overline{Pr} \rightarrow$ she
R.9. $\overline{Art} \rightarrow$ a | the
R.10. $\overline{Adj} \rightarrow$ pretty | little | blond
R.11. $\overline{Adv} \rightarrow$ pretty
R.12. $N \rightarrow$ girl | child
R.13. $V \rightarrow$ is | was
R.14. $C \rightarrow$ and | or | but

This grammar generates such sentences as "she is a pretty little pretty blond girl" or "a pretty little girl is a little pretty girl or a blond child is a pretty little child." (See exercises.)

Since a context-free grammar has the same monotone-increasing proof property as a context sensitive language, all such are recursive. However, we will prove a more useful statement of this fact in Section 8.2.

Definition 8.1.9. A grammar **G** is *finite state* iff it satisfies Condition 3. If **G** is finite state, then $L(\mathbf{G})$ is a *finite state language.*

We will see below that finite state languages are precisely the regular sets and that a finite state generator is in effect a n.f.s.a. "turned around" and conversely. Although we have deliberately refrained from commenting on the adequacy for natural languages of either context-sensitive or context-free languages, the poverty of the finite state grammars for modeling English, let us say, is clear. English includes, for example, nested sentences such as

the man the dog bit ran away (1)

It is clear that a grammar adequate to the generation of sentences such as (1) must be self-embedding in the sense that it includes proofs such as $S, \ldots, \alpha S\beta$. Here αS is a noun phrase which includes as part S (sentence) again. Condition 3 precludes such rules. More formally, if a finite state grammar could generate sentences like (1) it could also generate the set of words xx^{-1} where x^{-1} is the reflection of x (Definition 7.1.30). This set comprises an abstract paradigm for the nested sentences in question.

However, this set is not regular; yet it is context-free (see exercises). We will provide a precise discussion of the relationship between self-embedding and finite state languages in the exercises of Section 8.2. We further note here that finite state languages are, by the limitation just discussed, phrase structure languages in only a degenerate sense.

From the preceding discussion together with the way in which Condition 3 is formulated (as including Condition 2) it is clear that the family of finite state languages is *properly* included in the family of context-free languages. Also, the context-sensitive languages are properly included in the recursively enumerable languages, since the former are recursive by Theorem 8.1.7, whereas, by using Theorem 8.1.4 together with Corollary 4.4.11, the latter contains a recursively enumerable language which is not recursive. This fact takes us to the following theorem.

Theorem 8.1.10. Let $\mathscr{L}_0$, $\mathscr{L}_1$, $\mathscr{L}_2$, $\mathscr{L}_3$ be the families of languages whose grammars satisfy none of Conditions 1–3, Condition 1, Condition 2, and Condition 3, respectively. Then

$$\mathscr{L}_3 \subset \mathscr{L}_2 \subset \mathscr{L}_1 \subset \mathscr{L}_0$$

Proof. In view of previous discussions, we need only show $\mathscr{L}_2 \subset \mathscr{L}_1$. Since $\mathscr{L}_2 \subseteq \mathscr{L}_1$, this boils down to exhibiting a context-sensitive language which is not context-free. Such a language is the language made up of sentences of the form $0^n1^n0^n$, $n \geq 1$. We leave it to the student to construct a context-sensitive grammar for this language. The fact that the language is not context-free is the content of Corollary 8.2.6 of Section 8.2. Q.E.D.

In Chapter 4 we proved that Turing acceptors and generators are equivalent (Theorems 4.3.17 and 4.3.20). We will now show that the same holds for finite state acceptors and finite state grammars (f.s.g.).

Lemma 8.1.11. A sentence $x = s_{i_1} \cdots s_{i_n} \neq \Lambda$ is generated by an f.s.g. iff there exists a sequence of auxiliary symbols $q_{i_0}, q_{i_1}, \ldots, q_{i_{n-1}}$ such that

(*a*) $q_{i_0} = q_0$

(*b*) $q_{i_{j-1}} \rightarrow s_{i_j} q_{i_j}$ is an element of $\mathscr{P}$ $\quad j = 1, \ldots, n-1$

(*c*) $q_{i_{n-1}} \rightarrow s_{i_n}$ is an element of $\mathscr{P}$

Proof. For the student.

We state here separately as a hypothesis for the next theorem that Λ is in neither $x(\mathbf{A})$ or $L(\mathbf{G})$.

Theorem 8.1.12. For every f.s.a. **A** there is an f.s.g. **G** such that $x(\mathbf{A}) = L(\mathbf{G})$, and, conversely, for every f.s.g. **G** there is an f.s.a. **A** such that $x(\mathbf{A}) = L(\mathbf{G})$.

Proof. Let $\mathbf{A} = \langle S, Q, q_0, M, Q' \rangle$. Let $\mathbf{G} = \langle S, Q, q_0, \mathscr{P} \rangle$ with $\mathscr{P}$ as follows.

(i) $M(q_i, s_j) = q_l \Rightarrow q_i \to s_j q_l \in \mathscr{P}$.
(ii) $M(q_i, s_j) \in Q' \Rightarrow q_i \to s_j \in \mathscr{P}$.
(iii) A production is in $\mathscr{P}$ only if its being so follows from (i) or (ii).

Let $x \in x(\mathbf{A})$. Then considering $\mathbf{A}$ as a nondeterministic f.s.a. (cf. Theorem 7.2.15, first sentence of proof), there exists by Corollary 7.1.7, provided that $x = s_{i_1} \cdots s_{i_n}$, a sequence of states $q_{i_0}, \ldots, q_{i_n}$ such that

(1) $q_{i_0} = q_0$
(2) $q_{i_j} \in M(q_{i_{j-1}}, s_{i_j}) = \{q_{ij}\}$
(3) $q_{i_n} \in Q'$

It follows immediately that the sequences $s_{i_1} \ldots s_{i_n}, q_{i_0}, \ldots, q_{i_{n-1}}$ satisfy (*a*)–(*c*) of Lemma 8.1.11. Simply note that from (1) we have (*a*); from (i) and (2) we have (*b*); and from (ii), (2), and (3) we have (*c*). Therefore by the lemma, x is a theorem of $\mathbf{G}$. Suppose, oppositely, that $x \in L(\mathbf{G})$. By an exactly reverse argument we get $x \in x(\mathbf{A})$.

For the converse, let $\mathbf{G} = \langle S, Q, q_0, \mathscr{P} \rangle$, and let

$$\mathbf{N} = \langle S, Q \cup \{q'\}, \{q_0\}, M, Q' \rangle$$

be an n.f.s.a., where q' is new, $Q' = \{q'\}$, and M is determined as follows:

(i′) $q_i \to s_j q_l \in \mathscr{P} \Leftrightarrow q_l \in M(q_i, s_j)$
(ii′) $q_i \to s_j \in \mathscr{P} \Leftrightarrow M(q_i, s_j) \in Q'$

By Lemma 8.1.11, if $x = s_{i_1} \cdots s_{i_n} \in L(\mathbf{G})$, then there are $q_0, \ldots, q_{i_{n-1}}$ satisfying (*a*)–(*c*). Obviously the required facts (1)–(3) of Corollary 7.1.7 follow immediately from (i′), (ii′) and (*a*)–(*c*) of the lemma, thus $x \in x(\mathbf{N})$. Finally, by Theorem 7.2.15 there exists an f.s.a. $\mathbf{A}$ such that $x(\mathbf{N}) = x(\mathbf{A})$.

Q.E.D.

Corollary 8.1.13. For every regular set L, $L - \{\Lambda\}$ is a context-free language.

The limitation stated before Theorem 8.1.12 could be removed by permitting productions of the form $g \to \Lambda$ in our grammatical models. If we did so, however, the theorem would no longer have such a simple proof. We can have both, but the effort is not worth it.

We have found so far that for families of the weakest automata, that is, finite state machines and for the strongest, that is, Turing machines, the acceptors and the generators process exactly the same sets of words. So it necessarily holds that all of the closure properties for regular sets hold for finite state languages and similarly (owing to the effectiveness of the construction in Theorem 8.1.12) for questions of solvability, that is, the emptiness problem, the infinity problem, etc. (Theorems 7.1.29, 7.1.31, to 7.1.34, 7.1.38 to 7.1.40, and Theorems 7.2.1, 7.2.2, and 7.2.4.) Similarly recursively enumerable languages are not closed under negation and hence are not boolean; yet they are closed under existential quantification and bounded universal quantification (comment at end of Theorem 4.4.8). On the other hand, it follows from the unsolvability of the halting problem (Section 4.4—Example 1) that the question whether an unrestricted grammar produces any sentence at all is unsolvable (cf. 7.2.1). Similar questions will be taken up in somewhat more detail in Section 8.3, for the context-free languages.

EXERCISES 8.1

1. Show that the grammars $\mathbf{G}_1$ and $\mathbf{G}_2$ are weakly equivalent yet *inequivalent* in the strong sense mentioned after Definition 8.1.2.

$\mathbf{G}_1$	$\mathbf{G}_2$
$q_0 \rightarrow q_1q_2$	$q_0 \rightarrow q_1t$
$q_1 \rightarrow q_1q_1$	$q_1 \rightarrow q_1q_1$
$q_1 \rightarrow s$	$q_1 \rightarrow s$
$q_2 \rightarrow t$	

Use the trick of Section 8.0 for generating sentences with phrase markers.

2. Show that the copy language is not regular.

3. Show how a *tree* (cf. Section 5.4) may be associated to a proof in a phrase structure grammar in such a way that two sentences have the same parenthetical phrase marker iff they have the same tree. Construct an example of a proof tree for the copy language.

4. How many trees are there for "she is a pretty little pretty blond girl" (Example 5)?

5. Prove that the set of sentences of the form xx^{-1} is a context-free language but is not regular.

6. Show that the set of sentences $0^n1^n0^n$, $n \geq 1$ is context-sensitive.

7. Prove Lemma 8.1.11.

8.2 CONTEXT-FREE LANGUAGES

Our first task in this section will be to complete the proof of Theorem 8.1.10. We shall show that the language of sentences $0^n1^n0^n$, $n \geq 1$, is not context-free.

Definition 8.2.1. w *generates* w' iff there is a sequence $w = w_1, \ldots, w_n = w'$ such that w_{i+1} follows from (Definition 3.3.2) w_i, $i = 1, \ldots, n - 1$. We write $w \overset{*}{\Rightarrow} w'$. We also occasionally write $w_i \Rightarrow w_{i+1}$ for w_{i+1} follows from w_i. The context should obviate confusion with "if–then."

Corollary 8.2.2. (*a*) $\overset{*}{\Rightarrow}$ is transitive. (*b*) If $x_1 \overset{*}{\Rightarrow} y_1, \ldots, x_n \overset{*}{\Rightarrow} y_n$, then $x_1 \cdots x_n \overset{*}{\Rightarrow} y_1 \cdots y_n$. (*c*) If $x \overset{*}{\Rightarrow} y$ and $x = x_1 \cdots x_n$, then there are $y_1, \ldots, y_n$ such that $x_i \overset{*}{\Rightarrow} y_i$ and $y = y_1 \cdots y_n$, $i = 1, \ldots, n$.

Proof. For the student.

REMARK $q_0 \overset{*}{\Rightarrow} w'$ iff w' is a theorem iff there is a proof of w'.

In the following we use a, b, etc., as symbol variables over $S \cup Q$ and we use $A = S \cup Q$ as in Chapter 3 for the total vocabulary.

Theorem 8.2.3. For any context-free grammar $\mathbf{G} = \langle S, Q, q_0, \mathscr{P} \rangle$ there exists $\mathbf{G}' = \langle S, Q, q_0, \mathscr{P}' \rangle$ such that (*i*) if $l(x) \geq 2$, then $x \in L(\mathbf{G})$ iff $x \in L(\mathbf{G})'$; and (*ii*) $\mathbf{G}'$ has no productions of the form $q \rightarrow a$—all productions of $\mathbf{G}'$ have right-hand members of at least length 2.

REMARK. Thus for $\mathbf{G}'$ proofs are not merely monotonic increasing, as in Theorem 8.1.7, but are *strictly* so.

Proof. We define inductively for each $a \in A$ a chain of subsets:

$$V_1(a) = \{a\}$$
$$V_{k+1}(a) = V_k(a) \cup \{b \mid b \in A \wedge (\exists c)(c \in V_k(a) \wedge c \rightarrow b \in \mathscr{P})\}$$

Thus $V_{k+1}(a)$ includes $V_k(a)$ together with all symbols which follow, by productions, from symbols of $V_k(a)$. Clearly,

$$V_1(a) \subseteq \cdots \subseteq V_n(a) = V_{n+1}(a) = \cdots = V_{n+r}(a) \qquad (1)$$

since $V_k(a) \subseteq V_{k+1}(a)$ by construction; and if for some k, $V_k(a) = V_{k+1}(a)$ then $V_k(a) = V_m(a)$ for $m > k$; and $V_n(a) = V_{n+1}(a)$ for sure, where $K(Q) = n$. Likewise we note that $b \in V_n(a)$ iff $a \overset{*}{\Rightarrow} b$; and $a \in L(\mathbf{G})$ iff $q_0 \overset{*}{\Rightarrow} a$ and $a \in S \cap V_n(q_0)$.

Next, define[1]

$$\mathscr{P}^0 = \{q \rightarrow w \mid l(w) \geq 2 \wedge (\exists c)(c \in V_n(q) \wedge c \rightarrow w \in \mathscr{P})\}$$

To complete the construction of $\mathbf{G}'$, we have[2]

$$q \rightarrow a_1 \cdots a_r \in \mathscr{P}' \Leftrightarrow (\exists q \rightarrow b_1 \cdots b_r)(q \rightarrow b_1 \cdots b_r \in \mathscr{P}^0 \wedge a_i \in V_n(b_i)) \qquad i = 1, \ldots, r$$

So now $\mathbf{G}' = \langle S, Q, q_0, \mathscr{P}' \rangle$. By the construction, (*ii*) follows at once.

For (*i*), if $q \overset{*}{\Rightarrow} w$ in $\mathbf{G}'$ then $q \overset{*}{\Rightarrow} w$ in $\mathbf{G}$; conversely, if $q \overset{*}{\Rightarrow} w$ in $\mathbf{G}$ and $l(w) \geq 2$, then $q \overset{*}{\Rightarrow} w$ in $\mathbf{G}'$. This is left to the student to prove by induction on the length of the generation $q = w_1, \ldots, w_n = w$. Now specialize this to $q = q_0$ and (*i*) follows. Q.E.D.

[1] That is, the set of productions $q \rightarrow w$ satisfying $l(w) \geq 2$, etc.

[2] In the quantifier $(\exists q \rightarrow b_1 \cdots b_r)$ means "there is a production $q \rightarrow b_1 \cdots b_r$."

Corollary 8.2.4. The grammar **G**′ of Theorem 8.2.3 can be obtained effectively, that is, there is an algorithm for constructing it.

Proof. For the student.

Theorem 8.2.5. Let **G** be a grammar with the properties of **G**′ in Theorem 8.2.3. There exist nonnegative integers p, m such that for every $z \in L(\mathbf{G})$, if $l(z) > p$, then there are words $x, u, w, v, y \in S^*$ such that $z = xuwvy$, $u \neq \Lambda$ or $v \neq \Lambda$, $l(uwv) \leq m$, and for every $k \geq 1$,

$$z_k = xu^k wv^k y \in L(\mathbf{G})$$

Proof. Suppose $K(A) = n$, and consider the set of all generations $w_1, \ldots, w_k$ in **G** of length $k \leq n$, such that w_1 is an auxiliary symbol.

To each such generation there corresponds a *tree* [cf. Definitions 5.4.18–5.4.21 and Exercise 8.1(3)] with w_1 the label of a root, such that if a node is labeled q and the branches stemming from this node are labeled $a_1, \ldots, a_t$, then $q \to a_1 \cdots a_t \in \mathscr{P}$. Any such tree will have leaves labeled with symbols and the word (not necessarily a terminal theorem) formed from these by concatenation in the natural lexicographical order of leaves is a *final string* (the "natural" order is by row height and row position as in Definition 5.4.21 and the multiplication table algorithm in Section 5.4).

The set of trees whose construction was just indicated is finite and the lengths of the final strings thereof are bounded. Call this bound p. Now any sentence $z \in L(\mathbf{G})$ such that $l(z) > p$ is a final string of a tree with paths longer than n. If $a_1, \ldots, a_r$ is the longest such path, $r > n$, then in the subpath $a_{r-n}, \ldots, a_r$ some symbol must occur twice (because

$$r - (r - n) + 1 = n + 1$$

and $K(A) = n$). Let $a_i = a_j = q$, $r - n \leq i < j \leq r$, and consider the subtree of z's tree with root q. In this tree $q \overset{*}{\Rightarrow} u'qv' \overset{*}{\Rightarrow} uwv$ where $u' \overset{*}{\Rightarrow} u$, $v' \overset{*}{\Rightarrow} v$, and $q \overset{*}{\Rightarrow} w$, using Corollary 8.2.2. Since all productions are length increasing, either $u \neq \Lambda$ or $v \neq \Lambda$; uwv is a final string of the subtree and hence is a substring of the sentence z. Thus $z = xuwvy$ for some x, y.

Finally the generations $q \overset{*}{\Rightarrow} u'qv'$, $u' \overset{*}{\Rightarrow} u$, and $v' \overset{*}{\Rightarrow} v$ can be repeated k times. So we obtain $q \overset{*}{\Rightarrow} u^k wv^k$ and hence $q_0 \overset{*}{\Rightarrow} xu^k wv^k y$, k any positive integer. Since the longest path in the subtree is $n + 1$, there exists a bound $m \geq l(uwv)$. Q.E.D.

Corollary 8.2.6. The set of sentences $0^n 1^n 0^n$, $n \geq 1$, is not a context-free language.

Proof. Assume this set, call it L, is context-free and that it is generated by a grammar **G**′ as in Theorem 8.2.3. This is no restriction since even 010 is of length greater than 2. Let p be the integer known to exist by Theorem

8.2.5 and let $z = 0^p1^p0^p$. By that theorem, $z = xuwvy$, and also every $z_k = xu^kwv^ky \in L$. We will deduce contradictions for every one of a set of exhaustive cases about 1 occurring in z.

CASE 1. If 1 occurs in x then for some $x' \in \{0, 1\}^*$, $x = 0^p1x'$. So $z = xuwvy = 0^p1x'uwvy = 0^p1^p0^p$; likewise $z_k = 0^p1x'u^kwv^ky = 0^p1^p0^p$, which is absurd. The same argument applies by symmetry to y.

CASE 2. Suppose no 1 occurs in x but 1 does occur in u. (*a*) Suppose there is a 0 in u. Then for some u' and $i \geq 1$, $u = 0^i1u'$ or $u'10^i$. Consider $z_2 = zu^2wv^2y = x0^i1u'0^i1u'wv^2y \in L$, otherwise $z_2 = xu'10^iu'10^iwv^2y \in L$. Either case is impossible since $0^n1^n0^n$ for any n cannot have a subword $1\cdot\cdot0\cdot\cdot1$. (*b*) Suppose there is no 0 in u; thus $u = 1^i$ for some $i \geq 1$. But then $x = 0^p$. Let $z = xu^{2p}wv^{2p}y = 0^p1^{2pi}wv^{2p}y \in L$. However, this is absurd since z is assumed to be of the form $0^p1^p0^p$.

CASE 3. Suppose 1 occurs in w but not in x, u, v, or y. We leave it to the student to derive a contradiction proving in all that 1 cannot occur anywhere in z.

Hence $0^n1^n0^n$ is not context-free. Q.E.D.

This result also serves to complete the proof of Theorem 8.1.10, where the recursively enumerable, context-sensitive, context-free, and regular families of languages are simply ordered w.r.t. proper inclusion.

Our next aim is to prove closure properties of the family of context-free language. Of most moment is the interesting fact that unlike the regular sets—hence unlike the finite state languages—and unlike the recursive sets as a whole, the family of context-free languages is not closed under intersection or complementation. But first we see some positive results.

Theorem 8.2.7. (*a*) If L is a finite language, then $L - \{\Lambda\}$ is context-free. (*b*) If L is context-free, so is L^{-1} (cf. Theorem 7.1.32). (*c*) If L_1 and L_2 are context-free, so is $L_1 \cdot L_2$ (complex product—Definition 7.2.5). (*d*) If L is context-free, so is $L^* - \{\Lambda\}$. (*e*) If L_1 and L_2 are context-free, so is $L_1 \bigcup L_2$.

Proof. (*a*) By Corollaries 7.1.40 and 8.1.13.

(*b*) Let $L = L(\mathbf{G})$ where $\mathbf{G} = \langle S, Q, q_0, \mathscr{P}\rangle$; then $\mathbf{G}^{-1} = \langle S, Q, q_0, \mathscr{P}^{-1}\rangle$, where

$$\mathscr{P}^{-1} = \{q \to x^{-1} \mid q \to x \in \mathscr{P}\}$$

Obviously $L(\mathbf{G}^{-1}) = L^{-1}$.

(*c*) Let $L_i = L(\mathbf{G}_i)$, $\mathbf{G}_i = \langle S_i, Q_i, q_{0_i}, \mathscr{P}_i\rangle$, $i = 1, 2$. Assume that

$$Q_1 \bigcap (S_2 \bigcup Q_2) = (S_1 \bigcup Q_1) \bigcap Q_2 = \varnothing$$

otherwise one can replace the auxiliaries of Q_1, say, so that the disjointedness condition holds and yet $L(\mathbf{G}_1)$ is preserved. Assume that

$q_0 \notin Q_1 \cup Q_2$ and let $\mathbf{G} = \langle S, Q, q_0, \mathscr{P} \rangle$ where $S = S_1 \cup S_2$, $Q = Q_1 \cup Q_2 \cup \{q_0\}$, and $\mathscr{P} = \mathscr{P}_1 \cup \mathscr{P}_2 \cup \{q_0 \rightarrow q_{0_1} q_{0_2}\}$. It is obvious from this construction that $L(\mathbf{G}) = L(\mathbf{G}_1) \cdot L(\mathbf{G}_2)$.

(*d*) Again let $L = L(\mathbf{G})$, $\mathbf{G} = \langle S, Q, q_0, \mathscr{P} \rangle$ and let q_0' be a new auxiliary. Let $G^* = \langle S, Q', q_0', \mathscr{P} \rangle$ where $Q' = Q \cup \{q_0'\}$ and

$$\mathscr{P}' = \mathscr{P} \cup \{q_0' \rightarrow q_0 q_0', q_0' \rightarrow q_0\}$$

then the result follows by construction. If we had allowed rules $q \rightarrow \Lambda$ in Definition 8.1.2 we could of course have proved L^* is context-free.

(*e*) Use exactly the same construction as in (*c*), except that

$$\mathscr{P} = \mathscr{P}_1 \cup \mathscr{P}_2 \cup \{q_0 \rightarrow q_{0_1}, q_0 \rightarrow q_{0_2}\}$$

Q.E.D.

Theorem 8.2.8. The family of context-free languages is not closed under intersection.

Proof. Let $L = \{0^n 1^n 0^k \mid n, k \geq 1\}$. This language is generated by

$$\mathbf{G} = \langle \{0, 1\}, \{q_0, q_1, q_2\}, q_0, \mathscr{P} \rangle$$

where $\mathscr{P}$ is:

$$\begin{array}{ll} q_0 \rightarrow q_1 q_2 & q_2 \rightarrow 0 q_2 \\ q_1 \rightarrow 0 q_1 1 & q_2 \rightarrow 0 \\ q_1 \rightarrow 01 & \end{array}$$

We have here that $q_1 \overset{*}{\Rightarrow} 0^n 1^n$ for any n and similarly $q_2 \overset{*}{\Rightarrow} 0^k$. By Theorem 8.2.7(*b*), $L^{-1} = \{0^p 1^m 0^m \mid 0, m \geq 1\}$ is context-free as well. But $L \cap L^{-1} = \{0^n 1^n 0^n \mid n \geq 1\}$, which by Theorem 8.2.6 is not context-free.

Q.E.D.

Corollary 8.2.8a. The family of context-free languages is not closed under complementation.

Proof. If it were, then, since it is closed under union, it would be closed under intersection. Q.E.D.

By Theorem 8.1.11 and the fact that every f.s.a. can be constructed from a regular expression, we have at once an algorithmic procedure for constructing the grammar of a finite state language. Without attempting such an ambitious goal for the context-free case, we already have at hand some algorithms for constructing grammars buried in Theorem 8.2.7. We now resurrect them.

Theorem 8.2.9. (*a*) Given a finite language $\{x_1, \ldots, x_n\}$, $x_i \neq \Lambda$, there is an algorithm for constructing a grammar which generates it; (*b*) given $\mathbf{G}$, $L(\mathbf{G}) = L$, L^{-1} and $L^* - \{\Lambda\}$, there is an algorithm for $\mathbf{G}^{-1}$ and $\mathbf{G}^*$; (*c*) given $\mathbf{G}_1$, $\mathbf{G}_2$, $L(\mathbf{G}_1) = L_1$ and $L(\mathbf{G}_2) = L_2$, there is an algorithm for $\mathbf{G}_3$ and $\mathbf{G}_4$ where $L(\mathbf{G}_3) = L_1 L_2$ and $L(\mathbf{G}_4) = L_1 \cup L_2$.

Proof. (*a*) Let $L = \{x_1, \ldots, x_n\}$ on the alphabet S and

$$\mathbf{G} = \langle S, \{q_0\}, q_0, \{q_0 \to x_1, \ldots, q_0 \to x_n\}\rangle$$

The other parts all follow from the methods used in the proofs of 8.2.7.

Q.E.D.

We will now show that any context-free language is recursive and will do so in such a manner as to give a practical algorithm for actually testing theoremhood. (One such test for a regular language is made by injecting x into the f.s.a. whose defined set is that language.) First we need a lemma giving a definite bound on the length of a proof (cf. Theorem 8.1.7).

Lemma 8.2.10. Let $\mathbf{G} = \langle S, Q, q_0, \mathscr{P}\rangle$, and let $n = K(S \cup Q)$. A word $w \in S^*$ such that $l(w) = k$ is in $L(\mathbf{G})$ iff there is a proof $q_0 = w_1, w_2, \ldots, w_r = w$ such that $r \leq \sum_{j=1}^{k} n^j$.

Proof. Let $w \in S^*$ and $l(w) = k$. The proof from right to left follows from Definition 3.3.16. Conversely, suppose that $q_0 \stackrel{*}{\Rightarrow} w$. Let r be the smallest integer such that $q_0 = w_1, \ldots, w_r = w$ is a proof of w in $\mathbf{G}$. We known that $l(w_i) \leq l(w_{i+1})$, for every $i < r$ from Theorems 8.1.7 and 8.1.10. Suppose now, to derive a contradiction, that $r > \sum_{j=1}^{k} n^j$. Then since $l(w) = k$, it is easy to see that there are words w_i and w_j, $i < j < r$ such that $w_i = w_j$. It follows that the proof of w in $\mathbf{G}$ is $q_0 = w_1, \ldots, w_i, w_{j+1}, \ldots, w_r = w$, which contradicts the fact that r was chosen smallest.

Q.E.D.

This lemma suffices to establish the next theorem.

Theorem 8.2.11. For any context-free grammar $\mathbf{G}$, $L(\mathbf{G})$ is recursive.

In analogy to Theorems 7.2.2 and 7.2.4 we are also able to prove solvability of the emptiness and infinity problems.

Theorem 8.2.12. Given $\mathbf{G} = \langle S, Q, q_0, \mathscr{P}\rangle$ there is a method for deciding whether $L(\mathbf{G})$ is empty.

Proof. We will use the device of ascending chains of sets. Set

$$S_0 = S$$
$$S_i = S_{i-1} \cup \{a \mid a \in A \wedge (\exists x)((x \in S_{i-1}^* - \{\Lambda\}) \wedge a \Rightarrow x)\}$$

We leave it to the student to show that $S_0 \subseteq S_1 \subseteq \cdots$ strictly increases to an equality condition and to establish the appropriate bound β such that $S_k \subseteq S_\beta$ for all k. Finally

$$\begin{aligned}(\exists x)(x \in L(\mathbf{G})) &\Leftrightarrow (\exists x)(q_0 \stackrel{*}{\Rightarrow} x \wedge x \in S^* - \{\Lambda\}) \\ &\Leftrightarrow (\exists k)(q_0 \in S_k) \\ &\Leftrightarrow q_0 \in S_\beta\end{aligned}$$

Q.E.D.

Assumption. For the infinity result which follows we will assume (the fact can be proved) any $\mathbf{G}$ is such that for every $a \in A$, $q_0 \stackrel{*}{\Rightarrow} uav$ and for every $q \in Q$, there is $x \in S^*$ such that $q \overset{*}{\Rightarrow} x$; or else that **G** is weakly equivalent to **G**$'$ enjoying these properties.

Definition 8.2.13. **G** is *embedding* iff there is a $q \in Q$ such that $q \overset{*}{\Rightarrow} uqv$ for some $u \neq \Lambda$ or $v \neq \Lambda$.

Theorem 8.2.14. There is a decision procedure for determining of any given **G** whether $L(\mathbf{G})$ is infinite.

Proof. Suppose **G** has the properties of **G**$'$ of Theorem 8.2.3—all its proofs are strictly length increasing. If **G** is embedding, then for some q, u, and v we have $q \overset{*}{\Rightarrow} uqv$. By the assumption prior to Definition 8.2.13, we also have $q_0 \overset{*}{\Rightarrow} xqy$. Thus we have

$$q_0 \overset{*}{\Rightarrow} xqy \overset{*}{\Rightarrow} xuqvy \overset{*}{\Rightarrow} \cdots \overset{*}{\Rightarrow} xu^kqv^ky \overset{*}{\Rightarrow} \cdots$$

But by the assumption x, y, u, and v all are words on S^* or else the occurrences q_i generate words on S^*. Call these words x', y', u', and v'. Hence $q_0 \Rightarrow x'(u')^kw(v')^ky'$ for any k. Therefore $L(\mathbf{G})$ is infinite.

Conversely, if **G** is nonembedding, then it is immediate that $L(\mathbf{G})$ is finite. Hence we have so far proved that if **G** has strictly increasing productions, then $L(\mathbf{G})$ is infinite iff it is embedding.

If **G** does not have strictly increasing rules (if P includes a production $q \to a$) then by Theorem 8.2.5 we can effectively obtain **G**$'$ with this property which is weakly equivalent to **G** save for a finite number of sentences of length ≤ 1. Finally we observe that the embedding property is decidable [Exercise 8.2(7)]. Q.E.D.

Although the context-free languages are not closed under either complementation or intersection there are no doubt cases where one or the other does exist. Is there any way of deciding recursively the question of the existence of the intersection (or complement) in advance? Unfortunately the answer to this question is negative, as are several other decision problems related to it. The argument we now use turns on the correspondence problem of Post (Section 4.4, Example 6) which we know to be unsolvable for any vocabulary of more than two symbols. To simplify the ensuing proofs we use the further restriction that $K(S) > 2$. In general, however, the results all hold for $K(S) \geq 2$ (cf. Bar-Hillel, et al. [1960]).

Definition 8.2.15. Let $(x_1, \ldots, x_n)$ and $(y_1, \ldots, y_n)$ be n-tuples of non-null words over $\{0, 1\}$, $n \geq 1$. If there is a sequence $i_1, \ldots, i_k$ where $k \geq 1$ and $1 \leq i_j \leq n$ for $j = 1, \ldots, k$ such that $x_{i_1} \cdots x_{i_k} = y_{i_1} \cdots y_{i_k}$, then we write $P(x, y) = 1$; otherwise $P(x, y) = 0$.

Next we construct some languages, using the terminal vocabulary $S = \{0, 1, E\}$.

Definition 8.2.16. Let $(x_1, \ldots, x_n)$ be an n-tuple of non-null words on $\{0, 1\}$. Define:

$$L(x) = \{10^{i_k} \cdots 10^{i_1}Ex_{i_1} \cdots x_{i_k} \mid k \geq 1, 1 \leq i_j \leq n, j = 1, \ldots, k\}$$

Corollary 8.2.17. $L(x)$ is context-free.

Proof. $\mathbf{G} = \langle\{0, 1, E\}, \{q\}, q, \mathscr{P}\rangle$, where we have for $\mathscr{P}$:

$$\left.\begin{array}{l} q \to 10^iEx_i \\ q \to 10^iqx_i \end{array}\right\} i = 1, \ldots, n$$

Clearly this grammar generates $L(x)$. Q.E.D.

Definition 8.2.18. Let (x, y) be a pair of n-tuples $(x_1, \ldots, x_n)$, $(y_1, \ldots, y_n)$ of non-null words over $\{0, 1\}$; we define:

$$L(x, y) = L(x) \cdot E \cdot L(y)^{-1}$$

From Definition 8.2.16 this language may be more explicitly described, recalling $(xy)^{-1} = y^{-1}x^{-1}$ (Corollary 7.1.31):

$$\begin{aligned} L(x, y) = \{10^{i_k} \cdots 10^{i_1}Ex_{i_1} \cdots x_{i_k}Ey_{j_l}{}^{-1} \cdots y_{j_1}{}^{-1}E0^{j_1}1 \cdots 0^{j_l}1 \mid k \geq 1,& \\ l \geq 1, 1 \leq i_r \leq n \quad \text{for} \quad r = 1, \ldots, k& \\ \wedge\ 1 \leq j_r \leq n \quad \text{for} \quad r = 1, \ldots, l\}& \quad (2) \end{aligned}$$

One might think of 10^{i_k} as a code for the nonnegative integer i_k.

Corollary 8.2.19. $L(x, y)$ is context-free.

Proof. From Theorem 8.2.7 and Corollary 8.2.17. Q.E.D.

Definition 8.2.20. We define L_S by

$$L_S = \{x_1Ex_2Ex_2{}^{-1}Ex_1{}^{-1} \mid x_1, x_2 \in \{0, 1\}^*\}$$

Corollary 8.2.21. L_S is context-free.

Proof. $\mathbf{G}_S = \langle\{0, 1, E\}, \{q, U\}, q, \mathscr{P}\rangle$ where $\mathscr{P}$ is:

$$\begin{array}{c} q \to 0q0,\ q \to 1q1,\ q \to EUE \\ U \to 0U0,\ U \to 1U1,\ U \to E \end{array}$$

Q.E.D.

Finally we will use the intersection $L(x, y) \bigcap L_S$ which is expressed:

$$\begin{aligned} L = L(x, y) \bigcap L_S = \{10^{i_k} \cdots 10^{i_1}Ex_{i_1} \cdots x_{i_k}Ey_{i_k}{}^{-1} \cdots y_{i_1}{}^{-1}E0^{i_1}1 \cdots 0^{i_k}1 \mid& \\ k \geq 1 \wedge 1 \leq i_r \leq n \quad \text{for} \quad r = 1, \ldots, k& \\ \wedge\ x_{i_1} \cdots x_{i_k} = y_{i_1} \cdots y_{i_k}\}& \quad (3) \end{aligned}$$

REMARK. (3) comes from Definitions 8.2.16 and 8.2.20. Also, from (3),

$$(\exists z)(z \in L) \Leftrightarrow P(x, y) = 1$$

Note further that if $P(x, y) = 1$, then L is infinite because $x_{i_1} \cdots x_{i_k} = y_{i_1} \cdots y_{i_k}$ implies $(x_{i_1} \cdots x_{i_k})^m = (y_{i_1} \cdots y_{i_k})^m$ for all m. Similarly if

$P(x, y) = 0$, there is no $z \in L$, that is, $L = \varnothing$. Finally we already see that if there were a decision procedure for L then there would be one for the Post correspondence problem.

Theorem 8.2.22. If $P(x, y) = 1$ then L is not context-free.

Proof. From the remark above, L must be infinite. Assume L is context-free. By Theorem 8.2.5 there exist p and m such that if $l(z) > p$, then $z = xuwvy$, $l(u) + l(v) \geq 1$, $l(uwv) \leq m$ and $z_k = xu^k wv^k y \in L$ also, for all k.

Consider now $z = cEdEd^{-1}Ec^{-1} \in L$ with $l(z) \geq p$, $l(d) \geq m$ and $c, d \in \{0, 1\}^*$. We set

$$z = cEdEd^{-1}Ec^{-1} = xuwvy \tag{4}$$

Note that since $z \in L$, z is uniquely determined by c [check (3)]. From (4) we have

$$l(z) = 2l(c) + 2l(d) + 3 = l(x) + l(uwv) + l(y)$$

Using the fact that $l(d) \geq m \geq l(uwv)$

$$l(x) + l(y) \geq 2l(c) + 3 \tag{5}$$

From (5) we have at once that

$$(a) \quad l(x) \geq l(c) + 1 \qquad \text{or} \quad (b) \quad l(y) \geq l(c) + 1$$

Next consider

$$xu^2wv^2y = c_2Ec_2Ed_2{}^{-1}Ec_2{}^{-1} = z_2 \tag{6}$$

From (a), (4) and (6) it follows that $c = c_2$ and since c determines z uniquely, $z = z_2$, which is absurd. Similarly from (b) we deduce a contradiction. Therefore our assumption that L is context-free is false. It follows that if $P(x, y) = 1$, then L is not context-free. Q.E.D.

Theorem 8.2.23. The following problems are recursively unsolvable. Given two context-free grammars $\mathbf{G}_1$ and $\mathbf{G}_2$:

(a) Is $L(\mathbf{G}_1) \cap L(\mathbf{G}_2)$ empty?
(b) Is $L(\mathbf{G}_1) \cap L(\mathbf{G}_2)$ finite?
(c) Is $L(\mathbf{G}_1) \cap L(\mathbf{G}_2)$ finite state?
(d) Is $L(\mathbf{G}_1) \cap L(\mathbf{G}_2)$ context-free?

Proof. The parts of this theorem follow from Theorem 8.2.22, the remark before that theorem, the fact that every finite state language is context-free, and Theorem 8.2.7. Q.E.D.

By quite similar means one can show the unsolvability of problems companion to (a)–(d) above for the complements of context-free languages.

For example, the problem whether $(S^* - \{\Lambda\}) - L(\mathbf{G}), L(\mathbf{G})$ being context-free, is context-free is undecidable. However we omit further discussion and proofs of these facts except to state the following.

Theorem 8.2.24. The problem whether two context-free languages $L(\mathbf{G}_1)$ and $L(\mathbf{G}_2)$ are equal is recursively unsolvable as is, therefore, the problem whether $\mathbf{G}_1$ and $\mathbf{G}_2$ are weakly equivalent.

Proof. Let $\mathbf{G}_1$ generate all of S^* except for $\{\Lambda\}$. Now any grammar $\mathbf{G}_2$ with $S = \{0, 1\}$ is weakly equivalent to $\mathbf{G}_1$ iff

$$L(\mathbf{G}_1) = L(\mathbf{G}_2) \Leftrightarrow (S^* - \{\Lambda\}) - L(\mathbf{G}_2) = \varnothing$$

But by the foregoing informal remarks, the complementation problem is unsolvable. Q.E.D.

Definition 8.2.25. Given a grammar $\mathbf{G}$, if $w_1, \ldots, w_n$ is a proof in $\mathbf{G}$, then $w_1', \ldots, w_n'$ is a *strong proof* in $\mathbf{G}$ iff $w_1' = w_1$ and for all i, $1 < i \leq n$, w_i' follows from w_{i-1}' by $q_j \rightarrow (_j\, g)_j$ iff w_i follows from w_{i-1} by $q_j \rightarrow g$. A context-free grammar $\mathbf{G}$ is *ambiguous* iff there is a sentence $x \in L(\mathbf{G})$ such that x is the result of deleting parentheses from two distinct theorems of strong proofs.

An example of ambiguity was given in Section 8.0. We noted there that a necessary condition for the adequacy of a model for a grammar of a language is that it accounts for disparate structural descriptions when they exist. Now it would certainly be a convenience to linguistic theory if an algorithm were available to determine ambiguity. For example, it would be useful to know in advance whether certain programming (problem-oriented) languages are ambiguous. The reason, of course, is that we want to translate a sentence *with associated phrase markers* into the target sentence and not merely the sentence as a syntactical string. Unfortunately for any problem-oriented language[3] which is context-free there is in general no mechanical way of detecting ambiguity.

Theorem 8.2.26. The decision problem for ambiguity of context-free grammars is unsolvable.

Proof, Let $(x_1, \ldots, x_n)$ and $(y_1, \ldots, y_n)$ be n-tuples of words of $S^* - \{\Lambda\}$. Let t_i, $i = 1, \ldots, n$ be symbols other than those of S. Construct the two grammars

$$\mathbf{G}_1 = \langle S \cup \{t_1, \ldots, t_n, E\}, \{q_{0_1}\}, q_{0_1}, \mathscr{P}_1\rangle$$

and

$$\mathbf{G}_2 = \langle S \cup \{t_1, \ldots, t_n, E\}, \{q_{0_2}\}, q_{0_2}, \mathscr{P}_2\rangle$$

[3] The standard example is the Naur-Backus normal form fragment of ALGOL 60. See Section 8.4.

with

$$\mathscr{P}_1\colon q_{0_1} \to t_i E x_i^{-1} \qquad q_{0_1} \to t_i q_{0_1} x_i^{-1} \qquad i = 1, \ldots, n$$
$$\mathscr{P}_2\colon q_{0_2} \to t_i E y_i^{-1} \qquad q_{0_2} \to t_i q_{0_2} y_i^{-1} \qquad i = 1, \ldots, n$$

$\mathbf{G}_i$, $i = 1, 2$, is unambiguous since no right side of a production has more than one occurrence of one auxiliary in it—every generation tree is a Christmas tree. Let $\mathbf{G}_1 \cup \mathbf{G}_2$ be the grammar

$$\langle S \cup \{t_1, \ldots, t_n, E\}, \{q_0, q_{0_1}, q_{0_2}\}, q_0, \mathscr{P}'\rangle$$

where $\mathscr{P}'$ is $\mathscr{P}_1 \cup \mathscr{P}_2 \cup \{q_0 \to q_{0_1}, q_0 \to q_{0_2}\}$. It is clear from the construction that $x \in L(\mathbf{G}_1 \cup \mathbf{G}_2)$ has two proofs iff there is a proof of it in both $\mathbf{G}_1$ and $\mathbf{G}_2$. When there is, the situation may be described by the equation

$$t_{i_1} \cdots t_{i_k} E x_{i_k}^{-1} \cdots x_{i_1}^{-1} = t_{i_1} \cdots t_{i_k} E y_{i_k}^{-1} \cdots y_{i_1}^{-1}$$

From this fact it follows that $\mathbf{G}_1 \cup \mathbf{G}_2$ is ambiguous iff there is a sequence $i_1 \cdots i_k$ satisfying the Post correspondence condition. Q.E.D.

It is also possible to show that there are *inherently ambiguous* languages in the sense that one cannot find *any* unambiguous grammars for them, and further that there is no decision procedure for determining whether a language has this property.

This completes the discussion of the most important elementary properties of the context-free languages.

EXERCISES 8.2

1. Prove Corollary 8.2.2.

2. Complete the proof of Theorem 8.2.3. Prove Corollary 8.2.4.

3. A production is said to be *right* (*left*) *linear* iff it is of the form $q \to xq'$ ($q \to q'x$), $x \in S^* - \{\Lambda\}$. A production is *linear* iff it is of the form $q \to xq'y$, $x, y \in S^* - \{\Lambda\}$. A *grammar* is *right* (*left*) *linear* iff every production is right (left) linear or otherwise of the form $q \to x$, $x \in S^* - \{\Lambda\}$. A *grammar* is *linear* iff all its productions are linear or of the form $q \to x$, $x \in S^* - \{\Lambda\}$.

(*a*) Show that L is a finite state language iff it is generated by a right (left) linear grammar.

(*b*) Show that there exists a linear grammar which generates a context-free language which is not finite state.

(*c*) Show that not all context-free languages are generated by linear grammars.

4. Complete Case 3 of Corollary 8.2.6 and part (*a*) of Theorem 8.2.7.

5. Write a detailed proof for Theorem 8.2.23.

6. Show that the problem whether a context-free grammar is finite state is recursively unsolvable. (Use the fact that if L is context-free, then whether $(S^* - \{\Lambda\}) - L$ is finite state is unsolvable.)

7. A grammar **G** is *selfembedding* iff there is a $q \in Q$ such that $q \overset{*}{\Rightarrow} uqv$ for some $u \neq \Lambda$ and some $v \neq \Lambda$. Construct algorithms for deciding whether a grammar is embedding; selfembedding.

8. Let $A = \langle S, Q, q_0, M, Q' \rangle$ be an f.s.a. Show there is a context-free grammar **G** such that

$$L(\mathbf{G}) = \{y \mid (\exists x)(y = xEx^{-1} \wedge x \in x(A) \wedge E \notin S^*)\}$$

9. Prove that if **G** is nonself-embedding, then $L(\mathbf{G})$ is finite state. (*Hint:* Assume that **G** is *reduced*, that is, has the properties mentioned just before Definition 8.2.13. Then, if for every q there exists x, y such that $q \Rightarrow xq_0y$, $x, y \in (S \cup Q)^*$, show that all productions must satisfy Condition 3 of Section 8.1. If **G** does not have this property, complete the proof by induction on $K(Q)$.)

8.3 PUSHDOWN ACCEPTORS

We know from the results of Section 8.1 that there are context-free languages which are not regular; hence there are languages in the family which are not definable by an f.s.a. (or even an n.f.s.a.). What kind of automaton short of a Turing machine could perform such a task? We will now study a class of acceptors which is able to define the context-free languages. These automata are of more than theoretical interest since they represent in abstract form the principle of the pushdown memory or "stack" which is employed in computer programming technology. Informally speaking, a pushdown acceptor is capable of defining a set of words by use of the following means: (1) a single right-to-left input tape exactly as used by f.s.a.'s; (2) an auxiliary memory, the pushdown store, in which a record can be kept of everything scanned on the input but in which only the *last* such record entered is available for recall, then the *next* to last, and so forth. Such an automaton seems to be one of the simplest devices more powerful than an f.s.a. A pushdown acceptor which uses only one symbol in the auxiliary memory is called a *counter*. We will now attempt to make the pushdown concept precise.

Definition 8.3.1. A *pushdown storage acceptor*, p.d.a., is a semi-thue system with alphabet $S \cup Q \cup O$, $S \subseteq O$, $\Lambda \in S$, $Q \cap O = \varnothing$; a subset $Q' \subseteq Q$, the final states; an initial state q_0; an axiom scheme $\#q_0x\#$, $x \in S^*$. p.d.a. productions $\mathscr{P}$ are of the following three kinds only:

(*a*) $Po_hq_is_jR \rightarrow Po_hz_kq_lR$
(*b*) $Po_hq_is_jR \rightarrow Pq_lR$
(*c*) $\#q_i\# \rightarrow q_i$ if $q_i \in Q'$

q_i, q_l, and s_j are as usual internal state and input symbols, $o_h \in O$, and $z_k \in O^*$ where O is the output alphabet. A *deterministic* (that is, monogenic) p.d.a. is one such that each triple $o_h q_i s_j$ occurs at most once in the production set. A *nondeterministic* (that is, polygenic) p.d.a. is one not deterministic.

We will use the notation $\mathbf{P} = \langle S, Q, q_0, \mathscr{P}, O, Q' \rangle$ for p.d.a.'s always with the understanding that $\Lambda \in S$ (hence $\Lambda \in O$).

Definition 8.3.2. A word $x \in S^*$ is *accepted by a* p.d.a. **P** iff there is a terminal proof of some $q' \in Q'$ from $\# q_0 x \#$. $\mathscr{U}$ is definable by **P** iff every $x \in \mathscr{U}$ is accepted by **P**, and no $x \in S^*$ such that $x \notin \mathscr{U}$ is accepted by **P**.

It would be a relatively easy matter to alter our definitions so that x would be rejected by **P** iff $q \in Q'$ is terminal. But we will omit this elaboration except for one observation at the end of this section.

We may think of a p.d.a. in Turing machine style as a device with two tapes, I (input) and D (pushdown store). I is precisely the input tape to a finite transducer (considered as a unidirectional Turing machine—cf. Section 5.0). D, however, can be both written on and read and can move either left or right in a manner to be described. D grows, as does Turing tape, beginning with length zero.

A proof sequence is initiated by inscribing x on I with the p.d.a. in state q_0 scanning the leftmost symbol of x (Fig. 8.3.1).

Productions of the form (a) mean that if the acceptor is in state q_i scanning s_j on I and o_h on D, it shifts I one symbol left, shifts D $l(z_k)$ spaces left, and prints z_k to the right of o_h in these spaces of D. If $s_j = \Lambda$, it does *not* shift I.

Productions of the form (b) mean that I moves left, (unless $s_j = \Lambda$) while D moves right one symbol and sheds the o_h and the tape on which it is.

The significance of either $s = \Lambda$ or $o = \Lambda$ is that machine action does not depend on the non-null symbols $s' = \Lambda s = s\Lambda$, $o' = \Lambda o = o\Lambda$ being

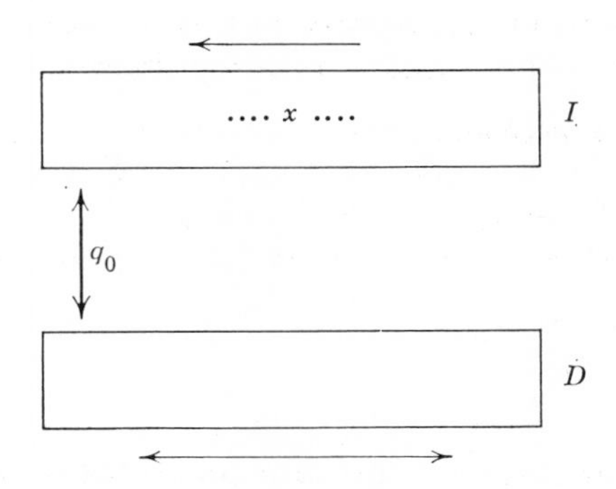

Fig. 8.3.1

read. Λ does not occupy tape. Hence we may and indeed shall frequently write, for example, $qs \to oq'$ for $\Lambda qs \to oq'$.

EXAMPLE 1. The p.d.a. below accepts the language xcx^{-1}, $x \in \{a, b\}^*$, $\{q_2\} = Q'$.

R.1. $q_0a \to aq_1$
R.2. $q_0b \to bq_1$
R.3. $q_1a \to aq_1$
R.4. $q_1b \to bq_1$
R.5. $q_1c \to q_2$
R.6. $aq_2a \to q_2$
R.7. $bq_2b \to q_2$
R.8. $\#q_2\# \to q_2$

An accepting proof of $\#q_0abcba\#$ appears below in further illustration.

1. $\#q_0abcba\#$ Axiom
2. $\#aq_1bcba\#$ **R.1.**

Here one may imagine that a has been printed on tape D of Fig. 8.3.1 yielding Fig. 8.3.2

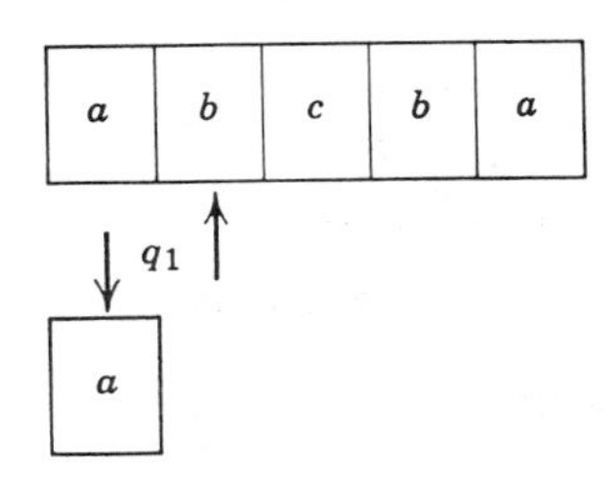

Fig. 8.3.2

from the initial situation of Fig. 8.3.3.

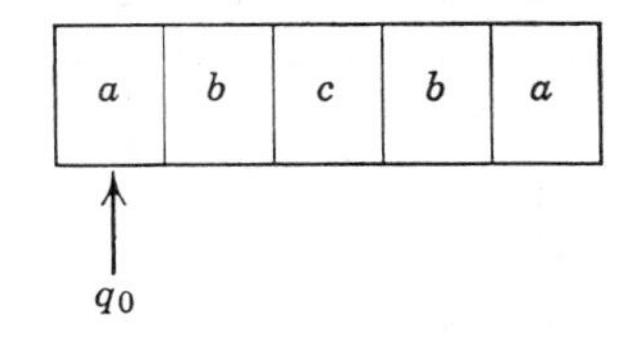

Fig. 8.3.3

Rule 4 applies next:

3. $\#abq_1cba\#$

and then

4. $\#abq_2ba\#$. ***R.5.***

The tape steps are shown in Figs. 8.3.4 and 8.3.5.

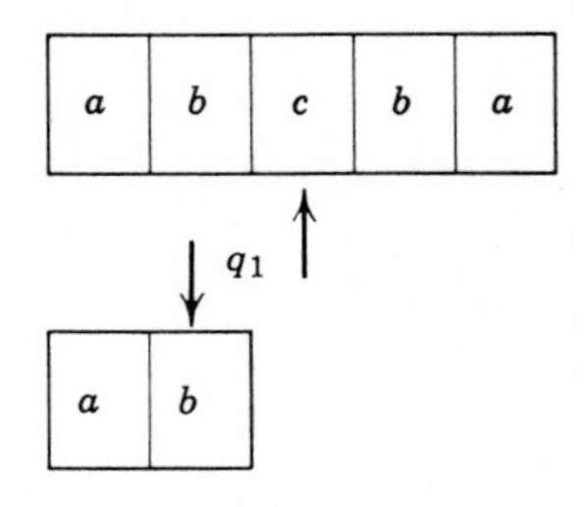

Fig. 8.3.4

and

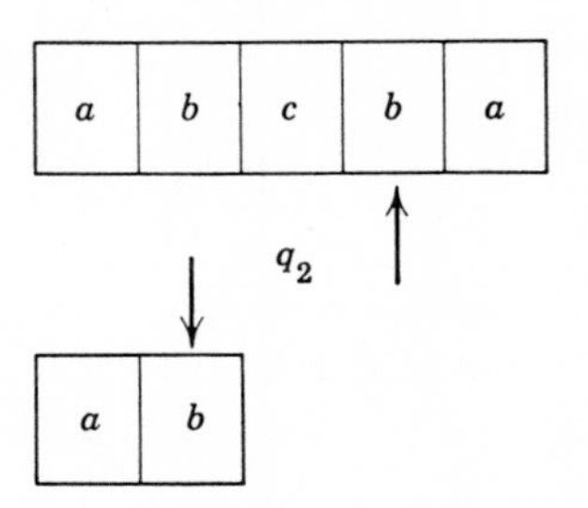

Fig. 8.3.5

Returning to the proof proper,

5. $\#aq_2a\#$ ***R.7.***

and tapewise, see Fig. 8.3.6.

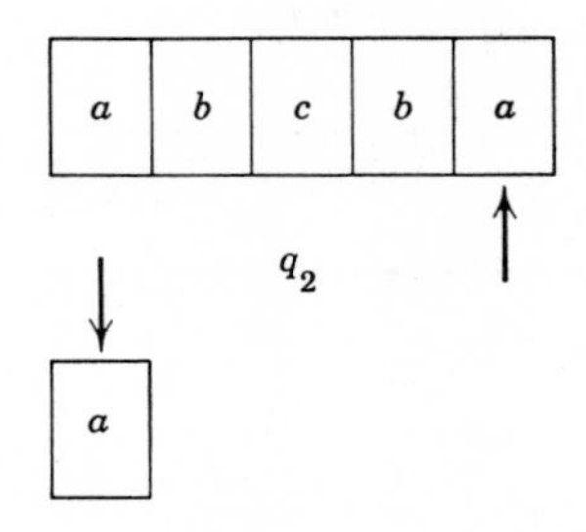

Fig. 8.3.6

Finally we have

6. q_2 ***R.6*** and ***R.8***

signifying acceptance. The ultimate tape picture is in Fig. 8.3.7, with the

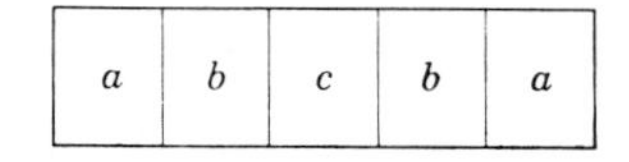

Fig. 8.3.7

pushdown store D having been completely shed.

EXAMPLE 2. A *boolean formula* is inductively defined to be either a variable a or b or an expression $-x$ if x is a formula or $(x \cup y)$ or $(x \cap y)$ if x and y are formulas. The following p.d.a. with accepting state q_5 accepts boolean formulas. In the productions α ranges over $\{a, b\}$.

R.1. $q_0\alpha \to q_5$
R.2. $q_0{}^- \to q_0$
R.3. $q_0(\to (q_1$
R.4. $q_1(\to (q_1$
R.5. $q_1\alpha \to q_2$
R.6. $q_1{}^- \to q_1$
R.7. $q_2 \cap \to q_3$
R.8. $q_2 \cup \to q_3$
R.9. $q_3(\to (q_1$
R.10. $q_3\alpha \to q_4$
R.11. $q_3- \to q_3$
R.12. $q_3{}^- \to q_1$
R.13. $(q_4) \to q_5$
R.14. $(q_5) \to q_5$
R.15. $q_5 \cap \to q_3$
R.16. $q_5 \cup \to q_3$
R.17. $\#q_5\# \to q_5$

Note that this automaton is nondeterministic, but a considerably simpler one is no doubt obtainable. The student should verify the action of this p.d.a. with examples.

It is not hard to see that a p.d.a. consisting solely of rules with $o_h = \Lambda$ is a transducer of a general kind, perhaps nondeterministic. Compare here Definition 5.1.1. The difference is that the transducer obtained in the manner indicated from a p.d.a. has $\Lambda \in S$ and also the output set will be comprised of *words* on O. Further the M and N functions of Definition 5.1.4 have become *relations* in the general case. Equivalently, in the same spirit as Definition 7.1.5, the ranges of M and N become sets of states and outputs respectively.

Definition 8.3.3. A *generalized finite transducer*, g.f.t., has alphabets as in Definition 8.3.1 except there are no designated final states; initial state q_0; axiom scheme $q_0x\#$, $x \in S^*$; and productions $\mathscr{R}$ of the following two forms only:

$$(a)\quad Pq_is_jR \to Pz_kq_lR \qquad z_k \in O^*$$
$$(b)\quad Pq_i\# \to P$$

A g.f.t. may be either polygenic or monogenic and need not be complete. We write $\mathbf{T} = \langle S, Q, q_0, \mathscr{R}, O' \rangle$ where O' is the finite subset of O^*

determined by $z \in O'$ iff z is in some production of $\mathscr{R}$. As we shall not discuss finite transducers at all there should be no confusion arising from our new use of "**T**."

EXAMPLE 3

$$\begin{aligned} q_1\Lambda &\to 01q_2 \\ q_20 &\to 10q_1 \\ q_11 &\to \Lambda q_2 \\ q_21 &\to 1q_1 \\ q_10 &\to 11q_2 \end{aligned}$$

Theorem 8.3.4. If **T** is a g.f.t., then there is a proof of $y \in O^*$ from $q_0x\#$, $x \in S^*$, iff when $x = s_{i_1} \cdots s_{i_n}$ and $y = z_{i_1} \cdots z_{i_n}$ there is a sequence $q_0 = q_{i_1}, \ldots, q_{i_n+1}$ such that

$$Pq_{i_j}s_{i_j}R \to Pz_{i_j}q_{i_{j+1}}R \qquad j = 1, \ldots, n$$

and

$$Pq_{i_n+1}\# \to P$$

are productions in $\mathscr{R}$ of **T**.

Proof. From Definitions 3.3.2, 3.3.3, and 8.3.3. Q.E.D.

Although the action of a g.f.t. is not necessarily functional, we will use the notation $\mathbf{T}(x, y)$ to indicate that y is an output from input x, that is, there is the required proof of y from $q_0x\#$. Also as a generalization of the direct and inverse image concepts we write $\mathbf{T}(\mathscr{U})$ and $\mathbf{T}^{-1}(\mathscr{V})$. $\mathbf{T}(\mathscr{U})$ is a possible set of outputs from a set of inputs $\mathscr{U}$. Likewise $\mathbf{T}^{-1}(\mathscr{V})$ is a possible set of inputs causing a set of outputs $\mathscr{V}$.

Definition 8.3.5. $\mathbf{T}' = \langle O', Q, q_0, \mathscr{R}', S\rangle$ is an *inverse* of

$$\mathbf{T} = \langle S, Q, q_0, \mathscr{R}, O'\rangle$$

iff for any $x \in S^*$, $y \in O^*$, $\mathbf{T}(x, y)$ iff $\mathbf{T}'(y, x)$.

Theorem 8.3.6. Every g.f.t. has an inverse.

Proof. Suppose **T** is a g.f.t. and that **T**′ is the transducer whose productions $\mathscr{R}'$ are

$$\begin{aligned} q_iz_k \to s_jq_l \in \mathscr{R}' &\Leftrightarrow q_is_j \to z_kq_l \in \mathscr{R} \\ Pq_i\# \to P \in \mathscr{R}' &\Leftrightarrow Pq_i\# \to P \in \mathscr{R} \end{aligned}$$

The obvious completion of the proof uses Theorem 8.3.4. Q.E.D.

EXAMPLE 4. An inverse to Example 3 is

$$\begin{aligned} q_101 &\to \Lambda q_2 \\ q_210 &\to 0q_1 \\ q_1\Lambda &\to 1q_2 \\ q_21 &\to 1q_1 \\ q_111 &\to 0q_2 \end{aligned}$$

Note that the construction used in Theorem 8.3.6 and applied in Example 4 simply takes the *words* z_k of the output of the initially given transducer to be the input *symbols* of the inverse automaton. This is reasonable since $\{z_k \mid z_k \in O'\}$ is a finite set.

Definition 8.3.3 allows g.f.t. as in the following example.

EXAMPLE 5.

$$\begin{aligned} q_0\Lambda &\to 1q_1 \\ q_1\Lambda &\to 11q_2 \\ q_2\Lambda &\to \Lambda q_0 \\ &\vdots \end{aligned}$$

In this example we see that it is possible to be in a state (here q_0) and to generate an indefinitely long output y without any input—in effect, that is to say, without moving across the input tape at all. Such a transducer is said to be *unbounded.*

Definition 8.3.7. A g.f.t. **T** is *unbounded* iff there is a sequence of states $q = q_{i_1}, \ldots, q_{i_n} = q$ such that $q_{i_j}\Lambda \to z_{i_j}q_{i_{j+1}}$ is a production of **T** for each $j = 1, \ldots, n - 1$ and $z_{i_1} \cdots z_{i_{n-1}} \neq \Lambda$. **T** is *bounded* iff it is not unbounded.

Definition 8.3.8. **T** and **T**$'$ are *equivalent* iff for every $x \in S^*$ and $y \in O^*$, $\mathbf{T}(x, y)$ iff $\mathbf{T}'(x, y)$.

Theorem 8.3.9. If **T** is bounded, there exists an equivalent g.f.t. **T**$'$ such that **T**$'$ has no productions of the form $q\Lambda \to g'$.

Proof. For the student.

We want now to show that if a language $L \subseteq S^*$ is input to a g.f.t. **T** and if $\mathbf{T}(L)$ is an output language, then $\mathbf{T}(L)$ is context-free provided L is. This fact is fundamental, as we shall see, to the proof that the language defined by a p.d.a. is context-free.

It will be very convenient in what follows to allow context-free grammars to have productions $g \to \Lambda$, $\Lambda \in S$. Such rules were precluded by *Condition* 1 of Section 8.1, since to have permitted them there would have led to uninteresting complications.[4] It is easy to show (which we will not) that context-free grammars with the new rules generate the same family of languages (except for Λ) as do those of Section 8.2 and that the essentials of the theory are the same.

Theorem 8.3.10. Let $\mathbf{T} = \langle S, Q, q_0, \mathscr{R}, O'\rangle$ be a g.f.t. and let

$$\mathbf{G} = \langle S, Q^G, a_0, \mathscr{P}\rangle$$

[4] To develop the part of the theory presented in Section 8.2 we would have had to show how to construct for an arbitrary **G** a weakly equivalent grammar with no rules $g \to \Lambda$ provided only that $\Lambda \notin L(\mathbf{G})$.

be a context-free grammar which generates $L(\mathbf{G})$. Then $\mathbf{T}(L(\mathbf{G}))$ is a context-free language. The property of being context-free is preserved under the operation of a g.f.t.

Proof.

CASE I. $\mathbf{T}$ is bounded. Hence by Theorem 8.3.9 we may assume $\mathbf{T}$ has no productions $q\Lambda \to g'$. We will construct a new context-free grammar $\mathbf{G}'$ and show that $L(\mathbf{G}') = \mathbf{T}(L(\mathbf{G}))$.

Let $\mathbf{G}' = \langle S', Q', q_0', \mathscr{P}' \rangle$ where $S' = O'$, $Q' = (Q \times A \times Q) \cup \{q_0'\}$, $A = S \cup Q^G$, and $\mathscr{P}'$ is a set of productions with membership as follows:

1. $(q_i, a, q_j) \to (q_i, a_1, q_{i_1}) \cdots (q_{i_{k-1}}, a_k, q_j) \in \mathscr{P}'$ provided that $a \to a_1 \cdots a_k \in \mathscr{P}$, for all possible indices $i, j, i_1, \ldots, i_{k-1}$ on the q's;
2. $q_0' \to (q_0, a_0, q_i) \in \mathscr{P}'$ for all $q_i \in Q$;
3. $(q_i, s_j, q_l) \to z_k \in \mathscr{P}'$ provided that $q_i s_j \to z_k q_l \in \mathscr{R}$;
4. $(q_i, s_j, q_l) \to (q_i, s_j, q_l)s_j \in \mathscr{P}'$ for all q_i, q_j, s_j such that there is no z_k for which $q_i s_j \to z_k q_l \in \mathscr{R}$.
5. No other rules are in $\mathscr{P}'$.

Production 4 is included above so as to satisfy Definition 8.1.1. Such rules obviously play no part in generating sentences.

Suppose now that $x = s_{i_1} \cdots s_{i_m} \in L(\mathbf{G})$; then by hypothesis $a_0 \overset{*}{\Rightarrow} x$. Also let $y = z_{i_1} \cdots z_{i_m} \in \mathbf{T}(L(\mathbf{G}))$ be a theorem from $q_0 x\#$ in $\mathbf{T}$.

All we have to do to prove that $y \in L(\mathbf{G}')$ is: (i) simulate the sequence of productions $P_1, \ldots, P_r$, $P_i \in \mathscr{P}$ $(i = 1, \ldots, r)$ which causes $a_0 \overset{*}{\Rightarrow} x$ by a companion sequence $P_1', \ldots, P_r'$, $P_i' \in \mathscr{P}'(i = 1, \ldots, r)$ using construction 1 above; (ii) add a production P_0' of the form 2 above in order to get the derivation in $\mathbf{G}'$ started; (iii) add productions of the form 3 so as to generate the proper sequence of output symbols z_k constituting y.

In more detail, steps (i) and (ii) yield a proof *scheme*

$$\begin{array}{c} q_0' \\ (q_0, a_0, \alpha_j) \\ \vdots \\ (q_0, s_{i_1}, \alpha_{i_1}) \cdots (q_{i_{m-1}}, s_{i_m}, \alpha_j) \end{array} \tag{1}$$

which is terminal w.r.t. Rule 1. Since by the construction 1, for every production in $\mathscr{P}$ and every possible sequence of states $q_i, q_j, q_{i_1}, \ldots, q_{i_k}$ there is an appropriate production in $\mathscr{P}'$, we may specify (1) w.r.t. q symbols in any way we wish. So we instantiate the scheme as follows: if $q_0 = q_{i_0}, q_{i_1}, \ldots, q_{i_{m+1}}$ is the sequence of states determined as in Theorem 8.3.4 by the proof of y from $q_0 x\#$ in $\mathbf{T}$, then set $\alpha_j = q_{i_{m+1}}$ and $\alpha_{i_k} = q_{i_k}$, $k < m + 1$. In this way (1) is forced to correspond to the sequence of states and inputs determining the output sequence y of $\mathbf{T}$.

Finally step (iii) calls for the addition of productions of the form 3 with appropriate choice of the q's and s's to generate $y = z_{i_1} \cdots z_{i_m}$.

Conversely, if $y \in L(\mathbf{G}')$, there is a derivation $q_0' \overset{*}{\Rightarrow} y$ in $\mathbf{G}'$. From the construction, arguing the above steps backwards, it is easily shown that there is an x such that $x \in L(\mathbf{G})$ and $\mathbf{T}(x, y)$.

CASE II. **T** is unbounded. We will indicate the change in the construction of $\mathbf{G}'$ which is required, leaving it to the reader to complete the detailed treatment. Replace each rule $a \to a_1 \cdots a_k \in \mathscr{P}$ of **G** by $a \to \beta a_1 \beta \cdots \beta a_k$ where $\beta \notin S \cup Q^G$; then remake the construction 1–5 performed in Case I. The effect of the addition of β will be to give $\mathbf{G}'$ the power to produce sentences y which are outputs of unbounded transducers. Consider the set

$$\mathscr{U}_{ij} = \{z \mid (\exists i_0) \cdots (\exists i_m)(\exists x_1), \ldots, (\exists x_m)(z = x_1 \cdots x_m \wedge (\forall k)(1 \leq k \leq m \Rightarrow q_{i_{k-1}}\Lambda \to x_k q_{i_k} \in \mathscr{R}) \wedge i_0 = i \wedge i_m = j)\}$$

$\mathscr{U}_{ij}$ is regular (why?) and there is only a finite number of pairs (i, j). Hence the union of all such sets is regular, and by Corollary 8.1.13 there is a finite set of context-free rules for generating it. Indeed, using the results of Chapter 7 and Section 8.1, such rules can be obtained effectively (see exercises); further, they generate exactly the same set as specified by the relations

$$(q_i, \alpha, q_j) \to \Lambda \qquad \text{and} \qquad (q_i, \alpha, q_j) \overset{*}{\Rightarrow} z$$

for all i, j, and $z \in \mathscr{U}_{ij}$. $\mathbf{G}'$, extended by the context-free rules to which we have alluded, therefore generates $\mathbf{T}(L(\mathbf{G}))$. Q.E.D.

By a similar kind of construction it is also possible to prove the following theorem.

Theorem 8.3.11. If **T** is a g.f.t. and **G** is a finite-state grammar which generates $L(\mathbf{G})$, then $\mathbf{T}(L(\mathbf{G}))$ is a regular language. The property of being a regular language is preserved under the operation of a generalized finite transducer.

Proof. For the student.

An interesting question which we have not so far considered concerns set-theoretic operations on languages of different kinds. We know that the regular sets are a boolean family and that the context-free languages are closed under union but do not comprise a boolean family. What about the union of a regular and a context-free language? Obviously the union is again a context-free language since every regular language is context-free. However the answer to the companion question about *intersection* is far from obvious since we do not have that the intersection of two context-free languages is context-free (Theorem 8.2.8). It is a remarkable fact that the intersection of context-free and regular languages is again context-free. This result turns out to have many interesting applications in mathematical linguistics. However, we shall use it here solely in our project to show the correspondence of p.d.a. and the family of context-free languages.

Theorem 8.3.12. If L_1 is context-free and L_2 is regular, then $L_1 \cap L_2$ is context-free.

Proof. Suppose $\mathbf{A} = \langle S, Q, q_0, M, Q^F \rangle$ and $\mathbf{G} = \langle S, Q^G, a_0, \mathscr{P} \rangle$, where $L_1 = L(\mathbf{G})$ and $L_2 = x(\mathbf{A})$. Let $A = S \cup Q^G$. Define $\mathbf{G}' = \langle S, Q', q_0', \mathscr{P}' \rangle$ where $Q' = (Q \times A \times Q) \cup \{q_0'\}$ and $\mathscr{P}'$ is as follows:

1′. $(q_i, a, q_j) \to (q_i, a_1, q_{i_1}) \cdots (q_{i_{k-1}}, a_k, q_j) \in \mathscr{P}'$ if $a \to a_1 \cdots a_k \in \mathscr{P}$, for all possible indices $i, j, i_1, \ldots, i_{k-1}$ on the q's.
2′. $q_0' \to (q_0, a_0, q_i) \in \mathscr{P}'$ for all $q_i \in Q^F$.
3′. $(q_i, s_j, q_l) \to s_j \in \mathscr{P}'$ if $M(q_i, s_j) = q_l$.
4′. No other rules are in $\mathscr{P}'$.

It is left to the student to complete the proof using this construction and a method analogous to that of Theorem 8.3.10. Q.E.D.

In order to prove Theorem 8.3.17 we shall need a certain standard form of context-free grammar for use in constructing a nondeterministic p.d.a. which will define a given language L. It was originally believed (Chomsky [1962]) that a *normal* grammar, that is, one whose productions are only of the form $q \to q'q''$ or $q \to s$ $(q' \neq q'')$ would be sufficient, given certain natural provisos.[5] However it turns out that the following quite complicated construction is actually needed.

Definition 8.3.13. A context-free grammar $\mathbf{G}$ is *α-normal* iff the following conditions are satisfied:

1. Q is partitioned into subsets Q^R and Q^L; elements of Q^R are denoted by q^R and of Q^L by q^L (throughout this definition only).
2. The productions of $\mathbf{G}$ are only of the four forms

$$q_i^R \to q_m^L q_n^R \qquad q_i^L \to q_k^L q_l^R$$
$$q^R \to s \qquad q^L \to s$$

3. There are no pairs of productions of the forms

$$q_j^L \to q_i^L q_k^R \qquad q_m^R \to q_i^L q_n^R$$

or

$$q_j^L \to q_i^L q_k^R \qquad q_m^R \to q_n^L q_k^R$$

[5] I am indebted to the publisher's Reader for pointing out my near perpetuation of an error in using simply normal grammars in the proof outline of Theorem 8.3.17. The more complicated α-normal grammar of Definition 8.3.13 is due to R. J. Stanley [1966]. A more economical approach to Theorem 8.3.17 appears in Ginsburg [1966].

4. If **G** contains a pair

$$q_i^{L(R)} \to q_j{}^L q_k{}^R \qquad q_p^{L(R)} \to q_j{}^L q_s{}^R$$

then, if it also contains $q_i^{L(R)} \to g'$, it contains $q_p^{L(R)} \to g'$, and conversely.

Explanation. 1 and 2 are clear. We say that if $g \to g'$ is of one of the forms in 2 above, g *dominates* the symbols in g'; for example, q_1 dominates q_2 and q_3 in $q_1 \to q_2q_3$. Condition 3 says that for no pair is it the case that an auxiliary is dominated by both a right and a left auxiliary. Roughly speaking, every node in a generation tree (cf. Theorem 8.2.5) has at most two branches growing from it and the left (right) node is always labeled with a left (right) auxiliary symbol; condition 3 guarantees that an auxiliary occurring on the left (right) in a tree stays to the left (right) in later arborization. Condition 4 states that if two auxiliaries dominate the same left auxiliary, they dominate the same symbols.

The next theorem tends to justify our intuitive idea that a sentence of a phrase structure language can be parsed by a sequence of bifurcations.

Theorem 8.3.14. For every context-free grammar **G** there exists a weakly equivalent α-normal context-free grammar **G**.

Proof (in outline). If $q \to x$, $x \in A^*$ is a production of **G** and if $x = a_1 \cdots a_k$, we replace this rule by

$$q \to a_1 \cdots a_{k-2}q'$$
$$q' \to a_{k-1}a_k$$

where $q' \notin Q$ of **G**. If this procedure is carried out exhaustively, we will obtain a new grammar with productions of the forms

(i) $q \to st$ $\qquad (s, t \in S \text{ or } = \Lambda)$
(ii) $q \to sq'$
(iii) $q \to q's$
(iv) $q \to q'q''$ $\qquad q' \neq q''$

and any such grammar can be seen to be weakly equivalent to **G**. By introducing further new auxiliaries and following a similar procedure all three unwanted varieties (i) to (iii) can be replaced by rules of the desired form. Q.E.D.

Recall our brief discussion of structural descriptions (phrase markers) in Section 8.0 [recall also, Exercises 8.1(3, 4)] and note that each labeled left parenthesis has as mate a unique identically labeled right parenthesis. If we have a language which uses parentheses, we say that two labeled pairs $(_i,)_i$ and $(_j,)_j$ *separate* each other iff they occur in the order $(_i, (_j,)_i,)_j$ where other parentheses may be interspersed among those displayed (Kleene [1952]). A one–one correspondence between the set of left parentheses and the set of right parentheses in an expression is *proper* iff a left is paired to a right to the right of it in the usual ordering and no two such pairs separate each other. It is easy to see that a sentence of a context-free language, owing to the nature of the rules of its generating grammar, always enjoys a proper pairing of phrase marking parentheses (see exercises). Furthermore, this property is easily detected by use of the following algorithm: if an expression has no parentheses, the property is satisfied; if there are parentheses, seek an innermost pair; if there is no such pair, the expression does not have the property; if there is a pair, cancel both members; return to the very first step.

It turns out that the proper pairing concept is a key one in the theory of definability of context-free languages. Indeed it is this idea that was used in the design of Examples 1 and 2; it also plays an important part in Theorems 8.3.17 and 8.3.19. The next definition formalizes the essential notion of cancellation that appears in the foregoing algorithm.

Definition 8.3.15. Given an arbitrary alphabet $A = \{a_1, \ldots, a_n\}$, we call $A^{-1} = \{a_1{}^{-1}, \ldots, a_n{}^{-1}\}$ the alphabet of *right inverses* with the rule that $xa_ia_i{}^{-1}y = xy$, $i = 1, \ldots, n$, and $x, y \in (A \bigcup A^{-1})^*$. We say that a word x *reduces* to y iff there is a sequence $x = z_1, \ldots, z_m = y$ such that for every $j < m$ there are words u_j, v_j, and a_{i_j} such that $z_j = u_ja_{i_j}a_{i_j}{}^{-1}v_j$ and $z_{j+i} = u_jv_j$. A word x is *blocked* iff $x = ya_iza_j{}^{-1}w$ for $i \neq j$ and for some perhaps empty words y, z, w such that z reduces to Λ.

Corollary 8.3.16. If x is blocked, it does not reduce to Λ; if x is blocked, then for every y, xy is blocked.

EXAMPLE 6. Suppose $x = a_1a_3a_2a_2{}^{-1}a_2a_3$ and $y = a_1a_3a_2a_3$. Then x reduces to y. y does not reduce to Λ. However, it is not blocked since yz is not blocked, where $z = a_3{}^{-1}a_2{}^{-1}a_3{}^{-1}a_1{}^{-1}$.

Theorem 8.3.17. If L is context-free, then there exists a nondeterministic p.d.a. **P** such that **P** defines L.

REMARK. The proof uses for the general case a construction that always leads to a polygenic set of rules. It is left to the student to show [Exercise 8.3(6)] that no monogenic construction exists in general.

Proof (outline). Suppose $\mathbf{G} = \langle S, Q, q_0, \mathscr{P}\rangle$ generates L. By Theorem 8.3.14 we may further suppose that **G** is α-normal. We could construct outright a p.d.a. which defines L; however, it is instructive to build a generalized transducer first; this transducer has the property that its output y reduces to Λ and $\mathbf{T}(x, y)$ iff $x \in L$ is generated by **G**.

So we let $\mathbf{T} = \langle S, Q', a_0, \mathscr{R}, O'\rangle$ where Q' is given by

$$a_0 \in Q'$$
$$q_i{}^l, q_i{}^r \in Q' \Leftrightarrow q_i \in Q$$

O is given by

$$a, a^{-1} \in O \Leftrightarrow a \in A = S \cup Q$$

where a^{-1} is the right inverse of a; and $\mathscr{R}$ is given by

1. $q_i \to s \in \mathscr{P} \Rightarrow q_i{}^l s \to q_i s s^{-1} q_i{}^{-1} q_i{}^r \in \mathscr{R}$
2. $q_i \to q_j q_k \in \mathscr{P} \Rightarrow \left\{\begin{matrix} q_i{}^l\Lambda \to q_i q_j{}^l \\ q_j{}^r\Lambda \to q_k{}^l \\ q_k{}^r\Lambda \to q_i{}^{-1} q_i{}^r \end{matrix}\right. \in \mathscr{R}$
3. $a_0\Lambda \to q_0{}^l \in \mathscr{R}$
4. $q_0{}^r\Lambda \to a_0 \in \mathscr{R}$
5. $Pa_0\# \to P \in \mathscr{R}$
6. $\mathscr{R}$ has no other productions.

From this construction it follows that x is generated by **G** iff **T**(x, y) and y reduces to Λ and y is equipped with phrase markers, except for two inessential facts: (*a*) the auxiliaries q_i have been substituted for labeled left parentheses $(_i$ and similarly $q_i{}^{-1}$ for the right $)_i$; (*b*) each terminal symbol $s \in S$ occurs with right s^{-1} inverse concatenated to the right. Without actually writing a complete proof of this fact, we will give an illustration of it after the discussion of the theorem. The student will then readily see how a detailed proof can be given (Example 7).

If the output y is a phrase marker with the additional property that each terminal symbol s occurs iff s^{-1} is concatenated to the right, then y reduces to Λ [Exercise 8.3(7)]. Similarly, again from the manner of the action of **T** and a straightforward application of Definition 8.3.15, the converse holds. Thus we have that x is accepted by **G** iff **T**(x, y) and y reduces to Λ.

Finally, we construct a p.d.a. **P** such that **P** accepts x iff **T**(x, y) and y reduces to Λ. $\mathbf{P} = \langle S, Q', a_0, \mathscr{P}', O, \{a_0\}\rangle$ where all components of the sextuple are like those of **T** except that **P** never actually uses the inverses a^{-1} and that the productions are as follows (note: they are derived directly from $\mathscr{R}$):

1′. $aq_i{}^l s \to a\Lambda q_i{}^r \in \mathscr{P}'$ for every $a \in O$

2′. $aq_i{}^l\Lambda \to aq_i q_j{}^l$ $\quad aq_j{}^r\Lambda \to aq_k{}^l$ and $aq_k{}^r\Lambda \to \Lambda q_i{}^r \in \mathscr{P}'$ for every $a \in O$

3′. $aa_0\Lambda \to a\Lambda q_0{}^l \in \mathscr{P}'$ for every $a \in O$

4′. $aq_0{}^r\Lambda \to a\Lambda a_0 \in \mathscr{P}'$ for every $a \in O$

5′. $\#a_0\# \to a_0 \in \mathscr{P}'$

From this construction we see by inspection that the action of **P** is no different than that of **T** except that **P** does nothing to the output when **T** prints $q_i s s^{-1} q_i{}^{-1}$ (compare 1 with 1′) and that **P** erases q_i when **T** prints $q_i{}^{-1}$. Hence it follows that **T**(x, y) and y reduces to Λ iff **P** accepts x. Q.E.D.

The following example should shed light on the construction of $\mathscr{R}$ and *mutatis mutandis* of $\mathscr{P}'$.

EXAMPLE 7. Let **G** be the grammar

R.1. $S \rightarrow CB$
R.2. $C \rightarrow AS$
R.3. $A \rightarrow a$
R.4. $B \rightarrow b$
R.5. $S \rightarrow c$

The following is a strong proof of

$$(_S\, (_C\, (_A\, a)_A\, (_S\, (_C\, (_A\, a)_A\, (_S\, c)_S\,)_C\, (_B\, b)_B\,)_S\,)_C\, (_B\, b)_B\,)_S :$$

1′. S
2′. $(_S\, CB)_S$ ***R.1.***
3′. $(_S\, (_C\, AS)_C\, B)_S$ ***R.2.***
4′. $(_S\, (_C\, A\, (_S\, CB)_S\,)_C\, B)_S$ ***R.1.***
5′. $(_S\, (_C\, A\, (_S\, (_C\, AS)_C\, B)_S\,)_C\, B)_S$ ***R.2.***
6′. $(_S\, (_C\, A\, (_S\, (_C\, A\, (_S\, c)_S\, B)_S\,)_C\, B)_S$ ***R.5.***
7′. $(_S\, (_C\, (_A\, a)_A\, (_S\, (_C\, (_A\, a)_A\, (_S\, c)_S\,)_C\, (_B\, b)_B\,)_S\,)_C\, (_B\, b)_B\,)_S$ by ***R.3***, ***3***, ***4*** and ***4***.

Observe that 7′ comes to *aacbb* in an ordinary proof and that *aacbb* may also be obtained by our parenthesis-removing algorithm presented prior to Definition 8.3.15.

Next we use the construction for a transducer given in the theorem to obtain the following automaton. Corresponding to ***R.1*** of the example machine:

R.1a. $S^l\Lambda \rightarrow SC^l$
R.1b. $C^r\Lambda \rightarrow B^l$
R.1c. $B^r\Lambda \rightarrow S^{-1}S^r$

and to ***R.2***:

R.2a. $C^l\Lambda \rightarrow CA^l$
R.2b. $A^r\Lambda \rightarrow S^l$
R.2c. $S^r\Lambda \rightarrow C^{-1}C^r$

to ***R.3***, ***R.4***, and ***R.5***:

R.3a. $A^la \rightarrow Aaa^{-1}A^{-1}A^r$
R.4a. $B^lb \rightarrow Bbb^{-1}B^{-1}B^r$
R.5a. $S^lc \rightarrow Scc^{-1}S^{-1}S^r$

Finally the "initial" and "terminal" rules are:

R.6. $a_0\Lambda \to S^l$
R.7. $S^r\Lambda \to a_0$
R.8. $Pa_0\# \to P$

where a_0 is the initial state of the transducer.

This automaton will produce from the axiom *aacbb* an output y which is the same as $7'$ except that S replaces $(_S$, S^{-1} replaces $)_S$, etc., and that aa^{-1} replaces a, etc. The desired terminal theorem in fact is

$$SCAaa^{-1}A^{-1}SCAaa^{-1}A^{-1}Scc^{-1}S^{-1}C^{-1}Bbb^{-1}B^{-1}S^{-1}C^{-1}Bbb^{-1}B^{-1}S^{-1}$$

The student is urged to verify this output since the trouble now will help ease the pain of doing Exercise 8.3(7).

In order to establish a kind of converse to Theorem 8.3.17 we shall need the next lemma.

Lemma 8.3.18. Given a p.d.a. **P**, there exists a generalized transducer **T** and a y such that $\mathbf{T}(x, y)$ and y reduces to Λ iff **P** accepts x.

Proof. Let $\mathbf{P} = \langle S, Q, q_0, \mathscr{P}, O, Q'\rangle$. Let $\mathbf{P}' = \langle S, Q, q_0, \mathscr{P}', O', Q'\rangle$ be a new p.d.a. where $O' = O \bigcup O^{-1}$, O^{-1} the alphabet of inverses, and where $\mathscr{P}'$ is determined thus:

1. $Po_hq_is_jR \to Po_hz_kq_lR \in \mathscr{P}' \Leftrightarrow$ it is in $\mathscr{P}$
2a. $Po_hq_is_jR \to Po_ho_h{}^{-1}q_lR \in \mathscr{P}'$ and
2b. $Po_hq_is_jR \to Po_ho_h{}^{-1}o^{-1}oq_lR \in \mathscr{P}'$ for all $o \in O$
$\Leftrightarrow Po_hq_is_jR \to Pq_lR \in \mathscr{P}$
3. $\#q_i\# \to q_i \in \mathscr{P}' \Leftrightarrow q_i \in Q'$

Thus **P′** is entirely like **P** except for the fact that whenever **P** sheds tape, **P′** instead *adds* to the storage tape either the inverse of the last output symbol printed on tape or that inverse followed by any pair $o^{-1}o$, $o \in O$. So **P′** is always nondeterministic while **P** need not be. The theorem statement leaves the question open. Note that **P′** cannot accept any word inasmuch as it cannot shed tape. Of course it is, nonetheless, a p.d.a. and a useful one in establishing our goal.

We say that a production of $\mathscr{P}$ *corresponds* to one of $\mathscr{P}'$ iff they have the same left-hand sides. If $w = \#yqx\#$ and $w' = \#zqx\#$ are lines of a proof in **P** and **P′** respectively such that z reduces to y (Definition 8.3.15), then w and w' *match*. If w and w' match, then there is a proof from the same axiom with a line w'' which matches w, and the productions applicable to w and w'' correspond [Exercise 8.3(9)].

Using the foregoing ideas we will now show:

(I) If **P** accepts x, then **P′** has a proof from $\#q_0x\#$ terminating in a word $w_n = \#yq_i\#$, $q_i \in Q'$ such that y reduces to Λ.

(II) If **P** does not accept x, then for every terminal w_n' from $\#q_0x\#$ in $\mathbf{P}'$ either $w_n' = \#yq\#$ for some y, $q \notin Q'$, and x; or $w_n' = \#yq_i\#$, $q_i \in Q'$, and y does not reduce to Λ.

To show (I) we will prove that for any nonterminal steps w_k and w_k' in proofs in **P** and $\mathbf{P}'$ respectively, if w_k matches w_k' and $w_k \Rightarrow w_{k+1}$ by a production of $\mathscr{P}$ by P_k then there is a P_k' of $\mathscr{P}'$ such that $w_k' \Rightarrow w_{k+1}'$ by P_k' and w_{k+1} and w_{k+1}' match. When we have done this, then since $w_1 = \#q_0x\#$ and $w_1' = \#q_0x\#$ match, (I) will follow immediately: if **P** accepts x, it will terminate in a word $\Lambda q = q$, where q is final, which will be matched by a terminal word yq; and since these words match, y reduces to Λ.

So assume that w_k and w_k' match, and P_k takes w_k into w_{k+1} and P_k is a rule of the form a, Definition 8.3.1. Then P_k' by its very construction (1 above) takes w_k' into w_{k+1}' and w_{k+1} and w_{k+1}' match. Suppose, however, that P_k is a rule of the form b of 8.3.1. Since w_k is not terminal it must be of the form $w_k = \#yo_hq_ix\#$, and $w_{k+1} = \#yq_lx'\#$. If $y = \Lambda$, then $w_k = \#o_hq_ix\#$ and $w_{k+1} = \#q_lx'\#$. Since $w_k' = \#zo_hq_ix\#$ matches w_k, z reduces to Λ. Now there exists by 2a of the construction a production P_k' which takes w_k' into $w_{k+1}' = \#zo_ho_h^{-1}q_lx'\#$. But clearly, then, w_{k+1}' matches w_{k+1} since $zo_ho_h^{-1}$ reduces to Λ. If $y \neq \Lambda$, then $w_k = \#y'o_ro_hq_ix\#$ where y' may or may not be null. P_k takes w_k into $w_{k+1} = \#y'o_rq_lx'\#$. Again $w_k' = \#zo_hq_ix\#$ matches w_k. So $z = vo_ru$ where v reduces to y' and where $u = \Lambda$ or else u reduces to Λ. Now there is an appropriate production taking w_k' into $w_{k+1}' = \#vo_ruo_ho_h^{-1}o_r^{-1}o_rq_lx'\#$ and $vo_ruo_ho_h^{-1}o_r^{-1}o_r$ reduces to $y'o_r$. This completes the proof of (I).

To demonstrate (II) we will prove that for nonterminal matching w_k and w_k', if P_k' takes w_k' into w_{k+1}', then either there exists P_k taking w_k into w_{k+1} and w_{k+1}' matches w_{k+1}', or else y in $w_{k+1}' = \#yq_lx\#$ is blocked (Definition 8.3.15). (II) will then follow immediately.

So we assume that w_{k+1}' follows from w_k' by P_k' and that there is no P_k taking w_k into w_{k+1} such that w_{k+1} matches w_{k+1}'. Assume also that P_k' is of type 2a in the construction; then $w_k = \#yo_hq_ix\#$ and $w_k' = \#zo_hq_ix\#$ match and z reduces to y. But $w_{k+1}' = \#zo_ho_h^{-1}q_lx'\#$. Moreover, there does exist P_k taking w_k into $w_{k+1} = \#yq_lx'\#$; and $zo_ho_h^{-1}$ reduces to y since z does. Hence P_k' cannot be of the form 2a but rather must be of the form 2b. In that case $w_{k+1}' = \#zo_ho_h^{-1}o_r^{-1}o_rq_lx'\#$ which reduces to $\#yo_r^{-1}o_rq_lx'\#$. Now if $y = \Lambda$, $yo_r^{-1}o_r$ is blocked. If $y \neq \Lambda$, then $y = y'o_s$ for some o_s, and moreover, as is easily seen, $w_{k+1} = \#y'o_sq_lx'\#$. If $s = r$, then w_{k+1}' reduces to $y'o_ro_r^{-1}o_r$ and further to $y'o_r$, in which case w_{k+1} and w_{k+1}' match. If $s \neq r$, then w_{k+1}' reduces to $y'o_so_r^{-1}o_r$, which is blocked.

This completes the proofs of (I) and (II). From these statements it follows at once that **P** accepts x iff **P**$'$ has a proof from $\#q_0x\#$ of a terminal word $\#yq\#$ where y reduces to Λ.

In order to obtain a transducer for the completion of the proof we take each production of $\mathscr{P}'$ and warp it into a transducer production by making the states of **T** pairs of output symbols and auxiliaries of **P**$'$. The construction is completely given, except for terminating productions of the form b of Definition 8.3.3, by

$$(o_h, q_i)s_j \to z_k(o_h', q_j) \in \mathscr{R}$$
$$\Leftrightarrow Po_hq_is_jR \to Po_hz_kq_lR \in \mathscr{P}'$$

where $o_h' \neq \Lambda$ and $z = yo_h'$ for some y or $z = \Lambda$ and $o_h' = o_h$, for all productions of $\mathscr{P}'$ except those of type 3. It is apparent that **T**(x, y) and y reduces to Λ if **P**$'$ has a proof of $\#yq\#$ from $\#q_0x\#$ such that y reduces to Λ. This statement taken together with (I) and (II) (or the summary following them) delivers the lemma. Q.E.D.

Theorem 8.3.19. If L is the language defined by a p.d.a. **P**, then L is context-free.

Proof. From Lemma 8.3.18, every $x \in L$ is accepted by **P** iff there is a g.f.t. **T** and a y such that **T**(x, y) and y reduces to Λ. Let K be the set of all words on $O \bigcup O^{-1}$ which reduce to Λ. Let $\mathbf{T}(S^*)$ be a set of output words. Let **T**$'$ be an inverse of **T** (which exists by Theorem 8.3.6). Then $\mathbf{T}'(K \bigcap \mathbf{T}(S^*)) = L$. But S^* is regular, and by Theorem 8.3.11 $\mathbf{T}(S^*)$ is likewise. K is context-free (see exercises). Hence by Theorem 8.3.12 $K \bigcap \mathbf{T}(S^*)$ is context-free. It follows, finally from Theorems 8.3.6 (already cited) and 8.3.10, that L is context-free. Q.E.D.

Note once again that in this theorem **P** may be either deterministic or nondeterministic while in Theorem 8.3.17, the p.d.a. *must* be nondeterministic. Thus the equivalence between determinism and nondeterminism which holds in the case of f.s.a. here fails. A somewhat amazing fact is that in the case of Turing machines one can also show for every nondeterministic machine (given the obvious definition) there is an equivalent deterministic one in the sense of turning out the same result from an initial instantaneous description (Evey [1963]).

The theory of context-free grammars discussed in Section 8.2 and above is far from elegant at this stage of its development. Except for some rather advanced work, notably that of Ginsburg and his co-workers and of Chomsky and Schutzenberger, most of the results come hard: little in the theory uses or seems to be amenable to the use of the relatively smoothly running kind of algebraic technique we were able to employ in Chapters 5 and 7. All depends on rather complicated constructions and case-by-case combinatorial arguments, many of which we have only sketched or left to the reader to fill in. In Turing machine theory the situation is not so bad, as one can deal with the interesting problems of Turing computability in terms of recursive function theory directly.

When it comes to context-sensitive grammars and languages, the situation is worse. Although there are important findings, some of which we shall sketch below, the theory about these systems is rather crude. It is not even certain that it is of much use in linguistics or elsewhere. Chomsky [1963] has given arguments showing quite conclusively that context-sensitive grammars are inadequate as models for the grammar of natural languages. The reason is easy to understand: such grammars permit *permutations* of sentential elements and thus in their strong proofs may allow counterintuitive phrase marker descriptions of phrase-like components. For instance, verbs may come to be identified as noun phrases. Thus, the strong theorems (phrase markers) may be too large a class, or inconsistent in the generalized sense discussed in Chapter 3. Yet the acceptors corresponding to context-sensitive languages, discussed immediately below, are in a class of machines (the linear bounded automata) which in point of behavior seem to be the closest models to digital computers available. However the situation may turn out in the future, it seems important at least to sketch an outline of the major aspects of the theory. Since the "mathematics" used in the theory is of an even more *ad hoc* character than that of the context-free languages, we feel it is appropriate to leave it out, particularly in an introductory book such as this one.

First, regarding closure properties, it turns out that the context-sensitive languages are closed under union and intersection. (Landweber [1963]). It is at the time of writing unknown (except for a certain subfamily) whether these languages are closed under complementation. A special case will be discussed briefly later.

Analogs with Theorems 8.2.12 and 8.2.14 fail: There are no decision procedures for the problems whether the output of a context-sensitive grammar is null or infinite. Furthermore, there is no algorithm for weak equivalence of such grammars.

A linear bounded acceptor (l.b.a.) is a Turing acceptor with tape whose length is bounded by a linear function of the length of the input x. Without loss of generality (by permitting additional states and/or output symbols) we may restrict our attention to l.b.a.'s with tape of length exactly $l(x)$, x the input. A deterministic l.b.a. is functional in the sense of an ordinary Turing acceptor while a nondeterministic l.b.a. has polygenic rules.

It is not known whether for every nondeterministic l.b.a. (n.l.b.a.) there is a deterministic l.b.a. with the same behavior. Thus, whereas n.f.s.a.'s and f.s.a.'s are the same (as are also full Turing acceptors) and whereas the deterministic and nondeterministic p.d.a. are of different powers, the question of equal strength of linear bounded automata has not been answered.

Having now the concept l.b.a. we may return to the definability and closure problems. Kuroda [1964] has shown that a language is context-sensitive iff it is the language defined by some (perhaps nondeterministic) l.b.a. Moreover, if L is accepted by a deterministic l.b.a., then it is context-sensitive. The converse to this is unknown; if it were known, we would also have a resolution to the problem of the relative powers of l.b.a. and n.l.b.a. mentioned above.

Moreover the same author has shown that the family of languages definable by l.b.a.'s is *boolean*, that is, in particular, it is closed under complementation. Again, a solution to the determinism–nondeterminism problem would as well be a solution to the complementation problem for the entire family. Since the context-sensitive languages are recursive, one can construct a linear bounded *detector* which not only accepts a given word from a context-sensitive grammar but which *rejects* words. Kuroda has also shown that a *rejected* language is context-sensitive. Note however, that if the rejecting automaton is nondeterministic, a given word x may be in *both* classes so that the rejected set and accepted set may overlap. For deterministic machines this cannot be the case, and for this reason the rejected set is the complement of the accepted sets and boolean closure follows.

Earlier results developed above in this section taken with the conclusions here stated about the context-sensitive languages imply that the powers of a p.d.a. are among those of an l.b.a. (see exercises). Furthermore, one can show that a deterministic l.b.a. can do anything a *nondeterministic* p.d.a. can do.

Summarizing Section 8.3 and the facts about acceptors just discussed, there are four main families of grammar, and four kinds of acceptors corresponding to them. The two families are ordered by proper inclusion as in Table 8.3.1.

TABLE 8.3.1

Type 0 (recursively enumerable)	Turing acceptor
Type 1 (context-sensitive)	n.l.b.a.
Type 2 (context-free)	n.p.d.a.
Type 3 (finite state)	n.f.s.a.

EXERCISES 8.3

1. Verify the action of the p.d.a. of Example 2.

2. Prove Theorem 8.3.9.

3. Fill out the details of Case II in the proof of Theorem 8.3.10: (*a*) determine $\mathscr{P}'$; (*b*) show that $\mathscr{U}_{ij}$ is regular; (*c*) show the construction of the necessary context-free rules.

4. Prove Theorem 8.3.11 and complete the proof of Theorem 8.3.12.

5. Show that phrase markers for context-free languages enjoy proper pairing.

6. Show that the Theorem 8.3.17 cannot be strengthened so as to assert the existence of a *deterministic* p.d.a. for accepting each context-free language.

7. Prove (Theorem 8.3.17) that x is generated by **G** iff there is a y such that $\mathbf{T}(x, y)$ and y reduces to Λ, and y is equipped with phrase markers except for use of auxiliaries instead of parentheses and for occurrences of right inverses s^{-1} concatenated to the right of each terminal symbol s in y.

8. Verify Example 7.

9. Prove that if $w = \#yqx\#$ and $w' = \#zqx\#$ are elements of a proof in **P** and one in **P**′, respectively, where **P**′ is constructed as in Lemma 8.3.18, and if w and w' match; then either $w = \#qx\#$ and for some $o_h{}^{-1} \in O'$, $z = z'o_h{}^{-1}$ reduces to Λ, or there is a proof from the same axiom with a line w'' which matches w and the productions applicable to w and w'' correspond.

10. Show K in Theorem 8.3.19 is context-free.

11. Show any language definable by a p.d.a. is definable by an l.b.a.

12. Is there an algorithm for determining whether a normal grammar generates a regular set?

13. Prove that there is no algorithm for determining for two context-free languages L_1 and L_2 whether there is a g.f.t. **T** such that $\mathbf{T}(L_1) = L_2$.

14. Consider the formulation of the propositional calculus in Definition 3.2.1 with the alphabet augmented with $\wedge$ (and). Abbreviate conjunctions $p \wedge q$ to pq. Also use p^n for $pp\cdots$(n times). Show that the set of theorems of the propositional calculus is context-sensitive but not context-free. *Hint*: Show the language of words $ut^nvt^nwt^nx$ is not context-free. Then consider formulas of the propositional calculus of the forms "$((\neg p^n \Rightarrow p^m) \Rightarrow p^k)$" and "$((\neg p^n \Rightarrow p^n) \Rightarrow p^n)$". (Hodes).

15. Prove that if L_1 is context-free and L_2 is finite, then $L_1 - L_2$ is context-free.

8.4 HISTORICAL AND BIBLIOGRAPHICAL REMARKS

The approach to mathematical (or algebraic) linguistics of this chapter stems mainly from Chomsky [1956], [1957], and Chomsky and Miller [1958]. Other approaches not using automata (generators in our sense) have been advocated by Harris [1951], Bar-Hillel [1953], Lambek [1958], and Curry [1961] among others. Elementary introductions to transformational grammar, including the study of phrase structure grammars, are those of Bach [1964] and Chomsky and Miller [1963]. A comprehensive study of context-free languages is made in Ginsburg [1966]. A detailed, technical account of generative grammars and other automata including a survey of many topics not included in our present chapter appears in Chomsky [1963].

Section 8.1 is essentially Chomsky [1959], which is another landmark in the field. The connection between finite state grammars and acceptors was shown by Bar-Hillel and Shamir [1960]. Section 8.2 is essentially Bar-Hillel, Perles, and Shamir [1961] except we do not allow productions $PgR \to P\Lambda R$. The unsolvability of the ambiguity problem was shown almost simultaneously by Chomsky and Schutzenberger [1962], Floyd [1962b], and Cantor [1962]; in the latter case it was shown w.r.t. the so-called Backus normal form of ALGOL (Backus [1959]); see also Naur [1960] and Ginsburg and Rice [1962]. Parikh [1961] showed the existence of inherently ambiguous languages.

Section 8.3 derives in the main from Chomsky [1962] and Chomsky [1963]. Similar results on preservation of context-free and regular languages under transducer action have been shown by Ginsburg and Rose [1963b]. That the intersection of a context-free and a regular language is context-free goes back to Bar-Hillel, Perles, and Shamir [1960]. Additional undecidability results have been obtained by Ginsburg and Rose [1963a]. The idea of a pushdown store seems to have originated with Burks, Warren, and Wright [1954] in connection with the design of a logic machine. In programming it was first used by Newell and Shaw [1957]. The concept of linear bounded acceptor is due to Myhill [1960].

For a summary discussion of various automata having powers between finite state machines and Turing machines see Fisher [1965].

Bibliography

This bibliography is divided into three parts. Part A lists books on switching circuits and boolean algebra which contain material which I assume the reader has as background for reading the present book. It also includes a few selected logic and algebra texts which (except for lack of material on switching circuits) should provide adequate background.

Part B lists books on automata theory which the student may want to consult from time to time. It also lists several survey papers on the theory of automata. The list also includes valuable books on mathematical linguistics.

Part C lists all other books and papers which are explicitly referred to in the present volume. With but few exceptions it includes only those works referenced in the "Historical and Bibliographical Remarks" sections at the ends of the chapters.

A somewhat more comprehensive bibliography including books and papers in switching theory and automata appears in Harrison [1965], Part B. A very complete bibliography to 1963 appears in Moore [1964], part B.

A. BACKGROUND BOOKS AND PAPERS

Arnold, B. H. [1962], *Logic and Boolean Algebra*, Prentice-Hall, Englewood Cliffs, N. J.

Bartee, T. C., I. L. Lebow, and I. S. Reed [1962], *Theory and Design of Digital Machines*, McGraw-Hill, New York.

Braun, E. L. [1963], *Digital Computer Design, Logic, Circuitry and Synthesis*, Academic Press, New York.

Birkhoff, G. and S. MacLane [1953], *A Survey of Modern Algebra* (Rev. Edition), Macmillan, New York.

Caldwell, S. H. [1958], *Switching Circuits and Logical Design*, John Wiley and Sons, New York.

Chevalley, C. [1956], *Fundamental Concepts of Algebra*, Academic Press, New York.

Copi, I. M. [1965], *Symbolic Logic* (2nd Edition), Macmillan, New York.

Culbertson, J. T. [1958], *Mathematics and Logic for Digital Devices*, Van Nostrand, Princeton.

Dubisch, R. [1964], *Lattices to Logic*, Blaisdell, New York.

Herstein, I. N. [1964], *Topics in Algebra*, Blaisdell, New York.

Hohn, F. E. [1960], *Applied Boolean Algebra; An Elementary Introduction*, Macmillan, New York.

Hu, S. [1965], *Elements of Modern Algebra*, Holden Day, San Francisco.

Korfhage, R. [1966], *Logic and Algorithms*, John Wiley and Sons, New York.

Marcus, M. P. [1962], *Switching Circuits for Engineers*, Prentice-Hall, Englewood Cliffs, N. J.

Miller, R. E. [1965], *Switching Theory*, Vol. 1: *Combinational Circuits*, John Wiley and Sons, New York.

Phister, M. Jr. [1958], *Logical Design of Digital Computers*, John Wiley and Sons, New York.

Quine, W. V. [1959], *Methods of Logic* (Rev. Edition), Holt, New York.

Rosenbloom, P. C. [1950], *The Elements of Mathematical Logic*, Dover, New York.

Stoll, R. R. [1961], *Set Theory and Logic*, W. H. Freeman and Co., San Francisco.

Whitesitt, J. E. [1961], *Boolean Algebra and its Applications*, Addison-Wesley, Reading, Mass.

B. BOOKS AND SURVEY PAPERS ON AUTOMATA THEORY

Arbib, M. [1964], *Brains, Machines, and Mathematics*, McGraw-Hill, New York.

Bach, E. [1964]. *Introduction to Transformational Grammars*, Holt, Rinehart and Winston, New York.

Bar-Hillel, Y. [1964], *Language and Information: Selected Essays on their Theory and Application*, Addison-Wesley, Reading, Mass.

Bazilevskii, Y. Y. [1963], *The Theory of Mathematical Machines*, Pergamon Press, New York.

Caianiello, E. R. [1966], *Automata Theory*, Academic Press, New York.

Chomsky, N. [1966], *Aspects of Linguistics*, M.I.T. Press, Cambridge, Mass.

Gill, A. [1962], *Introduction to the Theory of Finite-State Machines*, McGraw-Hill, New York.

Ginsburg, S. [1962], *An Introduction to Mathematical Machine Theory*, Addison-Wesley, Reading, Mass.

Ginsburg, S. [1966], *The Mathematical Theory of Context-Free Languages*, McGraw-Hill, New York.

Glushkov, V. M. [1966], *Introduction to Cybernetics*, Academic Press, New York.

Harrison, M. A. [1965], *Introduction to Switching and Automata Theory*, McGraw-Hill, New York.

Hartmanis, J. and R. E. Stearns [1966], *Algebraic Structure Theory of Sequential Machines*, Prentice-Hall, Englewood Cliffs, N. J.

Luce, R. D., R. R. Bush, and E. Galanter [1963], *Handbook of Mathematical Psychology*, Vol. II, Chaps. 11 and 12, John Wiley and Sons, New York.

Kobrinskii, N. E. and B. A. Trakhtenbrot [1965], *Introduction to the Theory of Finite Automata*, North-Holland, Amsterdam.

Marcus, S. [1966], *Algebraic Linguistics; Analytical Models*, Academic Press, New York.

McCarthy, J. and C. E. Shannon, (Eds.) [1956], *Automata Studies*, Princeton Univ. Press, Princeton.

McNaughton, R. [1961], "The Theory of Automata; A Survey," in *Advances in Computers*, Vol. 2, Academic Press, New York.

Moore, E. F. [1964], *Sequential Machines: Selected Papers*, Addison-Wesley, Reading, Mass.

Nelson, R. J. [1965], "Basic Concepts of Automata Theory," in *Proc. Assoc. Computing Mach.*, 20th Conference.

Trakhtenbrot, B. A. [1963], *Algorithms and Automatic Computing Machines*, Heath, Boston.

Von Neumann, J. [1951], "The General and Logical Theory of Automata," in *Cerebral Mechanisms and Behavior; the Hixon Symposium*, John Wiley and Sons, New York.

Von Neumann, J. [1958], *The Computer and the Brain*, Yale Univ. Press, New Haven.

Von Neumann, J. [1966], *Theory of Self Reproducing Automata* (ed. A. Burks), University of Illinois Press, Urbana.

C. OTHER BOOKS AND RESEARCH PAPERS

Arbib, M. [1961], "Turing Machines, Finite Automata, and Neural Nets," *J. Assoc. Computing Mach.*, Vol. 8, pp. 467–475.

Ashenhurst, R. L. [1953], "The Decomposition of Switching Functions," *Bell Lab. Rept.*, No. 1, pp. II–1, II–37.

Ashenhurst, R. L. [1959], "The Decomposition of Switching Functions," in *Proc. Int. Symp. Theory of Switching*, Harvard Univ. Press, Cambridge, Mass.

Backus, J. W. [1959], "The Syntax and Semantics of the Proposed International Algebraic Language of the Zurich ACM-GAMM Conference," ICIP, Paris.

Bar-Hillel, Y. [1953], "A Quasi-Arithmetical Notation for Syntactic Description," *Language*, Vol. 29, pp. 47–58. Also in Bar-Hillel [1964].

Bar-Hillel, Y. and E. Shamir [1960], "Finite State Languages," *Bull. Res. Council Israel*, Vol. 8F, pp. 143–172. Also in Bar-Hillel [1964].

Bar-Hillel, Y., M. Perles, and E. Shamir [1961], "On Formal Properties of Simple Phrase Structure Grammars," *Zeit. Phonetik, Sprachwissenschaft und Kommunikationsforschung*, Vol. 14, pp. 143–172. Also in Bar-Hillel [1964].

Birkhoff, G. [1935], "On the Structure of Abstract Algebras," *Proc. Camb. Phil. Soc.*, Vol. 31, pp. 433–454.

Birkhoff, G. [1948], *Lattice Theory*, Amer. Math. Soc. Coll. Pub., Vol. 25.

Brzozowski, J. A. [1964], "Derivatives of Regular Expressions," *J. Assoc. Computing Mach.*, Vol. 11, pp. 481–494.

Büchi, J. R. and J. B. Wright [1960], *Class Notes on a Mathematical Theory of Automata*, Univ. of Michigan, Ann Arbor.

Büchi, J. R. [1961], "Mathematische Theorie des Verhaltens Endlicher Automaten," *Zeit. Angew. Math. Mech.*, Vol. 42, pp. 9–16.

Burks, A. W. [1963], "Cellular Automata," in *Automata Theory*, Univ. of Michigan Engineering Summer Conference.

Burks, A. W. and I. M. Copi [1956], "The Logical Design of an Idealized General Purpose Computer," *J. Franklin Inst.*, Vol. 261, pp. 297–314, 421–436.

Burks, A. W. and H. Wang [1957], "The Logic of Automata," *J. Assoc. Computing Mach.*, Vol. 4, pp. 193–218, 279–297.

Burks, A. W., D. W. Warren, and J. B. Wright [1954], "An Analysis of a Logical Machine using Parenthesis-Free Notation," in *Math. Tables Aids Comp.*, Vol. 8, pp. 53–57.

Burks, A. W. and J. B. Wright [1953], "Theory of Logical Nets," *Proc. IRE*, Vol. 41, pp. 1357–1365. Also in Moore [1964].

Cantor, D. G. [1962], "On the Ambiguity Problem of Backus Systems," *J. Assoc. Computing Mach.*, Vol. 9, pp. 477–479.

Chomsky, N. [1956], "Three Models for the Description of Languages," *IRE Trans. Inform. Theory*, Vol. IT-2, pp. 113–124.

Chomsky, N. [1957], *Syntactic Structures*, Mouton and Co., The Hague.

Chomsky, N. [1959], "On Certain Formal Properties of Grammars," *Inform. Control*, Vol. 2, pp. 137–167.

Chomsky, N. [1962], "Context-Free Languages and Pushdown Storage," *M.I.T. Res. Lab. Electron. Quart. Prog. Rept.*, 65.

Chomsky, N. [1963], "Formal Properties of Grammars," in *Handbook of Mathematical Psychology*, Vol. 2, John Wiley and Sons, New York.

Chomsky, N. and G. A. Miller [1958], "Finite State Languages," *Inform. Control*, Vol. 1, pp. 91–112.

Chomsky, N. and G. A. Miller [1963], "Introduction to the Formal Analysis of Natural Languages," in *Handbook of Mathematical Psychology*, Vol. 2, John Wiley and Son, New York.

Chomsky, N. and M. P. Schutzenberger [1963], "The Algebraic Theory of Context-Free Languages," in *Computer Programming and Formal Systems*, North-Holland Pub. Co., Amsterdam.

Church, A. [1956], *Introduction to Mathematical Logic*, Princeton Univ. Press, Princeton, N.J.

Church, A. [1959], "Application of Recursive Arithmetic in the Theory of Computing and Automata," in *Notes in Advanced Theory of the Logical Design of Digital Computers*, Univ. of Michigan Engineering Summer Conference.

Clark, W. A. [1956], "The Logical Structure of Digital Computers," Lincoln Lab. M.I.T. Memo. 6M-3938, 1–5.

Cole, S. N. [1964], "Real-time Computation by Iterative Arrays of Finite State Machines," Ph.D. Thesis, Harvard.

Copi, I. M., C. C. Elgot, and J. B. Wright [1958], "Realization of Events by Logical Nets," *J. Assoc. Computing Mach.*, Vol. 5, pp. 181–196. Also in Moore [1964].

Curry, H. B. [1961], "Some Logical Aspects of Grammatical Structure," in *Structure of Language and its Mathematical Aspects*, Amer. Math. Soc., Providence, R.I.

Curtis, H. A. [1962], *A New Approach to the Design of Switching Circuits*, Van Nostrand, Princeton.

Davis, M. [1958], *Computability and Unsolvability*, McGraw-Hill, New York.

Ehrenfest, P. [1910], Review of L. Couturat, *L'Algebre de la Logique*, *Zhurnal Russkago Fiziko-Khimiceskago Obscestva*, Section of Physics, Vol. 42, pp. 382–387.

Elgot, C. C. [1959], *Lectures on Switching and Automata Theory*, Lecture Notes, Univ. of Michigan.

Elgot, C. C. [1961], "Decision Problems of Finite Automata Design and Related Arithmetics," *Trans. Amer. Math. Soc.*, Vol. 98, pp. 21–51.

Elgot, C. C. [1965], "A Perspective View of Discrete Automata and their Design," *Amer. Math. Monthly, Supplement on Computers and Computing*, Vol. 72, pp. 125–134.

Elgot, C. C. and J. Mezei [1965], "On Relations Defined by Generalized Finite Automata," IBM *J. Res. Dev.*, Vol. 9, pp. 47–68.

Elgot, C. C. and A. Robinson [1964], "Random-access Stored Program Machines: An Approach to Programming Languages," *J. Assoc. Computing Mach.*, Vol. 11, pp. 365–399.

Elgot, C. C. and J. D. Rutledge [1961], "Operations on Finite Automata, Extended Summary," in *AIEE Sec. Ann. Symp. Switching Theory and Logical Design.*

Evey, R. J. [1963], "The Theory and Application of Pushdown Store Machines," Ph.D. Thesis, Harvard.

Fisher, P. [1965]. "Multi-tape and Infinite-state Automata—A Survey," *Comm. Assoc. Computing Mach.*, Vol. 8, pp. 799–805.

Fleck, A. [1962], "Isomorphism Groups of Automata," *J. Assoc. Computing Mach.*, Vol. 4, pp. 469–476.

Floyd, R. W. [1962a], "On the nonexistence of a Phrase Structure Grammar for ALGOL 60," *Comm. Assoc. Computing Mach.*, Vol. 5, pp. 483–484.

Floyd, R. W. [1962b], "On Ambiguity in Phrase Structure Languages," *Comm. Assoc. Computing Mach.*, Vol. 5, pp. 526–534.

Gazale, M. J. [1957], "Irredundant Disjunctive and Conjunctive Forms of a Boolean Function," IBM *J. Res. Dev.*, Vol. 1, pp. 171–176.

Ginsburg, S. and H. G. Rice [1962], "Two Families of Languages related to ALGOL," *J. Assoc. Computing Mach.*, Vol. 9, pp. 350–371.

Ginsburg, S. and G. F. Rose [1963a], "Some Recursively Unsolvable Problems in ALGOL-like Languages," *J. Assoc. Computing Mach.*, Vol. 10, pp. 29–47.

Ginsburg, S. and G. F. Rose [1963b], "Operations which Preserve Definability in Languages," *J. Assoc. Computing Mach.*, Vol. 10, pp, 175–195.

Gödel, Kurt [1931], "Uber Formal unentscheidbäre Sätze der Principia Mathematische und Verwandter Systeme I," *Monatsh. Math. Phys.*, Vol. 38, pp. 173-198.

Harris, Z. S. [1951], *Methods in Structural Linguistics*, Univ. Chicago Press, Chicago.

Harrison, M. A. [1965], "On the Error Correcting Capacity of Finite Automata," *Inform. Control*, Vol. 8, pp. 430–450.

Hartmanis, J. [1960], "Symbolic Analysis of a Decomposition of Information Processing Machines," *Inform. Control*, Vol. 3, pp. 151–178.

Hartmanis, J. [1961], "On the State Assignment Problem for Sequential Machines I," *IRE Trans. Electron. Comp.*, Vol. EC-10, pp. 157–165.

Hartmanis, J. [1962], "Loop-free Structure of Sequential Machines," *Inform. Control*, Vol. 5, pp. 25–43. Also in Moore [1964].

Hartmanis, J. and R. E. Stearns [1964], "Pair Algebra and its Application to Automata Theory," *Inform. Control*, Vol. 7, pp. 485–507.

Hennie, F. C. [1961], *Iterative Arrays of Logical Circuits*, M.I.T. Press, Cambridge, Mass.

Hermes, H. [1954], "The Universalität Programmgesteuerter Rechenmaschine," *Math. Phys. Semsterberichte*, Vol. 4, pp. 42–53.

Holland, J. H. [1960], "Cycles in Logical Nets," *J. Franklin Inst.*, Vol. 270, pp. 202–226.

Holland, J. H. [1963], "Iterative Circuit Computers," in *Automata Theory*, Univ. of Michigan Engineering Summer Conference.

House, R. W. and T. Rado [1965], "A Generalization of Nelson's Algorithm for Obtaining Prime Implicants," *J. Symb. Logic*, Vol. 30, pp. 8–12.

Huffman, D. A. [1954], "The Synthesis of Sequential Switching Circuits," *J. Franklin Inst.*, Vol. 257, pp. 161–190; pp. 275–303. Also in Moore [1964].

Kaphengst, H. [1959], "Eine Abstrakte Programmgesteuerte Rechenmaschine," *Zeit. Math. Logic Grund. Math.*, Vol. 5, pp. 366–379.

Karp, R. M. [1965], *Algebraic Theory of Automata*, Lecture Notes, Univ. of Michigan.

Keister, W., A. E. Ritchie, and S. H. Washburn [1951], *The Design of Switching Circuits*, Van Nostrand, Princeton.

Keller, H. B. [1961], "Finite Automata, Pattern Recognition, and Perceptrons," *J. Assoc. Computing Mach.*, Vol. 8, pp. 1–20.

Kleene, S. C. [1952], *Introduction to Metamathematics*, Van Nostrand, Princeton.

Kleene, S. C. [1956], "Representation of Events in Nerve Nets and Finite Automata," in *Automata Studies*, Princeton Univ. Press, Princeton.

Kreider, D. and R. W. Ritchie, [1967], *Recursive Functions*, John Wiley and Sons, New York.

Krohn, K. B. and J. L. Rhodes [1963], "Algebraic Theory of Machines," in *Proc. Symp. Math. Theory Automata*, Polytechnic Press, Brooklyn, N.Y.

Krohn, K. B. and J. L. Rhodes [1965], "Algebraic Theory of Machines," *Trans. Amer. Math. Soc.*, Vol. 116, pp. 450–464.

Kuroda, S. Y. [1964], "Classes of Languages and Linear-bound Automata," *Inform. Control*, Vol. 7, pp. 207–223.

Lambek, J. [1958], "The Mathematics of Sentence Structure," *Amer. Math. Monthly*, Vol. 65, pp. 154–170.

Landweber, P. S. [1963], "Three Theorems on Phrase Structure Grammars of Type 1," *Inform. Control*, Vol. 6, pp. 131–136.

Lee, C. Y. [1960], "Automata and Finite Automata," *Bell System Tech. J.*, Vol. 39, pp. 1267–1295.

Lee, C. Y. [1961], "Categorizing Automata by W-Machine Programs," *J. Assoc. Computing Mach.*, Vol. 8, pp. 384–399.

Markov, A. A. [1954], *Theory of Algorithms*, Moscow (Available U.S. Dept. Commerce).

McCluskey, E. J. Jr. [1956], "Minimization of Boolean Functions," *Bell System Tech. J.*, Vol. 35, pp. 1417–1444.

McCulloch, W. S. and W. Pitts [1943], "A Logical Calculus of the Ideas Immanent in Nervous Activity," *Bull. Math. Biophys.*, Vol. 5, pp. 115–133.

McNaughton, R. [1964], "Badly Timed Elements and Well Timed Nets," Tech. Report, Moore School of Electrical Engineering, Univ. of Pennsylvania.

McNaughton, R. and H. Yamada [1960], "Regular Expressions and State Graphs for Automata," *IRE Trans. Electron. Comp.*, Vol. EC-9, pp. 39–47. Also in Moore [1964].

Mealy, G. H. [1955], "A Method for Synthesizing Sequential Circuits," *Bell System Tech. J.*, Vol. 34, pp. 1045–1079.

Medvedev, Y. T. [1958], "On a Class of Events Representable in a Finite Automaton," Transl. J. Schorr-Kon, Lincoln Lab. Report 34–73. Also in Moore [1964].

Moore, E. F. [1956], "Gedanken Experiments on Sequential Machines," in *Automata Studies*, Princeton Univ. Press, Princeton.

Moore, E. F. and C. E. Shannon [1956], "Reliable Circuits Using less Reliable Relays," *J. Franklin Inst.*, Vol. 262, pp. 191–208, 281–297.

Mott, T. H. [1960], "Determination of the Irredundant Normal Forms of a Truth Function by Iterated Consensus of Prime Implicants," *IRE Trans. Electron. Comp.*, Vol. EC-9, pp. 245–251.

Myhill, J. [1957], "Finite Automata and the Representation of Events," WADC Tech. Report, 57–624.

Myhill, J. [1960], "Linear Bounded Automata," WADD Tech. Note, 60–165.

Myhill, J. [1963a], "Finite Automata, Semi-Groups and Simulation," in *Automata Theory*, Univ. of Michigan Engineering Summer Conference.

Myhill, J. [1963b], "Notes for a Series of Lectures on Recursive Functions," in *Automata Theory*, Univ. of Michigan Engineering Summer Conference.

Muller, D. E. [1959], "Asynchronous Switching Theory," in *Notes in Advanced Theory of the Logical Design of Digital Computers*, Univ. of Michigan Engineering Summer Conference.

Naur, P. (Ed.) [1960], "Report on the Algorithmic Language ALGOL 60," *Comm. Assoc. Computing Mach.*, Vol. 3, pp. 299–314.

Nelson, R. J. [1955a], "Simplest Normal Truth Functions," *J. Symb. Logic*, Vol. 20, pp. 105–108.

Nelson, R. J. [1955b], "Weak Simplest Normal Truth Functions," *J. Symb. Logic*, Vol. 20, pp. 232–234.

Nerode, A. [1958], "Linear Automaton Transformations," *Proc. Amer. Math. Soc.*, Vol. 9, pp. 541–544.

Newell, A. and J. C. Shaw [1957], "Programming the Logic Theory Machine," *Proc. Western Joint Computer Conf.*, pp. 230–240.

Ott, G. and N. Feinstein [1961], "Design of Sequential Machines from their Regular Expressions," *J. Assoc. Computing Mach.*, Vol. 8, pp. 585–600.

Parikh, R. J. [1961], "Language Generating Devices," in M.I.T. *Res. Lab. Electron Quart. Report*, 60.

Paull, M. C. and S. H. Unger [1959], "Minimizing the Number of States of Incompletely Specified Sequential Machines," in *IRE Trans. Electron. Comp.*, Vol. EC-8, pp. 356–367.

Paz, A. [1962], "Homomorphisms between Finite Automata," in *Bull. Res. Council Israel*, Vol. 10F, pp. 93–100.

Perles, M., M. O. Rabin, and E. Shamir [1963], "The Theory of Definite Automata," *IEEE Trans. Electron. Comp.*, Vol. EC-12, pp. 233–243.

Petrick, S. R. [1956], "A Direct Determination of the Irredundant Forms of a Boolean Function from the Set of Prime Implicants," AFCRC, TR-56-110.

Post, E. L. [1936], "Finite Combinatory Processes—Formulation I," *J. Symb. Logic*, Vol. 1, pp. 103–105.

Post, E. L. [1943], "Formal Reduction of the General Combinatorial Decision Problem," *Amer. J. Math.*, Vol. 65, pp. 197–215.

Post, E. L. [1944], "Recursively Enumerable Sets of Positive Integers and Their Decision Problems," *Bull. Amer. Math. Soc.*, Vol. 50, pp. 284–316.

Post, E. L. [1946], "A Variant of a Recursively Unsolvable Problem," *Bull. Amer. Math. Soc.*, Vol. 52, pp. 264–268.

Quine, W. V. [1952], "The Problem of Simplifying Truth Functions," *Amer. Math. Monthly*, Vol. 59, pp. 521–531.

Quine, W. V. [1955], "A Way to Simplify Truth Functions," *Amer. Math. Monthly*, Vol. 62, pp. 627–631.

Rabin, M. O. [1963], "Probabilistic Automata," *Inform. Control*, Vol. 6, pp. 230–245. Also in Moore [1964].

Rabin, M. O. and D. Scott [1959], "Finite Automata and their Decision Problems, *IBM J. Res. Dev.*, Vol. 3, pp. 114–125. Also in Moore [1964].

Raney, G. [1958], "Sequential Functions," *J. Assoc. Computing Mach.*, Vol. 5, pp. 177–180.

Ritchie, R. W. [1963], "Classes of Recursive Functions of Predictable Complexity," Ph.D. Thesis, Princeton Univ.

Rogers, H. Jr. [1959], "The Present Theory of Turing Computability," *J. Soc. Ind. Appl. Math.*, Vol. 7, pp. 114–130.

Rogers, H. Jr. [in press], *Theory of Recursive Functions and Effective Computability*, McGraw-Hill, New York.

Roth, J. P. [1959], "Algebraic Topological Methods in Synthesis," *Proc. Int. Symp. Theory Switching*, Harvard Univ. Press, Cambridge, Mass.

Samson, E. W. and B. E. Mills [1954], "Circuit Minimization: Algebra and Algorithms for new Boolean Canonical Expressions," AFCRC, TR-54-21.

Shannon, C. E. [1938], "A Symbolic Analysis of Relay and Switching Circuits," *Trans. AIEE*, Vol. 57, pp. 713–723.

Shannon, C. E. [1956], "A Universal Turing Machine with Two Internal States," in *Automata Studies*, Princeton Univ. Press, Princeton.

Shepherdson, J. C. and H. E. Sturgis [1963], "Computability of Recursive Functions," *J. Assoc. Computing Mach.*, Vol. 10, pp. 217–255.

Stanley, R. J. [1965], "Finite State Representations of Context Free Languages," M.I.T. *Res. Lab. Electron. Quart. Report*, 76, pp. 276–279.

Stearns, R. E. and J. Hartmanis [1961], "On the State Assignment Problem for Sequential Machines II," *IRE Trans. Electron. Comp.*, Vol. EC-10, pp. 593–603.

Smullyan, R. M. [1961], *Theory of Formal Systems* (Rev. Edition), Princeton Univ. Press, Princeton.

Thatcher, J. W. [1963], "Notes on Mathematical Automata Theory," in *Papers in Automata Theory*, Univ. of Michigan.

Turing, A. M. [1936], "On Computable Numbers with applications to the Entscheidungsproblem," *Proc. London Math. Soc.*, Vol. 42, pp. 230–265.

Unger, S. H. [1959], "Hazards and Delays in Asynchronous Sequential Switching Circuits," *IRE Trans. Cir. Theory*, Vol. CT-6, pp. 12–25.

Von Neumann, J. [1956], "Probabilistic Logics," in *Automata Studies*, Princeton Univ. Press, Princeton.

Wang, H. [1957], "A Variant to Turing's Theory of Computing Machines," *J. Assoc. Computing Mach.*, Vol. 4, pp. 63–92.

Wang, H. [1965], "Logic and Computers," *Amer. Math. Monthly*, Supplement on Computers and Computing, Vol. 72, pp. 135 ff.

Winograd, S., "Input Error Limiting Automata," *J. Assoc. Computing Mach.*, Vol. 11, pp. 338–351.

Weeg, G. [1962], "The Structure of an Automaton and its Operation Preserving Transformation Group," *J. Assoc. Computing Mach.*, Vol. 3, pp. 345–349.

Yoeli, M. [1961], The Cascade Decomposition of Sequential Machines," *IRE Trans. Electron. Comp.*, Vol. EC-10, pp. 587–592.

Yoeli, M. [1963a], "Decomposition of Finite Automata," in *Technion*, Israel Inst. Tech. Report 10.

Yoeli, M. [1963b], "Cascade-Parallel Decomposition of Sequential Machines," *IRE Trans. Electron. Comp.*, Vol. EC-12, pp. 322–324.

Zeiger, H. P. [1964], "Loop-free Synthesis of Finite State Machines," Ph.D. Thesis, M.I.T.

Zeiger, H. P. [1965], "Cascade Synthesis of Finite State Machines," *IEEE Conf. Switching Theory Logical Design*, IEEE Inc., New York.

Index

Index of Symbols